Honda Civic
Owners Workshop Manual

Mark Storey

Models covered
Civic Hatchback (8th generation)
Petrol: 1.4 litre (1339cc) & 1.8 litre (1799cc)
Turbo-diesel: 2.2 litre (2204cc)

Does NOT cover 2.0 litre Type R or IMA Hybrid
Does NOT cover new Civic range introduced February 2012

(5913 - 400)

© Haynes Publishing 2015

ABCDE
FGHIJ
KLMNO
PQRS

A book in the **Haynes Owners Workshop Manual Series**

ISBN **978 0 85733 913 3**

British Library Cataloguing in Publication Data
A catalogue record for this book is available from the British Library.

Printed in Malaysia

Haynes Publishing
Sparkford, Yeovil, Somerset BA22 7JJ, England

Haynes North America, Inc
859 Lawrence Drive, Newbury Park, California 91320, USA

Printed using NORBRITE BOOK 48.8gsm (CODE: 40N6533) from NORPAC; procurement system certified under Sustainable Forestry Initiative standard. Paper produced is certified to the SFI Certified Fiber Sourcing Standard (CERT - 0094271)

Contents

LIVING WITH YOUR HONDA CIVIC

Introduction to the Honda Civic	Page	0•4
Safety first!	Page	0•5

Roadside Repairs

If your car won't start	Page	0•6
Jump starting	Page	0•7
Wheel changing	Page	0•8
Towing	Page	0•9
Identifying leaks	Page	0•10

Weekly Checks

Introduction	Page	0•11
Underbonnet check points	Page	0•11
Engine oil level	Page	0•13
Washer fluid level	Page	0•13
Coolant level	Page	0•14
Wiper blades	Page	0•14
Brake (and clutch) fluid level	Page	0•15
Tyre condition and pressure	Page	0•16
Battery	Page	0•17
Electrical systems	Page	0•17

Lubricants and fluids

	Page	0•18

Tyre pressures

	Page	0•18

MAINTENANCE

Routine maintenance and servicing

Petrol models

Servicing specifications	Page	1A•2
Maintenance schedule	Page	1A•3
Maintenance procedures	Page	1A•5

Diesel models

Servicing specifications	Page	1B•2
Maintenance schedule	Page	1B•3
Maintenance procedures	Page	1B•5

Contents

REPAIRS AND OVERHAUL

Engine and associated systems

1.4 litre petrol engine in-car repair procedures	Page 2A•1
1.8 litre petrol engine in-car repair procedures	Page 2B•1
2.2 litre diesel engine in-car repair procedures	Page 2C•1
Engine removal and overhaul procedures	Page 2D•1
Cooling, heating and air conditioning systems	Page 3•1
Fuel system – petrol engines	Page 4A•1
Fuel system – diesel engines	Page 4B•1
Emission control and exhaust systems	Page 4C•1
Starting and charging systems	Page 5A•1
Ignition system	Page 5B•1
Pre-heating system	Page 5C•1

Transmission

Clutch	Page 6•1
Manual transmission	Page 7A•1
Automatic transmission	Page 7B•1
Driveshafts	Page 8•1

Brakes and Suspension

Braking system	Page 9•1
Suspension and steering systems	Page 10•1

Body equipment

Bodywork and fittings	Page 11•1
Body electrical systems	Page 12•1
Wiring diagrams	Page 12•23

REFERENCE

Dimensions and weights	Page REF•1
Fuel economy	Page REF•2
Conversion factors	Page REF•6
Buying spare parts	Page REF•7
Vehicle identification numbers	Page REF•7
General repair procedures	Page REF•8
Jacking and vehicle support	Page REF•9
Tools and working facilities	Page REF•10
MOT test checks	Page REF•12
Fault finding	Page REF•18
Glossary of technical terms	Page REF•26

Index

	Page REF•32

The Honda Civic featured in this manual is the eight generation of the Civic. Production started in middle of 2005, with the model available for purchase in October 2005. Production continued until March 2012 when the next generation (the mark nine) became available. The Civic has remained largely unchanged since the start of production, apart from a minor facelift in 2009 that saw cosmetic changes to the front and rear bumpers and another minor facelift (an updated grille and a new design of alloy wheels) shortly before the end of production in 2011.

The Civic is available with a 1.4 litre petrol engine, a 1.8 litre petrol engine and a 2.2 litre diesel engine. Other engines are available but are not covered by this manual. The early 1.4 petrol engine (engine code L13A) fitted to the i-DSI was superseded by the later 1.4 litre (engine code L13Z) i-VTEC in 2009. Note that whilst these engines are described as '1.4' they are in fact 1339 cc engines. The 1.8 litre petrol engine is a newer design that has many of the features of the later 1.4 litre engine. The diesel engine is the common Honda diesel engine found in a wide variety of Honda vehicles.

Safety features include door side impact bars, four airbags as standard on all models, with some higher specification models having active front seat head restraints. All models have pre-tensioner seatbelts and ISO fixings for child seats. ABS is standard throughout the range, with many models also featuring stability and traction control – called VSA (Vehicle Stability Assist) by Honda.

The transversely-mounted engines drive the front roadwheels through a six-speed manual transmission with a hydraulically-operated clutch. I.8 litre models are also available with a standard fully automatic transmission. Note that the petrol models are also available with an automated mechanical transmission (i-SHIFT) but these models are not covered by this manual.

The fully-independent front suspension is by MacPherson struts and transverse lower arms at the front. A front anti-roll bar and EPS (Electric Power Steering) are standard on all models. The rear suspension is a simple torsion beam rear axle fitted with coil springs and shock absorbers.

Provided that regular servicing is carried out in accordance with the manufacturer's recommendations, the Civic should prove a reliable and economical car. The engine compartment is well-designed, and most of the items needing frequent attention are easily accessible.

Your Honda Civic manual

The aim of this manual is to help you get the best value from your vehicle. It can do so in several ways. It can help you decide what work must be done (even should you choose to get it done by a garage). It will also provide information on routine maintenance and servicing, and give a logical course of action and diagnosis when random faults occur. However, it is hoped that you will use the manual by tackling the work yourself. On simpler jobs it may even be quicker than booking the car into a garage and going there twice, to leave and collect it. Perhaps most important, a lot of money can be saved by avoiding the costs a garage must charge to cover its labour and overheads.

The manual has drawings and descriptions to show the function of the various components so that their layout can be understood. Tasks are described and photographed in a clear step-by-step sequence. The illustrations are numbered by the Section number and paragraph number to which they relate – if there is more than one illustration per paragraph, the sequence is denoted alphabetically.

References to the 'left' or 'right' of the vehicle are in the sense of a person in the driver's seat, facing forwards.

Acknowledgements

Thanks are due to AST Tools and Draper Tools Limited, who provided some of the workshop tools, and to all those people at Sparkford who helped in the production of this manual.

We take great pride in the accuracy of information given in this manual, but vehicle manufacturers make alterations and design changes during the production run of a particular vehicle of which they do not inform us. No liability can be accepted by the authors or publishers for loss, damage or injury caused by any errors in, or omissions from, the information given.

Working on your car can be dangerous. This page shows just some of the potential risks and hazards, with the aim of creating a safety-conscious attitude.

General hazards

Scalding

• Don't remove the radiator or expansion tank cap while the engine is hot.
• Engine oil, transmission fluid or power steering fluid may also be dangerously hot if the engine has recently been running.

Burning

• Beware of burns from the exhaust system and from any part of the engine. Brake discs and drums can also be extremely hot immediately after use.

Crushing

• When working under or near a raked vehicle, always supplement the jack with axle stands, or use drive-on ramps.
Never venture under a car which is only supported by a jack.
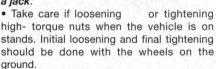
• Take care if loosening or tightening high- torque nuts when the vehicle is on stands. Initial loosening and final tightening should be done with the wheels on the ground.

Fire

• Fuel is highly flammable; fuel vapour is explosive.
• Don't let fuel spill onto a hot engine.
• Do not smoke or allow naked lights (including pilot lights) anywhere near a vehicle being worked on. Also beware of creating sparks (electrically or by use of tools).
• Fuel vapour is heavier than air, so don't work on the fuel system with the vehicle over an inspection pit.
• Another cause of fire is an electrical overload or short-circuit. Take care when repairing or modifying the vehicle wiring.
• Keep a fire extinguisher handy, of a type suitable for use on fuel and electrical fires.

Electric shock

• Ignition HT and Xenon headlight voltages can be dangerous, especially to people with heart problems or a pacemaker. Don't work on or near these systems with the engine running or the ignition switched on.

• Mains voltage is also dangerous. Make sure that any mains-operated equipment is correctly earthed. Mains power points should be protected by a residual current device (RCD) circuit breaker.

Fume or gas intoxication

• Exhaust fumes are poisonous; they can contain carbon monoxide, which is rapidly fatal if inhaled. Never run the engine in a confined space such as a garage with the doors shut.
• Fuel vapour is also poisonous, as are the vapours from some cleaning solvents and paint thinners.

Poisonous or irritant substances

• Avoid skin contact with battery acid and with any fuel, fluid or lubricant, especially antifreeze, brake hydraulic fluid and Diesel fuel. Don't syphon them by mouth. If such a substance is swallowed or gets into the eyes, seek medical advice.
• Prolonged contact with used engine oil can cause skin cancer. Wear gloves or use a barrier cream if necessary. Change out of oil-soaked clothes and do not keep oily rags in your pocket.
• Air conditioning refrigerant forms a poisonous gas if exposed to a naked flame (including a cigarette). It can also cause skin burns on contact.

Asbestos

• Asbestos dust can cause cancer if inhaled or swallowed. Asbestos may be found in gaskets and in brake and clutch linings. When dealing with such components it is safest to assume that they contain asbestos.

Special hazards

Hydrofluoric acid

• This extremely corrosive acid is formed when certain types of synthetic rubber, found in some O-rings, oil seals, fuel hoses etc, are exposed to temperatures above 4000C. The rubber changes into a charred or sticky substance containing the acid. *Once formed, the acid remains dangerous for years. If it gets onto the skin, it may be necessary to amputate the limb concerned.*
• When dealing with a vehicle which has suffered a fire, or with components salvaged from such a vehicle, wear protective gloves and discard them after use.

The battery

• Batteries contain sulphuric acid, which attacks clothing, eyes and skin. Take care when topping-up or carrying the battery.
• The hydrogen gas given off by the battery is highly explosive. Never cause a spark or allow a naked light nearby. Be careful when connecting and disconnecting battery chargers or jump leads.

Air bags

• Air bags can cause injury if they go off accidentally. Take care when removing the steering wheel and trim panels. Special storage instructions may apply.

Diesel injection equipment

• Diesel injection pumps supply fuel at very high pressure. Take care when working on the fuel injectors and fuel pipes.

⚠ *Warning: Never expose the hands, face or any other part of the body to injector spray; the fuel can penetrate the skin with potentially fatal results.*

Remember...

DO

• Do use eye protection when using power tools, and when working under the vehicle.

• Do wear gloves or use barrier cream to protect your hands when necessary.

• Do get someone to check periodically that all is well when working alone on the vehicle.

• Do keep loose clothing and long hair well out of the way of moving mechanical parts.

• Do remove rings, wristwatch etc, before working on the vehicle – especially the electrical system.

• Do ensure that any lifting or jacking equipment has a safe working load rating adequate for the job.

DON'T

• Don't attempt to lift a heavy component which may be beyond your capability – get assistance.

• Don't rush to finish a job, or take unverified short cuts.

• Don't use ill-fitting tools which may slip and cause injury.

• Don't leave tools or parts lying around where someone can trip over them. Mop up oil and fuel spills at once.

• Don't allow children or pets to play in or near a vehicle being worked on.

The following pages are intended to help in dealing with common roadside emergencies and breakdowns. You will find more detailed fault finding information at the back of the manual, and repair information in the main chapters.

If your car won't start and the starter motor doesn't turn

☐ Open the bonnet and make sure that the battery terminals are clean and tight (unclip the battery cover for access).
☐ Switch on the headlights and try to start the engine. If the headlights go very dim when you're trying to start, the battery is probably flat. Get out of trouble by jump starting (see next page) using a friend's car.

If your car won't start even though the starter motor turns as normal

☐ Is there fuel in the tank?
☐ Has the engine immobiliser been deactivated? This should happen automatically, on inserting the ignition key. However, if a replacement key has been obtained (other than from a Ford dealer), it may not contain the transponder chip necessary to deactivate the system. Even 'proper' replacement keys have to be coded to work properly – a procedure for this is outlined in the vehicle handbook.
☐ Is there moisture on electrical components under the bonnet? Switch off the ignition, then wipe off any obvious dampness with a dry cloth. Remove the plastic cover on the top of the engine (where applicable). Spray a water-repellent aerosol product (WD-40 or equivalent) on ignition and fuel system electrical connectors like those shown in the photos. Pay special attention to the ignition coil wiring connector and HT leads (where applicable).

A Check that electrical connections are secure (with the ignition switched off) and spray them with a water-dispersant spray like WD-40 if you suspect a problem due to damp.

B Check the security and condition of the battery connections.

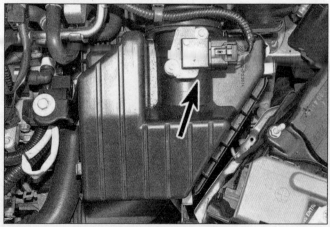

C Check the mass airflow sensor wiring plug

D Check that none of the engine compartment fuses have blown

Jump starting

When jump-starting a car using a booster battery, observe the following precautions:

✓ Before connecting the booster battery, make sure that the ignition is switched off.
✓ Ensure that all electrical equipment (lights, heater, wipers, etc) is switched off.
✓ Take note of any special precautions printed on the battery case.
✓ Make sure that the booster battery is the same voltage as the discharged one in the vehicle.

✓ If the battery is being jump-started from the battery in another vehicle, the two vehicles MUST NOT TOUCH each other.
✓ Make sure that the transmission is in neutral (or PARK, in the case of automatic transmission).

HAYNES HiNT *Jump starting will get you out of trouble, but you must correct whatever made the battery go flat in the first place. There are three possibilities:*

1 *The battery has been drained by repeated attempts to start, or by leaving the lights on.*

2 *The charging system is not working properly (alternator drivebelt slack or broken, alternator wiring fault or alternator itself faulty).*

3 *The battery itself is at fault (electrolyte low, or battery worn out).*

1 Connect one end of the red jump lead to the positive (+) terminal of the flat battery

2 Connect the other end of the red lead to the positive (+) terminal of the booster battery.

3 Connect one end of the black jump lead to the negative (-) terminal of the booster battery

4 Connect the other end of the black jump lead to a bolt or bracket on the engine block, well away from the battery, on the vehicle to be started.

5 Make sure that the jump leads will not come into contact with the fan, drivebelts or other moving parts of the engine. Start the engine using the booster battery and run it at idle speed. Switch on the lights, rear window demister and heater blower motor, then disconnect the junp leads in the reverse order of connection. Turn off the lights etc.

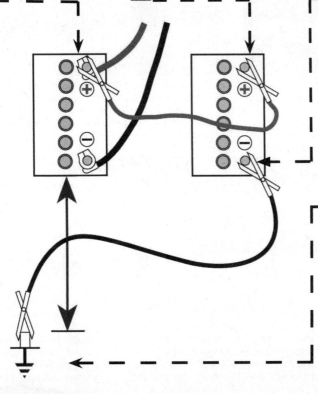

Wheel changing

Warning: Do not change a wheel in a situation where you risk being hit by other traffic. On busy roads, try to stop in a lay-by or a gateway. Be wary of passing traffic while changing the wheel – it is easy to become distracted by the job in hand.

Preparation

- ☐ When a puncture occurs, stop as soon as it is safe to do so.
- ☐ Park on firm level ground, if possible, and well out of the way of other traffic.
- ☐ Use hazard warning lights if necessary.

- ☐ If you have one, use a warning triangle to alert other drivers of your presence.
- ☐ Apply the handbrake and engage first or reverse gear (or P on models with automatic transmission).

- ☐ Chock the wheel diagonally opposite the one being removed – a couple of large stones will do for this.
- ☐ If the ground is soft, use a flat piece of wood to spread the load under the jack.

Changing the wheel

Note: *Most models are supplied a Tyre Repair Kit (TRK). A spare wheel and tyre are available and there is sufficient space in the load area to carry one. If possible always upgrade the TRK to a proper spare wheel and tyre.*

The spare wheel and tools are stored in the side storage pockets of the luggage compartment. Open the left-hand cover panel and remove the jack and tool kit.

Where applicable, using the flat end of the wheel brace, prise off the wheel trim or

centre cover for access to the wheel nuts. Models with alloy wheels may have special locking nuts – these are removed with a special tool, which should be provided with the wheel brace (or it may be in the glovebox).

1 Slacken each wheel nut by a half turn, using the wheel brace. If the nuts are too tight, DON'T stand on the wheelbrace to undo them – call for assistance from one of the motoring organisations.

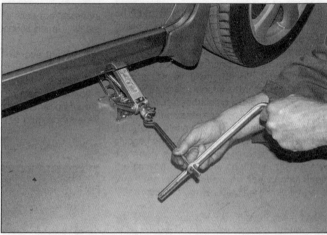

2 Two jacking points are provided on each side – use the one nearest the punctured wheel. Locate the jack head in the groove at the jacking point in the lowersill flange (don't jack the vehicle at any other point of the sill, nor on a plastic panel). Turn the jack handle clockwiseuntil the wheel is raised clear of the ground.

3 Remove the wheel nuts and store the punctured wheel under the sill while the spare is fitted

4 Fit the spare wheel, and screw on the nuts. Lightly tighten the nuts with the wheel brace. Remove the punctured wheel from the sill and then lower the vehicle to the ground. Securely tighten the wheel nuts, then refit the wheel trim or centre cover, as applicable.

Finally . . .

- ☐ Remove the wheel chocks. Stow the punctured wheel and tools back in the luggage compartment, and secure them in position.
- ☐ Check the tyre pressure on the tyre just fitted. If it is low, or if you don't have a pressure gauge with you, drive slowly to the next garage and inflate the tyre to the correct pressure. In the case of the narrow 'space-saver' spare wheel this pressure is much higher than for a normal tyre.
- ☐ The wheel nuts should be slackened and retightened to the specified torque at the earliest possible opportunity.
- ☐ Have the punctured wheel repaired as soon as possible, or another puncture will leave you stranded.

Tyre Repair Kit (TRK)

The TRK is located in the left-hand load area storage compartment. Remove the compressor and fluid.

Remove any nails or debris stuck in the tyre where possible. Note it is not possible to repair large splits are tyre wall damage with the TRK.

Note: *If the tyre does not inflate within 10 minutes, the tyre is beyond repair.*

Note: *Drive for 10 minutes and recheck the tyre pressure. Do not exceed 50 mph at any time. Have the tyre repaired or replaced at the earliest opportunity. The TRK is only a temporary solution.*

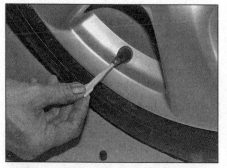

1 Remove the dust cap and (using the tool provided) remove the valve core

2 Shake the sealant bottle, remove the bottle cap and foil cover. Refit the cap and attach the hose to the bottle and tyre valve. Squeeze the bottle and fill the tyre with the sealant. Refit the valve core

3 Connect the compressor to the tyre valve and the electrical lead to the 12 power outlet. Turn the ignition on, switch on the compressor and inflate the tyre. When the tyre is inflated remove the compressor and fix the supplied warning labels to the wheel and the facia

Towing

When all else fails, you may find yourself having to get a tow home – or of course you may be helping somebody else. Long-distance recovery should only be done by a garage or breakdown service. For shorter distances, DIY towing using another car is easy enough, but observe the following points:

☐ Use a proper tow-rope – they are not expensive. The vehicle being towed must display an ON TOW sign in its rear window.

☐ Always turn the ignition key to the 'On' position when the vehicle is being towed, so that the steering lock is released, and

the direction indicator and brake lights work.

☐ The towing eye is of the screw-in type, and is found in the spare wheel well. The towing eye screws into a threaded hole, accessible after prising out a cover on the front bumper cover **(see illustrations)**.

☐ Before being towed, release the handbrake and make sure the transmission is in neutral. On models with automatic transmission, special precautions apply – do not exceed 30 mph or travel further than 30 miles, and the wheels must always roll forwards.

☐ Note that greater-than-usual pedal pressure will be required to operate the brakes, since the vacuum servo unit is only operational with the engine running.

☐ The driver of the car being towed must keep the tow-rope taut at all times to avoid snatching.

☐ Make sure that both drivers know the route before setting off.

☐ Only drive at moderate speeds and keep the distance towed to a minimum. Drive smoothly and allow plenty of time for slowing down at junctions.

Remove the cover

Screw in the towing eye...

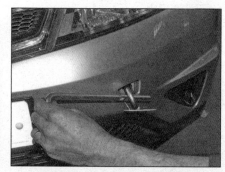

...and tighten it with the wheel brace

Identifying leaks

Puddles on the garage floor or drive, or obvious wetness under the bonnet or underneath the car, suggest a leak that needs investigating. It can sometimes be difficult to decide where the leak is coming from, especially if an engine undershield is fitted. Leaking oil or fluid can also be blown rearwards by the passage of air under the car, giving a false impression of where the problem lies.

 Warning: Most automotive oils and fluids are poisonous. Wash them off skin, and change out of contaminated clothing, without delay.

 The smell of a fluid leaking from the car may provide a clue to what's leaking. Some fluids are distinctively coloured. It may help to remove the engine undershield, clean the car carefully and to park it over some clean paper overnight as an aid to locating the source of the leak. Remember that some leaks may only occur while the engine is running.

Sump oil

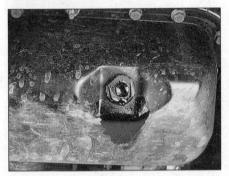

Engine oil may leak from the drain plug...

Oil from filter

...or from the base of the oil filter.

Gearbox oil

Gearbox oil can leak from the seals at the inboard ends of the driveshafts.

Antifreeze

Leaking antifreeze often leaves a crystalline deposit like this.

Brake fluid

A leak occurring at a wheel is almost certainly brake fluid.

Power steering fluid

Power steering fluid may leak from the pipe connectors on the steering rack.

Introduction

There are some very simple checks which need only take a few minutes to carry out, but which could save you a lot of inconvenience and expense.

These checks require no great skill or special tools, and the small amount of time they take to perform could prove to be very well spent, for example:

☐ Keeping an eye on tyre condition and pressures, will not only help to stop them wearing out prematurely, but could also save your life.

☐ Many breakdowns are caused by electrical problems. Battery-related faults are particularly common, and a quick check on a regular basis will often prevent the majority of these.

☐ If your car develops a brake fluid leak, the first time you might know about it is when your brakes don't work properly. Checking the level regularly will give advance warning of this kind of problem.

☐ If the oil or coolant levels run low, the cost of repairing any engine damage will be far greater than fixing the leak, for example.

Underbonnet check points

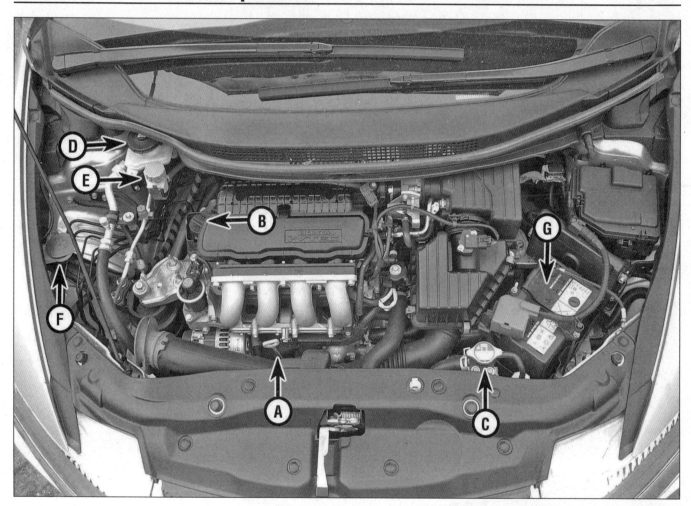

▲ **1.4 litre petrol engine**

A *Engine oil level dipstick*
B *Engine oil filler cap*
C *Coolant expansion tank*
D *Brake fluid reservoir*
E *Clutch fluid reservoir*
F *Screen washer fluid reservoir*
G *Battery*

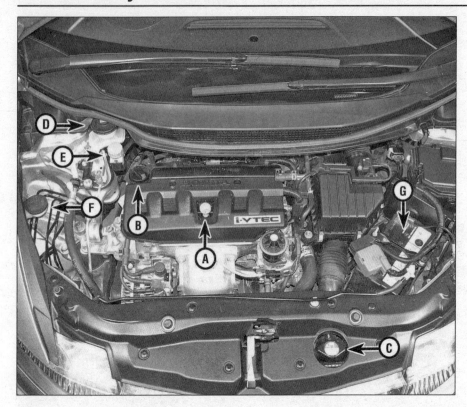

◄ 1.8 litre petrol engine

A *Engine oil level dipstick*
B *Engine oil filler cap*
C *Coolant expansion tank*
D *Brake fluid reservoir*
E *Clutch fluid reservoir*
F *Screen washer fluid reservoir*
G *Battery*

◄ 2.2 litre diesel engine

A *Engine oil level dipstick*
B *Engine oil filler cap*
C *Coolant expansion tank*
D *Brake fluid reservoir*
E *Clutch fluid reservoir*
F *Screen washer fluid reservoir*
G *Battery*

Engine oil level

Before you start

✔ Make sure that the car is on level ground.
✔ Check the oil level before the car is driven, or at least 5 minutes after the engine has been switched off.

 HAYNES HiNT *If the oil is checked immediately after driving the vehicle, some of the oil will remain in the upper engine components, resulting in an inaccurate reading on the dipstick.*

The correct oil

Modern engines place great demands on their oil. It is very important that the correct oil for your car is used **(see** *Lubricants and fluids***).**

Car care

● If you have to add oil frequently, you should check whether you have any oil leaks. Place some clean paper under the car overnight, and check for stains in the morning. If there are no leaks, then the engine may be burning oil.
● Always maintain the level between the upper and lower dipstick marks (see photo 2). If the level is too low, severe engine damage may occur. Oil seal failure may result if the engine is overfilled by adding too much oil.

1 The dipstick is located at the front of the engine (see Underbonnet check points for exact location). Withdraw the dipstick. Using a clean rag or paper towel, remove all oil from the dipstick.

2 Insert the dipstick into the tube as far as it will go, then withdraw it again.

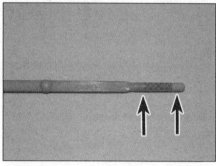

3 Note the oil level on the dipstick. It should be between the upper and lower marks. (1.8 litre shown, but all models are similar). If the oil level is only just above, or below, the MIN mark, topping-up is required.

4 Oil is added through the filler cap. Unscrew the filler cap and top.up the level. A funnel may be useful in reducing spillage. Add the oil slowly, checking the level on the dipstick often, and allowing time for the oil to run to the sump. Add oil until the level is just up to the MAX mark on the dipstick – don't overfill (see Car care)

Washer fluid level

● The windscreen washer reservoir also supplies the tailgate washer jet, where applicable. On models so equipped, the same reservoir also serves the headlight washers.
● Screenwash additives not only keep the windscreen clean during bad weather, they also prevent the washer system freezing in cold weather – which is when you are likely to need it most. Don't top-up using plain water, as the screenwash will become diluted, and will freeze in cold weather.

Caution: On no account use engine coolant antifreeze in the screen washer system – this may damage the paintwork.

1 The washer fluid reservoir filler neck is located in the right-hand side of the engine compartment. The filler cap incorporates a dipstick.

2 When topping-up the reservoir, add a screenwash additive in the quantities recommended on the additive bottle.

Coolant level

Warning: Do not attempt to remove the expansion tank pressure cap when the engine is hot, as there is a very great risk of scalding. Do not leave open containers of coolant about, as it is poisonous.

Car Care

● With a sealed-type cooling system, adding coolant should not be necessary on a regular basis. If frequent topping-up is required, it is likely there is a leak. Check the radiator, all hoses and joint faces for signs of staining or wetness, and rectify as necessary

● It is important that antifreeze is used in the cooling system all year round, not just during the winter months. Don't top up with water alone, as the antifreeze will become diluted.
● Petrol models have a coolant reservoir. If the reservoir is empty remove the radiator cap and check the level in the radiator

1 Coolant level varies with the temperature of the engine, and is visible through the expansion tank. Some models have a separate (non pressurised coolant reservoir). When the engine is cold, the coolant level should be between the MAX and MIN marks on the front of the reservoir. When the engine is hot, thelevel may rise slightly above the MAX mark.

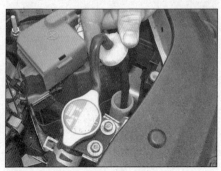

2 If topping-up is necessary, wait until the engine is cold. Slowly unscrew the expansion tank cap or remove to release any pressure present in the cooling system, and remove it. On models fitted with a separate reservoir remove the filler cap

3 Add a mixture of water and anti-freeze to the expansion tank until the coolant level is halfway between the level marks. Use only the specified antifreeze. Refit the cap and tighten it securely.

Wiper blades

✔ Only fit good-quality wiper blades.
✔ When removing an old wiper blade, note how it is fitted. Fitting new blades can be a tricky exercise, and noting how the old blade came off can save time.
✔ While the wiper blade is removed, take care not to knock the wiper arm from its locked position, or it could strike the glass.

● Offer the new blade into position the same way round as the old one. Ensure that it clicks home securely, otherwise it may come off in use, damaging the glass.
Note: *Fitting details for wiper blades vary according to model, and according to whether genuine Ford wiper blades have been fitted. Use the procedures and illustrations shown as a guide for your car.*

HAYNES HiNT *If smearing is still a problem despite fitting new wiper blades, try cleaning the glass with neat screenwash additive or methylated spirit.*

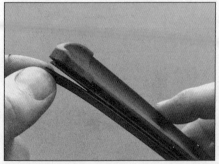

1 5.3q Check the condition of the wiper blades; if they are cracked or show any signs of deterioration, or if the glassswept area is smeared, renew them. Wiper blades should be renewed annually, regardless of their apparent condition.

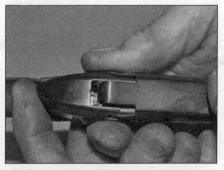

2 Depress the catch and...

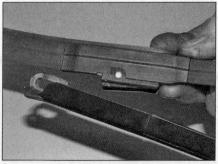

3 ...unhook the blade

Brake (and clutch) fluid level

Warning: Brake fluid can harm your eyes and damage painted surfaces, so use extreme caution when handling and pouring it.

Warning: Do not use fluid that has been standing open for some time, as it absorbs moisture from the air, which can cause a dangerous loss of braking effectiveness.

Warning: The fluid level in the reservoir will drop slightly as the brake pads wear down, but the fluid level must never be allowed to drop below the MIN mark.

Note: *All manual transmission models have a hydraulically-operated clutch, which uses the same fluid as the braking system.*

Before you start
✔ Make sure that your car is on level ground.

Safety first!
● If the reservoir requires repeated topping-up this is an indication of a fluid leak somewhere in the system, which should be investigated immediately.
● If a leak is suspected, the car should not be driven until the braking system has been checked. Never take any risks where brakes are concerned.

1 The brake fluid reservoir is located on the right-hand side of the engine compartment. Wipe clean the area around the filler cap, before removing the cap

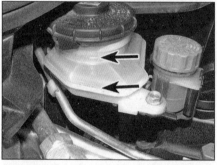

2 The MAX and MIN marks are indicated on the front of the reservoir. The fluid level must be kept between the marks at all times.

3 If topping-up is necessary, first wipe clean the area around the filler cap to prevent dirt entering the hydraulic system. Remove the reservoir cap and carefully lift it out of position. Inspect the reservoir; if the fluid is dirty, the hydraulic system should be drained and refilled.

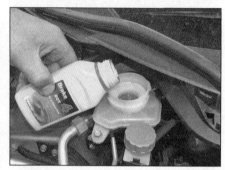

4 Carefully add fluid, taking care not to spill it onto the surrounding components. Use only the specified fluid; mixing different types can cause damage to the system. After topping-up to the correct level, securely refit the cap and wipe off any spilt fluid.

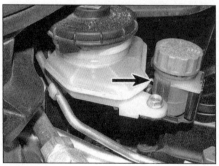

5 The clutch fluid reservoir sits in front of the brake fluid reservoir

6 The MIN and MAX marks are shown on the reservoir

7 Top up the reservoir as required. Note the cloth protecting the paint work

Tyre condition and pressure

It is very important that tyres are in good condition, and at the correct pressure – having a tyre failure at any speed is highly dangerous. Tyre wear is influenced by driving style – harsh braking and acceleration, or fast cornering, will all produce more rapid tyre wear. As a general rule, the front tyres wear out faster the the rears. Interchanging the tyres from front to rear ("rotating" the tyres) may result in more even wear. However, if this is completely effective, you may have the expense of replacing all four tyres at once!

Remove any nails or stones embedded in the tread before they penetrate the tyre to cause deflation. If removal of a nail does reveal that the tyre has been punctured, refit the nail so that its point of penetration is marked. Then immediately change the wheel, and have the tyre repaired by a tyre dealer.

Regularly check the tyres for damage in the form of cuts or bulges, especially in the side walls. Periodically remove the wheels, and clean any dirt or mud from the inside and outside surfaces. Examine the wheel rims for signs of rusting, corrosion or other damage. Light alloy wheels are easily damaged by "kerbing" whilst parking; steel wheels may also become dented or buckled. A new wheel is very often the only way to overcome severe damage.

New tyres should be balanced when they are fitted, but it may become necessary to re-balance them as they ear, or if the balance weights fitted to the wheel rim should fall off. Unbalanced tyres will wear more quickly, as will the steering and suspension components. Wheel imbalance is normally signified by vibration, particularly at t certain speed (typically around 50 mph). If this vibration is felt only through the steering wheel, then it is likely that just the front wheels need balancing. If, however, the vibration is felt through the whole car, the rear wheels could be out of balance. Wheel balancing should be carried out by a tyre dealer or garage.

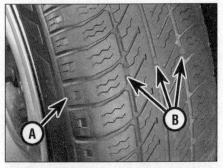

1 Tread Depth - visual check
The original tyres have tread wear safety bands (B), which will appear when the trad depth reaches approximately 1.6 mm. The band positions are indicated by a triangular mark on the tyre sidewall (A)

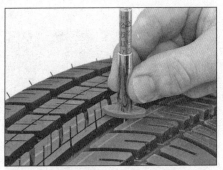

2 Tread Depth - manual check
Alternatively, tread wear can be monitored with a simple, inexpensive device known as a tread depth indicator gauge

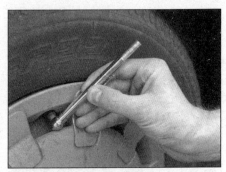

3 Tyre Pressure Check
Check the tyre pressures regularly with the tyres cold. Do not adjust the tyre pressures immediately after the vehicle has been used, or an inaccurate setting will result

Tyre tread wear patterns

Shoulder Wear

Underinflation (wear on both sides)
Under-inflation will cause overheating of the tyre, because the tyre will flex too much, and the tread will not sit correctly on the road surface. This will cause a loss of grip and excessive wear, not to mention the danger of sudden tyre failure due to heat build-up.
Check and adjust pressures
Incorrect wheel camber (wear on one side)
Repair or renew suspension parts
Hard cornering
Reduce speed!

Centre Wear

Overinflation
Over-inflation will cause rapid wear of the centre part of the tyre tread, coupled with reduced grip, harsher ride, and the danger of shock damage occurring in the tyre casing.
Check and adjust pressures

If you sometimes have to inflate your car's tyres to the higher pressures specified for maximum load or sustained high speed, don't forget to reduce the pressures to normal afterwards.

Uneven Wear

Front tyres may wear unevenly as a result of wheel misalignment. Most tyre dealers and garages can check and adjust the wheel alignment (or "tracking") for a modest charge.
Incorrect camber or castor
Repair or renew suspension parts
Malfunctioning suspension
Repair or renew suspension parts
Unbalanced wheel
Balance tyres
Incorrect toe setting
Adjust front wheel alignment
Note: *The feathered edge of the tread which typifies toe wear is best checked by feel.*

Battery

Caution: Before carrying out any work on the vehicle battery, read the precautions given in 'Safety first!' at the start of this manual.

✔ Make sure that the battery tray is in good condition, and that the clamp is tight. Corrosion on the tray, retaining clamp and the battery itself can be removed with a solution of water and baking soda. Thoroughly rinse all cleaned areas with water. Any metal parts damaged by corrosion should be covered with a zinc-based primer, then painted.

✔ Periodically (approximately every three months), check the charge condition of the battery, as described in Chapter #.

✔ If the battery is flat, and you need to jump start your vehicle, see *Jump Starting*.

1 The battery is located in the left-hand front corner of the engine compartment.

2 Check the tightness of battery clamps to ensure good electrical connections. You should not be able to move them. Also check each cable for cracks and frayed conductors.

3 If corrosion (white, fluffy deposits) is evident, remove the cables from the battery terminals, clean them with a small wire brush, then refit them. Automotive stores sell a tool for cleaning the battery post...

4 ...as well as the battery cable clamps

Electrical systems

✔ Check all external lights and the horn. Refer to Chapter 12 Section 2 for details if any of the circuits are found to be inoperative.

✔ Visually check all accessible wiring connectors, harnesses and retaining clips for security, and for signs of chafing or damage.

HAYNES HiNT *If you need to check your brake lights and indicators unaided, back up to a wall or garage door and operate the lights. The reflected light should show if they are working properly.*

1 If a single indicator light, stop-light or headlight has failed, it is likely that a bulb has blown and will need to be renewed. Refer to Chapter 12 for details. If both stop-lights have failed, it is possible that the switch has failed (see Chapter 9).

2 If more than one indicator light or tail light has failed, it is likely that either a fuse has blown or that there is a fault in the circuit (see Chapter 12). The main fusebox is located on the right-hand side of the facia below the steering wheel. The auxiliary fuse/relay box is located on the left-hand side of the engine compartment – unclip and remove the cover for access.

3 To renew a blown fuse, simply pull it out and fit a new fuse of the correct rating (see Chapter 12). Spare fuses, and a fuse removal tool, are provided on the inside of the auxiliary fusebox lid. If the fuse blows again, it is important that you find out why – a complete checking procedure is given in Chapter 12.

Lubricants and fluids

Engine oil:

Petrol engines . . . . Honda HFS 5/40 or Honda HFS 0/20 or oils conforming to ACEA A1/B1, A3/B3 or A5/B5 (0/30 0/40 5/30 or 5/40 weight oils)

Diesel engines. . . . . Honda diesel oil (0/30 synthetic)

Cooling system. . . . . Honda coolant Type 2

Automatic transmission . . . . Honda ATF-Z1

Manual transmission . . . . Honda MTF-3

Brake and clutch hydraulic system . . . . Honda brake fluid or DOT 3 or DOT 4

Tyre pressures

Tyre pressures (tyres cold):	Front	Rear
Normally-laden (up to 3 people):		
205/55 R16 91V	2.1 bars (30 psi)	2.1 bars 30 psi)
Fully-laden (with more than 3 persons):		
205/55 R16 91V	2.2 bars (31 psi)	2.2 bars (31 psi)
When towing:		
205/55 R16 91V	2.2 bars (31 psi)	2.6 bars (38 psi)

Note: *Pressures apply to original-equipment tyres, and may vary if any other make of tyre is fitted; check with the tyre manufacturer or supplier for the correct pressures if necessary.*

Chapter 1A
Routine maintenance and servicing – petrol models

Contents

Section number

Air filter element renewal 17
Auxiliary drivebelt check and renewal 20
Brake fluid renewal 23
Brake pads, shoes and discs check 7
Coolant strength check and renewal 25
Driveshaft rubber gaiter and joint check 10
Engine compartment wiring check 6
Engine oil and filter renewal 3
Exhaust system check 8
General Information 1
Handbrake check and adjustment 15
Hinge and lock lubrication 12
Lights and horn operation check 4

Section number

Pollen filter renewal 21
Regular maintenance 2
Remote control battery renewal 24
Road test 14
Roadwheel nut tightness check 13
Seat belt check 16
Spark plug renewal 19
Steering, suspension and roadwheel check 9
Transmission fluid 22
Underbody and fuel/brake line check 11
Underbonnet check for fluid leaks and hose condition 5
Valve clearances – check and adjust 18

Degrees of difficulty

Easy, suitable for
novice with little
experience

Fairly easy, suitable
for beginner with
some experience

Fairly difficult,
suitable for competent
DIY mechanic

Difficult, suitable
for experienced DIY
mechanic

Very difficult,
suitable for expert
DIY or professional

Lubricants and fluids .... Refer to end of *Weekly checks*

Capacities

Engine oil (including filter):
1.4 litre engines	3.6 litres
1.8 litre engines	3.7 litres

Cooling system (approximate at coolant change):
1.4 engines..	4.0 litres
1.8 engines..	5.3 litres
Manual transmission fluid (at change)	1.4 litres
Automatic transmission fluid (at change).....................	2.4 litres

Washer fluid reservoir:
Without headlamp washers	2.5 litres
With headlamp washers................................	5.8 litres
Fuel tank 50.0 litres	

Cooling system

Antifreeze mixture: ....
50% antifreeze	Protection down to –37°C
55% antifreeze	Protection down to –45°C

Note: *Refer to antifreeze manufacturer for latest recommendations.*

Brakes

Brake friction material. Minimum thickness (not including backing) ...	1.6 mm
Brake disc:	
Maximum runout	0.10 mm
Minimum thickness (front)	21.0 mm
Minimum thickness (rear)	7.0 mm

Ignition system

Spark plug gap
1.4 litre (engine code L13A)	1.2 – 1.3 mm
1.4 litre (engine code L13Z)	1.0 – 1.1 mm
1.8 litre	1.0 -1.1 mm

Valve clearances

1.4 litre engines:
Inlet	0.15-0.19 mm
Exhaust..	0.26 – 0.30 mm

1.8 litre engines
Inlet	0.18 – 0.22 mm
Exhaust..	0.23 – 0.27 mm

Remote control battery

Type	CR1616

Torque wrench settings

	Nm	lbf ft
Alternator bolts...	24	17
Battery tray bolts	22	16
Engine block coolant drain bolt	39	29
Engine oil drain plug....................................	39	29
Engine oil filter housing cap:	25	18
Fuel filter	15	11
Ignition coil bolts	12	9
Transmission drain plug (manual).........................	39	29
Transmission drain plug (automatic).......................	49	36
Transmission filler plug..................................	44	33
Transmission level plug	12	9
Roadwheel nuts	108	80
Spark Plugs	27	20
Valve adjuster lock nut	14	10

The maintenance intervals in this manual are provided with the assumption that you, not the dealer, will be carrying out the work. These are the minimum maintenance intervals recommended by us for vehicles driven daily. If you wish to keep your vehicle in peak condition at all times, you may wish to perform some of these procedures more often. We encourage frequent maintenance, because it enhances the efficiency, performance and resale value of your vehicle.

If the vehicle is driven in dusty areas, used to tow a trailer, or driven frequently at slow speeds (idling in traffic) or on short journeys, more frequent maintenance intervals are recommended.

When the vehicle is new, it should be serviced by a dealer service department (or other workshop recognised by the vehicle manufacturer as providing the same standard of service) in order to preserve the warranty. The vehicle manufacturer may reject warranty claims if you are unable to prove that servicing has been carried out as and when specified, using only original equipment parts or parts certified to be of equivalent quality.

Every 250 miles or weekly
☐ Refer to *Weekly checks*

Every 12 000 miles or 12 months, whichever comes first
In addition to the items listed above, carry out the following:
☐ Renew the engine oil and filter (Section 3)
☐ Check the operation of the lights and the horn (Section 4)
☐ Check under the bonnet for fluid leaks and hose condition (Section 5)
☐ Check the condition of the engine compartment wiring (Section 6)
☐ Check the condition of the seat belts (Section 16)
☐ Check the condition of the brake pads, shoes and discs (Section 7)
☐ Check the exhaust system (Section 8)
☐ Check the steering and suspension components for condition and security (Section 9)
☐ Check the condition of the driveshaft joints and gaiters (Section 10)
☐ Check the underbody and all fuel/brake lines (Section 11)
☐ Lubricate all hinges and locks (Section 12)
☐ Check roadwheel nut tightness (Section 13)
☐ Carry out a road test (Section 14)
☐ Check and if necessary adjust the handbrake (Section 15)
☐ Check the antifreeze/inhibitor strength (Section 25)

Every 25 000 miles or 2 years, whichever comes first
In addition to the items listed above, carry out the following:
☐ Renew the air filter (Section 17)
☐ Renew the pollen filter (Section 21)*
☐ Check the condition of the auxiliary drivebelt (Section 20)

Note: *If the vehicle is used in dusty conditions, the air filter and pollen filter should be renewed more frequently.*

Every 62 000 miles or 5 years, whichever comes first
☐ Renew the engine coolant (Section 25)

Note: *The second coolant replacement should be performed at 100 000 miles or 3 years after the first coolant change*

☐ Check the valve clearances (Section 18)

Every 75 000 or 8 years
☐ Replace the spark plugs (Section 19)

Note: *The second and subsequent spark plug changes should be after every 60 000 miles or 5 years*

☐ Renew the manual transmission fluid (Section 22)
☐ Renew the automatic transmission fluid (Section 22)

Every 3 years, regardless of mileage
☐ Renew the brake fluid (Section 23)
☐ Renew the remote control battery (Section 24)

Underbonnet view of a 1.8 litre model

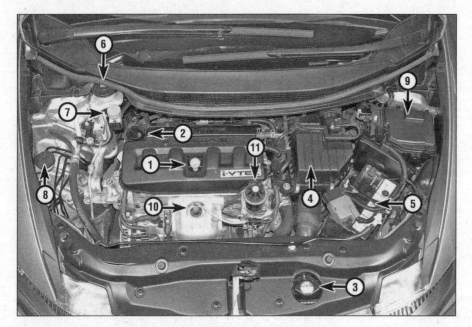

1 Engine oil level dipstick
2 Oil filler cap
3 Coolant expansion tank cap
4 Air filter element cover
5 Battery
6 Brake fluid reservoir
7 Clutch fluid reservoir
8 Washer fluid reservoir cap
9 Fuse/relay box
10 Oxygen sensor
11 EGR Valve

Front underbody view (undershield removed)

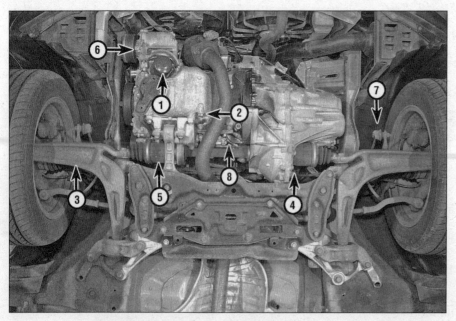

1 Oil filter
2 Engine oil drain plug
3 Suspension control arm
4 Transmission drain plug
5 Right-hand driveshaft
6 Air conditioning compressor
7 Anti-roll bar drop link
8 Starter motor

Rear underbody view

1 Rear silencer
2 Handbrake cable
3 Beam axle
4 Flexible brake hose
5 Shock absorber
6 EVAP Carbon canister
7 Coil spring

1 General Information

1 This Chapter is designed to help the home mechanic maintain his/her vehicle for safety, economy, long life and peak performance.
2 The Chapter contains a master maintenance schedule, followed by Sections dealing specifically with each task in the schedule. Visual checks, adjustments, component renewal and other helpful items are included. Refer to the accompanying illustrations of the engine compartment and the underside of the vehicle for the locations of the various components.
3 Servicing your vehicle in accordance with the mileage/time maintenance schedule and the following Sections will provide a planned maintenance programme, which should result in a long and reliable service life. This is a comprehensive plan, so maintaining some items but not others at the specified service intervals, will not produce the same results.
4 As you service your vehicle, you will discover that many of the procedures can – and should – be grouped together, because of the particular procedure being performed, or because of the proximity of two otherwise-unrelated components to one another. For example, if the vehicle is raised for any reason, the exhaust can be inspected at the same time as the suspension and steering components.
5 The first step in this maintenance programme is to prepare yourself before the actual work begins. Read through all the Sections relevant to the work to be carried out, then make a list and gather all the parts and tools required. If a problem is encountered, seek advice from a parts specialist, or a dealer service department.

2 Regular maintenance

1 If, from the time the vehicle is new, the routine maintenance schedule is followed closely, and frequent checks are made of fluid levels and high-wear items, as suggested throughout this manual, the engine will be kept in relatively good running condition, and the need for additional work will be minimised.
2 It is possible that there will be times when the engine is running poorly due to the lack of regular maintenance. This is even more likely if a used vehicle, which has not received regular and frequent maintenance checks, is purchased. In such cases, additional work may need to be carried out, outside of the regular maintenance intervals.
3 If engine wear is suspected, a compression test (refer to Chapter 2A or 2B, as applicable) will provide valuable information regarding the overall performance of the main internal components. Such a test can be used as a basis to decide on the extent of the work to be carried out. If, for example, a compression test indicates serious internal engine wear, conventional maintenance as described in this Chapter will not greatly improve the performance of the engine, and may prove a waste of time and money, unless extensive overhaul work is carried out first.
4 The following series of operations are those most often required to improve the performance of a generally poor-running engine:

Primary operations

a) Clean, inspect and test the battery (refer to 'Weekly checks').
b) Check all the engine-related fluids (refer to 'Weekly checks').
c) Check the condition and tension of the auxiliary drivebelt (Section 20).
d) Renew the spark plugs (Section 19).
e) Check the condition of the air filter, and renew if necessary (Section 17).
f) Check the condition of all hoses, and check for fluid leaks (Section 5).

5 If the above operations do not prove fully effective, carry out the following secondary operations:

Secondary operations

6 All items listed under Primary operations, plus the following:
a) Check the charging system (refer to Chapter 5A).
b) Check the ignition system (refer to Chapter 5B).
c) Check the fuel system (refer to Chapter 4A).

3.5 Unscrew the oil filler cap

3.6 Wearing gloves, remove the drain plug

3.8 Always fit a new sealing washer

3 Engine oil and filter renewal

1 Frequent oil and filter changes are the most important preventative maintenance procedures which can be undertaken by the DIY owner. As engine oil ages, it becomes diluted and contaminated, which leads to premature engine wear.

2 Before starting this procedure, gather together all the necessary tools and materials. Also make sure that you have plenty of clean rags and newspapers handy, to mop-up any spills. Ideally, the engine oil should be warm, as it will drain more easily, and more built-up sludge will be removed with it.

3 Take care not to touch the exhaust (especially the catalytic converter) or any other hot parts of the engine when working under the vehicle. To avoid any possibility of scalding, and to protect yourself from possible skin irritants and other harmful contaminants in used engine oils, it is advisable to wear gloves when carrying out this work.

4 Firmly apply the handbrake, then jack up the front of the vehicle and support it on axle stands (see *Jacking and vehicle support* in the Reference chapter). Release the fasteners and remove the engine access panel – where fitted.

5 Open the bonnet and remove the oil filler cap **(see illustration)**.

6 Using a spanner, or preferably a socket and bar, slacken the sump drain plug about half a turn. Position the draining container under the drain plug, then remove the plug completely **(see illustration)**.

7 Allow some time for the oil to drain, noting that it may be necessary to reposition the container as the oil flow slows to a trickle.

8 After all the oil has drained, wipe the drain plug with a clean rag. Discard the sealing washer – a new one must be fitted **(see illustration)**. Clean the area around the drain plug opening, and refit the plug complete with the seal and tighten it to the specified torque.

9 Move the container into position under the oil filter, which is located at the rear of the cylinder block.

10 Use an oil filter removal tool if necessary **(see illustrations)** to slacken the filter initially, then unscrew it by hand the rest of the way. Empty the oil from the old filter into the container, then puncture the top of the filter, and allow the remaining oil to drain from the filter into the container.

11 Use a clean rag to remove all oil, dirt and sludge from the filter sealing area on the engine.

12 Apply a light coating of clean engine oil to the sealing ring on the new filter, then screw the filter into position on the engine **(see illustrations)**. Tighten the filter firmly by hand only – do not use any tools.

13 Some genuine Honda filters have a series of numbers or triangles printed around the base of the filter. Where these are present, spin the filter into contact with the engine block and note the triangle that shows at the bottom of the filter and then:

● If 1 or one triangle is shown tighten the filter until 4 or four triangles are shown
● If 2 or two triangles are shown tighten the filter until 1 or one triangle is shown
● If 3 or three triangles are shown tighten the filter until 2 or two triangles are shown
● If 4 or four triangles are shown tighten the filter until 3 or three triangles are shown

14 Remove the old oil and all tools from under the car, refit the engine undershield (where applicable), then lower the car to the ground.

15 Fill the engine, using the correct grade and type of oil (refer to *Weekly checks* for details of topping-up). An oil can spout or funnel may help to reduce spillage. Pour in half the specified quantity of oil first, then wait a few minutes for the oil to run to the sump.

16 Continue adding oil a small quantity at a time until the level is up to the MIN mark on the dipstick. Adding around 0.5 litre of oil will now bring the level up to the MAX on the dipstick

3.10a Use the specific oil filter tool...

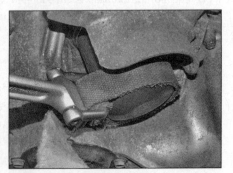

3.10b...or alternatively a strap wrench or similar tool

3.12a Oil the the seal on the new filter...

3.12b...and install it. Tighten by hand ONLY

– do not worry if a little too much goes in, as some of the excess will be taken up in filling the oil filter. Refit the dipstick and the filler cap.

17 Start the engine and run it for a few minutes; check for leaks around the oil filter and the sump drain plug. Note that there may be a few seconds delay before the oil pressure warning light goes out when the engine is started, as the oil circulates through the engine oil galleries and the new oil filter before the pressure builds-up.

18 Switch off the engine, and wait a few minutes for the oil to settle in the sump once more. With the new oil circulated and the filter completely full, recheck the level on the dipstick, and add more oil as necessary.

19 Dispose of the used engine oil and the old oil filter safely, with reference to General repair procedures in the Reference chapter of this manual. Many local recycling points have containers for waste oil, with oil filter disposal receptacles alongside.

4 Lights and horn operation check

1 With the ignition switched on where necessary, check the operation of all exterior lights.

2 Check the brake lights with the help of an assistant, or by reversing up close to a reflective door. Make sure that all the rear lights are capable of operating independently, without affecting any of the other lights – for example, switch on as many rear lights as possible, then try the brake lights. If any unusual results are found, this is usually due to an earth fault or other poor connection at that rear light unit.

3 Again with the help of an assistant or using a reflective surface, check as far as possible that the headlights work on both main and dipped beam.

4 Renew any defective bulbs with reference to Chapter 12.

5 Check the operation of all interior lights, including the glovebox and luggage area illumination lights. Switch on the ignition, and check that all relevant warning lights come on as expected – the vehicle handbook should give details of these. Now start the engine,

and check that the appropriate lights go out. When you are next driving at night, check that all the instrument panel and facia lighting works correctly. If any problems are found, refer to Chapter 12

6 Finally, choose an appropriate time of day to test the operation of the horn.

5 Underbonnet check for fluid leaks and hose condition

⚠️ *Warning: Renewal of air conditioning hoses must be left to a dealer service department or air conditioning specialist who has the equipment to depressurise the system safely. Never remove air conditioning components or hoses until the system has been depressurised.*

General

1 Visually inspect the engine joint faces, gaskets and seals for any signs of water or oil leaks. Pay particular attention to the areas around the cylinder head cover, cylinder head, oil filter and sump joint faces. Bear in mind that, over a period of time, some very slight seepage from these areas is to be expected – what you are really looking for is any indication of a serious leak. Should a leak be found, renew the offending gasket or oil seal by referring to the appropriate Chapters in this manual.

2 High temperatures in the engine compartment can cause the deterioration of the rubber and plastic hoses used for engine, accessory and emission systems operation. Periodic inspection should be made for cracks, loose clamps, material hardening and leaks.

3 When checking the hoses, ensure that all the cable-ties or clips used to retain the hoses are in place, and in good condition. Clips which are broken or missing can lead to chafing of the hoses, pipes or wiring, which could cause more serious problems in the future.

4 Carefully check the large top and bottom radiator hoses, along with the other smaller-diameter cooling system hoses and metal pipes; do not forget the heater hoses/pipes which run from the engine to the bulkhead. Inspect each hose along its entire length,

replacing any that is cracked, swollen or shows signs of deterioration. Cracks may become more apparent if the hose is squeezed, and may often be apparent at the hose ends.

5 Make sure that all hose connections are tight. If the large-diameter air hoses from the air cleaner are loose, they will leak air, and upset the engine idle quality **(see illustration)**. If the spring clamps that are used to secure some of the hoses appear to be slackening, they should be updated with worm-drive clips to prevent the possibility of leaks.

6 Some other hoses are secured to their fittings with clamps. Where clamps are used, check to be sure they haven't lost their tension, allowing the hose to leak. If clamps aren't used, make sure the hose has not expanded and/or hardened where it slips over the fitting, allowing it to leak.

7 Check all fluid reservoirs, filler caps, drain plugs and fittings, etc, looking for any signs of leakage of oil, transmission and/or brake hydraulic fluid, coolant and power steering fluid. Also check the clutch hydraulic fluid lines which lead from the fluid reservoir and slave cylinder (on the transmission).

8 If the vehicle is regularly parked in the same place, close inspection of the ground underneath it will soon show any leaks; ignore the puddle of water which will be left if the air conditioning system is in use. Place a clean piece of cardboard below the engine, and examine it for signs of contamination after the vehicle has been parked over it overnight – be aware, however, of the fire risk inherent in placing combustible material below the catalytic converter.

9 Remember that some leaks will only occur with the engine running, or when the engine is hot or cold. With the handbrake firmly applied, start the engine from cold, and let the engine idle while you examine the underside of the engine compartment for signs of leakage.

10 If an unusual smell is noticed inside or around the car, especially when the engine is thoroughly hot, this may point to the presence of a leak.

11 As soon as a leak is detected, its source must be traced and rectified. Where oil has been leaking for some time, it is usually necessary to use a steam cleaner, pressure washer or similar, to clean away the accumulated dirt, so that the exact source of the leak can be identified.

Vacuum hoses

12 It's quite common for vacuum hoses, especially those in the emissions system, to be colour-coded, or to be identified by coloured stripes moulded into them. Various systems require hoses with different wall thicknesses, collapse resistance and temperature resistance. When renewing hoses, be sure the new ones are made of the same material.

13 Often the only effective way to check a hose is to remove it completely from the vehicle. If more than one hose is removed, be sure to label the hoses and fittings to ensure correct installation **(see illustration)**.

5.5 Check the security of the air intake pipes

5.13 Check the security of the various vacuum hoses

5.16 Check the security of the fuel supply pipe.

6.5 Ensure all electrical connectors are securely clipped together

14 When checking vacuum hoses, be sure to include any plastic 'T' fittings in the check. Inspect the fittings for cracks, and check the hose where it fits over the fitting for distortion, which could cause leakage.

15 A small piece of vacuum hose (quarter-inch inside diameter) can be used as a stethoscope to detect vacuum leaks. Hold one end of the hose to your ear, and probe around vacuum hoses and fittings, listening for the 'hissing' sound characteristic of a vacuum leak.

⚠ *Warning: When probing with the vacuum hose stethoscope, be very careful not to come into contact with moving engine components such as the auxiliary drivebelt, radiator electric cooling fan, etc.*

Fuel hoses

⚠ *Warning: There are certain precautions which must be taken when inspecting or servicing fuel system components. Work in a well-ventilated area, and do not allow open flames (cigarettes, appliance pilot lights, etc) or bare light bulbs near the work area. Mop-up any spills immediately, and do not store fuel-soaked rags where they could ignite.*

16 Check all fuel hoses for deterioration and chafing. Check especially for cracks in areas where the hose bends, and also just before fittings, such as where a hose attaches to the fuel rail or pump **(see illustration)**.

17 High-quality fuel line, usually identified by the word 'Fluoroelastomer' printed on the hose, should be used for fuel line renewal. Never, under any circumstances, use non-reinforced vacuum line, clear plastic tubing or water hose as a substitute for fuel lines.

18 Spring type clamps may be used on fuel lines. These clamps often lose their tension over a period of time, and can be 'sprung' during removal. Renew all spring - type clamps with proper petrol pipe clips whenever a hose is renewed.

Metal pipes

19 Sections of metal piping are often used for fuel line between the fuel filter and the engine, and for some power steering and air conditioning applications. Check carefully to be sure the piping has not been bent or crimped, and that cracks have not started in the line; also check for signs of excessive corrosion.

20 If a section of metal fuel line must be renewed, only seamless steel piping should be used, since copper and aluminium piping don't have the strength necessary to withstand normal engine vibration.

21 Check the metal lines where they enter the brake master cylinder, ABS hydraulic unit or clutch master/slave cylinders (as applicable) for cracks in the lines or loose fittings. Any sign of brake fluid leakage calls for an immediate and thorough inspection.

6 Engine compartment wiring check

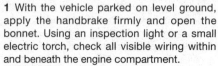

1 With the vehicle parked on level ground, apply the handbrake firmly and open the bonnet. Using an inspection light or a small electric torch, check all visible wiring within and beneath the engine compartment.

2 What you are looking for is wiring that is obviously damaged by chafing against sharp edges, or against moving suspension/transmission components and/or the auxiliary drivebelt, by being trapped or crushed between carelessly-refitted components, or melted by being forced into contact with the hot engine castings, coolant pipes, etc. In almost all cases, damage of this sort is caused in the first instance by incorrect routing on reassembly after previous work has been carried out.

3 Depending on the extent of the problem, damaged wiring may be repaired by rejoining the break or splicing-in a new length of wire, using solder to ensure a good connection, and remaking the insulation with adhesive insulating tape or heat-shrink tubing, as appropriate. If the damage is extensive, given the implications for the vehicle's future reliability, the best long-term answer may well be to renew that entire section of the loom, however expensive this may appear.

4 When the damage has been repaired, ensure that the wiring loom is re-routed correctly, so that it is clear of other components, and not stretched or kinked, and is secured out of harm's way using the plastic clips, guides and ties provided.

5 Check all electrical connectors, ensuring that they are clean, securely fastened, and that each is locked by its plastic tabs or wire clip, as appropriate **(see illustration)**. If any connector shows external signs of corrosion (accumulations of white or green deposits, or streaks of 'rust'), or if any is thought to be dirty, it must be unplugged and cleaned using electrical contact cleaner. If the connector pins are severely corroded, the connector must be renewed; note that this may mean the renewal of that entire section of the loom – see your local Honda dealer for details.

6 If the cleaner completely removes the corrosion to leave the connector in a satisfactory condition, it would be wise to pack the connector with a suitable material which will exclude dirt and moisture, preventing the corrosion from occurring again; a Honda dealer may be able to recommend a suitable product.

7 Check the condition of the battery connections – remake the connections or renew the leads if a fault is found (see Chapter 5A). Use the same techniques to ensure that all earth points in the engine compartment provide good electrical contact through clean, metal-to-metal joints, and that all are securely fastened.

7 Brake pads, shoes and discs check

1 The work described in this Sectionshould be carried out at the specified intervals, or whenever a defect is suspected in the braking system. Any of the following symptoms could indicate a potential brake system defect:

a) *The vehicle pulls to one side when the brake pedal is depressed.*

b) *The brakes make squealing, scraping or dragging noises when applied.*

c) *Brake pedal travel is excessive, or pedal feel is poor.*

d) *The brake fluid requires repeated topping-up. Note that, because the hydraulic clutch shares the same fluid as the braking system (see Chapter 6), this problem could be due to a leak in the clutch system.*

Front disc brakes

2 Apply the handbrake, then loosen the front wheel nuts. Jack up the front of the vehicle, and support it on axle stands (see *'Jacking and vehicle support'* in the Reference chapter).

3 For better access to the brake calipers, remove the wheels.

4 Look through the inspection window in the caliper, and check that the thickness of the friction lining material on each of the pads is not less than the recommended minimum

7.4 Measure the thickness of the brake pad friction material

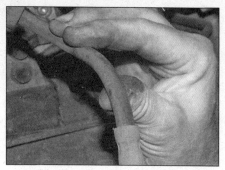

7.12 Check the condition of the rubber brake hoses by bending them slightly and looking for cracks

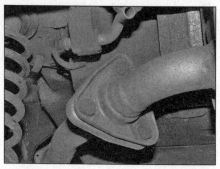

8.2 Check the condition of the exhaust joints and rubber mountings

thickness given in the Specifications **(see illustration)**.

5 If it is difficult to determine the exact thickness of the pad linings, or if you are at all concerned about the condition of the pads, then remove them from the calipers for further inspection (refer to Chapter 9).

6 Check the other caliper in the same way.

7 If any one of the brake pads has worn down to, or below, the specified limit, all four pads at that end of the car must be renewed as a set. If the pads on one side are significantly more worn than the other, this may indicate that the caliper pistons have partially seized – refer to the brake pad renewal procedure in Chapter 9, and push the pistons back into the caliper to free them.

8 Measure the thickness of the discs with a micrometer, if available, to make sure that they still have service life remaining. Do not be fooled by the lip of rust which often forms on the outer edge of the disc, which may make the disc appear thicker than it really is – scrape off the loose rust if necessary, without scoring the disc friction (shiny) surface.

9 If any disc is thinner than the specified minimum thickness, renew it (refer to Chapter 9).

10 Check the general condition of the discs. Look for excessive scoring and discolouration caused by overheating. If these conditions exist, remove the relevant disc and have it resurfaced or renewed (refer to Chapter 9).

11 Make sure that the handbrake is firmly applied, then check that the transmission is in neutral. Spin the wheel, and check that the brake is not binding. Some drag is normal with a disc brake, but it should not require any great effort to turn the wheel – also, do not confuse brake drag with resistance from the transmission.

12 Before refitting the wheels, check all brake lines and hoses (refer to Chapter 9). In particular, check the flexible hoses in the vicinity of the calipers, where they are subjected to most movement **(see illustration)**. Bend them between the fingers (but do not actually bend them double, or the casing may be damaged) and check that this does not reveal previously-hidden cracks, cuts or splits.

13 On completion, refit the wheels and lower the car to the ground. Tighten the wheel nuts to the specified torque.

Rear disc brakes

14 Loosen the rear wheel nuts, then chock the front wheels. Jack up the rear of the car, and support it on axle stands. Release the handbrake and remove the rear wheels.

15 The procedure for checking the rear brakes is much the same as described in paragraphs 2 to 13 above. Check that the rear brakes are not binding, noting that transmission resistance is not a factor on the rear wheels. Abnormal effort may indicate that the handbrake needs adjusting – see Chapter 9.

8 Exhaust system check

1 With the engine cold (at least three hours after the vehicle has been driven), check the complete exhaust system, from its starting point at the engine to the end of the tailpipe. Ideally, this should be done on a hoist, where unrestricted access is available; if a hoist is not available, raise and support the vehicle on axle stands (see *'Jacking and vehicle support'* in the Reference chapter).

2 Make sure that all brackets and rubber mountings are in good condition, and tight; if any of the mountings are to be renewed, ensure that the new ones are of the correct type – in the case of the rubber mountings, their colour is a good guide. Those nearest to the catalytic converter are more heat-resistant than the others **(see illustration)**.

3 Check the pipes and connections for evidence of leaks, severe corrosion, or damage. One of the most common points for a leak to develop is around the welded joints between the pipes and silencers. Leakage at any of the joints or in other parts of the system will usually show up as a black sooty stain in the vicinity of the leak. **Note:** *Exhaust sealants should not be used on any part of the exhaust system upstream of the catalytic converter (between the converter and engine) – even if the sealant does not contain additives harmful to the converter, pieces of it may break off and foul the element, causing local overheating.*

4 At the same time, inspect the underside of the body for holes, corrosion, open seams, etc, which may allow exhaust gases to enter the passenger compartment. Seal all body openings with silicone or body putty.

5 Rattles and other noises can often be traced to the exhaust system, especially the rubber mountings. Try to move the system, silencer(s), heat shields and catalytic converter. If any components can touch the body or suspension parts, secure the exhaust system with new mountings.

6 Check the running condition of the engine by inspecting inside the end of the tailpipe; the exhaust deposits here are an indication of the engine's state of tune. The inside of the tailpipe should be dry, and should vary in colour from dark grey to light grey/brown; if it is black and sooty, or coated with white deposits, this may indicate the need for a full fuel system inspection.

9 Steering, suspension and roadwheel check

Front suspension and steering

1 Apply the handbrake, then raise the front of the vehicle and support it on axle stands (see *'Jacking and vehicle support'* in the Reference chapter).

2 Visually inspect the balljoint dust covers and the steering rack gaiters for splits, chafing or deterioration **(see illustration)**. Any wear of

9.2 Check the condition of the steering rack gaiters

these components will cause loss of lubricant, together with dirt and water entry, resulting in rapid deterioration of the balljoints or steering gear.

3 Where fitted, check the power-assisted steering fluid hoses for chafing or deterioration, and the pipe and hose unions for fluid leaks. Also check for signs of fluid leakage under pressure from the steering gear rubber gaiters, which would indicate failed fluid seals within the steering gear.

4 Grasp the roadwheel at the 12 o'clock and 6 o'clock positions, and try to rock it **(see illustration)**. Very slight free play may be felt, but if the movement is appreciable, further investigation is necessary to determine the source. Continue rocking the wheel while an assistant depresses the footbrake. If the movement is now eliminated or significantly reduced, it is likely that the hub bearings are at fault. If the free play is still evident with the footbrake depressed, then there is wear in the suspension joints or mountings.

5 Now grasp the wheel at the 9 o'clock and 3 o'clock positions, and try to rock it as before. Any movement felt now may again be caused by wear in the hub bearings or the steering track rod balljoints. If the outer track rod balljoint is worn, the visual movement will be obvious. If the inner joint is suspect, it can be felt by placing a hand over the rack-and-pinion rubber gaiter, and gripping the track rod. If the wheel is now rocked, movement will be felt at the inner joint if wear has taken place.

6 Using a large screwdriver or flat bar, check for wear in the suspension mounting and subframe bushes by levering between the relevant suspension component and its attachment point. Some movement is to be expected as the mountings are made of rubber, but excessive wear should be obvious. Also check the condition of any visible rubber bushes, looking for splits, cracks or contamination of the rubber.

7 With the vehicle standing on its wheels, have an assistant turn the steering wheel back-and-forth, about an eighth of a turn each way. There should be very little, if any, lost movement between the steering wheel and roadwheels. If this is not the case, closely observe the joints and mountings previously described, but in addition, check the steering column joints for wear, and also check the rack-and-pinion steering gear itself.

Rear suspension

8 Chock the front wheels, then raise the rear of the vehicle and support it on axle stands (see *'Jacking and vehicle support'* in the Reference chapter).

9 Check the rear hub bearings for wear, using the method described for the front hub bearings (paragraph 4).

10 Using a large screwdriver or flat bar, check for wear in the suspension mounting bushes by levering between the relevant suspension component and its attachment point. Some movement is to be expected as the mountings are made of rubber, but excessive wear should be obvious.

Roadwheel check and balancing

11 Periodically remove the roadwheels, and clean any dirt or mud from the inside and outside surfaces. Examine the wheel rims for signs of rusting, corrosion or other damage. Light alloy wheels are easily damaged by 'kerbing' whilst parking, and similarly, steel wheels may become dented or buckled. Renewal of the wheel is very often the only course of remedial action possible.

12 The balance of each wheel and tyre assembly should be maintained, not only to avoid excessive tyre wear, but also to avoid wear in the steering and suspension components. Wheel imbalance is normally signified by vibration through the vehicle's bodyshell, although in many cases it is particularly noticeable through the steering wheel. Conversely, it should be noted that wear or damage in suspension or steering components may cause excessive tyre wear. Out-of-round or out-of-true tyres, damaged wheels and wheel bearing wear/maladjustment also fall into this category. Balancing will not usually cure vibration caused by such wear.

13 Wheel balancing may be carried out with the wheel either on or off the vehicle. If balanced on the vehicle, ensure that the wheel-to-hub relationship is marked in some way prior to subsequent wheel removal, so that it may be refitted in its original position.

10 Driveshaft rubber gaiter and joint check

1 The driveshaft rubber gaiters are very important, because they prevent dirt, water and foreign material from entering and damaging the joints. External contamination can cause the gaiter material to deteriorate prematurely, so it's a good idea to wash the gaiters with soap and water occasionally.

2 With the vehicle raised and securely supported on axle stands (see *'Jacking and vehicle support'* in the Reference chapter), turn the steering onto full-lock, then slowly rotate each front wheel in turn. Inspect the condition of the outer constant velocity (CV) joint rubber gaiters, squeezing the gaiters to open out the folds. Check for signs of cracking, splits, or deterioration of the rubber, which may allow the escape of grease, and lead to the ingress of water and grit into the joint. Also check the security and condition of the retaining clips. Repeat these checks on the inner tripod joints **(see illustration)**. If any damage or deterioration is found, the gaiters should be renewed as described in Chapter 8.

3 At the same time, check the general condition of the outer CV joints themselves, by first holding the driveshaft and attempting to rotate the wheels. Repeat this check on the inner joints, by holding the inner joint yoke and attempting to rotate the driveshaft.

4 Any appreciable movement in the joint indicates wear in the joint, wear in the driveshaft splines, or a loose driveshaft retaining bolt.

11 Underbody and fuel/brake line check

1 With the vehicle raised and supported on axle stands or over an inspection pit, thoroughly inspect the underbody and wheel arches for signs of damage and corrosion. In particular, examine the bottom of the side sills, and any concealed areas where mud can collect.

2 Where corrosion and rust is evident, press and tap firmly on the panel with a screwdriver, and check for any serious corrosion which would necessitate repairs.

3 If the panel is not seriously corroded, clean away the rust, and apply a new coating of underseal. Refer to Chapter 11 for more details of body repairs.

4 At the same time, inspect the lower body panels for stone damage and general condition.

5 Inspect all of the fuel and brake lines on the underbody for damage, rust, corrosion and leakage. Also make sure that they are correctly

9.4 Check for wear in the wheel bearing by grasping the wheel and trying to rock it

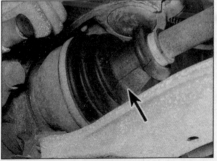

10.2 Squeeze the driveshaft gaiters and check for cracks

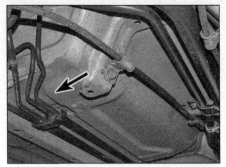

11.5 Check the fuel and brake pipes under the vehicle body

supported in their clips **(see illustration)**. Where applicable, check the PVC coating on the lines for damage.

12 Hinge and lock lubrication

1 Work around the vehicle and lubricate the hinges of the bonnet, doors and tailgate with a light machine oil.
2 Check carefully the security and operation of all hinges, latches and locks, adjusting them where required. Check the operation of the central locking system (if fitted).
3 Where applicable, check the condition and operation of the tailgate struts, renewing them if either is leaking or no longer able to support the tailgate securely when raised.

13 Roadwheel nut tightness check

1 Checking the tightness of the wheel nuts is more relevant than you might think. Apart from the obvious safety aspect of ensuring they are sufficiently tight, this check will reveal whether they have been overtightened, as may have happened the last time new tyres were fitted, for example. If the car suffers a puncture, you may find that the wheel nuts cannot be loosened with the wheel brace.
2 Apply the handbrake, chock the wheels, and engage 1st gear.
3 Remove the wheel cover (or wheel centre cover), using the flat end of the wheel brace supplied in the tool kit.
4 Loosen the first wheel nut, using the wheel brace if possible. If the nut proves stubborn, use a close-fitting socket and a long extension bar.
Warning: Do not use makeshift means to loosen the wheel nuts if the proper tools are not available. If extra force is required, make sure that the tools fit properly, and are of good quality. Even so, consider the consequences of the tool slipping or breaking, and take precautions – wearing

stout gloves is advisable to protect your hands. Do not be tempted to stand on the tools used – they are not designed for this, and there is a high risk of personal injury if the tool slips or breaks. If the wheel nuts are simply too tight, take the car to a garage equipped with suitable power tools.
5 Once the nut has been loosened, remove it and check that the wheel stud threads are clean. Use a small wire brush to clean any rust or dirt from the threads, if necessary.
6 Refit the nut, with the tapered side facing inwards. Tighten it fully, using the wheel brace alone – no other tools. This will ensure that the wheel nuts can be loosened using the wheel brace if a puncture occurs. However, if a torque wrench is available, tighten the nut to the specified torque wrench setting.
7 Repeat the procedure for the remaining nuts, then refit the wheel cover or centre cover, as applicable.
8 Work around the car, checking and retightening the nuts for all four wheels.

14 Road test

Braking system

1 Make sure that the vehicle does not pull to one side when braking, and that the wheels do not lock when braking hard.
2 Check that there is no vibration through the steering when braking. As all models are equipped with ABS brakes, if vibration is felt through the pedal under heavy braking, this is a normal characteristic of the system operation, and is not a cause for concern.
3 Check that the handbrake operates correctly, without excessive movement of the lever, and that it holds the vehicle stationary on a slope, in both directions (facing up and down a slope).
4 With the engine switched off, test the operation of the brake servo unit as follows. Depress the footbrake four or five times to exhaust the vacuum, then start the engine. As the engine starts, there should be a noticeable 'give' in the brake pedal as vacuum builds-up. Allow the engine to run for at least two minutes, and then switch it off. If the brake pedal is now depressed again, it should be possible to detect a hiss from the servo as the pedal is depressed. After about four or five applications, no further hissing should be heard, and the pedal should feel considerably harder.

Steering and suspension

5 Check for any abnormalities in the steering, suspension, handling or road 'feel'.
6 Drive the vehicle, and check that there are no unusual vibrations or noises.
7 Check that the steering feels positive, with no excessive sloppiness or roughness,

and check for any suspension noises when cornering and driving over bumps.

Drivetrain

8 Check the performance of the engine, transmission and driveshafts.
9 Check that the engine starts correctly, both when cold and when hot.
10 Listen for any unusual noises from the engine and transmission.
11 Make sure that the engine runs smoothly when idling, and that there is no hesitation when accelerating.
12 Check that all gears can be engaged smoothly without noise, and that the gear lever action is smooth and not abnormally vague or 'notchy'.
13 Listen for a metallic clicking sound from the front of the vehicle as the vehicle is driven slowly in a circle with the steering on full-lock. Carry out this check in both directions. If a clicking noise is heard, this indicates wear in a driveshaft joint, in which case renew the joint if necessary.

Clutch

14 Check that the clutch pedal moves smoothly and easily through its full travel, and that the clutch itself functions correctly, with no trace of slip or drag.
15 If the clutch is slow to release, it is possible that the system requires bleeding (see Chapter 6). Also check the fluid pipes under the bonnet for signs of leakage.
16 Check the clutch as described in Chapter 6.

Instruments and electrical equipment

17 Check the operation of all instruments and electrical equipment.
18 Make sure that all instruments read correctly, and switch on all electrical equipment in turn, to check that it functions properly.

15 Handbrake check and adjustment

1 In service, the handbrake should be fully applied within 6 to 7 clicks of the handbrake lever ratchet. Should adjustment be necessary, refer to Chapter 9, Section 18, for the full procedure description.

16 Seat belt check

1 Check the seat belts for satisfactory operation and condition. Inspect the webbing for fraying and cuts. Check that they retract smoothly and without binding into their reels.
2 Check the seat belt mountings, ensuring that all the bolts are securely tightened.

17.2a Release the locking clips...

17.2b...and disconnect the MAF sensor wiring plug

17.2c On 1.8 litre models remove the wiring loom

17 Air filter element renewal

Caution: Never drive the vehicle with the air filter element removed. Excessive engine wear could result, and backfiring could even cause a fire under the bonnet.

1 If carrying out a routine service, the element should be renewed regardless of its apparent condition.

2 Release the locking clips and lift the cover from the filter housing. Lift out the filter **(see illustrations)**.

3 With the filter removed, wipe out the inside of the housing.

4 Refitting is the reverse of the removal procedure.

18 Valve clearances – check and adjust

Note: *Valves clearance should be checked and adjust when the engine is cold.*

1 Remove the cylinder head cover as described in Chapter 2A or Chapter 2B.

2 To allow the the engine to be turned over easily, remove the spark plugs. Rotate the engine by means of either the crankshaft pulley or by raising the right-hand wheel, engaging third gear and rotating the roadwheel.

17.2d Remove the lid...

17.2e...and lift out the air filter

3 Rotate the engine until the 'UP' mark is visible on the camshaft sprocket and the grooves on the sprocket are in line with the top edge of the cylinder head.

Note: *Number 1 cylinder is next to the timing chain and the inlet valves are at the front of the engine with the exhaust valves at the rear.*

4 With the engine at TDC on number 1 cylinder slide the correct feeler gauge between the rocker arm and the valve stem on the inlet side. The gauge should be a snug sliding fit with a slight dragging feel as you remove the feeler gauge. On 16 valve engines repeat the procedure for the second inlet valve.

5 If adjustment is required slacken the lock nut and using a screw driver, adjust the adjusting screw until the correct gap is achieved.Tighten the lock nut whilst holding

the adjuster screw steady with screwdriver. Recheck the clearance after the lock nut has been fully tightened.

6 Repeat the checking and adjustment procedure for the exhaust valve clearance(s) on number 1 cylinder.

7 Rotate the engine until the mark for number 3 cylinder appears on the camshaft sprocket. Continue to rotate the engine until the groove mark on the sprocket is flush with the cylinder head. At this point the inlet and exhaust valves for number 3 cylinder can be checked and adjusted.

8 With number 3 cylinder all checked and adjusted, rotate the engine until the the mark for cylinder number 4 appears on the camshaft sprocket. Continue to rotate the engine until the groove mark on the sprocket is flush with

18.3 The camshaft UP marking on the 1.4 i-DSI engine

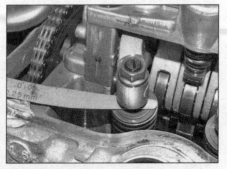

18.4 The feeler gauge should be a snug sliding fit

18.5 Slacken the locknut and turn the screw to adjust the valve clearance. Tighten the locknut when the correct clearance is set

19.6 Rotate the bayonet screws to remove the cover on 1.8 litre engines

19.8a Disconnect the coil wiring plugs

19.8b The ignition coil mounting bolts on the 1.4 i-DSI engine (front bank shown)

the cylinder head. At this point the inlet and exhaust valves for number 4 cylinder can be checked and adjusted.

9 Finally, with number 4 cylinder all checked and adjusted, rotate the engine until the the mark for cylinder number 2 appears on the camshaft sprocket. Continue to rotate the engine until the groove mark on the sprocket is flush with the cylinder head. At this point the inlet and exhaust valves for number 2 cylinder can be checked and adjusted.

10 Refit the spark plugs and valve cover and if raised lower the vehicle to the ground.

19 Spark plug renewal

1 Early 1.4 litre models (designated i-DSI and with an L13A engine code) use two spark plugs per cylinder (eight in total). Later 1.4 litre i-VTEC models (engine code L13Z) are more conventional with a single spark plug per cylinder.

2 Removal and replacement of the spark plugs is similar on both 1.4 litre engines.

3 The correct functioning of the spark plugs is vital for the correct running and efficiency of the engine. It is essential that the plugs fitted are appropriate for the engine.

4 If the correct type is used and the engine is in good condition, the spark plugs should not need attention between scheduled intervals.

5 Spark plug removal and refitting requires a spark plug socket, with an extension which can be turned by a ratchet handle or similar. This socket is lined with a rubber sleeve, to protect the porcelain insulator of the spark plug, and to hold the plug while you insert it into the spark plug hole. You will also need feeler blades to check the spark plug electrode gap, and (ideally) a torque wrench to tighten the new plugs to the specified torque. **Note:** *Do not attempt to adjust the spark plug gap. If the gap is wider than that specified the plug must be replaced.*

6 Where fitted, remove the engine cover **(see illustration)** or on some 1.4 litre engines the inlet manifold cover.

7 If working on the early L137A engine

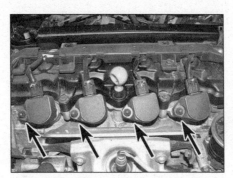

19.8c The ignition coils mounting bolts on the 1.8 litre engine

remove the wiring loom support from the rear of the cylinder head.

8 Disconnect the wiring plugs from each coil and then remove the ignition coils **(see illustrations)**. Whilst not essential, keeping the ignition coils in cylinder order (and front or rear on i-DSI models) is a good idea.

9 Unscrew the spark plugs, ensuring that the socket is kept in alignment with each plug – if the socket is forcibly moved to either side, the porcelain top of the plug may be broken off. Remove the plug from the engine **(see illustration)**.

10 As each plug is removed, examine it as follows – this will give a good indication of the condition of the engine:

a) If the insulator nose of the spark plug is clean and white, with no deposits, this is indicative of a weak mixture.

b) If the tip and insulator nose are covered

19.8d Remove the ignition coils (1.4 L13Z engine)

with hard black-looking deposits, then this is indicative that the mixture is too rich.

c) Should the plug be black and oily, then it is likely that the engine is fairly worn, as well as the mixture being too rich.

d) If the insulator nose is covered with light tan to greyish-brown deposits, then the mixture is correct, and it is likely that the engine is in good condition.

e) Inspect the main ceramic body of the plug. Check carefully for pitting and any tracking marks running down the side of the insulator.

11 If you are renewing the spark plugs, purchase the new plugs, then check each of them first for faults such as cracked insulators or damaged threads. New plugs are supplied with a preset gap. Do not attempt to adjust the gap.

12 If the plugs were removed to inspect them, then the gap can be checked **(see illustration)**.

19.9 Remove the spark plugs

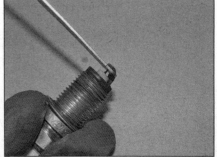

19.12 Check the electrode gap with a set of feeler gauges

If the gap is not as specified do not attempt to adjust the gap or clean the spark plug. If there is any doubt as to the condition of the spark plugs they should be replaced.

13 Before fitting the spark plugs, check that the threaded connector sleeves at the top of the plugs are tight (where fitted), and that the plug exterior surfaces and threads are clean. Brown staining on the porcelain, immediately above the metal body, is quite normal, and does not necessarily indicate a leak between the body and insulator.

14 On installing the spark plugs, first check that the cylinder head thread and sealing surface are as clean as possible; use a clean rag wrapped around a paintbrush to wipe clean the sealing surface. Apply a smear of copper-based grease or anti-seize compound to the threads of each plug, and screw them in by hand where possible. Take extra care to enter the plug threads correctly, as the cylinder head is made of aluminium alloy – it's often difficult to insert spark plugs into their holes without cross - threading them (see **Haynes Hint**).

HAYNES HINT *It is often difficult to insert spark plugs into their holes without dross-threading them. To avoid this possibility, fit a short length of rubber or plastic hose over the end of the spark plug. The flexible hose acts as a universal joint, to help align the plug with the plug hole. Should the plug begin to cross thread, the hose will slip on the spark plug, preventing thread damage to the cylinder head.*

15 When each spark plug is started correctly on its threads, screw it down until it just seats lightly, then tighten it to the specified torque wrench setting. If a torque wrench is not available – and this is one case where the use of a torque wrench is strongly recommended – tighten each spark plug through no more than 1/16th of a turn. Do not exceed the specified torque setting, and NEVER overtighten spark plugs.

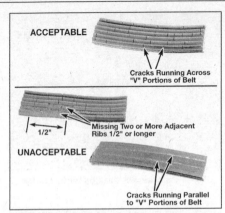

20.3 Check very carefully for some of the more common faults found on multi-ribbed auxiliary drivebelts

16 Refit the coils (in the correct order) and tighten the retaining bolts.
17 Reconnect the wiring plugs, refit the wiring loom (where removed) and the refit the manifold cover and where fitted engine cover.

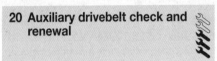

20 Auxiliary drivebelt check and renewal

Note: *Only rotate the engine in the normal (clockwise) direction.*

Drivebelt check

1 A single auxiliary drivebelt is fitted at the right-hand side of the engine. On early models adjustment is carried out by moving the alternator. All later models have an automatic adjuster fitted. Checking the drivebelt tension is unnecessary on these models.
2 Due to their function and material make-up, drivebelts are prone to failure after a long period of time, and should therefore be inspected regularly.
3 With the engine stopped, inspect the full length of the drivebelt for cracks and separation of the belt plies. It will be necessary to turn the

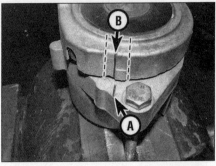

20.5 Note the location of the tensioner fixed line (A). The dotted lines indicate the normal range marked by the tensioner long and short rectangular reference marks – tensioner fixed line (A) should be within this range if the drivebelt is unworn

engine (using a spanner or socket and bar on the crankshaft pulley bolt) in order to move the belt from the pulleys so that the belt can be inspected thoroughly. Twist the belt between the pulleys so that both sides can be viewed. Also check for fraying, and glazing which gives the belt a shiny appearance. Check the pulleys for nicks, cracks, distortion and corrosion **(see illustration)**.
4 Note that it is not unusual for a ribbed belt to exhibit small cracks in the edges of the belt ribs, and unless these are extensive or very deep, belt renewal is not essential.
5 The automatic tensioner incorporates a wear guide. The index mark on the fixed base of the tensioner must lie within the long and short marks on the movable section of the tensioner **(see illustration)**.

Drivebelt tension check and adjustment
Note: *Models not fitted with an automatic adjuster only.*
6 The belt tension is checked by pushing the belt at a distance halfway between the pulleys. Push firmly with your thumb and see how much the belt moves (deflects) **(see illustrations)**.

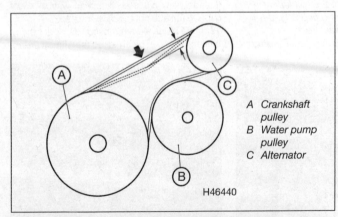

A Crankshaft pulley
B Water pump pulley
C Alternator

H46440

20.6 Auxiliary drivebelt tension checking point – models without air conditioning. Apply moderate thumb pressure at the point shown. The belt should deflect between 7 to 10 mm

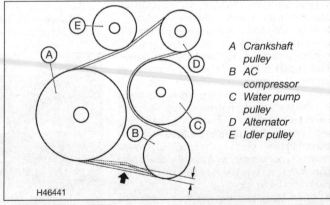

A Crankshaft pulley
B AC compressor
C Water pump pulley
D Alternator
E Idler pulley

H46441

20.6b Auxiliary drivebelt tension checking point – models with air conditioning. Apply moderate thumb pressure at the point shown. The belt should deflect between 6 to 9 mm

20.9 The auxiliary drivebelt adjuster bolt

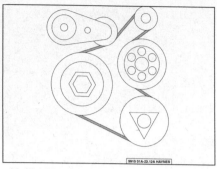

20.12a Alternator belt routing 1.4 models with AC

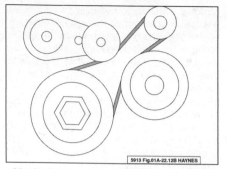

20.12b Alternator belt routing 1.4 models without AC

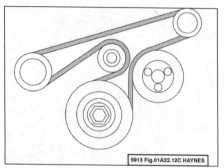

20.12c Alternator belt routing 1.8 petrol models without AC

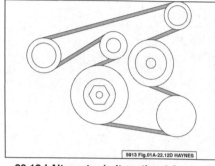

20.12d Alternator belt routing 1.8 petrol models with 1.855 mm belt

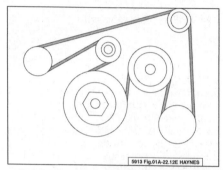

20.12e Alternator belt routing 1.8 petrol models with 2.061 mm belt

7 If adjustment of the belt is required, jack up and support the front of the vehicle – see *'Jacking and vehicle support'* in the Reference chapter

8 Remove the roadwheel and and slacken off the alternator lower mounting bolt.

9 Slacken off the upper mounting bolt and then using the adjuster bolt, slacken or tighten the alternator belt **(see illustration)**.

10 When the adjustment is correct, tighten the alternator bolts to the specified torque.

Drivebelt renewal

11 Honda do not specify a replacement interval for belt replacement. It should be inspected regularly and the position of the tensioner noted. It may be prudent to replace it if any component driven by the belt is replaced or removed as part of another procedure.

12 Jack up the front of the vehicle (see *'Jacking and vehicle support'* in the Reference chapter) and remove the right-hand road wheel to gain access to the belt and crankshaft pulley. Note the routing of the belt before removing it **(see illustrations)**.

13 Special long handled belt release spanners are commercially available, however it is possible to release the tension with a pair of spanners locked together. If the original belt is to be refitted mark the direction of rotation on the belt before removing it.

14 With a long spanner (or two shorter spanners used together) applied to the tensioner pulley bolt, move the tensioner pulley slowly and evenly until the drivebelt can be slipped off the first pulley **(see illustrations)**. Release the tensioner slowly and carefully. Do NOT allow the tensioner arm

to snap back against spring pressure – it will break.

15 On 1.4 petrol model release the tensioner from below, on 1.8 petrol models release the tensioner from above. On models not fitted with an automatic tension fully slacken of the belt by moving the alternator as described in paragraphs 8 and 9 above.

16 Working from the wheel arch or engine compartment as necessary, and noting its routing, slip the drivebelt off the remaining pulleys and withdraw it.

17 With the belt removed checked the operation of the pulleys. They can all (apart from the crankshaft pulley) be rotated by hand. Listen for any noise as the pulleys are rotated and check for any excess play. Where necessary clean the grooves in the pulleys.

18 Refitting the belt is a reversal of the

20.14a Two spanners locked together can be used to release the tensioner

20.14b The tensioner can be held in the relaxed position with a heavy duty cable tie

20.14c Remove the auxiliary drivebelt

removal procedure, however the aid of an assistant makes fitting the belt considerably easier. With the belt fitted, rotate the engine (via the crankshaft pulley) several times to settle the belt. Check that the belt is correctly located in the pulley grooves as it is rotated.

19 On models not fitted with an automatic adjuster after the belt tension has been adjusted the engine should be started and run for several minutes to settle the belt. Stop the engine and recheck the tension. Adjust the tensioner if necessary.

20 Refit the road wheel, remove the axle stand and lower the vehicle to the ground.

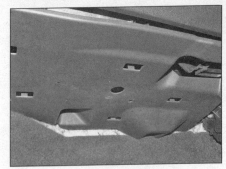
21.1a Unclip and then...

21.1b...remove the lower panel from below the glovebox

21 Pollen filter renewal

1 Working in the passengers footwell pull down and release the facia under cover and then unhook it from the rear mounting point. Replacement of the filter is slightly easier if the glovebox is removed before removing the pollen filter **(see illustrations)**.

2 Unclip and remove the cover from the filter and then slide the filter from the housing **(see illustrations)**. Note the air flow direction – marked on the filter.

3 Fit the new filter using a reversal of the removal procedure, ensuring that the filter is fitted with the airflow arrows pointing straight back into the cabin. Refit the lower facia cover.

21.2a Unclip the filter cover...

21.2b...and slide out the filter

22 Transmission fluid

Manual transmission – level checking

1 Jack up and support the front of the vehicle – see *'Jacking and vehicle support'* in the Reference chapter. Remove the engine undershield.

2 Slacken the combined filler/level plug. This located close to the left-hand driveshaft, on the differential housing. Have a container

ready to catch any fluid and then remove the filler/level plug **(see illustration)**.

3 The level check should be made with the vehicle on level ground. Lowering the vehicle to do this will make access to the filler/level plug difficult. The easiest way to check the level is to first check that the level is just below the filler plug with a home made dipstick – a length of welding rod makes an ideal dipstick – whilst the vehicle is raised. If there are no apparent leaks the chances are that the level is correct.

4 If the level is low (or believed to be) then feed a length of hose into the filler hole. Feed the hose up an out of the vehicle and attach a small funnel. Lower the vehicle to the ground and then pour fresh transmission oil into the transmission through the funnel, stopping as soon as oil drips from the filler hole into the container.

5 When the level is correct raise the front of the vehicle, support it on axle stands and refit the filler/level plug – using a new washer and tightening to the specified torque. Refit the engine undershield and lower the vehicle to the ground.

Manual transmission – fluid renewal

6 Jack up and support the front of the vehicle – see *'Jacking and vehicle support'* in the Reference chapter. Remove the engine undershield.

7 Remove the filler/level plug. Place a clean container beneath the transmission and then remove the drain plug **(see illustrations)**. Allow the fluid to drain into the container.

8 Clean the area around the drain plug, fit a new sealing washer to the drain plug and tighten the bolt to the specified torque.

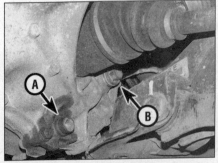
22.2 Manual transmission drain (A) and filler/level check (B)

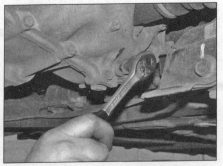
22.7a Remove the drain plug...

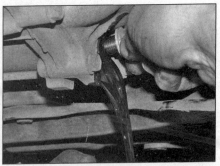
22.7b...and drain the transmission

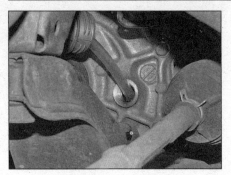

22.9 Filling the transmission

9 Fill the transmission with fresh transmission oil using a length of hose and small funnel **(see illustration)**. The vehicle should be on the ground and level. To achieve this it may be necessary to lower the vehicle to the ground.

10 As soon as fluid flows from the filler/level hole, refit the filler plug – using a new washer – and tighten it to the specified torque.

11 Refit the engine undershield and lower the vehicle.

Automatic transmission fluid – checking

12 The engine should be at normal operating temperature. Park the vehicle on level ground, open the bonnet and remove the transmission fluid dipstick. This is located on the front left-hand side of the engine bay close to the air filter housing.

13 Remove the dipstick, wipe it with a cloth and then refit it. Pull out the dipstick and check that the fluid level is between the marks on the dipstick. If necessary add transmission fluid though the dip stick hole.

Note: *When refitting the dipstick, ensure that the arrow on the dipstick points to the front of the vehicle.*

Automatic transmission fluid – replacement

14 Jack up and support the front of the vehicle – see '*Jacking and vehicle support*' in the Reference chapter. Remove the engine undershield.

Caution: If the transmission fluid is changed with a hot engine the transmission fluid will be hot. Wear safety glasses and suitable gloves if this is the case.

15 Have a suitable container ready beneath the drain plug. Remove the drain plug and recover the sealing washer. Discard the washer, a new one must be used.

16 Fit a new sealing washer and tighten it to the specified torque.

17 Refit the engine undershield and lower the vehicle to the ground.

18 Remove the transmission dipstick and using a suitable length of hose and a funnel slowly fill the transmission with fresh fluid. Do not overfill the transmission.

23 Brake fluid renewal

⚠ *Warning: Brake hydraulic fluid can harm your eyes and damage painted surfaces, so use extreme caution when handling and pouring it. Do not use fluid that has been standing open for some time, as it absorbs moisture from the air. Excess moisture can cause a dangerous loss of braking effectiveness. Brake fluid is also highly flammable – treat it with the same respect as petrol.*

1 The procedure is similar to that for the bleeding of the hydraulic system as described in Chapter 9.

2 Reduce the fluid level in the reservoir (by syphoning or using a poultry baster), but do not allow the fluid level to drop far enough to allow air into the system.

Warning: Do not syphon the fluid by mouth; it is poisonous.

3 The brakes must be bled in sequence.
a) *Front right*
b) *Front left*
c) *Rear right*
d) *Rear left*

4 Working in order, open the first bleed screw in the sequence, and pump the brake pedal gently until nearly all the old fluid has been emptied from the master cylinder reservoir. Top-up to the MAX level with new fluid, and continue pumping until only the new fluid remains in the reservoir, and new fluid can be seen emerging from the bleed screw. Tighten the screw, and top the reservoir level up to the MAX level line. Old hydraulic fluid is invariably much darker in colour than the new, making it easy to distinguish the two.

5 Work through all the remaining bleed screws in the sequence until new fluid can be seen at all of them. Be careful to keep the master cylinder reservoir topped-up to above the MIN level at all times, or air may enter the system and greatly increase the length of the task.

6 When the operation is complete, check that all bleed screws are securely tightened, and that their dust caps are refitted. Wash off all traces of spilt fluid, and recheck the master cylinder reservoir fluid level.

7 Check the operation of the brakes before taking the car on the road.

24 Remote control battery renewal

1 Although not in the Honda maintenance schedule, we recommend that the battery is changed every 2 years, regardless of the vehicle's mileage. However, if the door locks repeatedly fail to respond to signals from the remote control at the normal distance, change the battery in the remote control before attempting to troubleshoot any of the vehicle's other systems.

2 Remove the single small cross head screw from base of the key fob. Separate the two halves of the fob using a small flat bladed screwdriver.

3 Release the inner cover from the upper switch housing (use a small screwdriver) and remove the battery.

4 Fit the new battery with the + side facing down. Refit the inner cover.

5 Refit the upper and the lower sections back together. Refit the screw nd test the operation of the remote fob.

25 Coolant strength check and renewal

⚠ *Warning: Do not allow antifreeze to come in contact with your skin or painted surfaces of the vehicle. Flush contaminated areas immediately with plenty of water. Don't store new coolant, or leave old coolant lying around, where it's accessible to children or pets – they're attracted by its sweet smell. Ingestion of even a small amount of coolant can be fatal. Wipe up garage-floor and drip-pan spills immediately. Keep antifreeze containers covered, and repair cooling system leaks as soon as they're noticed.*

⚠ *Warning: Never remove the expansion tank filler cap when the engine is running, or has just been switched off, as the cooling system will be hot, and the consequent escaping steam and scalding coolant could cause serious injury.*

⚠ *Warning: Wait until the engine is cold before starting these procedures.*

Strength check

1 Use a hydrometer to check the strength of the antifreeze. Follow the instructions provided with your hydrometer. The antifreeze strength should be approximately 50%. If it is significantly less than this, drain a little coolant from the radiator (see this Section), add antifreeze to the coolant expansion tank, then recheck the strength.

Coolant draining

2 To drain the system, first remove the expansion tank filler cap.

3 If the additional working clearance is required, raise the front of the vehicle and support it securely on axle stands (see '*Jacking and vehicle support*' in the Reference chapter). Undo the fasteners and remove the engine undershield.

4 Place a large drain tray underneath,

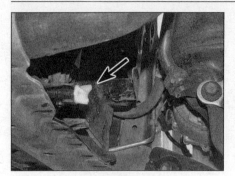

25.4a The radiator drain tap

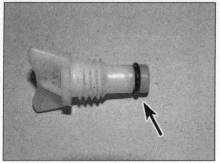

25.4b Check the condition of the drain plug O-ring. Replace it if it is poor condition

and unscrew the radiator drain plug **(see illustrations)**. Direct as much of the escaping coolant as possible into the tray.

5 Once the coolant has stopped draining from the radiator, close the drain plug.

6 On models fitted with a separate (non pressurised) reservoir, the reservoir must be removed to drain the coolant.

System flushing

7 With time, the cooling system may gradually lose its efficiency, as the radiator core becomes choked with rust, scale deposits from the water, and other sediment. To minimise this, as well as using only good-quality antifreeze and clean soft water, the system should be flushed as follows whenever any part of it is disturbed, and/or when the coolant is renewed.

8 With the coolant drained, refit the drain plug and refill the system with fresh water. Refit the expansion tank filler cap, start the engine and warm it up to normal operating temperature, then stop it and (after allowing it to cool down completely) drain the system again. Repeat as necessary until only clean water can be seen to emerge, then refill finally with the specified coolant mixture.

9 If only clean, soft water and good-quality antifreeze (even if not to Honda's specification) has been used, and the coolant has been renewed at the suggested intervals, the above procedure will be sufficient to keep clean the system for a considerable length of time. If, however, the system has been neglected, a more thorough operation will be required, as follows.

10 First drain the coolant, then disconnect the radiator top and bottom hoses. Insert a garden hose into the radiator top hose connection, and allow water to circulate through the radiator until it runs clean from the bottom outlet.

11 To flush the engine, insert the garden hose into the radiator bottom hose, wrap a piece of rag around the garden hose to seal the connection, and allow water to circulate until it runs clear.

12 Try the effect of repeating this procedure in the top hose, although this may not be effective, since the thermostat will probably close and prevent the flow of water.

13 In severe cases of contamination, reverse-flushing of the radiator may be necessary. This may be achieved by inserting the garden hose into the bottom outlet, wrapping a piece of rag around the hose to seal the connection, then flushing the radiator until clear water emerges from the top hose outlet.

14 If the radiator is suspected of being severely choked, remove the radiator (Chapter 3), turn it upside-down, and repeat the procedure described in paragraph 12.

15 Flushing the heater matrix can be achieved using a similar procedure to that described in paragraph 12, once the heater inlet and outlet hoses have been identified. These two hoses will be of the same diameter, and pass through the engine compartment bulkhead (refer to the heater matrix removal procedure in Chapter 3 for more details).

16 The use of chemical cleaners is not recommended, and should be necessary only as a last resort; the scouring action of some chemical cleaners may lead to other cooling system problems. Normally, regular renewal of the coolant will prevent excessive contamination of the system.

Coolant filling

Note: *It is increasingly common for manufactures to supply anti-freeze/coolant pre-mixed with distilled water. Check that the replacement coolant/anti-freeze is not a ready mixed type before adding water.*

17 With the cooling system drained and flushed, ensure that all disturbed hose unions are correctly secured, and that the radiator/engine drain plug(s) is securely tightened. Refit the engine undershield (where applicable). If it was raised, lower the vehicle to the ground.

18 Set the heater temperature control to maximum heat, but ensure the blower is turned off.

19 Prepare a sufficient quantity of the specified coolant mixture (see below); allow for a surplus, so as to have a reserve supply for topping-up.

20 Slowly fill the system through the expansion tank. Since the tank is the highest point in the system, all the air in the system should be displaced into the tank by the rising liquid. Slow pouring reduces the possibility of air being trapped and forming airlocks.

21 Continue filling until the coolant level reaches the expansion tank MAX level line (see *Weekly checks*), then cover the filler opening to prevent coolant splashing out.

22 Start the engine and run it at 2500 rpm for 2 minutes. If the level in the expansion tank drops significantly, top-up to the MAX level line, to minimise the amount of air circulating in the system.

23 Fill the expansion tank to the MAX level line, refit the expansion tank cap, and run the engine at 2500 rpm until the thermostat opens and the engine is at normal operating temperature. Check this by feeling the radiator bottom hose – if it's hot, then the thermostat has opened.

24 Briefly run the engine at 4000 rpm, then run it at 2500 rpm for approximately 3 minutes.

25 Stop the engine, wash off any spilt coolant from the engine compartment and bodywork, then leave the car to cool down completely (overnight, if possible).

26 With the system cool, open the expansion tank, and top-up the tank to the MAX level line. Refit the filler cap, tightening it securely, and clean up any further spillage.

27 After refilling, always check carefully all components of the system (but especially any unions disturbed during draining and flushing) for signs of coolant leaks. Fresh antifreeze has a searching action, which will rapidly expose any weak points in the system.

Antifreeze type and mixture

Note: *Do not use engine antifreeze in the windscreen/tailgate washer system, as it will damage the vehicle's paintwork. A screenwash additive should be added to the washer system in its maker's recommended quantities.*

28 If the vehicle's history (and therefore the quality of the antifreeze in it) is unknown, owners are advised to drain and thoroughly reverse-flush the system, before refilling with fresh coolant mixture.

29 If the antifreeze used is to Honda's specification, the levels of protection it affords are indicated in the coolant packaging.

30 To give the recommended standard mixture ratio for antifreeze, 50% (by volume) of antifreeze must be mixed with 50% of clean, soft water; if you are using any other type of antifreeze, follow its manufacturer's instructions to achieve the correct ratio.

31 You are unlikely to fully drain the system at any one time (unless the engine is being completely stripped), and the capacities quoted in Specifications are therefore slightly academic for routine coolant renewal. As a guide, only two-thirds of the system's total capacity is likely to be needed for coolant renewal.

32 As the drained system will be partially filled with flushing water, in order to establish the recommended mixture ratio, measure out 50% of the system capacity in antifreeze and pour it into the hose/expansion tank as described above, then top-up with water. Any topping-up while refilling the system should be done with water – for *Weekly checks* use a suitable mixture.

33 Before adding antifreeze, the cooling system should be drained, preferably flushed, and all hoses checked for condition and security. As noted earlier, fresh antifreeze will rapidly find any weaknesses in the system.

34 After filling with antifreeze, a label should be attached to the expansion tank, stating the type and concentration of antifreeze used, and the date installed. Any subsequent topping-up should be made with the same type and concentration of antifreeze.

General cooling system checks

35 The engine should be cold for the cooling system checks, so perform the following procedure before driving the vehicle, or after it has been shut off for at least three hours.

36 Remove the expansion tank filler cap, and clean it thoroughly inside and out with a rag. Also clean the filler neck on the expansion tank. The presence of rust or corrosion in the filler neck indicates that the coolant should be changed. The coolant inside the expansion tank should be relatively clean and transparent. If it is rust-coloured, drain and flush the system, and refill with a fresh coolant mixture.

37 Carefully check the radiator hoses and heater hoses along their entire length; renew any hose which is cracked, swollen or deteriorated.

38 Inspect all other cooling system components (joint faces, etc) for leaks. A leak in the cooling system will usually show up as white- or antifreeze-coloured deposits on the area adjoining the leak (see **Haynes Hint**). Where any problems of this nature are found on system components, renew the component or gasket with reference to Chapter 3.

39 Clean the front of the radiator with a

A leak in the cooling system will usually show up as white or antifreeze coloured deposits on the areas adjoining the leak.

soft brush to remove all insects, leaves, etc, embedded in the radiator fins. Be careful not to damage the radiator fins, or cut your fingers on them. To do a more thorough job, remove the radiator grille as described in Chapter 11.

Airlocks

40 If, after draining and refilling the system, symptoms of overheating are found which did not occur previously, then the fault is almost certainly due to trapped air at some point in the system, causing an airlock and restricting the flow of coolant; usually, the air is trapped because the system was refilled too quickly.

41 If an airlock is suspected, first try gently squeezing all visible coolant hoses. A coolant hose which is full of air feels quite different to one full of coolant when squeezed. After refilling the system, most airlocks will clear once the system has cooled, and been topped-up.

42 While the engine is running at operating temperature, switch on the heater and heater fan, and check for heat output. Provided there

is sufficient coolant in the system, lack of heat output could be due to an airlock in the system.

43 Airlocks can have more serious effects than simply reducing heater output – a severe airlock could reduce coolant flow around the engine. Check that the radiator top hose is hot when the engine is at operating temperature – a top hose which stays cold could be the result of an airlock (or a non-opening thermostat).

44 If the problem persists, stop the engine and allow it to cool down completely, before unscrewing the expansion tank filler cap or loosening the hose clips and squeezing the hoses to bleed out the trapped air. In the worst case, the system will have to be at least partially drained (this time, the coolant can be saved for re-use) and flushed to clear the problem. If all else fails, have the system evacuated and vacuum filled by a suitably-equipped garage.

Expansion tank pressure cap check

45 Wait until the engine is completely cold – perform this check before the engine is started for the first time in the day.

46 Place a wad of cloth over the expansion tank cap, then unscrew it slowly and remove it.

47 Examine the condition of the rubber seal on the underside of the cap. If the rubber appears to have hardened, or cracks are visible in the seal edges, a new cap should be fitted.

48 If the car is several years old, or has covered a large mileage, consider renewing the cap regardless of its apparent condition – they are not expensive. If the pressure relief valve built into the cap fails, excess pressure in the system will lead to puzzling failures of hoses and other cooling system components.

Chapter 1B
Routine maintenance and servicing – diesel models

Contents

Section number

Air filter element renewal 19
Auxiliary drivebelt check and renewal 20
Brake fluid renewal. 24
Brake pads, shoes and discs check 9
Coolant strength check and renewal 25
Driveshaft rubber gaiter and joint check 12
Engine compartment wiring check. 7
Engine oil and filter renewal 3
Exhaust system check 10
Fuel filter renewal 18
Fuel filter water draining 4
General Information 1
Handbrake check and adjustment 17

Section number

Hinge and lock lubrication 14
Lights and horn operation check 5
Pollen filter renewal 21
Regular maintenance 2
Remote control battery renewal 23
Road test 16
Roadwheel nut tightness check 15
Seat belt check. 8
Steering, suspension and roadwheel check 11
Transmission fluid. 22
Underbody and fuel/brake line check 13
Underbonnet check for fluid leaks and hose condition 6

Degrees of difficulty

| **Easy,** suitable for novice with little experience | 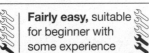 | **Fairly easy,** suitable for beginner with some experience | | **Fairly difficult,** suitable for competent DIY mechanic | 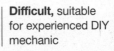 | **Difficult,** suitable for experienced DIY mechanic | | **Very difficult,** suitable for expert DIY or professional | 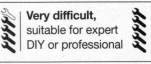 |

Lubricants and fluids.. Refer to end of *Weekly checks*

Capacities

Engine oil (including filter)...................................	5.9 litres
Cooling system (approximate at coolant change)	6.6 litres

Washer fluid reservoir:

With headlight washer system	5.8 litres
Without headlight washer system	2.5 litres
Fuel tank	50.0 litres
Transmission fluid..	2.2 litres

Cooling system

Antifreeze mixture:......................................

50% antifreeze	Protection down to −37°C
55% antifreeze	Protection down to −45°C

Note: *Refer to antifreeze manufacturer for latest recommendations.*

Brakes

Brake friction material.

Minimum thickness (not including backing)	1.6 mm

Brake disc:

Maximum runout	0.10 mm
Minimum thickness (front)	21.0 mm
Minimum thickness (rear)	7.0 mm

Remote control battery

Type	CR1616

Torque wrench settinngs

	Nm	lbf ft
Battery tray bolts	22	16
Engine block coolant drain bolt	39	29
Engine oil drain plug......................................	39	29
Engine oil filter housing cap:	25	18
Fuel filter	15	11
Fuel filter water level sensor...............................	5	4
Transmission drain plug	39	29
Transmission filler plug....................................	44	33
Transmission level plug	12	9
Roadwheel nuts	108	80

The maintenance intervals in this manual are provided with the assumption that you, not the dealer, will be carrying out the work. These are the minimum maintenance intervals recommended by us for vehicles driven daily. If you wish to keep your vehicle in peak condition at all times, you may wish to perform some of these procedures more often. We encourage frequent maintenance, because it enhances the efficiency, performance and resale value of your vehicle.

If the vehicle is driven in dusty areas, used to tow a trailer, or driven frequently at slow speeds (idling in traffic) or on short journeys, more frequent maintenance intervals are recommended.

When the vehicle is new, it should be serviced by a dealer service department (or other workshop recognised by the vehicle manufacturer as providing the same standard of service) in order to preserve the warranty. The vehicle manufacturer may reject warranty claims if you are unable to prove that servicing has been carried out as and when specified, using only original equipment parts or parts certified to be of equivalent quality.

Every 250 miles or weekly
☐ Refer to *Weekly checks*

Every 12 000 miles or 12 months, whichever comes first
In addition to the items listed above, carry out the following:
☐ Renew the engine oil and filter (Section 3)
☐ Drain the fuel filter (Section 4)
☐ Check the operation of the lights and the horn (Section 5)
☐ Check under the bonnet for fluid leaks and hose condition (Section 6)
☐ Check the condition of the engine compartment wiring (Section 7)
☐ Check the condition of the seat belts (Section 8)
☐ Check the condition of the brake pads, shoes and discs (Section 9)
☐ Check the exhaust system (Section 10)
☐ Check the steering and suspension components for condition and security (Section 11)
☐ Check the condition of the driveshaft joints and gaiters (Section 12)
☐ Check the underbody and all fuel/brake lines (Section 13)
☐ Lubricate all hinges and locks (Section 14)
☐ Check roadwheel nut tightness (Section 15)
☐ Carry out a road test (Section 16)
☐ Check and if necessary adjust the handbrake (Section 17)
☐ Check the antifreeze/inhibitor strength (Section 25)

Every 25 000 miles or 2 years, whichever comes first
In addition to the items listed above, carry out the following:
☐ Renew the air filter (Section 19)*
☐ Renew the fuel filter (Section 18)
☐ Renew the pollen filter (Section 21)*
☐ Check the condition of the auxiliary drivebelt (Section 20)

Note: *If the vehicle is used in dusty conditions, the air filter and pollen filter should be renewed more frequently.*

Every 62 000 miles or 5 years, whichever comes first
☐ Renew the engine coolant (Section 25)

Note: *The second coolant replacement should be performed at 100 000 miles or 3 years after the first coolant change*

Every 75 000 or 8 years
☐ Renew the manual transmission fluid (Section 22)

Every 3 years, regardless of mileage
☐ Renew the brake fluid (Section 24)
☐ Renew the remote control battery (Section 23)

Underbonnet view

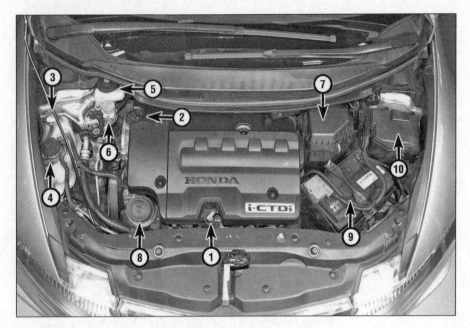

1 Engine oil level dipstick
2 Oil filler cap
3 Coolant expansion tank cap
4 Washer fluid reservoir cap
5 Brake fluid reservoir
6 Clutch fluid reservoir
7 Air filter element cover
8 Oil filter
9 Battery
10 Fuse/relay box cover

Front underbody view

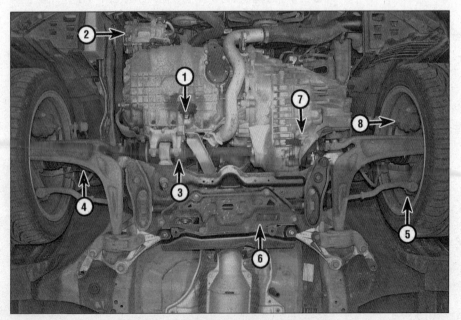

1 Engine oil sump drain plug
2 Air conditioning compressor
3 Right-hand driveshaft intermediate bearing
4 Control arm
5 Track rod end
6 Front subframe
7 Transmission drain plug
8 Front brake caliper

Rear underbody view

1 Rear silencer
2 Coil spring
3 Beam axle
4 Handbrake cable
5 Shock absorber

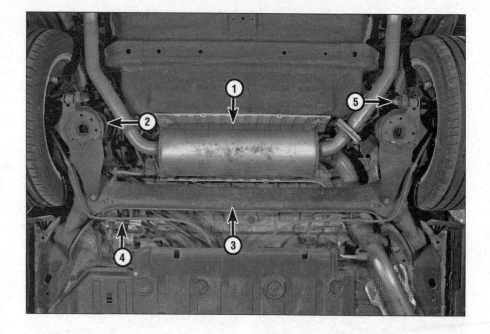

1 General Information

1 This Chapter is designed to help the home mechanic maintain his/her vehicle for safety, economy, long life and peak performance.
2 The Chapter contains a master maintenance schedule, followed by Sections dealing specifically with each task in the schedule. Visual checks, adjustments, component renewal and other helpful items are included. Refer to the accompanying illustrations of the engine compartment and the underside of the vehicle for the locations of the various components.
3 Servicing your vehicle in accordance with the mileage/time maintenance schedule and the following Sections will provide a planned maintenance programme, which should result in a long and reliable service life. This is a comprehensive plan, so maintaining some items but not others at the specified service intervals will not produce the same results.
4 As you service your vehicle, you will discover that many of the procedures can – and should – be grouped together, because of the particular procedure being performed, or because of the proximity of two otherwise-unrelated components to one another. For example, if the vehicle is raised for any reason, the exhaust can be inspected at the same time as the suspension and steering components.
5 The first step in this maintenance programme is to prepare yourself before the actual work begins. Read through all the Sections relevant to the work to be carried out, then make a list and gather all the parts and tools required. If a problem is encountered, seek advice from a parts specialist, or a dealer service department.

2 Regular maintenance

1 If, from the time the vehicle is new, the routine maintenance schedule is followed closely, and frequent checks are made of fluid levels and high-wear items, as suggested throughout this manual, the engine will be kept in relatively good running condition, and the need for additional work will be minimised.
2 It is possible that there will be times when the engine is running poorly due to the lack of regular maintenance. This is even more likely if a used vehicle, which has not received regular and frequent maintenance checks, is purchased. In such cases, additional work may need to be carried out, outside of the regular maintenance intervals.
3 If engine wear is suspected, a compression test or leakdown test (refer to the relevant part of Chapter 2A) will provide valuable information regarding the overall performance of the main internal components. Such a test can be used as a basis to decide on the extent of the work to be carried out. If, for example, a compression or leakdown test indicates serious internal engine wear, conventional maintenance as described in this Chapter will not greatly improve the performance of the engine, and may prove a waste of time and money, unless extensive overhaul work is carried out first.
4 The following series of operations are those most often required to improve the performance of a generally poor-running engine:

Primary operations

a) Clean, inspect and test the battery (refer to 'Weekly checks ').
b) Check all the engine-related fluids (refer to 'Weekly checks ').
c) Check the condition and tension of the auxiliary drivebelt (Section 23).
d) Check the condition of the air filter, and renew if necessary (Section 22).
e) Renew the fuel filter (Section 21).
f) Check the condition of all hoses, and check for fluid leaks (Section 9).

5 If the above operations do not prove fully effective, carry out the following secondary operations:

Secondary operations

6 All items listed under Primary operations, plus the following:
a) Check the charging system (refer to Chapter 5A).
b) Check the preheating system (refer to Chapter 5A).
c) Check the fuel system (refer to Chapter 4B).

3 Engine oil and filter renewal

1 Frequent oil and filter changes are the most important preventative maintenance procedures which can be undertaken by the DIY owner. As engine oil ages, it becomes diluted and contaminated, which leads to premature engine wear.

2 Before starting this procedure, gather together all the necessary tools and materials. Also make sure that you have plenty of clean rags and newspapers handy, to mop-up any spills. Ideally, the engine oil should be warm, as it will drain more easily, and more built-up sludge will be removed with it. Take care not to touch the exhaust or any other hot parts of the engine when working under the vehicle. To avoid any possibility of scalding, and to protect yourself from possible skin irritants and other harmful contaminants in used engine

oils, it is advisable to wear gloves when carrying out this work.

3 Open the bonnet and remove the oil filler cap.

4 Firmly apply the handbrake, then jack up the front of the vehicle and support it securely on axle stands (see 'Jacking and vehicle support' in the Reference chapter).

5 Working underneath the vehicle, undo the bolts and remove the access flap. This provides access to the engine oil (sump) drain plug **(see illustration)**.

6 Using a spanner, or preferably a suitable socket and bar, slacken the drain plug (at the rear of the sump) about half a turn **(see illustrations)**. Position the draining container under the drain plug, then remove the plug completely and discard the sealing washer – this must be renewed as a matter of course whenever it is disturbed.

7 Allow some time for the oil to drain, noting that it may be necessary to reposition the container as the oil flow slows to a trickle.

 As the drain plug releases from the threads, move it away sharply so the stream of oil issuing from the sump runs into the container, not up your sleeve.

8 Place clean rag around the oil filter, which is located at the front right-hand end of the engine, to prevent old oil from being spilt on to surrounding components, particularly the auxiliary drivebelt. Use an oil filter removal tool to slacken the filter cap, then unscrew it by hand the rest of the way **(see illustrations)**. The Honda service tool for this task is Part No. 04151-RBD-305, but note that commercial equivalents are widely available.

Note: *Ensure the oil draining tray is in position beneath the drain plug, as oil will flow from the filter/filter housing as the filter cover is released.*

3.5 Remove the cover

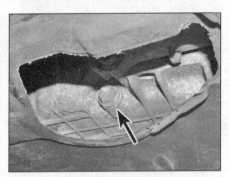
3.6a The oil drain plug

3.6b Use a socket and bar to slacken the drain plug

3.6c Remove the drain plug...

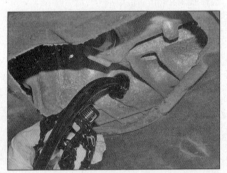
3.6d...and allow the oil to drain

3.8a Use the correct tool...

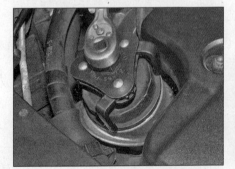
3.8b...a three legged tool...

3.8c...or even a strap wrench

3.8d Remove the cover

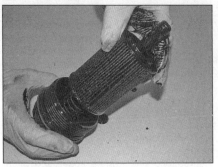

3.10 Pull the filter from the housing

3.11a Components of the engine oil filter assembly

3.11b Fit the largest O-ring to the cap...

3.11c...the medium sized O-ring to cap stem middle groove...

3.11d...and the smallest O-ring to the groove at the cap tip

9 Carefully lift out the filter assembly; place it immediately in a drip tray or other suitable container and do not allow oil to drip on other components. Very carefully wipe out the filter chamber using kitchen towel or clean rag; remove all traces of old oil and any other deposits from inside the chamber and be careful not to leave pieces of paper or lint from the rag caught on any sharp edges inside the chamber. Check that all three sealing O-rings are present on the filter assembly and not left inside the chamber. Cover the chamber while the filter is removed (plug its opening with clean rag or similar).

10 Remove the old filter element and all three sealing O-rings from the filter cap. Wash the filter cap in solvent and clean it with a brush, then wipe it dry. The filter cap and chamber

must be scrupulously clean before reassembly can commence **(see illustration)**.

11 Fit the large sealing O-ring to the groove in the cap, then the medium-sized O-ring to the mid-point of the filter cap's stem and the smallest O-ring to the groove at its tip. Carefully fit the new filter element to the cap's stem, ensuring that the seals at either end of the element are not dislodged or damaged, then lubricate the O-rings with clean engine oil before fitting the filter assembly to the chamber **(see illustrations)**.

12 Tighten the filter cap to the specified torque wrench setting. Do NOT overtighten the cap. It is made of synthetic material and will break or distort if over-stressed.

13 After all the oil has drained, wipe the drain plug with a clean rag and fit the new sealing

washer **(see illustration)**. Clean the area around the drain plug opening, and refit the plug complete with washer and tighten it to the specified torque. Refit the access flap and tighten its bolt securely; note the specified torque wrench setting. Remove the draining container with the old oil and all tools from under the vehicle and lower the vehicle to the ground.

14 Fill the engine through the oil filler hole, using the correct grade and type of oil (refer to Weekly checks for details of topping-up). Pour in half the specified quantity of oil first, then wait a few minutes for the oil to drain into the sump. Continue to add oil, a small quantity at a time, until the level is up to the lower mark on the dipstick.

15 Start the engine and run it for a few minutes, while checking for leaks around the oil filter seal and the sump drain plug. Note that there may be a delay of a few seconds before the low oil pressure warning light goes out when the engine is first started, as the oil circulates through the new oil filter and the engine oil galleries before the pressure builds-up.

16 Refit the access cover to the engine undershield, remove the axle stands and lower the vehicle to the ground.

17 With the vehicle on the ground check the oil level, adding oil to bring the level up to the maximum mark on the dipstick as necessary. Refit the oil filler cap.

18 Dispose of the used engine oil and the old oil filter safely, with reference to *General*

3.11e Take care not to dislodge or damage the seals when fitting the new filter element to the cap

3.11f Lubricate the O-rings and fit the filter assembly to the filter chamber

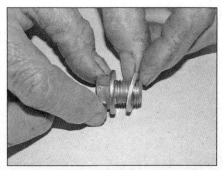

3.13 Fit a new sealing washer and tighten the drain plug to specified torque wrench setting

repair procedures in the Reference chapter of this manual. Many local recycling points have containers for waste oil with oil filter disposal receptacles alongside.

4 Fuel filter water draining

1 Access to the base of the fuel filter is limited. Consider removing the entire filter assembly to drain the water if necessary.
2 Remove the air filter housing as described in Chapter 4B **(see illustration)**.
3 Jack up and support the front of the vehicle (see '*Jacking and vehicle support*' in the Reference chapter) and then remove the engine undershield.
4 Place a suitable container beneath the filter and then attach a short length of hose to the filter drain plug **(see illustration)**.
5 Open the drain plug and allow the water to drain from the filter. There should be no need to drain a large amount of fuel **(see illustration)**.
6 Tighten the drain plug and refit the air filter assembly.
7 Refit the engine undershield and lower the vehicle to the ground.
8 Start the engine and ensure that the 'water in the fuel' warning light is not on.
9 If the engine fails to start, remove the cover and operate the hand primer bulb until it feels firm. Crank the engine for a maximum of 20 seconds. If the engine still fails to start repeat the procedure.

5 Lights and horn operation check

1 With the ignition switched on where necessary, check the operation of all exterior lights.
2 Check the brake lights with the help of an assistant, or by reversing up close to a reflective door. Make sure that all the rear lights are capable of operating independently, without affecting any of the other lights – for example, switch on as many rear lights as possible, then try the brake lights. If any

unusual results are found, this is usually due to an earth fault or other poor connection at that rear light unit.
3 Again with the help of an assistant or using a reflective surface, check as far as possible that the headlights work on both main and dipped beam.
4 Renew any defective bulbs with reference to Chapter 12.
5 Check the operation of all interior lights, including the glovebox and luggage area illumination lights. Switch on the ignition, and check that all relevant warning lights come on as expected – the vehicle handbook should give details of these. Now start the engine, and check that the appropriate lights go out. When you are next driving at night, check that all the instrument panel and facia lighting works correctly. If any problems are found, refer to Chapter 12
6 Finally, choose an appropriate time of day to test the operation of the horn.

6 Underbonnet check for fluid leaks and hose condition

⚠️ **Warning: Renewal of air conditioning hoses must be left to a dealer service department or air conditioning specialist who has the equipment to depressurise the system safely. Never remove air conditioning components or hoses until the system has been depressurised.**

1 Visually inspect the engine joint faces, gaskets and seals for any signs of water or oil leaks. Pay particular attention to the areas around the cylinder head cover, cylinder head, oil filter and sump joint faces. Bear in mind that, over a period of time, some very slight seepage from these areas is to be expected – what you are really looking for is any indication of a serious leak. Should a leak be found, renew the offending gasket or oil seal by referring to the appropriate Chapters in this manual.
2 High temperatures in the engine compartment can cause the deterioration of the rubber and plastic hoses used for engine, accessory and emission systems operation.

Periodic inspection should be made for cracks, loose clamps, material hardening and leaks.
3 When checking the hoses, ensure that all the cable-ties or clips used to retain the hoses are in place, and in good condition. Clips which are broken or missing can lead to chafing of the hoses, pipes or wiring, which could cause more serious problems in the future.
4 Carefully check the large top and bottom radiator hoses, along with the other smaller-diameter cooling system hoses and metal pipes; do not forget the heater hoses/pipes which run from the engine to the bulkhead. Inspect each hose along its entire length, replacing any that is cracked, swollen or shows signs of deterioration. Cracks may become more apparent if the hose is squeezed, and may often be apparent at the hose ends.
5 Make sure that all hose connections are tight. If the large-diameter air hoses from the air cleaner are loose, they will leak air, and upset the engine idle quality. If the spring clamps that are used to secure many of the hoses appear to be slackening, they should be updated with worm-drive clips to prevent the possibility of leaks.
6 Some other hoses are secured to their fittings with clamps. Where clamps are used, check to be sure they haven't lost their tension, allowing the hose to leak. If clamps aren't used, make sure the hose has not expanded and/or hardened where it slips over the fitting, allowing it to leak.
7 Check all fluid reservoirs, filler caps, drain plugs and fittings, etc, looking for any signs of leakage of oil, transmission and/or brake hydraulic fluid, coolant and power steering fluid. Also check the clutch hydraulic fluid lines which lead from the fluid reservoir and slave cylinder (on the transmission).
8 If the vehicle is regularly parked in the same place, close inspection of the ground underneath it will soon show any leaks; ignore the puddle of water which will be left if the air conditioning system is in use. Place a clean piece of cardboard below the engine, and examine it for signs of contamination after the vehicle has been parked over it overnight.

4.2 The fuel filter location

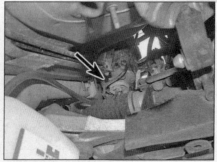

4.4 Attach a drain hose to the filter

4.5 Reach in from above and open the drain tap

9 Remember that some leaks will only occur with the engine running, or when the engine is hot or cold. With the handbrake firmly applied, start the engine from cold, and let the engine idle while you examine the underside of the engine compartment for signs of leakage.

10 If an unusual smell is noticed inside or around the car, especially when the engine is thoroughly hot, this may point to the presence of a leak.

11 As soon as a leak is detected, its source must be traced and rectified. Where oil has been leaking for some time, it is usually necessary to use a steam cleaner, pressure washer or similar to clean away the accumulated dirt, so that the exact source of the leak can be identified.

Vacuum hoses

12 It's quite common for vacuum hoses, especially those in the emissions system, to be colour-coded, or to be identified by coloured stripes moulded into them. Various systems require hoses with different wall thicknesses, collapse resistance and temperature resistance. When renewing hoses, be sure the new ones are made of the same material.

13 Often the only effective way to check a hose is to remove it completely from the vehicle. If more than one hose is removed, be sure to label the hoses and fittings to ensure correct installation.

14 When checking vacuum hoses, be sure to include any plastic T-fittings in the check. Inspect the fittings for cracks, and check the hose where it fits over the fitting for distortion, which could cause leakage.

15 A small piece of vacuum hose (quarter-inch inside diameter) can be used as a stethoscope to detect vacuum leaks. Hold one end of the hose to your ear, and probe around vacuum hoses and fittings, listening for the 'hissing' sound characteristic of a vacuum leak.

⚠️ **Warning: When probing with the vacuum hose stethoscope, be very careful not to come into contact with moving engine components such as the auxiliary drivebelt, radiator electric cooling fan, etc.**

Fuel hoses

⚠️ **Warning: There are certain precautions which must be taken when inspecting or servicing fuel system components. Work in a well-ventilated area, and do not allow open flames (cigarettes, appliance pilot lights, etc) or bare light bulbs near the work area. Mop-up any spills immediately, and do not store fuel-soaked rags where they could ignite.**

16 Check all fuel hoses for deterioration and chafing. Check especially for cracks in areas where the hose bends, and also just before fittings, such as where a hose attaches to the fuel filter.

17 It is not unusual for a high-mileage diesel engine to exhibit a 'film' of diesel fuel around the injectors, resulting in an oily appearance. Unless there is clear evidence of a significant fuel leak, this is not normally a matter for concern. The best course of action would be to first clean the engine thoroughly; then, after several more miles have been covered, the source of the leak can be identified and its severity assessed.

18 High-quality fuel line, usually identified by the word 'Fluoroelastomer' printed on the hose, should be used for fuel line renewal. Never, under any circumstances, use non-reinforced vacuum line, clear plastic tubing or water hose as a substitute for fuel lines.

19 Springtype clamps are commonly used on fuel lines. These clamps often lose their tension over a period of time, and can be 'sprung' during removal. Renew all spring-type clamps with proper petrol pipe clips whenever a hose is renewed.

Metal lines

20 Sections of metal piping are often used for fuel line between the fuel filter and the engine. Check carefully to be sure the piping has not been bent or crimped, and that cracks have not started in the line.

21 If a section of metal fuel line must be renewed, only seamless steel piping should be used, since copper and aluminium piping don't have the strength necessary to withstand normal engine vibration.

22 Check the metal lines where they enter the brake master cylinder, ABS hydraulic unit or clutch master/slave cylinders (as applicable) for cracks in the lines or loose fittings. Any sign of brake fluid leakage calls for an immediate and thorough inspection.

7   Engine compartment wiring check

1 With the vehicle parked on level ground, apply the handbrake firmly and open the bonnet. Using an inspection light or a small electric torch, check all visible wiring within and beneath the engine compartment. Make sure that the ignition is switched off – take out the key.

2 What you are looking for is wiring that is obviously damaged by chafing against sharp edges, or against moving suspension/transmission components and/or the auxiliary drivebelt, by being trapped or crushed between carelessly-refitted components, or melted by being forced into contact with the hot engine castings, coolant pipes, etc. In almost all cases, damage of this sort is caused in the first instance by incorrect routing on reassembly after previous work has been carried out.

3 Depending on the extent of the problem, damaged wiring may be repaired by rejoining the break or splicing-in a new length of wire, using solder to ensure a good connection, and remaking the insulation with adhesive insulating tape or heat-shrink tubing, as appropriate. If the damage is extensive, given the implications for the vehicle's future reliability, the best long-term answer may well be to renew that entire section of the loom, however expensive this may appear.

4 When the actual damage has been repaired, ensure that the wiring loom is re-routed correctly, so that it is clear of other components, and not stretched or kinked, and is secured out of harm's way using the plastic clips, guides and ties provided.

5 Check all electrical connectors, ensuring that they are clean, securely fastened, and that each is locked by its plastic tabs or wire clip, as appropriate. If any connector shows external signs of corrosion (accumulations of white or green deposits, or streaks of 'rust'), or if any is thought to be dirty, it must be unplugged and cleaned using electrical contact cleaner. If the connector pins are severely corroded, the connector must be renewed; note that this may mean the renewal of that entire section of the loom – see your local Ford dealer for details.

6 If the cleaner completely removes the corrosion to leave the connector in a satisfactory condition, it would be wise to pack the connector with a suitable material which will exclude dirt and moisture, preventing the corrosion from occurring again; a Ford dealer may be able to recommend a suitable product.

7 Check the condition of the battery connections – remake the connections or renew the leads if a fault is found (see Chapter 5A). Use the same techniques to ensure that all earth points in the engine compartment provide good electrical contact through clean, metal-to-metal joints, and that all are securely fastened.

8 Check the wiring to the glow plugs, referring to Chapter 5C necessary.

8   Seat belt check

1 Check the seat belts for satisfactory operation and condition. Inspect the webbing for fraying and cuts. Check that they retract smoothly and without binding into their reels.

2 Check the seat belt mountings, ensuring that all the bolts are securely tightened.

9   Brake pads, shoes and discs check

1 The work described in this Section should be carried out at the specified intervals, or whenever a defect is suspected in the braking system. Any of the following symptoms could indicate a potential brake system defect:

a) *The vehicle pulls to one side when the brake pedal is depressed.*

b) *The brakes make squealing, scraping or dragging noises when applied.*

c) *Brake pedal travel is excessive, or pedal feel is poor.*

d) *The brake fluid requires repeated topping-up. Note that, because the hydraulic clutch shares the same fluid as the braking system (see Chapter 6), this problem could be due to a leak in the clutch system.*

Front disc brakes

2 Apply the handbrake, then loosen the front wheel nuts. Jack up the front of the vehicle, and support it on axle stands (see *'Jacking and vehicle support'* in the Reference chapter).

3 For better access to the brake calipers, remove the wheels.

4 Look through the inspection window in the caliper, and check that the thickness of the friction lining material on each of the pads is not less than the recommended minimum thickness given in the Specifications **(see illustration)**.

5 If it is difficult to determine the exact thickness of the pad linings, or if you are at all concerned about the condition of the pads, then remove them from the calipers for further inspection (refer to Chapter 9).

6 Check the other caliper in the same way.

7 If any one of the brake pads has worn down to, or below, the specified limit, all four pads at that end of the car must be renewed as a set. If the pads on one side are significantly more worn than the other, this may indicate that the caliper pistons have partially seized – refer to the brake pad renewal procedure in Chapter 9, and push the pistons back into the caliper to free them.

8 Measure the thickness of the discs with a micrometer, if available, to make sure that they still have service life remaining. Do not be fooled by the lip of rust which often forms on the outer edge of the disc, which may make the disc appear thicker than it really is – scrape off the loose rust if necessary, without scoring the disc friction (shiny) surface.

9 If any disc is thinner than the specified minimum thickness, renew it (refer to Chapter 9).

10 Check the general condition of the discs. Look for excessive scoring and discolouration caused by overheating. If these conditions exist, remove the relevant disc and have it resurfaced or renewed (refer to Chapter 9).

11 Make sure that the handbrake is firmly applied, then check that the transmission is in neutral. Spin the wheel, and check that the brake is not binding. Some drag is normal with a disc brake, but it should not require any great effort to turn the wheel – also, do not confuse brake drag with resistance from the transmission.

12 Before refitting the wheels, check all brake lines and hoses (refer to Chapter 9). In particular, check the flexible hoses in the vicinity of the calipers, where they are subjected to most movement **(see illustration)**. Bend them between the fingers (but do not actually bend them double, or the casing may be damaged) and check that this does not reveal previously-hidden cracks, cuts or splits.

13 On completion, refit the wheels and lower the car to the ground. Tighten the wheel nuts to the specified torque.

Rear disc brakes

14 Loosen the rear wheel nuts, then chock the front wheels. Jack up the rear of the car, and support it on axle stands. Release the handbrake and remove the rear wheels.

15 The procedure for checking the rear brakes is much the same as described in paragraphs 2 to 13 above. Check that the rear brakes are not binding, noting that transmission resistance is not a factor on the rear wheels. Abnormal effort may indicate that the handbrake needs adjusting – see Chapter 9.

10 Exhaust system check

1 With the engine cold (at least three hours after the vehicle has been driven), check the complete exhaust system, from its starting point at the engine to the end of the tailpipe. Ideally, this should be done on a hoist, where unrestricted access is available; if a hoist is not available, raise and support the vehicle on axle stands.

2 Make sure that all brackets and rubber mountings are in good condition, and tight; if any of the mountings are to be renewed, ensure that the new ones are of the correct type – in the case of the rubber mountings, their colour is a good guide. Those nearest to the catalytic converter are more heat-resistant than the others.

3 Check the pipes and connections for evidence of leaks, severe corrosion, or damage. Leakage at any of the joints or in other parts of the system will usually show up as a black sooty stain in the vicinity of the leak. **Note:** *Exhaust sealants should not be used on any part of the exhaust system upstream of the catalytic converter (between the engine and the converter) – even if the sealant does not contain additives harmful to the converter, pieces of it may break off and foul the element, causing local overheating.*

4 At the same time, inspect the underside of the body for holes, corrosion, open seams, etc, which may allow exhaust gases to enter the passenger compartment. Seal all body openings with silicone or body putty.

5 Rattles and other noises can often be traced to the exhaust system, especially the rubber mountings **(see illustration)**. Try to move the system, silencer(s) and catalytic converter. If any components can touch the body or suspension parts, secure the exhaust system with new mountings.

11 Steering, suspension and roadwheel check

Front suspension and steering

1 Apply the handbrake, then raise the front of the vehicle and support it on axle stands.

2 Visually inspect the balljoint dust covers and the steering gear gaiters for splits, chafing

9.4 Check the brake pad friction material thickness (arrowed)

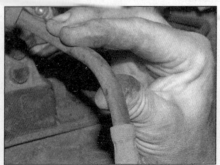
9.12 Bend the flexible hoses and check for cracks

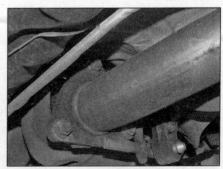
10.5 Check the condition of the exhaust joints and the rubber mountings

11.2 Check the condition of the steering rack gaiters

11.4 Grasp the roadwheel at the 12 o'clock and 6 o'clock positions, and try to rock it

12.2 Check the condition of the driveshaft gaiters

or deterioration **(see illustration)**. Any wear of these components will cause loss of lubricant, together with dirt and water entry, resulting in rapid deterioration of the balljoints or steering gear.

3 Check the power-assisted steering fluid hoses for chafing or deterioration, and the pipe and hose unions for fluid leaks. Also check for signs of fluid leakage under pressure from the steering gear rubber gaiters, which would indicate failed fluid seals within the steering gear.

4 Grasp the roadwheel at the 12 o'clock and 6 o'clock positions, and try to rock it **(see illustration)**. Very slight free play may be felt, but if the movement is appreciable, further investigation is necessary to determine the source. Continue rocking the wheel while an assistant depresses the footbrake. If the movement is now eliminated or significantly reduced, it is likely that the hub bearings are at fault. If the free play is still evident with the footbrake depressed, then there is wear in the suspension joints or mountings.

5 Now grasp the wheel at the 9 o'clock and 3 o'clock positions, and try to rock it as before. Any movement felt now may again be caused by wear in the hub bearings or the steering track rod balljoints. If the outer track rod balljoint is worn, the visual movement will be obvious. If the inner joint is suspect, it can be felt by placing a hand over the rack-and-pinion rubber gaiter, and gripping the track rod. If the wheel is now rocked, movement will be felt at the inner joint if wear has taken place.

6 Using a large screwdriver or flat bar, check for wear in the suspension mounting and subframe bushes by levering between the relevant suspension component and its attachment point. Some movement is to be expected as the mountings are made of rubber, but excessive wear should be obvious. Also check the condition of any visible rubber bushes, looking for splits, cracks or contamination of the rubber.

7 With the vehicle standing on its wheels, have an assistant turn the steering wheel back-and-forth, about an eighth of a turn each way. There should be very little, if any, lost movement between the steering wheel

and roadwheels. If this is not the case, closely observe the joints and mountings previously described, but in addition, check the steering column joints for wear, and also check the rack-and-pinion steering gear itself.

Rear suspension

8 Chock the front wheels, then raise the rear of the vehicle and support it on axle stands.

9 Check the rear hub bearings for wear, using the method described for the front hub bearings (paragraph 4).

10 Using a large screwdriver or flat bar, check for wear in the suspension mounting bushes by levering between the relevant suspension component and its attachment point. Some movement is to be expected as the mountings are made of rubber, but excessive wear should be obvious.

Roadwheel check and balancing

11 Periodically remove the roadwheels, and clean any dirt or mud from the inside and outside surfaces. Examine the wheel rims for signs of rusting, corrosion or other damage. Light alloy wheels are easily damaged by 'kerbing' whilst parking, and similarly, steel wheels may become dented or buckled. Renewal of the wheel is very often the only course of remedial action possible.

12 The balance of each wheel and tyre assembly should be maintained, not only to avoid excessive tyre wear, but also to avoid wear in the steering and suspension components. Wheel imbalance is normally signified by vibration through the vehicle's bodyshell, although in many cases it is particularly noticeable through the steering wheel. Conversely, it should be noted that wear or damage in suspension or steering components may cause excessive tyre wear. Out-of-round or out-of-true tyres, damaged wheels and wheel bearing wear/maladjustment also fall into this category. Balancing will not usually cure vibration caused by such wear.

13 Wheel balancing may be carried out with the wheel either on or off the vehicle. If balanced on the vehicle, ensure that the wheel-to-hub relationship is marked in some way prior to subsequent wheel removal, so that it may be refitted in its original position.

12 Driveshaft rubber gaiter and joint check

1 The driveshaft rubber gaiters are very important, because they prevent dirt, water and foreign material from entering and damaging the joints. External contamination can cause the gaiter material to deteriorate prematurely, so it's a good idea to wash the gaiters with soap and water occasionally.

2 With the vehicle raised and securely supported on axle stands, turn the steering onto full-lock, then slowly rotate each front wheel in turn. Inspect the condition of the outer constant velocity (CV) joint rubber gaiters, squeezing the gaiters to open out the folds. Check for signs of cracking, splits, or deterioration of the rubber, which may allow the escape of grease, and lead to the ingress of water and grit into the joint. Also check the security and condition of the retaining clips. Repeat these checks on the inner joints **(see illustration)**. If any damage or deterioration is found, the gaiters should be renewed as described in Chapter 8.

3 At the same time, check the general condition of the outer CV joints themselves, by first holding the driveshaft and attempting to rotate the wheels. Repeat this check on the inner joints, by holding the inner joint yoke and attempting to rotate the driveshaft.

4 Any appreciable movement in the joint indicates wear in the joint, wear in the driveshaft splines, or a loose driveshaft retaining bolt.

13 Underbody and fuel/brake line check

1 With the vehicle raised and supported on axle stands or over an inspection pit, thoroughly inspect the underbody and wheel arches for signs of damage and corrosion. In particular, examine the bottom of the side sills, and any concealed areas where mud can collect.

2 Where corrosion and rust is evident, press

13.5 Ensure the pipes are correctly supported in their clips

and tap firmly on the panel with a screwdriver, and check for any serious corrosion which would necessitate repairs.

3 If the panel is not seriously corroded, clean away the rust, and apply a new coating of underseal. Refer to Chapter 11 for more details of body repairs.

4 At the same time, inspect the lower body panels for stone damage and general condition.

5 Inspect all of the fuel and brake lines on the underbody for damage, rust, corrosion and leakage. Also make sure that they are correctly supported in their clips **(see illustration)**. Where applicable, check the PVC coating on the lines for damage.

14 Hinge and lock lubrication

1 Work around the vehicle and lubricate the hinges of the bonnet, doors and tailgate with a light machine oil.

2 Check carefully the security and operation of all hinges, latches and locks, adjusting them where required. Check the operation of the central locking system (if fitted).

3 Where applicable, check the condition and operation of the tailgate struts, renewing them if either is leaking or no longer able to support the tailgate securely when raised.

15 Roadwheel nut tightness check

1 Checking the tightness of the wheel nuts is more relevant than you might think. Apart from the obvious safety aspect of ensuring they are sufficiently tight, this check will reveal whether they have been overtightened, as may have happened the last time new tyres were fitted, for example. If the car suffers a puncture, you may find that the wheel nuts cannot be loosened with the wheel brace.

2 Apply the handbrake, chock the wheels, and engage 1st gear.

3 Remove the wheel cover (or wheel centre cover), using the flat end of the wheel brace supplied in the tool kit.

4 Loosen the first wheel nut, using the wheel brace if possible. If the nut proves stubborn, use a close-fitting socket and a long extension bar.

 Warning: Do not use makeshift means to loosen the wheel nuts if the proper tools are not available. If extra force is required, make sure that the tools fit properly, and are of good quality. Even so, consider the consequences of the tool slipping or breaking, and take precautions – wearing stout gloves is advisable to protect your hands. Do not be tempted to stand on the tools used – they are not designed for this, and there is a high risk of personal injury if the tool slips or breaks. If the wheel nuts are simply too tight, take the car to a garage equipped with suitable power tools.

5 Once the nut has been loosened, remove it and check that the wheel stud threads are clean. Use a small wire brush to clean any rust or dirt from the threads, if necessary.

6 Refit the nut, with the tapered side facing inwards. Tighten it fully, using the wheel brace alone – no other tools. This will ensure that the wheel nuts can be loosened using the wheel brace if a puncture occurs. However, if a torque wrench is available, tighten the nut to the specified torque wrench setting.

7 Repeat the procedure for the remaining nuts, then refit the wheel cover or centre cover, as applicable.

8 Work around the car, checking and retightening the nuts for all four wheels.

16 Road test

Braking system

1 Make sure that the vehicle does not pull to one side when braking, and that the wheels do not lock when braking hard.

2 Check that there is no vibration through the steering when braking. On models equipped with ABS brakes, if vibration is felt through the pedal under heavy braking, this is a normal characteristic of the system operation, and is not a cause for concern.

3 Check that the handbrake operates correctly, without excessive movement of the lever, and that it holds the vehicle stationary on a slope, in both directions (facing up and down a slope).

4 With the engine switched off, test the operation of the brake servo unit as follows. Depress the footbrake four or five times to exhaust the vacuum, then start the engine. As the engine starts, there should be a noticeable 'give' in the brake pedal as vacuum builds-up. Allow the engine to run for at least two minutes, and then switch it off. If the brake pedal is now depressed again, it should be possible to detect a hiss from the servo as the pedal is depressed. After about four or five applications, no further hissing should be heard, and the pedal should feel considerably harder.

Steering and suspension

5 Check for any abnormalities in the steering, suspension, handling or road 'feel'.

6 Drive the vehicle, and check that there are no unusual vibrations or noises.

7 Check that the steering feels positive, with no excessive sloppiness or roughness, and check for any suspension noises when cornering and driving over bumps.

Drivetrain

8 Check the performance of the engine, transmission and driveshafts.

9 Check that the engine starts correctly, both when cold and when hot. Observe the glow plug warning light, and check that it comes on and goes off correctly.

10 Listen for any unusual noises from the engine and transmission.

11 Make sure that the engine runs smoothly when idling, and that there is no hesitation when accelerating.

12 Check that all gears can be engaged smoothly without noise, and that the gear lever action is smooth and not abnormally vague or 'notchy'.

13 Listen for a metallic clicking sound from the front of the vehicle as the vehicle is driven slowly in a circle with the steering on full-lock. Carry out this check in both directions. If a clicking noise is heard, this indicates wear in a driveshaft joint, in which case renew the joint if necessary.

Clutch

14 Check that the clutch pedal moves smoothly and easily through its full travel, and that the clutch itself functions correctly, with no trace of slip or drag.

15 If the clutch is slow to release, it is possible that the system requires bleeding (see Chapter 6). Also check the fluid pipes under the bonnet for signs of leakage.

16 Check the clutch as described in Chapter 6.

Instruments and electrical equipment

17 Check the operation of all instruments and electrical equipment.

18 Make sure that all instruments read correctly, and switch on all electrical equipment in turn, to check that it functions properly.

17 Handbrake check and adjustment

1 In service, the handbrake should be fully applied within 8 to 9 clicks of the handbrake lever ratchet. Should adjustment be necessary, refer to Chapter 9 for the full procedure description.

18.3 Disconnect the fuel hoses

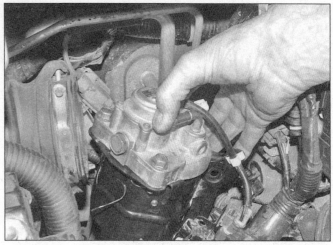

18.4 Remove the filter

18.5a Remove the bolts...

18.5b...and slide off the protective cage

18 Fuel filter renewal

1 Remove the air filter assembly as described in Chapter 4B.

2 Disconnect the wiring plugs
3 Disconnect the fuel supply and return pipes from the filter **(see illustration)**. Plug the openings to prevent contamination.
4 Remove the filter mounting bolts and pull the filter free from the filter housing **(see illustration)**.

5 Mount the filter head in a vice (use soft jaws to protect the filter head) and then remove the housing **(see illustration)**.
6 Remove the water level sensor and then unscrew the filter from the filter head **(see illustrations)**.
7 On reassembly, renew the sealing O-ring on

18.6a Remove the level sensor – anticipate some fuel spillage

18.6b Slacken and then...

18.6c...remove the fuel filter

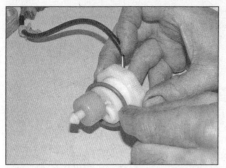

18.7a Fit a new O-ring (supplied with the filter)

18.7b Lubricate the O-rings

18.7c Tighten the filter. Note the cable tie used to avoid crushing the filter

18.7d Fit the level sensor...

18.7e...and tighten it to the specified torque

the water level switch (see illustrations). To tighten the filter, Honda service tool Part No. 070AA-RMAC100 is required. We found that a commercial cup-type equivalent was not deep enough to tighten the filter to the specified torque. We improvised with a three-legged oil filter tool. Tighten the filter to the specified torque.

8 Refit the filter assembly to the vehicle and operate the hand primer to prime the fuel system. Refit the air filter assembly and start the vehicle. If the vehicle does not start operate the hand priming bulb and try again.

Caution: Do not operate the starter motor for more than 20 seconds.

9 Check carefully for any signs of fuel leaks from the filter assembly. On completion, dispose safely of the drained fuel and the used filter. Most local authority used oil 'banks' also have used filter disposal points alongside.

19 Air filter element renewal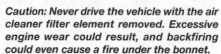

Caution: Never drive the vehicle with the air cleaner filter element removed. Excessive engine wear could result, and backfiring could even cause a fire under the bonnet.

1 If carrying out a routine service, the element must be renewed regardless of its apparent condition.

2 Release the locking clips, lift up the cover and remove the air filter from the housing (see illustrations).

3 With the air cleaner cover removed, wipe out the inside of the housing.

4 Refitting is the reverse of the removal procedure.

20 Auxiliary drivebelt check and renewal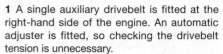

Note: *Only rotate the engine in the normal (clockwise) direction.*

Drivebelt check

1 A single auxiliary drivebelt is fitted at the right-hand side of the engine. An automatic adjuster is fitted, so checking the drivebelt tension is unnecessary.

2 Due to their function and material make-up, drivebelts are prone to failure after a long period of time, and should therefore be inspected regularly.

3 With the engine stopped, inspect the full length of the drivebelt for cracks and separation of the belt plies. It will be necessary to turn the engine (using a spanner or socket and bar on the crankshaft pulley bolt) in order to move the belt from the pulleys so that the belt can be inspected thoroughly. Twist the belt between the pulleys so that both sides can be viewed. Also check for fraying, and glazing which gives the belt a shiny appearance. Check the pulleys for nicks, cracks, distortion and corrosion (see illustration).

4 Note that it is not unusual for a ribbed belt

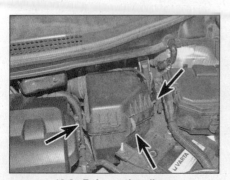

19.2a Release the clips...

19.2b...lift the lid and extract the air filter

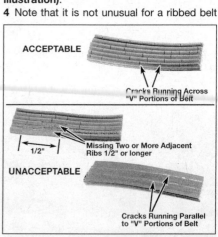

20.3 Check very carefully for some of the more common faults found on multi-ribbed auxiliary drivebelts

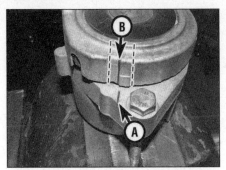

20.5 Note the location of the tensioner fixed line (A). The dotted lines indicate the normal range marked by the tensioner long and short rectangular reference marks – tensioner fixed line (A) should be within this range if the drivebelt is unworn

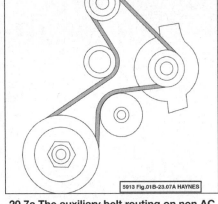

20.7a The auxiliary belt routing on non AC models

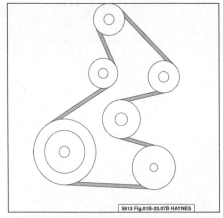

20.7b The auxiliary belt routing on AC models

to exhibit small cracks in the edges of the belt ribs, and unless these are extensive or very deep, belt renewal is not essential.

5 The automatic tensioner incorporates a wear guide. The index mark on the fixed base of the tensioner must lie within the long and short marks on the movable section of the tensioner **(see illustration)**.

Drivebelt renewal

6 Honda do not specify a replacement interval for belt replacement. It should be inspected regularly and the position of the tensioner noted. It may be prudent to replace it if any component driven by the belt is replaced or removed as part of another procedure.

7 Jack up the front of the vehicle (see "*Jacking and vehicle support*" in the Reference chapter

and remove the right-hand road wheel to gain access to the belt and crankshaft pulley. Note the routing of the belt before removing it **(see illustrations)**.

8 Special long handled belt release spanners are commercially available, however it is possible to release the tension with a pair of spanners locked together. If the original belt is to be refitted mark the direction of rotation on the belt before removing it.

9 With a long spanner (or two shorter spanners used together) applied to the tensioner pulley bolt, move the tensioner pulley and arm clockwise until the drivebelt can be slipped off the first pulley, then release them slowly and carefully. Do NOT allow the tensioner arm to snap back against spring pressure – it will break **(see illustration)**.

10 Working from the wheel arch or engine compartment as necessary, and noting its routing, slip the drivebelt off the remaining pulleys and withdraw it.

11 With the belt removed checked the operation of the pulleys. They can all (apart from the crankshaft pulley) be rotated by hand. Listen for any noise as the pulleys are rotated and check for any excess play. Where necessary clean the grooves in the pulleys.

12 If there is any doubt about the condition of the tensioner then remove it and mount it in a vice **(see illustrations)**.

13 Mount the tensioner in a vice and check that the torque required to align the fixed and movable marks on the tensioner lies within the range of 47 to 59 Nm.

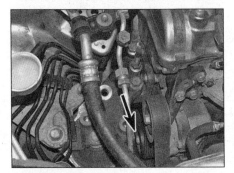

20.9 Access to the belt tensioner is limited

20.12a Remove the idler pulley

20.12b The tensioner mounting bolts

20.12c Unbolt and then...

20.12d...remove the tensioner

20.13 Mount the tensioner in a vice using two M8 bolts and check the force required to align the index marks

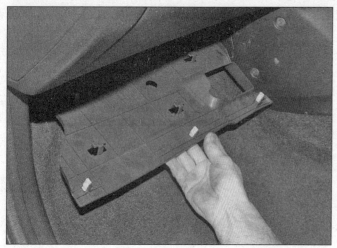

21.1a Unclip and then...

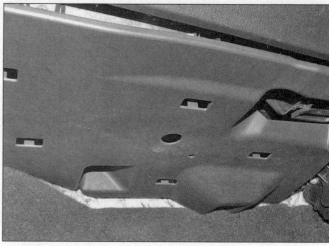

21.1b...remove the lower panel from below the glovebox

14 Refitting the belt is a reversal of the removal procedure, however the aid of an assistant makes fitting the belt considerably easier. With the belt fitted, rotate the engine (via the crankshaft pulley) several times to settle the belt. Check that the belt is correctly located in the pulley grooves as it is rotated.

15 Refit the road wheel, remove the axle stand and lower the vehicle to the ground.

21 Pollen filter renewal

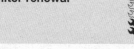

1 Working in the passengers footwell pull down and release the facia under cover and then unhook it from the rear mounting point **(see illustrations)**. Replacement of the filter is slightly easier if the glovebox is removed before removing the pollen filter.
2 Unclip and remove the cover from the filter and then slide the filter from the housing **(see illustration)**. Note the air flow direction – marked on the filter.
3 Fit the new filter using a reversal of the removal procedure, ensuring that the filter is fitted with the airflow arrows pointing straight back into the cabin. Refit the lower facia cover.

22 Transmission fluid

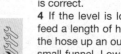

Transmission oil – level checking

1 Jack up and support the front of the vehicle – see '*Jacking and vehicle support*' in the Reference chapter. Remove the engine undershield.
2 Slacken the combined filler/level plug. This located close to the left-hand driveshaft, on the differential housing **(see illustration)**. Have a container ready to catch any fluid and then remove the filler/level plug.
3 The level check should be made with the vehicle on level ground. Lowering the vehicle to do this will make access to the filler/level plug difficult. The easiest way to check the level is to first check that the level is just below

the filler plug with a home made dipstick – a length of welding rod makes an ideal dipstick – whilst the vehicle is raised. If there are no apparent leaks the chances are that the level is correct.
4 If the level is low (or believed to be) then feed a length of hose into the filler hole. Feed the hose up an out of the vehicle and attach a small funnel. Lower the vehicle to the ground and then pour fresh transmission oil into the transmission through the funnel, stopping as soon as oil drips from the filler hole into the container.
5 When the level is correct raise the front of the vehicle, support it on axle stands and refit the filler/level plug – using a new washer and tightening to the specified torque. Refit the engine undershield and lower the vehicle to the ground.

Transmission – fluid renewal

6 Jack up and support the front of the vehicle – see '*Jacking and vehicle support*' in the Reference chapter. Remove the engine undershield.
7 Remove the filler/level plug. Place a clean container beneath the transmission and then

21.2a Unclip the filter cover...

21.2b...and slide out the filter

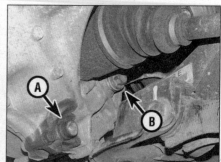

22.2 Manual transmission drain (A) and filler/level check (B)

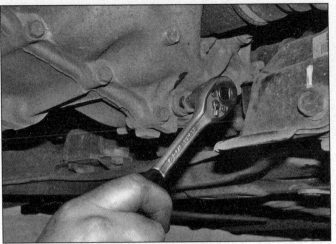

22.7a Remove the drain plug...

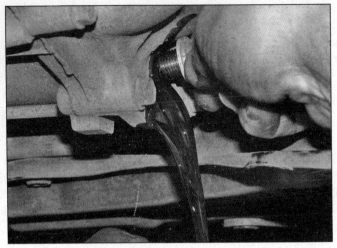

22.7b...and drain the transmission

remove the drain plug (see illustrations). Allow the fluid to drain into the container.

8 Clean the area around the drain plug, fit a new sealing washer to the drain plug and tighten the bolt to the specified torque.

9 Fill the transmission with fresh transmission oil using a length of hose and small funnel (see illustration). The vehicle should be on the ground and level. To achieve this it may be necessary to lower the vehicle to the ground.

10 As soon as fluid flows from the filler/level hole, refit the filler plug – using a new washer – and tighten it to the specified torque.

11 Refit the engine undershield and lower the vehicle.

23 Remote control battery renewal

1 Although not in the Honda maintenance schedule, we recommend that the battery is changed every 2 years, regardless of the vehicle's mileage. However, if the door locks repeatedly fail to respond to signals from the remote control at the normal distance, change the battery in the remote control before

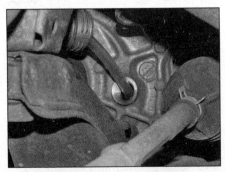

22.9 Filling the transmission

attempting to troubleshoot any of the vehicle's other systems.

2 Remove the single small cross head screw from base of the key fob. Separate the two halves of the fob using a small flat bladed screwdriver.

3 Release the inner cover from the upper switch housing (use a small screwdriver) and remove the battery.

4 Fit the new battery with the + side facing down. Refit the the inner cover.

5 Refit the upper and the lower sections back together. Refit the screw nd test the operation of the remote fob.

24 Brake fluid renewal

⚠ **Warning: Brake hydraulic fluid can harm your eyes and damage painted surfaces, so use extreme caution when handling and pouring it. Do not use fluid that has been standing open for some time, as it absorbs moisture from the air. Excess moisture can cause a dangerous loss of braking effectiveness. Brake fluid is also highly flammable – treat it with the same respect as petrol.**

1 The procedure is similar to that for the bleeding of the hydraulic system as described in Chapter 9.

2 Reduce the fluid level in the reservoir (by syphoning or using a poultry baster), but do not allow the fluid level to drop far enough to allow air into the system.

⚠ **Warning: Do not syphon the fluid by mouth; it is poisonous.**

3 The brakes must be bled in sequence.
a) Front right
b) Front left
c) Rear right
d) Rear left

4 Working in order, open the first bleed screw in the sequence, and pump the brake pedal gently until nearly all the old fluid has been emptied from the master cylinder reservoir. Top-up to the MAX level with new fluid, and continue pumping until only the new fluid remains in the reservoir, and new fluid can be seen emerging from the bleed screw. Tighten the screw, and top the reservoir level up to the MAX level line. Old hydraulic fluid is invariably much darker in colour than the new, making it easy to distinguish the two.

5 Work through all the remaining bleed screws in the sequence until new fluid can be seen at all of them. Be careful to keep the master cylinder reservoir topped-up to above the MIN level at all times, or air may enter the system and greatly increase the length of the task.

6 When the operation is complete, check that all bleed screws are securely tightened, and that their dust caps are refitted. Wash off all traces of spilt fluid, and recheck the master cylinder reservoir fluid level.

7 Check the operation of the brakes before taking the car on the road.

25 Coolant strength check and renewal

⚠ **Warning: Do not allow antifreeze to come in contact with your skin or painted surfaces of the vehicle. Flush contaminated areas immediately with plenty of water. Don't store new coolant, or leave old coolant lying around, where it's accessible to children or pets – they're attracted by its sweet smell. Ingestion of even a small amount of coolant can be fatal. Wipe up garage-floor and drip-pan spills immediately. Keep antifreeze containers covered, and repair cooling system leaks as soon as they're noticed.**

Warning: Never remove the expansion tank filler cap when the engine is running, or has just been switched off, as the cooling system will be hot, and the consequent escaping steam and scalding coolant could cause serious injury.

Warning: Wait until the engine is cold before starting these procedures.

Strength check

1 Use a hydrometer to check the strength of the antifreeze. Follow the instructions provided with your hydrometer. The antifreeze strength should be approximately 50%. If it is significantly less than this, drain a little coolant from the radiator (see this Section), add antifreeze to the coolant expansion tank, then recheck the strength.

Coolant draining

2 To drain the system, first remove the expansion tank filler cap.
3 If the additional working clearance is required, raise the front of the vehicle and support it securely on axle stands (see 'Jacking and vehicle support' in the Reference chapter). Undo the fasteners and remove the engine undershield.
4 Place a large drain tray underneath, and unscrew the radiator drain plug **(see illustrations)**. Direct as much of the escaping coolant as possible into the tray.
5 Once the coolant has stopped draining from the radiator, close the drain plug.

System flushing

6 With time, the cooling system may gradually lose its efficiency, as the radiator core becomes choked with rust, scale deposits from the water, and other sediment. To minimise this, as well as using only good-quality antifreeze and clean soft water, the system should be flushed as follows whenever any part of it is disturbed, and/or when the coolant is renewed.
7 With the coolant drained, refit the drain plug and refill the system with fresh water. Refit the expansion tank filler cap, start the engine and warm it up to normal operating temperature, then stop it and (after allowing it to cool down completely) drain the system again. Repeat as necessary until only clean water can be seen to emerge, then refill finally with the specified coolant mixture.
8 If only clean, soft water and good-quality antifreeze (even if not to Honda's specification) has been used, and the coolant has been renewed at the suggested intervals, the above procedure will be sufficient to keep clean the system for a considerable length of time. If, however, the system has been neglected, a more thorough operation will be required, as follows.
9 First drain the coolant, then disconnect the radiator top and bottom hoses. Insert a garden hose into the radiator top hose

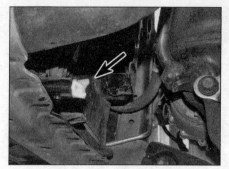

25.4a The radiator drain tap

connection, and allow water to circulate through the radiator until it runs clean from the bottom outlet.
10 To flush the engine, insert the garden hose into the radiator bottom hose, wrap a piece of rag around the garden hose to seal the connection, and allow water to circulate until it runs clear.
11 Try the effect of repeating this procedure in the top hose, although this may not be effective, since the thermostat will probably close and prevent the flow of water.
12 In severe cases of contamination, reverse-flushing of the radiator may be necessary. This may be achieved by inserting the garden hose into the bottom outlet, wrapping a piece of rag around the hose to seal the connection, then flushing the radiator until clear water emerges from the top hose outlet.
13 If the radiator is suspected of being severely choked, remove the radiator (Chapter 3), turn it upside-down, and repeat the procedure described in paragraph 12.
14 Flushing the heater matrix can be achieved using a similar procedure to that described in paragraph 12, once the heater inlet and outlet hoses have been identified. These two hoses will be of the same diameter, and pass through the engine compartment bulkhead (refer to the heater matrix removal procedure in Chapter 3 for more details).
15 The use of chemical cleaners is not recommended, and should be necessary only as a last resort; the scouring action of some chemical cleaners may lead to other cooling system problems. Normally, regular renewal of the coolant will prevent excessive contamination of the system.

Coolant filling

Note: *It is increasingly common for manufactures to supply anti-freeze/coolant pre-mixed with distilled water. Check that the replacement coolant/anti-freeze is not a ready mixed type before adding water.*

16 With the cooling system drained and flushed, ensure that all disturbed hose unions are correctly secured, and that the radiator/ engine drain plug(s) is securely tightened. Refit the engine undershield (where applicable). If it was raised, lower the vehicle to the ground.
17 Set the heater temperature control to

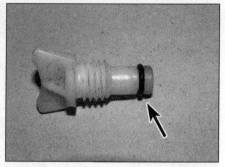

25.4b Check the condition of the drain plug O-ring. Replace it if it is poor condition

maximum heat, but ensure the blower is turned off.
18 Prepare a sufficient quantity of the specified coolant mixture (see below); allow for a surplus, so as to have a reserve supply for topping-up.
19 Slowly fill the system through the expansion tank. Since the tank is the highest point in the system, all the air in the system should be displaced into the tank by the rising liquid. Slow pouring reduces the possibility of air being trapped and forming airlocks.
20 Continue filling until the coolant level reaches the expansion tank MAX level line (see *Weekly checks*), then cover the filler opening to prevent coolant splashing out.
21 Start the engine and run it at 2500 rpm for 2 minutes. If the level in the expansion tank drops significantly, top-up to the MAX level line, to minimise the amount of air circulating in the system.
22 Fill the expansion tank to the MAX level line, refit the expansion tank cap, and run the engine at 2500 rpm until the thermostat opens and the engine is at normal operating temperature. Check this by feeling the radiator bottom hose – if it's hot, then the thermostat has opened.
23 Briefly run the engine at 4000 rpm, then run it at 2500 rpm for approximately 3 minutes.
24 Stop the engine, wash off any spilt coolant from the engine compartment and bodywork, then leave the car to cool down completely (overnight, if possible).
25 With the system cool, open the expansion tank, and top-up the tank to the MAX level line. Refit the filler cap, tightening it securely, and clean up any further spillage.
26 After refilling, always check carefully all components of the system (but especially any unions disturbed during draining and flushing) for signs of coolant leaks. Fresh antifreeze has a searching action, which will rapidly expose any weak points in the system.

Antifreeze type and mixture

Note: *Do not use engine antifreeze in the windscreen/tailgate washer system, as it will damage the vehicle's paintwork. A screenwash additive should be added to the washer system in its maker's recommended quantities.*

27 If the vehicle's history (and therefore the quality of the antifreeze in it) is unknown, owners are advised to drain and thoroughly reverse-flush the system, before refilling with fresh coolant mixture.

28 If the antifreeze used is to Honda's specification, the levels of protection it affords are indicated in the coolant packaging.

29 To give the recommended standard mixture ratio for antifreeze, 50% (by volume) of antifreeze must be mixed with 50% of clean, soft water; if you are using any other type of antifreeze, follow its manufacturer's instructions to achieve the correct ratio.

30 You are unlikely to fully drain the system at any one time (unless the engine is being completely stripped), and the capacities quoted in Specifications are therefore slightly academic for routine coolant renewal. As a guide, only two-thirds of the system's total capacity is likely to be needed for coolant renewal.

31 As the drained system will be partially filled with flushing water, in order to establish the recommended mixture ratio, measure out 50% of the system capacity in antifreeze and pour it into the hose/expansion tank as described above, then top-up with water. Any topping-up while refilling the system should be done with water – for *Weekly checks* use a suitable mixture.

32 Before adding antifreeze, the cooling system should be drained, preferably flushed, and all hoses checked for condition and security. As noted earlier, fresh antifreeze will rapidly find any weaknesses in the system.

33 After filling with antifreeze, a label should be attached to the expansion tank, stating the type and concentration of antifreeze used, and the date installed. Any subsequent topping-up should be made with the same type and concentration of antifreeze.

General cooling system checks

34 The engine should be cold for the cooling system checks, so perform the following procedure before driving the vehicle, or after it has been shut off for at least three hours.

35 Remove the expansion tank filler cap, and clean it thoroughly inside and out with a rag. Also clean the filler neck on the expansion tank. The presence of rust or corrosion in the filler neck indicates that the coolant should be changed. The coolant inside the expansion tank should be relatively clean and transparent. If it is rust-coloured, drain and flush the system, and refill with a fresh coolant mixture.

36 Carefully check the radiator hoses and heater hoses along their entire length; renew any hose which is cracked, swollen or deteriorated.

37 Inspect all other cooling system components (joint faces, etc) for leaks. A leak in the cooling system will usually show up as white- or antifreeze-coloured deposits on the area adjoining the leak (see **Haynes Hint**). Where any problems of this nature are found on system components, renew the component or gasket with reference to Chapter 3.

38 Clean the front of the radiator with a soft brush to remove all insects, leaves, etc, embedded in the radiator fins. Be careful not to damage the radiator fins, or cut your fingers on them. To do a more thorough job, remove the radiator grille as described in Chapter 11.

Airlocks

39 If, after draining and refilling the system, symptoms of overheating are found which did not occur previously, then the fault is almost certainly due to trapped air at some point in the system, causing an airlock and restricting the flow of coolant; usually, the air is trapped because the system was refilled too quickly.

40 If an airlock is suspected, first try gently squeezing all visible coolant hoses. A coolant hose which is full of air feels quite different to one full of coolant when squeezed. After refilling the system, most airlocks will clear once the system has cooled, and been topped-up.

41 While the engine is running at operating temperature, switch on the heater and heater fan, and check for heat output. Provided there is sufficient coolant in the system, lack of heat output could be due to an airlock in the system.

42 Airlocks can have more serious effects than simply reducing heater output – a severe airlock could reduce coolant flow around the engine. Check that the radiator top hose is hot when the engine is at operating temperature – a top hose which stays cold could be the result of an airlock (or a non-opening thermostat).

A leak in the cooling system will usually show up as white or antifreeze coloured deposits on the areas adjoining the leak.

43 If the problem persists, stop the engine and allow it to cool down completely, before unscrewing the expansion tank filler cap or loosening the hose clips and squeezing the hoses to bleed out the trapped air. In the worst case, the system will have to be at least partially drained (this time, the coolant can be saved for re-use) and flushed to clear the problem. If all else fails, have the system evacuated and vacuum filled by a suitably-equipped garage.

Expansion tank pressure cap check

44 Wait until the engine is completely cold – perform this check before the engine is started for the first time in the day.

45 Place a wad of cloth over the expansion tank cap, then unscrew it slowly and remove it.

46 Examine the condition of the rubber seal on the underside of the cap. If the rubber appears to have hardened, or cracks are visible in the seal edges, a new cap should be fitted.

47 If the car is several years old, or has covered a large mileage, consider renewing the cap regardless of its apparent condition – they are not expensive. If the pressure relief valve built into the cap fails, excess pressure in the system will lead to puzzling failures of hoses and other cooling system components.

Chapter 2 Part A
1.4 litre petrol engine in-car repair procedures

Contents

Section number

Camshaft – removal, inspection and refitting. 8
Camshaft oil seals – renewal 13
Compression test – description and interpretation 2
Crankshaft oil seals – renewal 14
Crankshaft pulley – removal and refitting. 6
Cylinder head – removal, inspection and refitting 9
Cylinder head cover – removal and refitting. 4
Engine/transmission mountings – inspection and renewal 17
Flywheel – removal, inspection and refitting 15

Section number

General Information 1
Oil pressure switch – removal and refitting 12
Oil pump – removal, inspection and refitting 11
Pilot bearing – renewal 16
Rocker shaft assembly – removal, inspection and refitting 7
Sump – removal and refitting 10
Timing chain and related components – removal inspection
    and refitting. 5
Top Dead Centre (TDC) for No 1 piston – locating. 3

Degrees of difficulty

| **Easy,** suitable for novice with little experience | 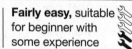 | **Fairly easy,** suitable for beginner with some experience | | **Fairly difficult,** suitable for competent DIY mechanic | | **Difficult,** suitable for experienced DIY mechanic | | **Very difficult,** suitable for expert DIY or professional | |

Specifications

General

Engine type.	Single overhead cam, with 8 or 16 valves
Designation	i-DSI and i-VTEC (L series)
Engine codes:	
i-DSI	L13A
i-VTEC	L13Z
Capacity	1339 cc
Bore	73.0 mm
Stroke	80.0 mm
Compression ratio	10.5 : 1
Firing order.	1-4-3-2 (No 1 cylinder at timing chain end)
Direction of crankshaft rotation	Clockwise (seen from right-hand side of car)

Compression pressures

Minimum	142 psi
Maximum variation between cylinders.	28 psi

Valves

Valve clearances (cold):	
Inlet	0.15 to 0.19 mm
Exhaust.	0.26 to 0.30 mm
Valve stem diameter:	
Inlet	5.48 to 5.49 mm
Exhaust.	5.45 to 5.46 mm
Stem to guide clearance:	
Inlet	0.020 to 0.050 mm
Exhaust.	0.050 to 0.080
Valve spring free length (L13A):	
Inlet	50.52 mm
Exhaust.	57.37 mm
Valve spring free length (L13Z):	
Inlet	51.17 mm
Exhaust.	57.26 mm

Timing chain

Standard distance (see text)	19 mm
Service limit	15 mm

Cylinder head

Maximum permissible warpage	0.07 mm
Height	119.9 to 120.1 mm

Camshaft

Running clearance	0.045 to 0.084 mm (limit 0.1 mm)
Endfloat	0.05 to 0.25 mm (limit 0.5 mm)

Cylinder block

Gasket face warpage	0.07 mm max
Bore diameter	73.0 to 73.015 mm (limit 73.065 mm)
Bore taper (service limit)	0.05 mm
Reboring limit	0.25 mm

Pistons and piston rings

Piston diameter	72.97 to 72.98 mm

Piston ring end gap (installed):

Top compression ring	0.15 to 0.30 mm (limit 0.60 mm)
Second compression ring	0.30 to 0.42 mm (limit 0.80 mm)
Oil control ring	0.20 to 0.70 mm (limit 0.031 mm)

Piston ring to groove clearance:

Top compression ring	0.065 to 0.090 mm (limit 0.15 mm)
Second compression ring	0.030 to 0.055 mm (limit 0.15 mm)

Gudgeon pin

Diameter	17.997 to 18.00 mm
Pin to piston clearance	0.010 to 0.017 mm

Crankshaft and bearings

Main bearings	5
Main bearing journal diameter	49.976 to 50.00 mm
Big end bearing journal diameter	39.976 to 40.00 mm
Crankshaft endfloat	0.10 to 0.35 mm (limit 0.45)
Runout	0.04 max

Connecting rods

Big end bore diameter	43.00 mm
Small end bore diameter	17.964 to 17.977 mm
Running clearance	0.020 to 0.036 mm
Endfloat	0.15 to 0.30 mm

Lubrication

L13A Engine:

Oil pressure (minimum, warm engine) at idle	0.7 bars
Oil pressure (minimum, warm engine) at 3000 rpm	3.4 bars

Oil pump clearances:

Inner rotor to outer rotor clearance	0.02 to 0.14 mm (limit 0.20 mm)
Pump housing to outer rotor clearance	0.10 to 0.18 mm (limit 0.20 mm)
Pump housing to outer rotor axial clearance	0.02 to 0.07 mm (limit 0.15 mm)

L13Z engine:

Oil pressure (minimum, warm engine) at idle	0.7 bars
Oil pressure (minimum, warm engine) at 3000 rpm	3.4 bars

Oil pump clearances:

Inner rotor to outer rotor clearance	0.06 to 0.16 mm (limit 0.20 mm)
Pump housing to outer rotor clearance	0.10 to 0.175 mm (limit 0.20 mm)
Pump housing to outer rotor axial clearance	0.02 to 0.06 mm (limit 0.15 mm)

Torque wrench settings

	Nm	lbf ft
Air conditioning compressor mounting bolts	22	16
Alternator mounting bolts	24	17
Auxiliary drivebelt belt idler pulley bolt	24	17
Auxiliary drivebelt tensioner bolts	24	17
Camshaft position sensors	12	9
Camshaft sprocket bolt	56	41
Camshaft thrust cover bolts	10	7
Crankshaft position sensor	12	9
Crankshaft pulley bolt:		
Stage 1 (new bolt or new pulley ONLY)	177	130
Stage 2 (new bolt or new pulley ONLY)	Fully slacken	
Stage 3 (all)	37	27
Stage 4 (all)	Angle-tighten a further 90°	
Cylinder head bolts:		
Stage 1	29	22
Stage 2	Angle-tighten a further 130°	
Cylinder head cover bolts:		
L13A engines	12	9
L13Z engines	10	7
Engine mountings:		
Right-hand mounting		
Bracket to engine nuts*	49	36
Bracket to body mounting bolt	72	52
Support bracket bolt/nuts*	38	28
Left-hand mounting		
Mounting bracket to transmission nuts/bolt*	76	56
Support bracket nuts/bolts	22	16
Bracket to body bolts*	64	47
Bracket base (on transmission) bolts*	59	43
Rear mounting:		
Subframe and rear bracket through bolt*	103	76
Mounting to transmission bolts*	103	76
Mounting on transmission:		
M12 bolt*	54	40
M14 bolt*	83	61
Flywheel bolts	118	87
Main bearing bridge bolts		
Stage 1	25	18
Stage 2	Angle-tighten a further 40°	
Oil pressure switch	18	13
Oil pump mounting bolts	12	9
Oil pump pick up pipe nut/bolts	12	9
Oil level sensor cover plate	10	7
Rocker shaft bolts:		
Rocker shaft mounting bolts (L13A engines)	29	22
Rocker shaft mounting bolts (L13Z engines, bolts 1-10)	15	11
Rocker shaft mounting bolts (L13Z engines, bolt 11)	10	7
Sump drain plug	39	29
Sump bolts:		
Front bolt (transmission end)	24	18
Sump to transmission bolts	64	47
All other bolts	12	9
Timing chain cover bolts:		
6 mm bolts	12	9
8 mm bolts	31	23
Timing chain front guide bolts	12	9
Timing chain tensioner lower pivot bolt	22	16
Timing chain tensioner slider bolt	12	9
Water pump pulley bolts	14	10

*New nuts/bolts must be used

1 General Information

How to use this Chapter

1 This Part of Chapter 2 is devoted to in-car repair procedures on the 1.4 litre petrol engines. All procedures concerning engine removal, refitting and engine block/cylinder head overhaul can be found in Chapter 2D.

2 Refer to Vehicle identification numbers in the Reference chapter at the end of this manual for details of engine code locations.

3 Most of the operations included in this Chapter are based on the assumption that the engine is still installed in the car. Therefore, if this information is being used during a complete engine overhaul, with the engine already removed, many of the steps included here will not apply.

Engine description

4 There are two versions of the 1.4 litre engine fitted to the Honda Civic. Early models (up to around 2008/09) were designated i-DSI (Intelligent Dual Sequential Ignition) and later model use the familiar i-VTEC (Intelligent-Variable Valve Timing and Lift Electronic Control) designation. Both engines have similar bottom ends with five main crankshaft bearings, a crankshaft driven oil pump and a spring tensioned timing chain.

5 The connecting rod big-end bearings are split shell-type and the small ends are attached to the pistons by interference-fit gudgeon pins. Each piston is fitted with two compression rings and one oil control ring.

6 The valves are operated by a rocker shaft assembly, with screw-and-locknut adjustment on the rocker arms for the valve clearances; the valves are each closed by a single valve spring, and operate in guides integral in the aluminium alloy cylinder head. i-DSI models have 8 valves and i-VTEC models have 16 valves. Both engines use a single overhead camshaft.

Operations with engine in car

7 The following work can be carried out with the engine in the car:

a) Rocker shaft and camshaft – removal, inspection and refitting.
b) Cylinder head – removal and refitting.
c) Crankshaft oil seals – renewal.
d) Timing chain, sprockets and tensioner – removal, inspection and refitting.
e) Oil pump – removal and refitting.
f) Sump – removal and refitting..
g) Connecting rods and pistons – removal and refitting*.
h) Flywheel/driveplate – removal, inspection and refitting.
i) Engine/transmission mountings – removal and refitting.

Note: *It is possible to remove the pistons and connecting rods (after removing the cylinder head and sump) without removing the engine. However, this is not recommended. Work of this nature is more easily and thoroughly completed with the engine on the bench, as described in Chapter 2D.

2 Compression test – description and interpretation

Note: Cranking the engine with the coils removed will set a DTC (Diagnostic Trouble Code). Completing several drive cycles after carrying out a compression test may erase the fault codes. If the MIL (Malfunction Indicator Light) remains illuminated, suitable diagnostic equipment will be required to erase the fault codes.

1 When engine performance is down, or if misfiring occurs which cannot be attributed to the ignition or fuel systems, a compression test can provide diagnostic clues as to the engine's condition. If the test is performed regularly, it can give warning of trouble before any other symptoms become apparent.

2 The engine must be fully warmed-up to operating temperature, the oil level must be correct and the battery must be fully-charged. The help of an assistant will also be required.

3 Remove fuse number 2 from the passenger compartment fusebox. This is the fuse for the fuel pump – further details are to be found in Chapter 4A. Now start the engine and allow it to run until it stalls.

4 With reference to Chapter 1A remove the spark plugs. Note on i-DSI engines, remove only the front row of spark plugs, but disconnect the rear spark plug coil connectors.

5 Fit a compression tester to the No 1 cylinder spark plug hole – the type of tester which screws into the spark plug thread is preferable.

6 Arrange for an assistant to hold the accelerator pedal fully depressed to the floor, while at the same time cranking the engine over for several seconds on the starter motor. Observe the compression gauge reading. The compression will build-up fairly quickly in a healthy engine. Low compression on the first stroke, followed by gradually-increasing pressure on successive strokes, indicates worn piston rings. A low compression on the first stroke which does not rise on successive strokes, indicates leaking valves or a blown head gasket (a cracked cylinder head could also be the cause). Deposits on the underside of the valve heads can also cause low compression. Record the highest gauge reading obtained, then repeat the procedure for the remaining cylinders.

7 Add some engine oil (about three squirts from a plunger type oil can) to each cylinder through the spark plug holes, and then repeat the test.

8 If the compression increases after the oil is added, the piston rings are probably worn. If the compression does not increase significantly, the leakage is occurring at the valves or the head gasket. Leakage past the valves may be caused by burned valve seats and/or faces, or warped, cracked or bent valves.

9 If two adjacent cylinders have equally low compressions, it is most likely that the head gasket has blown between them. The appearance of coolant in the combustion chambers or on the engine oil dipstick would verify this condition.

10 If one cylinder is about 20 percent lower than the other, and the engine has a slightly rough idle, a worn lobe on the camshaft could be the cause.

11 On completion of the checks, refit the spark plugs and ignition coils. Refit the fuel pump fuse to the fusebox.

3 Top Dead Centre (TDC) for No 1 piston – locating

1 Top dead centre (TDC) is the highest point of the cylinder that each piston reaches as the crankshaft turns. Each piston reaches its TDC position at the end of its compression stroke, and then again at the end of its exhaust stroke. For the purpose of engine timing, TDC on the compression stroke for No 1 piston is used. No 1 cylinder is at the timing chain end of the engine. Proceed as follows.

2 Disconnect the battery negative (earth) lead (see Chapter 5A). Remove the spark plugs as described in Chapter 1A.

3 Turn the engine over by hand (using a 19 mm socket or spanner on the crankshaft pulley bolt) until the TDC notch in the crankshaft pulley (which may be painted white) is aligned with the pointer above the pulley. Note that the crankshaft pulley will also have an ignition timing mark before top dead centre (BTDC), which may be painted red – as the pulley is turned clockwise, the TDC notch will be the second of the two marks to come into alignment (see illustration).

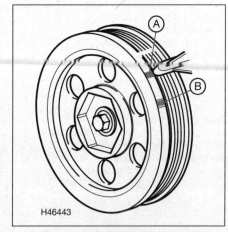

3.3 The crankshaft pulley marks: White TDC (A) and red (B) ignition timing

3.5 The UP markings and the horizontal lines confirm the engine is set at TDC

4.4 Removing the cylinder head cover

4.6 Fit the gasket into the grooves

4 In this position, No 1 and No 4 pistons will be at TDC, but one will be on the compression stroke, and the other on exhaust. Without removing the cylinder head cover as described in Section 4, the only way to check this is as follows. Remove the spark plug from No 1 cylinder as described in Chapter 1A, then turn the engine back from TDC by approximately 90°. Have an assistant cover the open spark plug hole with their hand, then turn the engine forwards to TDC – as this is done, it should be possible to feel compressed air coming from the open plug hole. If not, turn the engine round a full turn until the TDC mark is again aligned, and repeat the check.

5 Further confirmation of TDC on No1 cylinder can only be achieved by removing the cylinder head cover as described in Section 4 – as this involves removing the inlet manifold, the importance of this will depend on what other work is being carried out. With the cylinder head cover removed, check that the UP marking on the camshaft sprocket is visible, and the two horizontal marks are aligned with the cylinder head top surface **(see illustration)**.

6 Once No 1 cylinder has been positioned at TDC on the compression stroke, TDC for any of the other cylinders can then be located by rotating the crankshaft clockwise

(in its normal direction of rotation), 180° at a time, and following the firing order (see Specifications).

7 Where removed, refit the spark plug(s) and cylinder head cover, referring to Chapter 1A and Section 4 as necessary.

4 Cylinder head cover – removal and refitting

Removal

1 Remove the inlet manifold as described in Chapter 4A.

2 Disconnect the wiring plugs from the ignition coils. On L13A engines remove the ignition coils and the earth terminal. On all engines remove the wiring loom supports and the ventilation hoses.

3 Slacken the cover bolts evenly (a half turn to start) and then remove them fully.

4 Remove the cover from the engine **(see illustration)**.

Refitting

5 Thoroughly clean the cylinder head cover, and the mating surface of the cylinder head. Besides removing any oil, in particular, clean

off any sealant at the cylinder head-to-timing chain cover joint.

6 Check the condition of the old gasket. Providing it's not crushed, perished or distorted, it can be refitted into the cover groove **(see illustration)**. Similarly, check the condition of the cover bolt washers, and fit new ones if necessary.

7 Apply two 2.5 mm beads of RTV sealant (Honda Liquid Gasket, part number 08C70-K0334M, or equivalent) to the joint between the cylinder head and the timing chain cover **(see illustration)**. Once the sealant has been applied, the cover should be fitted within 5 minutes

8 Refit the cylinder head cover, making sure the gasket stays in place. Once the cover is down, slide it back-and-forth very slightly, to ensure that the gasket is properly seated

9 Fit the cover bolts and washers. Working in stages tighten the bolts in the order shown to the specified torque **(see illustration)**.

10 Further refitting is a reversal of removal, noting the following points:

a) Refit the ignition coils as described in Chapter 5B.

b) Refit the inlet manifold as described in Chapter 4A.

c) Wait at least 30 minutes before starting the engine, to give the sealant time to cure.

4.7 Apply sealant to the joint between the cylinder head and timing chain cover

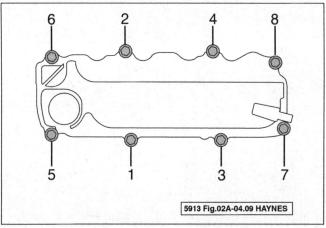

4.9 Valve cover bolt tightening sequence

5.4 Remove the idler pulley

5.5 Remove the waterpump pulley

5.10 Disconnect the crankshaft position sensor wiring plug

5 Timing chain and related components – removal inspection and refitting

Removal

1 Loosen (but do not yet remove) the three water pump pulley bolts – this is more easily done before the auxiliary drivebelt is removed.
2 Jack up and support the front of the vehicle and then remove the right-hand road wheel. Remove the engine under cover and then remove the wing liner.
3 Remove the auxiliary drivebelt as described in Chapter 1A. On models fitted with manual belt adjustment unbolt and remove the alternator adjuster bolt bracket from the engine, and ensure that the alternator lower mounting bolt is loose enough that the alternator can pivot forwards, clear of the timing chain cover.On models fitted with an automatic belt adjuster remove the automatic tensioner.
4 On L13A engines,where fitted unbolt and remove the drivebelt idler pulley, noting carefully the fitted sequence of washers and spacers **(see illustration)**.
5 Remove the three water pump pulley bolts

and then remove the water pump pulley **(see illustration)**.
6 Remove the cylinder head cover as described in Section 4.
7 Set the engine to TDC on No 1 cylinder, as described in Section 3. As the cylinder head cover has been removed, check that the camshaft sprocket UP mark and horizontal lines are correctly aligned.
8 Remove the crankshaft pulley as described in Section 6.
9 On L13A engines only remove the sump as described in Section 10.
10 At the back of the timing chain cover (L13A engines only) disconnect the wiring plug from the crankshaft position sensor **(see illustration)**. Trace the wiring up the back of the timing chain cover, release the two harness clips and move the wiring clear.
11 The weight of the engine must now be supported, as the right-hand mounting must be removed. Where the the sump has been removed, supporting from below is made more difficult – take care not to involve the crankshaft, nor to damage the oil pump pick-up. Use a jack, with a block of wood on the edge of the block, and just take the weight of the engine.
12 Where applicable, unbolt the earth strap

in front of the right-hand mounting, and move it clear.
13 With the engine supported from below, loosen the bolts securing the right-hand mounting to the inner wing and then remove the mounting as described in Section 17.
14 The timing chain cover is secured by a total of twelve bolts, of 6 mm and 8 mm diameter. Remove the bolts, and store them carefully – we pushed the bolts through a piece of card, in their fitted pattern **(see illustration)**. If not already done, pivot the alternator forwards, clear of the cover (or, if preferred, remove it completely, referring to Chapter 5A).
15 The cover is fitted using a bead of sealant, so will probably be stuck. Start by pulling it at the top, and work downwards until it is free, and can be removed – prising between the joint faces may cause damage and an oil leak on reassembly. Slide the cover off the nose of the crankshaft, and remove it **(see illustration)**. *Note: While the timing chain cover is removed, consider fitting a new crankshaft oil seal which is fitted to it – this job is far easier to do with the cover off. Refer to Section 14.*
16 On the early L13A engine, slide off the crankshaft position sensor's pulse generator

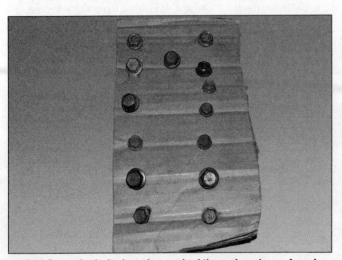

5.14 Store the bolts in order, pushed through a piece of card

5.15 Removing the timing chain cover

5.16 Remove the crankshaft sensor pulse plate

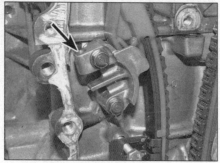

5.18a The chain tensioner has two bolts and a screwdriver slot

5.18b Hold the tensioner with a screwdriver and then remove the upper bolt

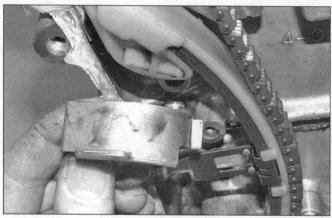

5.19 Remove the tensioner

5.20 Remove the tensioner arm

plate (this looks like a slim sprocket), noting how it is fitted (see illustration).

17 Before removing the chain check the distance between the chain sides at a the narrowest point opposite the chain tensioner. Compare the distance to that specified.

18 Apply a little oil as necessary to the timing chain tensioner's slider. Use a screwdriver in the hole provided at the back of the tensioner to release the chain tension. As this is done, loosen the tensioner's lower bolt, and remove the upper bolt (see illustrations).

19 Withdraw the screwdriver, then take out the lower bolt and remove the tensioner from the engine (see illustrations).

20 Remove the lower pivot bolt, and take off the curved tensioner arm from the back of the chain (see illustration).

21 Remove the two bolts securing the guide in front of the chain, and take off the guide (see illustration).

22 Before removing the chain, note the fitted positions of the blue-steel links – there should be one at the base of the crankshaft sprocket, and two more at the top of the camshaft sprocket. If the chain is to be re-used, if necessary, clean the marked links and apply fresh paint.

23 With all tension removed from the chain, it can be checked for wear (the chain should be renewed as a matter of course if the engine is being overhauled). Try to lift the chain upwards off the camshaft sprocket, at the top. If the chain is worn, it may be possible to lift it

clear so that the sprocket teeth are visible – a chain this worn should always be renewed.

24 Using an open-ended spanner on the camshaft flats provided, hold the camshaft while the sprocket bolt is loosened. Unscrew the sprocket bolt, then slide the sprocket and chain from the camshaft (note the position of the locating keyway – at the top), and withdraw it (see illustration). Remove the camshaft sprocket from the chain.

25 Slide the crankshaft sprocket and the chain off the nose of the crankshaft (see illustration). Remove the sprocket from the chain. Note that the sprocket's Woodruff key (which is fitted with its curved surfaces pointing downwards) will be loose – remove it for safekeeping.

26 Note that, while it is removed, Honda

5.21 Remove the front guide arm

5.24 Remove the bolt and slide off the chain and sprocket

5.25 Slide off the crankshaft sprocket and chain

5.39 The coloured links must sit on either side of the vertical mark on the sprocket

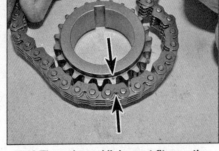

5.40 The coloured link must fit over the punch mark

5.41a Refit the woodruff key with the curved face down...

advise keeping the chain away from magnetic fields (presumably, this also applies to a new chain).

Camshaft sprocket

27 In theory, the camshaft sprocket can be removed without removing the chain completely – this would also save removing the timing chain cover. For details, refer to the camshaft removal procedure in Section 8.

28 In practice, removing the camshaft sprocket from the chain, and then refitting it, is nearly impossible while the timing cover is still in place – there is just too little working room. If the sprocket must be removed, refer to the timing chain removal procedure described previously in this Section.

Crankshaft sprocket

29 The crankshaft sprocket can only be removed or refitted with the timing chain, as described previously in this Section.

Timing chain tensioner

30 The chain tensioner can be removed as described previously in this Section. If the tensioner is being renewed, attention should also be paid to the tensioner arm and the chain front guide. Note that best practise is to replace the the timing chain, both chain guides and the tensioner.

Inspection

31 Check the chain for wear, which will be evident in the form of excess play between the links. If the chain can be lifted at either 'end' of its run so that the sprocket teeth are visible, it has stretched excessively. If there is any doubt as to the chain's condition, a new one should be fitted – timing chain failure is a lot rarer than timing belt failure, but would still be catastrophic to the engine.

32 If the chain is worn, examine the sprocket teeth closely – if their teeth have taken on a 'hooked' appearance, new ones should be fitted. It is generally considered a false economy to fit a new timing chain on worn sprockets.

33 Assessing wear in the chain tensioner is not easy. Particularly if the tensioner is known to have covered a very high mileage, and/or if a new chain is being fitted, it is recommended that an old tensioner is not re-used.

34 Examine the tensioner arm and front guide for scoring or wear ridges, and renew if necessary. If a new timing chain is being fitted, the guide arms and tensioner should always be replaced.

Refitting

35 Check that the crankshaft is set to TDC – in this position, a punched mark on one of the crankshaft sprocket teeth will be aligned with an arrowhead marking on the oil pump. Temporarily refit the crankshaft sprocket (the right way round) to check.

36 The camshaft should also be set to TDC – in this position, the word UP should be uppermost, and the two horizontal lines should align with the top of the cylinder head. Temporarily refit the camshaft sprocket to check. If the marks are not aligned, turn the camshaft sprocket only very slightly, as turning it by more than a few degrees could bend the valves. If the camshaft must be turned significantly, turn the crankshaft approximately 90° first, so the pistons are down the bores – reset the camshaft, then bring the crankshaft back to TDC.

37 Remove the camshaft and crankshaft sprockets, if they were temporarily refitted.

38 Find a clean working area, to lay out the timing chain and the two sprockets.

39 Fit the chain around the camshaft sprocket. The two blue-steel links should sit either side of a near-vertical line, just to the right of the word UP on the sprocket **(see illustration)**.

40 Now fit the timing chain around the crankshaft sprocket, so that the single blue-steel link sits exactly over the sprocket tooth with the punched mark on it **(see illustration)**.

41 If removed, refit the crankshaft's Woodruff key, with its curved surface pointing downwards **(see illustrations)**.

42 Offer in the chain and two sprockets as an assembly **(see illustration)**. Slide the crankshaft sprocket onto the crankshaft, and over the Woodruff key, then fit the camshaft sprocket onto the camshaft's locating keyway. Refit the camshaft sprocket bolt.

43 With the chain in place, again check that the two sprockets are correctly aligned. Note that the single blue-steel link around the crankshaft sprocket should align with the arrowhead on the oil pump **(see illustration)**.

44 Fit the chain front guide, and tighten

5.41b...so that it fits in the groove as shown

5.42 Fit the chain and sprockets as a complete assembly

5.43 The link, punch mark and mark on the oil pump must all be in alighment

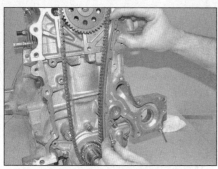

5.44 Fit the front chain guide and secure in place

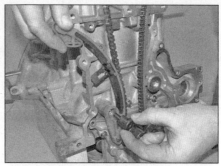

5.45 Fit the tensioner arm and the lower pivot bolt

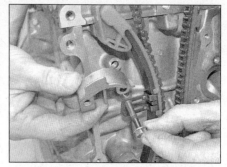

5.46 Fit the tensioner and lower bolt hand tight

5.47a Oil the tensioner surface and...

5.47b...then use a screwdriver to rotate the tensioner so that the upper bolt can be fitted

5.49 Use a spanner to hold the camshaft and then tighten the sprocket bolt

the two bolts to the specified torque **(see illustration)**.

45 Fit the curved tensioner arm in position on the rear run of the chain, then oil the pivot bolt, and tighten it to the specified torque **(see illustration)**.

46 Offer up the chain tensioner, and fit the lower bolt, hand-tight only at this stage **(see illustration)**.

47 Apply a little engine oil to the tensioner's sliding surface (where it contacts the curved tensioner arm). Using a screwdriver in the hole provided, turn the tensioner clockwise (towards the chain), and refit the upper bolt **(see illustrations)**. Tighten the upper and lower bolts to the specified torque.

48 Fully tighten the upper and lower tensioner bolts

49 Using an open-ended spanner on the camshaft flats provided, hold the camshaft in position. Tighten the camshaft sprocket bolt to the specified torque **(see illustration)**.

50 Where fitted, slide on the crankshaft position sensor's pulse plate, as noted on removal. Note that this plate has an arrowhead marking, which, at TDC, should align with the identical marking on the oil pump **(see illustrations)**.

51 Temporarily refit the crankshaft pulley bolt, and use a spanner or socket to slowly turn the engine through two complete revolutions. Check that the TDC marks come back into alignment. If the crankshaft binds or seems to hit something, do not force it, as the valves may be hitting the pistons. If this happens, the chain is incorrectly fitted. If necessary, reset the engine to TDC, then remove the chain and repeat the refitting procedure.

52 Remove the crankshaft pulley bolt.

5.50a On the L13A engine refit the crankshaft position sensor plate...

5.50b...ensuring that at TDC the mark on the plate aligns with the mark on the oil pump

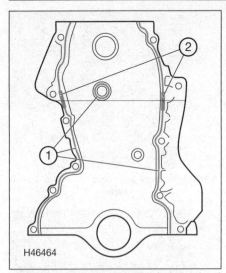

5.55a Apply the sealant as shown. Note that on L13Z engines the bead of sealant must be 2.5 mm alround

1 Bead of sealant 1.5 mm diameter
2 Bead of sealant 3.0 mm diameter

53 Before refitting the timing cover, check the condition of the crankshaft oil seal which is fitted to it. This seal is much easier to renew when the cover is removed – see Section for details.
54 Clean off all traces of old sealant from the cover, engine faces, cover bolts and bolt holes. Take care not to mark the mating faces. Wash the cover and engine mating faces with suitable solvent, and dry them before continuing.
55 Apply a bead of RTV sealant (Honda Liquid Gasket, part number 08C70-K0334M, or equivalent) to the timing cover mating faces on the engine block and cylinder head, as shown. The bead should be 2.5 mm diameter all round **(see illustrations)**. Run the sealant inside the bolt holes – try not to get any down

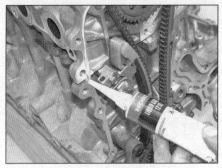

5.55b Applying the sealant

the holes themselves, as this may affect the bolt tightening. Once the sealant has been applied, the cover should be fitted within 5 minutes.
56 On the L13Z engines apply a 2.5 mm diameter of sealant along the outer edges of the sump and a 5.0 mm diameter bead around the curved section.
57 Offer the cover over the end of the crankshaft, taking care not to damage the oil seal in the cover. Do not slide the cover into place on 1L13Z engines, but rather sit the bottom of the cover on the sump and pivot the cover into position. Settle the cover onto the engine, and guide it into place by fitting two or more of the bolts (the bolts are two different sizes, and should be fitted to their original locations) **(see illustrations)**.
58 The cover will 'float' on the sealant, even with all the bolts in place (there are no locating dowels). Although the cover alignment doesn't appear to be critical, use a straight-edge across the top surfaces of the cover and cylinder head, to ensure they are level.
59 Fit all the remaining cover bolts. Starting in the middle of the cover, tighten the bolts evenly, and finally to their respective torques.
60 Clip the crankshaft position sensor wiring harness to the rear of the timing cover, and reconnect the wiring plug.

61 Refit the engine right-hand mounting with reference to Section 17. Also refit the earth strap in front of the mounting.
62 The remainder of refitting is a reversal of removal, noting the following points:
a) *Where removed, refit the sump as described in Section 10.*
b) *Refit the crankshaft pulley as described in Section 6.*
c) *Refit the cylinder head cover as described in Section 4.*
d) *If the alternator was removed, refit it as described in Chapter 5A.*
e) *Refit the water pump pulley, with the bolts hand-tight to begin with (it will be easier to tighten them to the specified torque once the auxiliary drivebelt has been refitted and tensioned, as described in Chapter 1A).*

6 Crankshaft pulley –
   removal and refitting

Removal

1 Remove the auxiliary drivebelt as described in Chapter 1A.
2 The crankshaft pulley has a white TDC marking on its outer rim (there is also a red mark, indicating the BTDC ignition timing point). The engine does not have to be set to TDC if just the pulley is being removed, but if other work is to be carried out requiring the engine to be at TDC, the engine should be set in this position as described in Section 3 before the pulley is removed.
3 The crankshaft pulley must now be held stationary while the bolt is loosened. Honda specify a special tool that engages with the pulley and allows a socket to pass through the tool and onto the crankshaft pulley bolt. The procedure described below allows the bolt (and pulley) to be removed without the special tool.
4 Jack up the front of the car, and support

5.57a Offer up the cover and...

5.57b...use the bolts to guide it into place

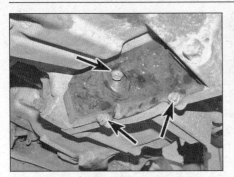

6.4a At the base of the bell housing, remove the bolts...

6.4b...and take off the cover plate

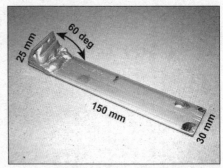

6.5a The fabricated flywheel locking tool

it on axle stands (see 'Jacking and vehicle support' in the Reference chapter). Remove the metal cover plate on the base of the transmission bellhousing, which is secured by three bolts – this gives access to the flywheel ring gear **(see illustrations)**. By jamming a suitable tool into the ring gear, the engine will be locked, and the pulley bolt can be loosened.

5 The pulley bolt is tight, and while it is possible to remove it with a lever jammed into the ring gear, we opted to fabricated our own specific tool. We fabricated an angled tool from some thick steel strip – this could have been bent over at the end, but we welded on a piece of angled steel bar instead. This tool slots into the base of the bellhousing, and into the ring gear **(see illustration)**. It worked very well, and can also be turned around to hold the flywheel for tightening the pulley bolt.

6 Before loosening the pulley bolt, ensure that the car is securely supported. Only use good-quality, close-fitting tools for this job – if something slips, it may result in injury. For extra leverage, use a long-handled breaker (or 'cracker') bar, or slip a piece of substantial tubing over the socket handle, to make it longer. Don't use a ratchet handle if possible – the ratchet may fail under load. If an extension bar is used on the socket, rest the outer end of the extension bar (the end nearest the handle) on another axle stand, to keep it horizontal

6.5b Fit the tool into the bell housing

– this improves leverage, and reduces the chance of the socket slipping off under load.

7 Unscrew and remove the bolt (which has an integral washer), and slip off the pulley **(see illustration)**. Note which way up the pulley fits – it engages on a keyway. Where applicable, the Woodruff key which sits in the crankshaft may be loose – it's best to recover it, and store it with the pulley.

8 If the engine had to be set to TDC before the pulley was removed (see paragraph 2), loosely refit the pulley and bolt, and reset the engine to TDC, as it is likely that the pulley may have turned during removal. Once the setting is conformed, remove the bolt and pulley again.

6.7 Removing the crankshaft pulley

Refitting

9 Wipe clean the pulley and the mating surfaces of the crankshaft and its sprocket. Also clean the pulley bolt and washer. Though not specifically required by Honda, consider using a new bolt when refitting – this should be done in any case if the bolt appears damaged.

10 Offer up the pulley, the same way up as was noted on removal, and fit it over the crankshaft key. Lightly oil the bolt threads and the underside of the bolt head, then tighten the bolt by hand, and check that the pulley is properly seated **(see illustrations)**.

11 Using the same method as for removal, prevent the crankshaft pulley from turning as the bolt is tightened.

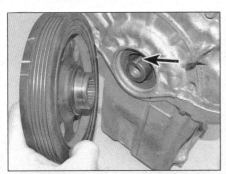

6.10a Fit the crankshaft pulley over the woodruff key

6.10b Oil the bolt threads and under the head of the washer

6.10c Fit the bolt and hand tighten it

6.12a After tightening the bolt to the specified torque, paint marks at 90 degrees apart

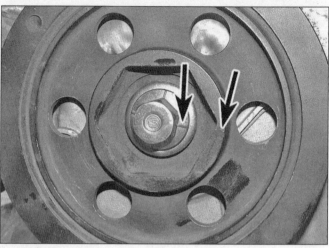

6.12b The marks will align after the specified angle (90 degrees) has been achieved

12 If a new bolt is being used (or if a new crankshaft has been fitted), there are two initial stages to tightening to be observed first. Otherwise, just tighten the bolt to the specified Stage 3 torque, then through the Stage 4 angle (which is equivalent to a quarter-turn). A quarter-turn can be made easier to judge by painting a mark on the bolt and the pulley, as we did **(see illustrations)**.

13 Refit and tension the auxiliary drivebelt as described in Chapter 1A.

7 Rocker shaft assembly
  – removal, inspection and
  refitting

Removal

1 Remove the cylinder head cover (see Section 4).

2 Completely loosen (but do not remove) all the valve adjuster screws, to remove all valve spring pressure from the rocker shaft components.

3 Set the engine to No 1 on TDC as described in Section 3.

4 Loosen the five rocker shaft mounting bolts on i-DSI engines and the eleven bolts on i-VTEC engines a half-turn at a time, working in the reverse of the tightening sequence shown later in this Section.

5 When all the bolts are loose, remove them. Lift off the rocker shaft assembly, noting that it i-DSI engines have a single on a dowel at the timing chain end **(see illustration)** and i-VTEC engines have a dowel beneath each retaining bolt.

Inspection

6 If you wish to dismantle and inspect the rocker arm assembly, the locating dowel at the timing chain end of the shaft should be removed first. Slip the rocker arms, washers and springs off the timing chain end of the shaft, keeping them in fitted order – they must

be reassembled in the same positions they were removed from.

7 Thoroughly clean the components and inspect them for wear and damage. Check the rocker arm faces that contact the camshaft – if any wear is found, the corresponding camshaft lobes should also be checked – and the rocker arm tips. Check the surfaces of the rocker shaft that the rocker arms ride on, as well as the bearing surfaces inside the rocker arms, for scoring and excessive wear. Renew any parts that are damaged or excessively worn. Also, make sure the oil holes in the shaft are not blocked.

7.5 Remove the rocker shaft assembly

7.10 Oil all the cylinder head moving parts

Refitting

8 Lubricate all components with clean engine oil, and reassemble the rocker arms, washers and springs onto the timing chain end of the shaft, in their correct fitted order.

9 Refit the shaft locating dowel or dowels to the head **(see illustration)**.

10 Coat the camshaft lobes, valve tops, and the bolt threads and heads, with clean engine oil **(see illustration)**.

11 Before offering the assembled shaft into place, each pair of rockers should be 'tied' together with a cable-tie, to compress the springs **(see illustration)**. We found this was

7.9 Refit the dowels

7.11 Secure the rocker arms on the shaft with cable ties

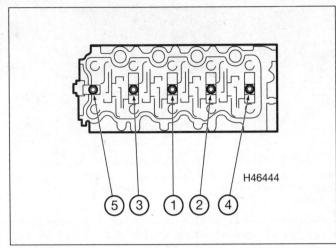

7.12a The rocker shaft bolt tightening sequence – L13A engines

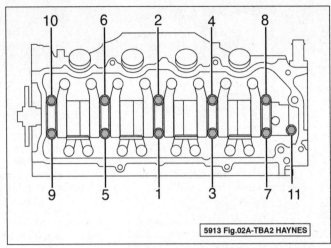

7.12b The rocker shaft bolt tightening sequence L13Z engines

necessary, otherwise the rockers and washers catch on the camshaft bearing housings as the shaft is tightened down, which carries a risk of component damage.

12 Refit the rocker bolts. Starting with the centre bolt and working outwards, tighten the bolts half a turn at a time until they are all seated fully. Working in the same sequence, tighten the bolts to the specified torque **(see illustrations)**. Note that the final bolt on i-VTEC engines is set to a lower value than the rest.

13 When the shaft is fully tightened, cut the cable-ties and remove them **(see illustration)**.

14 Adjust the valve clearances as described in Chapter 1A, then refit the cylinder head cover as described in Section 4.

15 Run the engine and check for oil leaks and proper operation.

8   Camshaft – removal, inspection and refitting

Removal

1 Remove the air filter housing as described in Chapter 4A.

2 Remove cylinder head cover (Section 4)

and then the the rocker shaft assembly as described in Section 7.

3 The following procedure assumes that the timing chain will not be removed completely. If the chain is to be removed, refer to Section 5.

4 There are no camshaft bearing caps to remove – therefore, the camshaft can only be withdrawn by sliding it out of the head, at the transmission end. This means that the camshaft sprocket has to be unbolted, and removed from the camshaft with the timing chain still attached.

5 Support the engine from below, as the right-hand mounting must be removed. Use a large piece of wood between the jack head and the sump, to spread the load, and just take the weight of the engine.

6 Where applicable, unbolt the earth strap in front of the right-hand mounting, and move it clear.

7 With the engine supported from below remove the right-hand engine mounting as described in Section 17.

8 Using the spout of an oil can through the cylinder head's oil return hole behind the camshaft sprocket, lightly lubricate the sliding surfaces of the chain tensioner.

9 Unscrew and remove the access bolt and washer, located halfway down the timing

7.13 Remove the cable ties

cover, at the rear (the access bolt is brass-coloured, unlike the silver cover bolts) **(see illustrations)**. Have ready a 6 mm diameter bolt, approximately 60 mm in length, to insert into this hole.

10 Prise out the large plastic plug from the end of the head, which covers the camshaft sprocket bolt **(see illustration)**. Recover the plug's O-ring seal – note that a new plug and O-ring must be obtained for refitting.

11 The crankshaft must now be prevented from turning for the next step. This could be achieved by holding the pulley bolt itself

8.9a The tensioner access bolt

8.9b Remove the bolt

8.10 Remove the blanking plug

8.12 Turning the sprocket moves the bracket to expose a bolt hole

8.13 Fit the 60 mm bolt into the hole (shown with the timing chain cover removed for clarity)

8.14 Tie the camshaft sprocket and chain together

(though this is the direction for unscrewing the pulley bolt, the bolt is so tight, there should be no danger of it loosening). Alternatively, refer to Section 6 and use the ring gear locking method described.

12 With the crankshaft locked, have an assistant use a spanner on the camshaft sprocket bolt to apply firm pressure on the sprocket clockwise (the sprocket should hardly turn) – this will force the tensioner and its arm rearwards. Attached to the tensioner arm is a slotted bracket – when the arm is forced back by the chain, the slot uncovers a 6 mm threaded hole in the end of the block **(see illustration)**.

13 Holding the camshaft sprocket clockwise, insert a 6 mm bolt, at least 60 mm long, into the threaded hole, and screw it in as far as possible (the bolt will be under some strain,

8.15 Hold the camshaft steady with an open ended spanner and remove the camshaft sprocket bolt

and screwing in by a few threads will not be enough) **(see illustration)**. Have the assistant release the sprocket. The tensioner arm is now locked in the retracted position, releasing the chain tension – this can be confirmed by the play that will now be present in the camshaft sprocket.

14 The chain and camshaft sprocket are removed together. Pass a cable-tie through one of the camshaft sprocket holes, and wrap it tight around the chain – this keeps the chain and sprocket together, in the correct fitted position**(see illustration)**.

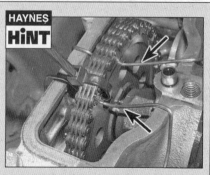

HAYNES HINT

We found that two short pieces of stiff wire could be passed through the sprocket's upper holes, and folded over the head and timing cover, to support the sprocket and chain. This method of support will only work if the timing cover is not being removed.

15 Using an open-ended spanner on the camshaft flats provided, hold the camshaft while the sprocket bolt is loosened **(see illustration)**. Only loosen the bolt by half a turn at this stage – do not remove it.

16 There is a slight risk that, if upward tension is not maintained on the chain, the chain will drop off the crankshaft sprocket, making it near-impossible to put back on without removing the sump. We found that the guide below the crankshaft sprocket always kept the chain engaged with it, however.

17 With the timing cover still fitted, the danger is that the camshaft sprocket and chain might drop down inside the cover, and that they would be impossible to retrieve, so it is advisable to keep the chain and sprocket supported while removed. This can be done by passing some stiff wire or cable-ties through the camshaft sprocket holes (see **Haynes Hint**).

18 With the camshaft sprocket supported, remove the bolt and release the sprocket from the keyway at the top of the camshaft, by moving it to the side. Once the sprocket is released, support the chain and sprocket before continuing.

19 Remove the battery as described in Chapter 5A.

20 Remove the lower bolt securing the wiring harness to the end of the head, and also unbolt the earth strap from the camshaft thrust cover. Release the wiring harness from the support bracket at the rear **(see illustrations)**.

8.20a Remove the bolt securing the wiring loom to the cylinder head...

8.20b...and then unbolt the earth cable

8.20c Unhook the wiring loom from the support bracket

8.21a Where fitted unbolt...

8.21b...and remove the support bracket

8.22a Disconnect the camshaft position sensor wiring plug...

8.22b...and then unbolt and remove the sensor

8.23a Remove the thrust cover bolts...

8.23b...and remove the cover. Note the O-ring

21 To improve access, remove the two bolts securing the wiring harness support bracket, and remove it from the head **(see illustrations)**.

22 At the rear of the head, disconnect the wiring plug from the camshaft position (TDC) sensor, then remove the single mounting bolt and remove the sensor, recovering its O-ring seal – a new seal should be used when refitting **(see illustrations)**.

23 Remove the two camshaft thrust cover bolts, and withdraw the cover. It's likely that the cover will prove difficult to remove, as there is a large O-ring seal inside – take care not to damage the mating faces if the cover has to be prised off **(see illustrations)**. Recover the O-ring seal – a new one should be used when refitting.

24 Before removing the camshaft, note that

the camshaft sprocket locating keyway is positioned at 12 o'clock, at TDC.

25 Carefully slide out the camshaft, keeping it as horizontal as possible **(see illustration)**. If the shaft catches as it is withdrawn, slide it back in and try to free it by turning it slightly – there is a danger of damaging the cam lobes if the shaft is roughly handled. Once it is completely removed, rest the shaft on clean newspaper or rags, to protect the lobes.

Inspection

26 Examine the camshaft lobes for score marks, pitting, galling (wear due to rubbing) and evidence of overheating (blue, discoloured areas). Look for flaking away of the hardened surface layer of each lobe. Renew the camshaft if any of these conditions are apparent.

27 If any of the lobes is damaged, check the

corresponding rocker finger's surfaces for similar signs – it probably wouldn't be wise to fit a new camshaft and re-use the old rocker shaft assembly, as both would have suffered wear. Seek the advice of an engine rebuilding specialist if in doubt.

28 As far as possible, examine the condition of the camshaft bearing surfaces in the cylinder head. If the head bearing surfaces are worn excessively, the cylinder head will need to be renewed.

Refitting

29 Liberally oil the camshaft lobes and the camshaft bearings in the cylinder head **(see illustration)**.

30 Slide the camshaft into the head, keeping it horizontal to avoid catching the lobes, which might cause damage **(see illustration)**. Turn

8.25 Remove the camshaft

8.29 Oil the camshaft bearings

8.30 Slide the camshaft into the cylinder head

8.31a Fit a new O-ring to the thrust cover...

8.31b...and then refit the cover

8.40 Fit a new sealing plug to the timing chain cover

the camshaft so that the sprocket locating keyway is in the TDC position (12 o'clock), as noted before removal.

31 Fit a new (lightly oiled) O-ring seal to the thrust cover, then press the cover into position and secure with the two bolts, tightened to the specified torque **(see illustrations)**.

32 Similarly, refit the camshaft position (TDC) sensor to the back of the engine, with a new, lightly-oiled O-ring. Tighten the sensor mounting bolt to the specified torque.

33 Refit the wiring harness support bracket. Fit the harness itself back onto the bracket, then refit the earth strap and lower bolt.

34 Align the sprocket onto the keyway, and refit the bolt. Once the bolt is at least hand-tight, the wire and/or cable-ties can be removed from the sprocket.

35 Check that the sprocket is aligned in the TDC position (UP mark uppermost, horizontal marks in line with the head), turning the camshaft if necessary to achieve this. The alignment mark made prior to removal between the chain and sprocket should also correspond.

36 Hold the camshaft using a spanner on the flats provided, and tighten the sprocket bolt to the specified torque.

37 Use the method employed during removal to stop the crankshaft turning during the next step.

38 Have an assistant apply firm pressure clockwise on the camshaft sprocket bolt, so that the 6 mm bolt fitted to the timing cover earlier is released. Unscrew the 6 mm bolt, then release the pressure on the sprocket,

so that the chain tensioner arm takes up the chain tension once more. Refit the access bolt and washer, and tighten it securely.

39 Use a spanner or socket on the crankshaft pulley bolt to slowly turn the engine through two complete revolutions. Check that the TDC marks described in Section 3 come back into alignment. If the crankshaft binds or seems to hit something, do not force it, as the valves may be hitting the pistons. If this happens, the chain is incorrectly fitted. If necessary, reset the engine to TDC, then remove the chain from the camshaft sprocket and repeat the refitting procedure.

40 Fit a new cylinder head plug (and O-ring) into the camshaft sprocket bolt access hole, and tap it home **(see illustration)**.

41 Refit the engine right-hand mounting with reference to Section 17. Also (where removed) refit the earth strap in front of the mounting, and the refrigerant hose mounting bracket bolt.

42 Refit the rocker shaft assembly as described in Section 7 and then refit the cylinder head cover as described in Section 4.

43 Refit the air filter housing as described in Chapter 4A.

9 Cylinder head – removal, inspection and refitting

Removal

Note: *To avoid the possibility of warping the cylinder head, the cylinder head bolts should*

only be loosened when the engine has cooled down completely.

1 Remove the fuse from the fusebox and run the engine until it stops (Chapter 4A). Disconnect the battery (Chapter 5A). Refer to Chapter 1A and drain the cooling system.

2 Remove the air cleaner assembly as described in Chapter 4A.

3 Disconnect the evaporative emissions (EVAP) hose and coolant hoses from the throttle body **(see illustration)**.

4 Release the spring clips, and disconnect the radiator top and bottom hoses from the thermostat housing **(see illustration)**. Similarly, disconnect the two smaller hoses at the rear of the housing, and the remaining heater hose from the back of the head – mark the hoses for position using tape.

5 Loosen (but do not yet remove) the three water pump pulley bolts – this is more easily done before the auxiliary drivebelt is removed.

6 Remove the auxiliary drivebelt as described in Chapter 1A. On models with manual belt adjustment, unbolt and remove the alternator adjuster bolt bracket from the engine. Slacken the alternator lower mounting bolt and pivot the alternator forwards.

7 On models fitted with an automatic belt tensioner, remove the tensioner.

8 On models with air conditioning, unbolt and remove the drivebelt idler pulley, noting carefully the fitted sequence of washers and spacers **(see illustration)**.

9.4 Disconnect the coolant hoses

9.8 Where fitted, remove the idler pulley

9.3 Disconnect the coolant hoses from the throttle body

9.9 Remove the water pump pulley

9.14a Release the hose clips

9.14b Slide the hose along the rigid pipe

9.14c Remove the rigid pipe

9.15a Release the hose clip...

9.15b...and remove the EGR coolant hose

9 Remove the three water pump pulley bolts, and take off the pulley **(see illustration)**.

10 Remove the inlet manifold and fuel rail as described in Chapter 4A.

11 Either remove the exhaust manifold, or disconnect the catalytic converter from it, as described in Chapter 4A. Removing the manifold will make it easier to lift the head off, and out of the engine compartment.

12 Disconnect the following wiring plugs from the following components around the engine:
a) *Camshaft position (TDC) sensor, from the rear of the head, at the transmission end.*
b) *Coolant temperature sensor, below the TDC sensor.*
c) *Oil pressure switch*
d) *Knock sensor connector*
e) *Exhaust gas recirculation connector (EGR).*
f) *Rocker oil control solenoid (i-VTEC engines only)*

13 At the transmission end of the head, remove the two bolts from above, and take off the air cleaner mounting bracket (where applicable). Remove the lower bolt securing the wiring harness to the end of the head, and also unbolt the earth strap from the camshaft thrust cover. Release the wiring harness from the support bracket at the rear.

14 The rigid coolant pipe at the front of the head must now be removed. Release the clips, and slide the rubber hose section down the pipe. Unscrew the single bolt securing the coolant pipe to the front of the thermostat housing, and pull the pipe off, noting that it

has an O-ring seal which must be renewed when reconnecting **(see illustrations)**.

15 Release the spring clip and disconnect the coolant hose from the base of the EGR valve (at the front corner of the head) **(see illustrations)**.

16 Remove the cylinder head cover as described in Section 4.

17 Set the engine to TDC on No 1 cylinder, as described in Section 3. As the cylinder head cover has been removed, check that the camshaft sprocket UP mark and horizontal lines are correctly aligned.

18 Remove the crankshaft pulley as described in Section 6.

19 At the back of the timing chain cover, disconnect the wiring plug from the crankshaft position sensor. Trace the wiring up the back of the timing chain cover, release the two harness clips and move the wiring clear.

20 The weight of the engine must now be supported from below, as the right-hand mounting must be removed. Use a large piece of wood between the jack head and the sump, to spread the load, and just take the weight of the engine.

21 Where applicable, unbolt the earth strap in front of the right-hand mounting, and move it clear **(see illustration)**.

22 With the engine supported from below, loosen the bolts securing the right-hand mounting to the inner wing as described in Section 17.

23 Remove the timing chain cover, timing chain and camshaft sprocket as described in Section 5.

24 Remove the top bolt from the chain front guide, so that the guide is released from the head **(see illustration)**.

25 Working in the reverse of the tightening

9.21 Remove the earth connection

9.24 Remove the bolt from the timing chain guide

9.25 Slacken the head bolts

9.26 Remove the cylinder head

9.27 Recover the old head gasket

sequence shown later in this Section, loosen each head bolt by a quarter-turn each time, repeating the sequence until all bolts are completely loose, and can be removed **(see illustration)**. If new bolts are not being fitted (this is not something we would recommend), lay the old bolts out in their fitted order, so they can be refitted in the same place.

26 Carefully lift off the head, and place it on a clean surface – do not allow the lower face to be damaged, or even a new gasket will not seal properly **(see illustration)**. If the head is stuck, try rocking it backwards to free it, using a blunt lever (such as a wooden hammer handle) in the inlet ports on the front – space permitting, try the same approach on the exhaust ports at the rear. Once the gasket seal has been broken, the head should come off. Hitting the head is not advisable, as the alloy is easily damaged. Also note that the head is located on two dowels.

27 Recover the old head gasket **(see illustration)**. It must not be re-used, but it will be useful to hold onto it for now, to compare with the new one as verification.

28 If the head is to be dismantled for overhaul, remove the rocker shaft and camshaft as described in Section 7 and Section 8, then refer to Part 2D of this Chapter.

Preparation for refitting

29 The mating faces of the cylinder head and cylinder block/crankcase must be perfectly clean before refitting the head. Remove the two dowels (note their positions) and use a hard plastic or wood scraper to remove all traces of gasket and carbon; also clean the piston crowns.

30 Take particular care during the cleaning operations, as aluminium alloy is easily damaged. Also, make sure that the carbon is not allowed to enter the oil and water passages – this is particularly important for the lubrication system, as carbon could block the oil supply to the engine's components. Using adhesive tape and paper, seal the water, oil and bolt holes in the cylinder block/crankcase.

31 Take care that as little debris as possible gets onto the timing chain (and that the supported chain is not disturbed during cleaning) – anything more than a little dirt will risk getting caught up in the crankshaft sprocket, and may cause damage to the timing chain.

32 Check the mating surfaces of the cylinder block/crankcase and the cylinder head for nicks, deep scratches and other damage. If slight, they may be removed carefully with a file, but if excessive, machining may be the only alternative to renewal.

33 If warpage of the cylinder head gasket surface is suspected, use a straight-edge to check it for distortion. Refer to Chapter 2D if necessary.

34 As stated previously, we recommend that the old head bolts should not be re-used. Do not be tempted, either for convenience or saving money, to ignore this advice – if the bolts or their threads 'let go' when they're tightened, the bottom half of the engine could be reduced to scrap very quickly

35 Although not essential, if a suitable tap-and-die set is available, it's worth running the correct-size tap down the bolt threads in the cylinder block. This will clean the threads of any debris, and go some way to restoring any damaged threads. Make absolutely sure the tap is the right size and thread pitch, and lightly oil the tap before starting. Failing this, choose one of the old head bolts, clean its threads with a wire brush, then lightly oil it, and run it fully into each bolt hole, cleaning it between each one.

36 If possible, clean out the bolt holes in the block using compressed air, to ensure no oil or water is present. Screwing a bolt into an oil- or water-filled hole can (in extreme cases) cause the block to fracture, due to the hydraulic pressure created.

Refitting

37 Ensure the two locating dowels are refitted to their original positions on the block top surface – the dowels correspond to bolts 3 and 10 in the tightening sequence. Check that the new cylinder head gasket is the same type as the original, and that any TOP or UP marking is facing upwards, then locate it onto the top face of the cylinder block and over the dowels. Ensure that it is correctly aligned with the coolant passages and oilways **(see illustrations)**.

38 Fit the cylinder head onto the block, making sure the gasket does not move. Locate the head on the two dowels **(see illustration)**.

39 Lightly oil the threads and heads of the new head bolts before fitting them.

9.37a Refit the dowels to their original locations and...

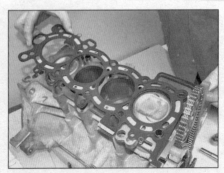

9.37b...lay the new gasket on the engine block

9.38 Fit the cylinder head to the engine block

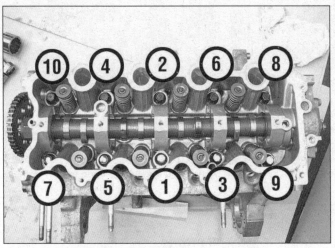

9.40 The head bolt tightening sequence

9.42 Refit the guide chain upper bolt

40 Following the tightening sequence, first tighten the bolts to the specified Stage 1 torque **(see illustration)**. **Note:** *If any bolt starts creaking during tightening, Honda suggest loosening it completely, and start tightening again. If the bolts are lubricated as stated in the previous paragraph, no creaking should be evident.*

41 Now the head bolts should be tightened further, to their specified Stage 2 angle. It is strongly recommended that an angle gauge is used for this task – these are not expensive, and are available from any good car accessory shop or motor factors. Again, follow the tightening sequence.

42 Refit the timing chain and sprocket as described in Section 5. Remember to refit the chains front guide's top bolt, and tighten it to the specified torque **(see illustration)**.

43 Clip the crankshaft position sensor wiring harness to the rear of the timing cover, and reconnect the wiring plug.

44 Refit the engine right-hand mounting with reference to Section 17. Also (where removed) refit the earth strap in front of the mounting, and the refrigerant hose mounting bracket bolt.

45 The remainder of refitting is a reversal of removal, noting the following points:

a) *Use a new O-ring when reconnecting the rigid coolant pipe to the front of the thermostat housing.*

b) *Refit the crankshaft pulley as described in Section 6.*

c) *Before refitting the cylinder head cover (Section 4), check and adjust the valve clearances as described in Chapter 1A.*

d) *Refit the water pump pulley, with the bolts hand-tight to begin with (it will be easier to tighten them to the specified torque once the auxiliary drivebelt has been refitted and tensioned, as described in Chapter 1A).*

e) *Refit the fuel rail and inlet manifold as*

described in Chapter 4A. On completion, switch the ignition on and off a few times, to run the fuel pump, then check for signs of fuel leakage.

f) *When all the coolant pipes and hoses have been reconnected, refill the cooling system as described in Chapter 1A.*

g) *Check the oil level and run the engine up to temperature whilst watching carefully for fuel, oil and coolant leaks.*

10 Sump – removal and refitting

Removal

1 Jack up the front of the car, and support it on axle stands (see *'Jacking and vehicle support'* in the Reference chapter). Remove the engine undershield.

2 Drain the engine oil as described in Chapter 1A, then refit the drain plug. Remove the oil filter – unusually, this is mounted on the sump's front face. It makes sense to fit a new oil filter on completion, but this is not essential.

 Warning: Do not disconnect the air conditioning pipes. It is an offence to knowingly discharge refrigerant to the atmosphere.

3 On models with air conditioning, the compressor is bolted to the sump's front face. Disconnect the compressor wiring plug. Remove the four bolts, then move the compressor forwards, clear of the sump. Support the compressor using wire or cable-ties, so that the refrigerant hoses (which must not be disturbed) are not strained **(see illustration)**.

4 Withdraw the dipstick, and place it to one side. Remove the single bolt securing the dipstick tube to the front of the engine, then pull the tube upwards to release its lower O-ring, and remove it **(see illustration)**. A new O-ring should be used when refitting.

5 With reference to Section 17, unbolt and remove the lower torque rod.

6 Remove the cover from the oil level sensor, disconnect the wiring plug and remove the bolt securing the sensor wiring loom. On i-VTEC models (engine code L13Z) remove the cover, unbolt the crankshaft position sensor and disconnect the wiring plug.

7 Where the sump meets the transmission, remove the bolts and take off the small cover

10.3 Unbolt the AC compressor

10.4 Remove the dipstick guide tube

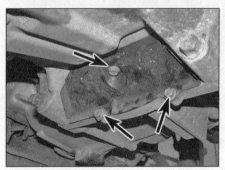

10.7a Remove the bolts...

10.7b...and take off the cover plate

10.14 Fit a new U-shaped gasket to the sump

10.15a Fit a new O-ring to the oil filter supply passage (not the locating dowel)

10.15b Make sure the other locating dowel is in place at the transmission end

plate from below the flywheel. Also remove the two large sump to transmission bolts **(see illustrations)**.

8 Remove the remaining bolts securing the sump to the base of the engine – note that the front bolt at the transmission end is larger than the others, and that the two bolts next to the flywheel are longer. The sump is fitted using sealant, so will likely remain stuck. Note that the sump is located on two dowels.

9 Prise the sump down at the four corners and nowhere else. Because the sump is bonded to the engine block with a sealant and not a gasket, removing it can be difficult. An alternative method is to remove the drain plug and use a tool such as a screwdriver inserted in the drain hole as a lever to prise the sump free (take care not to damage the

drain hole threads). Keep the sump level as it is lowered, to prevent spillage of any remaining oil in it. Also be prepared for oil drips from the crankcase when the sump is removed.

10 Recover the U-shaped gasket from the transmission end of the sump – a new one must be used when refitting.

11 Similarly, recover the O-ring fitted to the oil filter supply passage, and the locating dowel behind it, if it is loose. A new O-ring must be used when refitting.

12 A further small dowel is fitted at the transmission end of the sump – recover this dowel if it is loose.

13 Clean any sealant from the sump and engine mating faces – care must be taken not to damage the soft aluminium of the sump. Wipe the mating faces with a suitable solvent, and allow to dry. While the sump is off, check

that the oil pick-up/strainer on the base of the engine is clear, cleaning it if necessary.

Refitting

14 Fit a new U-shaped gasket to the transmission end of the sump, ensuring that it locates fully in the groove **(see illustration)**.

15 Fit a new O-ring to the oil filter supply passage at the front of the sump. Ensure that the two sump locating dowels are still in place **(see illustrations)**.

16 Apply a bead of RTV sealant (Honda Liquid Gasket, part number 08C70-K0334M, or equivalent) to the sump's mating face. The bead should be 1.5 mm diameter all round, except in the curved area where the sump meets the timing chain cover – here the bead should be 5.0 mm. Run the sealant inside the bolt holes **(see illustrations)**. Once the sealant has been applied, the sump should be fitted within 5 minutes.

17 Lining up the sump is tricky. It is helpful to have an assistant available to guide the sump over the timing cover end – the large bead of sealant has a tendency to apply itself to the teeth of crankshaft position sensor pulse plate otherwise. We temporarily fitted a longer bolt at the timing cover end, to get the alignment right.

18 Offer up the sump, and locate it on the two dowels **(see illustration)**. Fit the bolts to retain it, tightened by hand only initially. Note that the two longer bolts are fitted at the flywheel end, and the larger-diameter bolt is number 1 in the tightening sequence.

19 Working in sequence, and in two or three

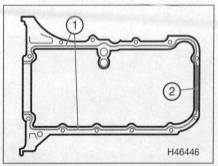

10.16a Sealant application details when refitting the sump

1 Bead of sealant, 1.5mm diameter
2 Bead of sealant, 5 mm diameter

10.16b Run the sealant inside the bolt holes

10.18 Offer the sump into position

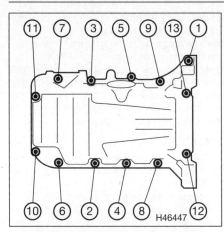

10.19 Sump bolt tightening sequence

11.3 Unscrew the oil pump mounting bolts

11.4 Oil pump pressure relief valve bolt, spring and plunger

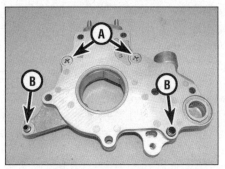

11.5a Remove the two screws (A) – note the locating dowels (B)...

11.5b...and take off the inner cover

stages, tighten the nuts and bolts to the specified torque (see illustration). Note that the larger bolt on the front at the transmission end (number 1 in the tightening sequence) has a higher tightening torque than the others.

20 Refit the two sump to transmission bolts, and tighten them to the specified torque.

21 Remove any surplus sealant from the sump before it fully hardens.

22 Refit the small cover plate from below the flywheel and secure with the three bolts.

23 Connect the wiring plug and then refit the oil level sensor cover. Refit the bolt securing the wiring loom bracket. On -VTEC models (engine code L13Z) connect the crankshaft sensor wiring plug and refit the cover.

24 Refit the dipstick tube, using a new O-ring, and tighten the tube mounting bolt securely.

25 On models with air conditioning, refit the compressor, and tighten the four bolts to the specified torque. Reconnect the compressor wiring plug.

26 Fit the oil filter, tightening it by hand only – do not use any tools.

27 Refit the engine undershield and lower the vehicle to the ground.

28 Allow at least 30 minutes (and preferably, several hours) for the sealant used on the sump to cure, then refill the engine with oil as described in Chapter 1A.

11 Oil pump – removal, inspection and refitting

Removal

1 Remove the timing chain and crankshaft sprocket as described in Section 5.

2 Remove the two nuts and bolt securing the oil pick-up/strainer to the bottom of the engine. Recover the gasket from the oil pump flange – a new one must be used when refitting.

3 Unscrew and remove the seven bolts securing the oil pump to the block (note that three of the bolts are shorter than the rest) (see illustration). Withdraw the oil pump from the front of the crankshaft – recover the two locating dowels, and the O-ring from the oil

supply passage.

Inspection

4 Remove the pressure relief valve bolt, and extract the spring and pressure relief valve plunger from the pump housing (see illustration). Check the spring for distortion and the relief valve plunger for scoring. Renew parts as necessary.

5 Undo the screws and dismantle the oil pump. You may need to use an impact screwdriver to loosen the two pump inner cover screws without stripping the heads (see illustrations).

6 Check the oil pump inner-to-outer rotor clearance, housing-to-outer rotor clearance, and the housing-to-rotor endfloat (see illustrations). Compare your measurements to the figures listed in the Specifications. Renew the pump if any of the measurements

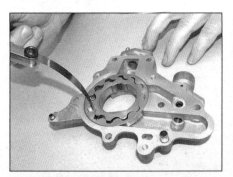

11.6a Check the inner to outer rotor clearance...

11.6b...the housing to the to the outer rotor clearance...

11.6c...and the housing to rotor end float

11.7 Lightly oil the pump rotors when refitting

11.9 Fit a new O-ring to the back of the oil pump

exceed the specified limits. It is generally considered good practice to fit a new oil pump if the engine is being overhauled.

7 If removed, lightly oil and refit the pump rotors **(see illustration)**.

8 Apply thread-locking compound to the pump inner cover screws, refit the cover and tighten the screws securely. Refit the oil pressure relief valve and spring assembly, then refit the bolt, and tighten to the specified torque.

Refitting

9 Refit the two locating dowels on the back of the pump, and fit a new O-ring to the oil supply passage **(see illustration)**.

10 Offer the pump onto the engine, aligning the pump's inner rotor with the drive slot on the crankshaft, and refit the seven bolts **(see illustrations)**.

11 Tighten the oil pump mounting bolts to the specified torque.

12 Refit the oil pick-up/strainer using a new gasket on the pipe flange, and tighten the nuts/bolt to the specified torque **(see illustrations)**.

13 Refit the crankshaft sprocket and timing chain as described in Section 5.

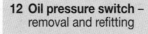
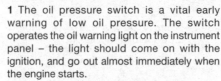

12 Oil pressure switch – removal and refitting

1 The oil pressure switch is a vital early warning of low oil pressure. The switch operates the oil warning light on the instrument panel – the light should come on with the ignition, and go out almost immediately when the engine starts.

2 If the light does not come on, there could be a fault on the instrument panel, the switch wiring, or the switch itself. If the light does not

go out, low oil level, worn oil pump (or sump pick-up blocked), blocked oil filter, or worn main bearings could be to blame – or again, the switch may be faulty.

3 If the light comes on while driving, the best advice is to turn the engine off immediately, and not to drive the car until the problem has been investigated – ignoring the light could mean expensive engine damage.

Removal

4 The oil pressure switch is located on the front face of the engine, directly above the oil filter.

5 Access to the switch is easiest from below – raise the front of the car, and support it on axle stands (see *'Jacking and vehicle support'* in the Reference chapter). Remove the engine undershield. Though not essential, access to the switch is improved by unscrewing the oil filter – anticipate some oil spillage when this is done.

6 Disconnect the wiring plug from the switch.

7 Unscrew the switch from the block and remove it – a deep socket or large spanner will be required **(see illustration)**. There should only be a very slight loss of oil when this is done.

Refitting

8 Refitting is the reverse of the removal procedure, noting the following points:

a) *If the same switch is being refitted, clean any old sealant from the switch threads.*

b) *Apply a little RTV sealant to the switch threads, then tighten the switch to the specified torque* **(see illustrations)**.

11.10a Offer the oil pump into position...

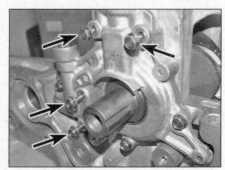

11.10b...and refit the bolts

11.12a Fit a new pipe flange gasket...

11.12b...then refit the oil pick up pipe...

11.12c...and secure with the flange nuts and mounting bolt

12.7 Unscrew and remove the oil pressure switch

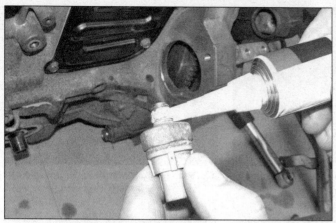

12.8a Apply a little sealant to the switch threads...

12.8b...before refitting and tightening it

c) *Reconnect the switch connector, making sure it clicks home properly. Ensure that the wiring is routed away from any hot or moving parts.*

d) *If removed, refit the oil filter, tightening it securely by hand only (do not use any tools).*

e) *Check the engine oil level and top-up if necessary (see Weekly checks).*

f) *Check for signs of oil leaks once the engine has been restarted and warmed-up to normal operating temperature.*

13 Camshaft oil seals – renewal

1 There are no conventional camshaft oil seals on this engine, but O-ring seals are fitted to covers at either end of the camshaft.

Timing chain end

2 If an oil leak has been noted from the timing chain end of the engine, it may be coming from the cylinder head cover (Section 4) or the timing chain cover (Section 5).

3 However, there is a small plastic plug fitted to the timing chain cover, in line with the camshaft. If oil is weeping from this plug, the seal can be renewed as follows.

4 Support the engine from below, as the right-hand mounting must be removed. Use a large piece of wood between the jack head and the sump, to spread the load, and just take the weight of the engine.

5 Where applicable, unbolt the earth strap in front of the right-hand mounting, and move it clear.

6 On models with air conditioning, one of the refrigerant hoses passes close to the right-hand mounting, and is secured to the inner wing by a support bracket. It may be useful to remove the hose support bracket bolt, to give some movement in the hose.

7 With the engine supported from below, loosen the bolts securing the right-hand mounting to the inner wing. The mounting upper bracket is secured to the engine by two nuts – one on top, and the other removed from

below. Remove the two nuts, then unscrew the mounting-to-wing bolts, and lift out the mounting assembly, manoeuvring it past the refrigerant hose where applicable.

8 Prise out the large plastic plug from the end of the head, which covers the camshaft sprocket bolt. Recover the plug's O-ring seal.

9 Clean the location in the timing chain cover, then fit a new plug and O-ring, pressing the plug home firmly **(see illustration)**.

10 Refit the engine right-hand mounting with reference to Section 17. Also refit the earth strap in front of the mounting, and (where removed) the refrigerant hose mounting bracket bolt.

Transmission end

11 If an oil leak has been noted from the

13.9 Fit the new timing cover plug and O-ring

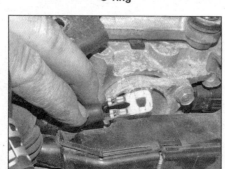

13.14b...and unbolt the earth strap from the camshaft thrust cover

transmission end of the engine, it may be coming from the cylinder head cover (Section 4).

12 However, the thrust cover fitted over the transmission end of the camshaft could be responsible. If oil is weeping from this cover, the seal can be renewed as follows.

13 Remove the air cleaner as described in Chapter 4A.

14 Remove the two bolts from above, and take off the air cleaner mounting bracket at the transmission end of the cylinder head. Remove the lower bolt securing the wiring harness to the end of the head, and also unbolt the earth strap from the camshaft thrust cover. Release the wiring harness from the support bracket at the rear **(see illustrations)**.

13.14a Remove the bolt securing the wiring loom to the end of the cylinder head...

13.14c Slide the wiring loom off the support bracket

15 Remove the two camshaft thrust cover bolts, and withdraw the cover. It's likely that the cover will prove difficult to remove, as there is a large O-ring seal inside – take care not to damage the mating faces if the cover has to be prised off **(see illustrations)**.

16 Fit a new (lightly oiled) O-ring seal to the thrust cover, then press the cover into position and secure with the two bolts, tightened to the specified torque **(see illustrations)**.

17 Refit the wiring harness to the mounting bracket, then refit the earth strap and lower bolt. Refit the air cleaner mounting bracket, and tighten the two bolts to the specified torque.

18 Refit the air cleaner as described in Chapter 4A.

13.15a Remove the two thrust cover mounting bolts...

13.15b...and then withdraw the cover. Note the large O-ring seal

14 Crankshaft oil seals – renewal

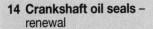

Timing chain end

1 Remove the crankshaft pulley as described in Section 6.

2 Before removing the old seal, note its fitted depth in the timing cover carefully, especially if the seal is being renewed with the timing cover still fitted. The specified distance is 30.3 to 31.0 mm to the front of the seal when measured from the rear of the timing chain cover.

3 Using a suitable claw tool, extract the oil seal, but take care not to damage the seal housing. As it is removed, note the fitted orientation of the seal in the cover.

4 Clean the seal location in the timing cover as far as possible. Also, check for any sharp edges which may damage the new seal, either during fitting or in service.

5 Honda do not state whether the new seal should be oiled before fitting, so we fitted our (genuine Honda) seal without oiling it first. If possible, seek clarification on this from your parts supplier.

6 Offer the new seal into position. If the timing cover has been removed, the seal can be tapped home to the fitted depth noted previously, using a tube or socket of roughly

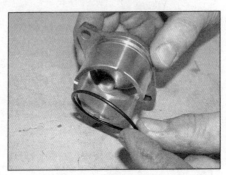

13.16a Fit a new O-ring to the thrust cover...

13.16b...then press the cover back into place and secure with the bolts

the same outside diameter as the seal **(see illustration)**. If the timing cover is still fitted, there is limited working room to tap the seal home, and it may have to be pressed in with a suitable blunt instrument – make sure the seal isn't damaged, and is fitted to the same depth as the old one.

7 Refit the crankshaft pulley as described in Section 6.

Transmission end

8 Remove the flywheel as described in Section 15.

9 Using a suitable claw tool, extract the oil seal, but take care not to damage the seal housing. Alternatively, carefully drill a small hole in the seal, then fit a self-tapping screw and pull out the seal **(see illustrations)**. As it

is removed, note the fitted orientation of the seal, and its fitted depth.

10 Clean the seal location as far as possible. Also, check for any sharp edges which may damage the new seal, either during fitting or in service.

11 Honda do not state whether the new seal should be oiled before fitting, so we fitted our (genuine Honda) seal without oiling it first. If possible, seek clarification on this from your parts supplier.

12 Offer the new seal into position, and tap it home to the fitted depth noted previously (this is effectively flush with the crankcase/block). If possible, use a tube or socket of roughly the same outside diameter as the seal – failing this, work around the seal, tapping it progressively home with a blunt instrument

14.6 Tap the oil seal into the timing cover using a tube or socket

14.9a Drill a small hole in the seal...

14.9b...then fit a screw and use it to pull out the seal

14.12a Offer the seal into position...

14.12b...and tap it home using a block of wood

to make sure the seal isn't damaged **(see illustrations)**.

13 Refit the flywheel described in Section 15.

15 Flywheel – removal, inspection and refitting

Removal

1 Remove the transmission as described in Chapter 7A, then remove the clutch as described in Chapter 6.

2 Jam a suitable tool into the ring gear teeth to prevent the flywheel/crankshaft from rotating as the bolts are removed **(see illustration)**.

3 Unscrew the six retaining bolts, and remove the flywheel from the rear flange of the crankshaft – take care not to drop the flywheel, as it is heavy **(see illustrations)**.

Inspection

4 If on removal, the flywheel bolts are found to be in poor condition (stretched threads, etc) they must be renewed.

5 Inspect the starter ring gear on the flywheel for any broken or excessively-worn teeth. If evident, the ring gear must be renewed; this is a task best entrusted to a Honda dealer or a competent garage. Alternatively, obtain a complete new flywheel.

6 On manual transmission models, the clutch friction surface on the flywheel must be carefully inspected for grooving or hairline cracks (caused by overheating). If these

conditions are evident, it may be possible to have the flywheel surface-ground, however this work must be carried out by an engine overhaul specialist. If surface-grinding is not possible, the flywheel must be renewed.

Refitting

7 Check that the mating faces of the flywheel/driveplate and crankshaft are clean before refitting. Lubricate the threads of the retaining bolts with engine oil before they are screwed into position.

8 Locate the flywheel onto the crankshaft, then insert and hand-tighten the bolts.

9 Prevent the flywheel turning as for removal. Tighten the bolts progressively to the specified torque.

10 If removed, refit the starter motor as described in Chapter 5A. Refit the clutch as described in Chapter 6, then refit the transmission as described in Chapter 7A.

16 Pilot bearing – renewal

1 The pilot bearing is located in the end of the crankshaft, and supports the end of the transmission input shaft. Whenever the transmission is removed (such as when the clutch is being renewed), the pilot bearing should be checked for wear.

2 Remove the transmission as described in Chapter 7A.

3 The pilot bearing can be accessed through

the centre of the flywheel. Turn the bearing by hand, and check it for roughness, excess play, or any other sign of wear.

4 The bearing is press-fitted into the end of the crankshaft, and the only way to remove it is by using a suitable slide hammer.

5 The new bearing should be lightly oiled, then tapped home to the shoulder inside the crankshaft, using a socket or tube which bears on the new bearing's outer race.

6 Refit the transmission as described in Chapter 7A.

17 Engine/transmission mountings – inspection and renewal

General

1 The engine/transmission mountings seldom require attention, but broken or deteriorated mountings should be renewed immediately, or the added strain placed on the driveline components may cause damage or wear.

2 While separate mountings may be removed and refitted individually, if more than one is disturbed at a time – such as if the engine/transmission unit is removed from its mountings – they must be reassembled and their fasteners tightened in the position marked on removal.

3 On reassembly, the complete weight of the engine/transmission unit must not be taken by the mountings until all are correctly aligned with the marks made on removal. Tighten the engine/transmission mounting fasteners to their specified torque wrench settings.

Inspection

4 During the check, the engine/transmission unit must be raised slightly, to remove its weight from the mountings.

5 Raise the front of the vehicle, and support it securely on axle stands. Position a jack under the sump, with a large block of wood between the jack head and the sump, then carefully raise the engine/transmission just enough to take the weight off the mountings.

⚠️ *Warning: DO NOT place any part of your body under the engine when it is supported only by a jack.*

15.2 Using a home made tool to lock the flywheel ring gear

15.3a Unscrew the six flywheel bolts...

15.3b...and take off the flywheel

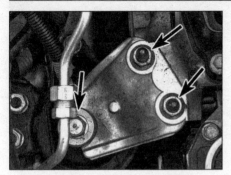

17.10 Remove the bolt and nuts

17.11 Remove the nuts and bolt (hidden) from the stiffener

6 Check the mountings to see if the rubber is cracked, hardened or separated from the metal components. Sometimes the rubber will split right down the centre.

7 Check for relative movement between each mounting's brackets and the engine/transmission or body (use a large screwdriver or lever to attempt to move the mountings). If movement is noted, lower the engine and check that the mounting bolts are secure.

Renewal

Note: *Honda recommend that whenever a mount is disturbed the opposite mount and the lower rear mount (torque rod) should always be slackened off to settle the engine and then re-tightened.*

Right-hand mounting

8 Jack up and support the front of the vehicle (see *'Jacking and vehicle support'* in the Reference chapter). Remove the engine undershield.

9 Support the weight of the engine from below. Use a large piece of wood between the jack head and the sump, to spread the load, and just take the weight of the engine.

10 Unbolt the earth strap in front of the mounting, and move it clear **(see illustration)**. Remove the single bolt and the two nuts – dispose of the nuts as they must be replaced.

11 Unbolt and remove the main body mounting stiffener **(see illustration)**. Dispose of the bolt – it must be replaced.

12 Remove the two bolts and then remove the main flexible mounting from the body.

13 Refit the main flexible body mounting and support bracket. If marks were made prior to removal, align the mounting and then tighten the mounting and bracket to the specified torque.

14 Refit the mounting bracket loosely, using new nuts where specified. If alignment marks were made prior to removal, lower the engine and align the mounting with the marks. Tighten the nuts/bolt to the specified torque on completion.

15 The remainder of refitting is a reversal of removal.

Left-hand mounting

16 Jack up and support the front of the vehicle (see *'Jacking and vehicle support'* in the Reference chapter. Remove the engine undershield.

17 Support the weight of the transmission from below. Use a large piece of wood between the jack head and the transmission, to spread the load, and just take the weight of the engine.

18 Remove the air cleaner assembly as described in Chapter 4A.

19 Disconnect the battery – see *'disconnecting the battery'* in Chapter 5A.

20 Remove the cover from the engine control unit (ECU) disconnect the wiring plugs and then unbolt and remove the ECU.

21 Unbolt and then remove the ECU mounting bracket.

22 Release the fusebox from the support bracket.

23 Unbolt and remove the stiffener form the top of the flexible mounting.

24 Make alignment marks between the mounting and the body and between the mounting and the transmission.Where fitted unbolt the earth cable and then remove the the two nuts and single bolt from the top of the transmission. Dispose of the nuts – they must be replaced.

25 Remove the flexible mounting to body bolts. Lift the mounting from the studs on the transmission and remove it. Dispose of the bolts – they must be replaced.

26 If required the bracket base (on the transmission) can now be unbolted and removed. If removed, dispose of the bolts – they must be replaced.

27 Where removed refit the bracket base to the transmission, using new bolts tightened to the specified torque. Refit the mounting loosely and align it with the previously made marks. Tighten the bolts to the specified torque and lower the transmission using the jack.

28 The remainder of refitting is a reversal of removal.

Rear mounting (torque rod)

29 To remove the engine rear mounting, apply the handbrake, then jack up the front of the car and support it on axle stands (see *'Jacking and vehicle support'* in the Reference chapter). Remove the engine undershield.

30 Removing the rear mounting will only allow the engine to move on its remaining mountings, so providing they are in sound condition, removing the rear mounting will not leave the engine dangerously unsupported.

31 To separate the mounting, unscrew and remove the through bolt and then remove the two mounting bolts from the transmission. Dispose of the bolts – they must be replaced.

32 If required the transmission mounted bracket can now be unbolted and removed. Remove the three bolts and dispose of them – they must be replaced.

33 Refitting is a reversal of removal, but fully tighten the mounting to transmission bolts before tightening the subframe bolt to the specified torque.

Chapter 2 Part B
1.8 litre petrol engines in-car repair procedures

Contents

Section number

Camshaft – removal, inspection and refitting................... 8
Camshaft oil seals – renewal 13
Compression test – description and interpretation 2
Crankshaft oil seals – renewal 14
Crankshaft pulley – removal and refitting..................... 6
Cylinder head – removal, inspection and refitting 9
Cylinder head cover – removal and refitting................... 4
Engine/transmission mountings – inspection and renewal 17
Flywheel/driveplate – removal, inspection and refitting 15

Section number

General Information 1
Oil pressure switch – removal and refitting 12
Oil pump – removal and refitting 11
Pilot bearing – renewal.. 16
Rocker shaft and VTEC control – removal and refitting.......... 7
Sump – removal and refitting................................... 10
Timing chain and related components – removal inspection and
    refitting 5
Top Dead Centre (TDC) for No 1 piston – locating.............. 3

Degrees of difficulty

Easy, suitable for novice with little experience	Fairly easy, suitable for beginner with some experience	Fairly difficult, suitable for competent DIY mechanic	Difficult, suitable for experienced DIY mechanic	Very difficult, suitable for expert DIY or professional

Specifications

General

Engine type.	Four cylinder single overhead camshaft engine
Engine code	R18A
Capacity	1799 cc
Bore	81.0 mm
Stroke	87.3 mm
Compression ratio	10.5: 1
Firing order	1-3-4-2 (No 1 cylinder at timing belt end)
Direction of crankshaft rotation	Clockwise (seen from right-hand side of car)

Compression pressures

Minimum	128 psi
Maximum difference between cylinders	28 psi

Cylinder head

Maximum permissible distortion	0.08 mm
Cylinder head height	114.95 to 115.05 mm

Cylinder head bolts

Minimum diameter 45 mm from the base of the bolt	10.6 mm
Minimum diameter 50 mm from the base of the bolt	10.6 mm

Cylinder block

Maximum warpage	0.10 mm
Bore diameter (nominal)	81.000 to 81.015 mm
Bore diameter service limit	81.070 mm

Piston and piston rings

	Standard	Service limit
Piston diameter (14 mm from base of the piston)		
New	80.980 to 80.990 mm	80.93 mm
Oversize	81.230 to 81.240 mm	
Piston ring end gap (installed)		
Top ring.	0.20 to 0.35 mm	0.60 mm
Second ring	0.40 to 0.55 mm	0.70 mm
Oil control ring	0.20 to 0.70 mm	0.80 mm
Piston ring groove clearance		
Top ring.	0.45 to 0.070 mm	0.13
Second ring	0.035 to 0.060 mm	0.13 mm

Gudgeon pin

	Standard	Service limit
Pin to piston clearance.	-0.004 to +0.003 mm	0.006 mm
Pin diameter	19.960 to 19.964 mm	19.960 mm

Valves

Valve clearance (cold):	
Inlet	0.18 – 0.22 mm
Exhaust.	0.23 – 0.27 mm
Valve spring length:	
Inlet	55.31 mm
Exhaust	56.97 mm
Valve to guide clearance:	
Inlet	0.02 – 0.05 mm (limit 0.08 mm)
Exhaust.	0.05 – 0.08 mm (limit 0.11 mm)

Crankshaft and bearings

	Standard	Service limit
Crankshaft endfloat	0.10 to 0.35 mm	0.45 mm
Main bearing to journal clearance	0.018 to 0.034 mm	0.055 mm

Camshaft

Camshaft endfloat	0.05 – 0.25 mm (limit 0.04 mm)
Cam lobe height:	
Inlet (primary)	35.754 mm
Inlet secondary (A)	35.358 mm
Inlet secondary (B)	36.027 mm
Exhaust	35.813 mm

Connecting rods

	Standard	Service limit
Big end free play	0.15 to 0.35 mm	0.45 mm
Big end bearing clearance	0.024 to 0.042 mm	0.055 mm

Lubrication

Oil pressure (minimum, warm engine):	
At idle	10 psi (min)
At 3,000 rpm.	50 psi (min)
Oil pump clearances:	
Inner to outer rotor clearance.	0.02 -0.16 mm (limit 0.20 mm)
Housing to outer rotor clearance	0.1 – 0.175 mm (limit 0.20 mm)
Housing to outer rotor endfloat	0.02 – 0.07 mm (limit 0.12 mm)
Piston cooling jet opening pressure.	46 psi

Torque wrench settings

	Nm	lbf ft
Air conditioning compressor mounting bolts.	22	16
Air conditioning compressor support bracket	44	33
Auxiliary drivebelt tensioner:		
M10 bolt.	54	40
M8 bolt.	24	17
Camshaft position sensor	12	9
Camshaft position sensor pick-up ring bolt.	34	25
Camshaft thrust plate bolts	10	7
Coolant pump pulley bolts.	14	10
Connecting rod bolts		
Stage 1.	20	14
Stage 2.	Angle-tighten a further 90°	
Crankshaft position sensor	12	9
Crankshaft pulley:		
Stage 1.	69	51
Stage 2.	Angle-tighten a further 90°	

Torque wrench settings

	Nm	lbf ft
Cylinder head bolts:		
Stage 1	39	29
Stage 2	Angle-tighten a further 90°	
Stage 3	Angle-tighten a further 90°	
Stage 4 (new bolts ONLY)	Angle-tighten a further 60°	
Cylinder head cover	10	7
Cylinder head cover loom support bolts	10	7
Driveplate	74	55
EGR pipe nuts/bolts	22	16
EGR valve nuts	24	17
Engine mountings:		
Left-hand mounting		
Left-hand bracket to transmission nuts*	74	54
Left-hand mounting bracket to body bolts*	64	47
Left-hand stiffener bracket	22	14
Bracket base (on transmission) bolts*	59	43
Rear torque rod bolts:		
On transmission	64	47
On subframe	103	76
Right-hand mounting		
Bracket to engine nut/bolt*	74	54
Bracket to flexible mounting bolt	72	52
Flexible mounting to body*	64	47
Stiffener bracket (inner wing)*	64	47
Torque rod*	64	47
Exhaust front pipe:		
Pipe to catalytic converter nuts	93	69
Exhaust pipe to silencer bolts	22	16
Support bracket	22	16
Flywheel bolts	103	76
Main bearing ladder:		
10 mm bolts		
Stage 1	25	18
Stage 2	Angle-tighten a further 57°	
8 mm bolts	24	17
Oil baffle plate bolts	10	7
Oil drain plug	39	29
Oil pickup pipe bolts	12	9
Oil pressure switch	18	13
Piston cooling jet	39	29
Rocker shaft bolts	15	11
Sump bolts	18	13
Sump to transmission bolts	64	47
Timing chain cover:		
M8 bolts	31	23
M6 bolts (upper front cover)	10	7
M6 bolts (lower outer 2 bolts)	12	9
M6 bolts (vertical bolts through sump)	18	13
Timing chain fixed guide bolts	12	9
Timing chain tensioner arm	22	16
Timing chain tensioner bolts	10	7
Thermostat housing bolts	10	7

*Use new nut/bolts

---

1 General Information

How to use this Chapter

1 This Part of Chapter 2 is devoted to in-car repair procedures on the 1.8 litre petrol engine. All procedures concerning engine removal and refitting, and engine block/cylinder head overhaul can be found in Chapter 2D.

2 Refer to Vehicle identification numbers in the Reference chapter at the end of this manual for details of engine code locations.

3 Most of the operations included in this Chapter are based on the assumption that the engine is still installed in the car. Therefore, if this information is being used during a complete engine overhaul, with the engine already removed, many of the steps included here will not apply.

Engine description

4 The engine is a single overhead cam, sixteen valve, water cooled in-line design designated i-VTEC (intelligent Variable lift Timing and Electronic Control) by Honda. The engine features a further development of the familiar i-VTEC valve control first developed by Honda's motorcycle division in the early 1980s.

5 The new i-VTEC system allows the engine to operate in two distinct, but complimentary modes. At idle, low speed and steady cruise a sliding pin engages the economy lobe on the camshaft, retarding the closure of the inlet valve. In the economy mode the throttle plate is held open by the engine management system aiding fuel economy by eliminating the pumping losses associated with a closed throttle plate (on a conventional engine the throttle plate would be almost closed at idle). When combined with a variable length inlet manifold sufficient air enters the combustion chamber with minimum resistance. When accelerating or driving under high load conditions the engine operates exactly the same as a conventional sixteen valve engine.

6 The camshaft is driven by a spring tensioned timing chain and the valves are operated via a rocker shaft assembly. Adjustment of the valve clearances is by a conventional screw and lock nut arrangement. The valves are closed by a single spring. A spring is also fitted to the economy cam rocker arms to control the backlash when the i-VTEC economy mode is not engaged.

7 The oil pump is integrated into the timing chain case and is driven by the 'nose' of the crankshaft.

8 The crankshaft is supported in five shell-type main bearings, combined into a one-piece bearing ladder that forms part of the engine block. The connecting rod big-end bearings are also split shell-type, and the small ends are attached to the pistons by circlip retained gudgeon pins. Each piston is fitted with two compression rings and one oil control ring.

9 The crankshaft runs in five main bearings, the centre main bearing's upper half incorporating thrustwashers to control crankshaft endfloat. Due to the very fine bearing clearances and bearing shell tolerances incorporated during manufacture, it is not possible to renew the crankshaft separate to the cylinder block; in fact it is not possible to remove and refit the crankshaft accurately using conventional tooling. This means that if the crankshaft is worn excessively, it must be renewed together with the cylinder block.

Operations with engine in car

10 The following work can be carried out with the engine in the car:
a) *Cylinder head cover – removal and refitting.*
b) *Timing chain tensioner and sprockets – removal and refitting.*
c) *Camshaft oil seals – renewal.*
d) *Camshafts, tappets and shims – removal and refitting.*
e) *Cylinder head – removal and refitting.*
f) *Sump – removal and refitting.*
g) *Crankshaft oil seals – renewal.*
h) *Oil pump – removal and refitting.*
i) *Flywheel/driveplate – removal and refitting.*
j) *Engine/transmission mountings – removal and refitting.*

2 Compression test – description and interpretation

Note: *Cranking the engine with the coils removed will set a DTC (Diagnostic Trouble Code). Completing several drive cycles after carrying out a compression test may erase the fault codes. If the MIL (Malfunction Indicator Light) remains illuminated, suitable diagnostic equipment will be required to erase the fault codes.*

1 When engine performance is down, or if misfiring occurs which cannot be attributed to the ignition or fuel systems, a compression test can provide diagnostic clues as to the engine's condition. If the test is performed regularly, it can give warning of trouble before any other symptoms become apparent.

2 The engine must be fully warmed-up to operating temperature, the oil level must be correct and the battery must be fully-charged. The help of an assistant will also be required.

3 Remove fuse number 2 from the passenger compartment fusebox. This is the fuse for the fuel pump – further details are to be found in Chapter 4A. Now start the engine and allow it to run until it stalls.

4 With reference to Chapter 1A remove the ignition coils and spark plugs.

5 Fit a compression tester to the No 1 cylinder spark plug hole – the type of tester which screws into the spark plug thread is preferable.

6 Arrange for an assistant to hold the accelerator pedal fully depressed to the floor, while at the same time cranking the engine over for several seconds on the starter motor. Observe the compression gauge reading. The compression will build-up fairly quickly in a healthy engine. Low compression on the first stroke, followed by gradually-increasing pressure on successive strokes, indicates worn piston rings. A low compression on the first stroke which does not rise on successive strokes, indicates leaking valves or a blown head gasket (a cracked cylinder head could also be the cause). Deposits on the underside of the valve heads can also cause low compression. Record the highest gauge reading obtained, then repeat the procedure for the remaining cylinders.

7 Add some engine oil (about three squirts from a plunger type oil can) to each cylinder through the spark plug holes, and then repeat the test.

8 If the compression increases after the oil is added, the piston rings are probably worn. If the compression does not increase significantly, the leakage is occurring at the valves or the head gasket. Leakage past the valves may be caused by burned valve seats and/or faces, or warped, cracked or bent valves.

9 If two adjacent cylinders have equally low compressions, it is most likely that the head gasket has blown between them. The

appearance of coolant in the combustion chambers or on the engine oil dipstick would verify this condition.

10 If one cylinder is about 20 percent lower than the other, and the engine has a slightly rough idle, a worn lobe on the camshaft could be the cause.

11 On completion of the checks, refit the spark plugs and ignition coils. Refit the fuel pump fuse to the fusebox.

3 Top Dead Centre (TDC) for No 1 piston – locating

1 Top dead centre (TDC) is the highest point of the cylinder that each piston reaches as the crankshaft turns. Each piston reaches its TDC position at the end of its compression stroke, and then again at the end of its exhaust stroke. For the purpose of engine timing, TDC on the compression stroke for No 1 piston is used. No 1 cylinder is at the timing chain end of the engine. Proceed as follows.

2 Disconnect the battery negative (earth) lead (see Chapter 5A). Remove the spark plugs as described in Chapter 1A.

3 Turn the engine over by hand (using a socket or spanner on the crankshaft pulley bolt) until the TDC notch in the crankshaft pulley (which may be painted white) is aligned with the pointer above the pulley. Note that the crankshaft pulley will also have an ignition timing mark before top dead centre (BTDC), which may be painted red – as the pulley is turned clockwise, the TDC notch will be the second of the two marks to come into alignment **(see illustration)**.

4 In this position, No 1 and No 4 pistons will be at TDC, but one will be on the compression stroke, and the other on exhaust. Without removing the cylinder head cover as described in Section, the only way to check this is as follows. Remove the spark plug from No 1

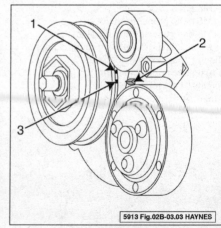

5913 Fig.02B-03.03 HAYNES

3.3 The engine timing marks

1 TDC (Top Dead Centre)
2 Index mark
3 BTDC (Before Top Dead Centre)

3.5 The engine set at TDC. Note the marks and the position of the coloured chain link

4.1a Remove the engine cover...

cylinder as described in Chapter 1A, then turn the engine back from TDC by approximately 90°. Have an assistant cover the open spark plug hole with their hand, then turn the engine forwards to TDC – as this is done, it should be possible to feel compressed air coming from the open plug hole. If not, turn the engine round a full turn until the TDC mark is again aligned, and repeat the check.

5 Further confirmation of TDC on No1 cylinder can only be achieved by removing the cylinder head cover as described in Section. With the cylinder head cover removed, check that the UP marking on the camshaft sprocket is visible, and the two horizontal marks are aligned with the cylinder head top surface **(see illustration)**.

6 Once No 1 cylinder has been positioned at TDC on the compression stroke, TDC for any of the other cylinders can then be located by rotating the crankshaft clockwise (in its normal direction of rotation), 180° at a time, and following the firing order (see Section 0).

7 Where removed, refit the spark plug(s) and cylinder head cover, referring to Chapter 1A and Chapter 2A Section 4 as necessary.

4.1b...and then remove the fuel rail cover

4.2a Disconnect the ignition coils...

4.2b...and remove the wiring loom support bolts

4.4a Pull out the dipstick...

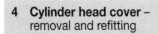

4 Cylinder head cover –
remove and refitting

Removal

1 Remove the engine cover and then remove the fuel injector cover **(see illustrations)**.

2 Disconnect the wiring plugs from the ignition coils and then remove the bolts from the loom supports **(see illustrations)**.

3 Disconnect the wiring plugs from the AC compressor and alternator. Work the loom free from the support bracket.

4 Pull out the dipstick and disconnect the vapour hose from the left-hand end of the cylinder head. On some engines remove the cover from the fuel rail **(see illustrations)**.

4.4b...remove the fuel rail cover...

4.4c...and the breather pipe

4.5a Special peg bolts are fitted to the right-hand end...

4.5b...and the left-hand end of the valve cover

4.5c Remove the valve cover

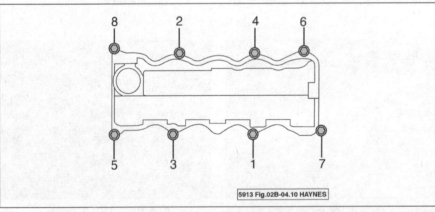

4.8 Apply sealant as shown

5 Note the location of the bolts and then unbolt and remove the cylinder head cover **(see illustrations)**. Recover from the gasket from the engine if necessary.

Refitting

6 Thoroughly clean the cylinder head cover, and the mating surface of the cylinder head. Besides removing any oil, in particular, clean off any sealant at the cylinder head-to-timing chain cover joint.
7 Check the condition of the old gasket. Providing it's not crushed, perished or distorted, it can be refitted into the cover groove.
8 Apply two, 2.5 mm beads of RTV sealant (Honda Liquid Gasket, part number 08C70-K0334M, or equivalent) to the joint

between the cylinder head and the timing chain/oil pump cover **(see illustration)**. Once the sealant has been applied, the cover should be fitted within 5 minutes
9 Refit the cylinder head cover, making sure the gasket stays in place.
10 Fit the cover bolts. Working in stages tighten the bolts in the order shown to the specified torque **(see illustration)**.
11 Refit the remaining components in reverse order and then wait at least 30 minutes before starting the engine.

5 Timing chain and related components – removal inspection and refitting

Removal

Note: *There is very little working room between the timing chain and the inner wing. For clarity most of the images show in this section are taken with the engine removed from the vehicle.*

1 Loosen (but do not yet remove) the three water pump pulley bolts – this is more easily done before the auxiliary drivebelt is removed.
2 Jack up and support the front of the vehicle and then remove the right-hand road wheel. Remove the engine undershield and then remove the wing liner.
3 Have a clean container ready and then remove the sump plug and drain the engine oil. Fit a new seal to the sump plug and tighten it to the specified torque.
4 Remove the auxiliary drivebelt as described in Chapter 1A and then remove the waterpump pulley **(see illustration)**.
5 With reference to Chapter 5A, disconnect the wiring plug and remove the alternator.
6 Unbolt and remove the automatic tensioner **(see illustration)**. Check the damper assembly for oil leaks as it is removed.
7 Remove the cylinder head cover as described in Section 4.
8 Set the engine to TDC on No 1 cylinder, as described in Section 3. As the cylinder head cover has been removed, check that the camshaft sprocket UP mark and horizontal lines are correctly aligned.
9 Disconnect the breather hose and then

4.10

5.4 Remove the pulley

5.6 Remove the automatic auxiliary belt tensioner

5.15 Removing the timing chain cover

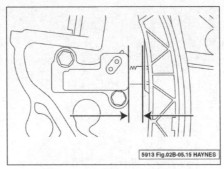

5.16 Measure the exposed length of the plunger. It must not exceed 14.15 mm

5.18a The plunger locking hole

remove the crankshaft pulley as described in Section 6.

10 The weight of the engine must now be supported, as the right-hand mounting must be removed. Use a jack, with a block of wood on the edge of the sump and just take the weight of the engine.

11 With the engine supported from below, remove the AC hose support bracket from the upper torque rod and then unbolt and remove the torque rod – note the position of the bolts as they are removed.

12 Unbolt the earth cable from the upper engine mounting and then with reference to Section 17, remove the engine mounting.

13 The timing chain cover also incorporates the oil pump. Anticipate some oil spillage as the cover is removed.

14 The timing chain cover is secured by a total of fifteen horizontal bolts bolts, of 6 mm and 8 mm diameter and two vertical bolts. Remove the bolts, and store them carefully – we pushed the bolts through a piece of card, in their fitted pattern.

15 The cover is fitted using a bead of sealant, so will probably be stuck. Start by pulling it at the top, and work downwards until it is free, and can be removed – prising between the joint faces may cause damage and an oil leak on reassembly. Slide the cover off the nose of the crankshaft, and remove it **(see illustration)**.

Note: *While the timing chain cover is removed, consider fitting a new crankshaft oil seal which is fitted to it – this job is far easier to do with the cover off. Refer to Section 14.*

16 With the cover removed check the position of the chain tensioner plunger. The amount of the plunger that is exposed will determine if the timing chain requires replacement **(see illustration)**.

Note: *A removable plate is fitted to the timing chain cover. If the plate is removed then the exposed length of the plunger can be measured before the cover is removed. With the engine installed access is difficult and the full length of the plunger is hard to see and equally hard to measure.*

17 Refit the crankshaft pulley and tighten the bolt so that the crankshaft can be turned anti-clockwise to compress the chain tensioner.

5.18b Compress the plunger, rotate the sliding plate and lock the tensioner

18 Apply a little oil as necessary to the timing chain tensioner's slider and then turn the crankshaft backwards – anti-clockwise – so that the tension is compressed and a 1 mm pin (a hex key or split pin is ideal for this purpose) can be inserted into the tension to hold the plunger in the retracted position **(see illustrations)**.

19 Unbolt and remove the tensioner **(see illustration)** and then remove the crankshaft pulley.

20 Remove the lower pivot bolt, and take off the movable guide and then remove the fixed chain guide **(see illustration)**.

21 Before removing the chain, note the fitted positions of the coloured steel links – there should be one at the base of the crankshaft sprocket in the 7 o'clock position, and one

5.19 Remove the tensioner

at the top of the camshaft sprocket in the 1 o'clock position **(see illustration)**. If the chain is to be re-used (and if necessary) clean the marked links and apply fresh paint.

22 The best guide as to whether the chain is worn is the previously checked position of the plunger. However with all the tension removed from the chain, it can be further checked for wear. Try to lift the chain upwards off the camshaft sprocket, at the top. If the chain is worn, it may be possible to lift it clear so that the sprocket teeth are visible – a chain this worn should always be renewed.

23 Using an open-ended spanner on the camshaft flats provided, hold the camshaft while the sprocket bolt is loosened. Unscrew the sprocket bolt, then slide the sprocket and chain from the camshaft (note the position

5.20 Note the special bolt at the chain guide pivot point

5.21 The upper (gold) link opposite the index mark

5.23 Remove the camshaft sprocket bolt

5.24 Note the alignment marks

of the locating keyway – at the top), and withdraw it **(see illustration)**. Remove the camshaft sprocket from the chain.

24 Unhook the chain from the crankshaft sprocket and then slide the sprocket off the nose of the crankshaft **(see illustration)**.

Camshaft sprocket

25 In theory, the camshaft sprocket can be removed without removing the chain completely – this would also save removing the timing chain cover. For details, refer to the camshaft removal procedure in Section 8.

26 In practice, removing the camshaft sprocket from the chain, and then refitting it, is nearly impossible while the timing cover is still in place. If the sprocket must be removed, then tension must be keep on the chain at all times. If the chain is not tensioned it will fall easily of the crankshaft sprocket and then without removing the timing chain cover it will be impossible to see if the coloured link is correctly aligned on the crankshaft sprocket.

Crankshaft sprocket

27 The crankshaft sprocket can only be removed or refitted with the timing chain, as described previously in this Section.

Timing chain tensioner

28 The chain tensioner can be removed as described previously in this Section. If the tensioner is being renewed, attention should also be paid to the tensioner arm and the chain front guide. Note that best practise is to replace the the timing chain, both chain guides and the tensioner.

Inspection

29 Check the chain for wear, which will be evident in the form of excess play between the links. If the chain can be lifted at either 'end' of its run so that the sprocket teeth are visible, it has stretched excessively. If there is any doubt as to the chain's condition, a new one should be fitted – timing chain failure is a lot rarer than timing belt failure, but would still be catastrophic to the engine.

30 If the chain is worn, examine the sprocket teeth closely – if their teeth have taken on a 'hooked' appearance, new ones should be fitted. It is generally considered a false economy to fit a new timing chain on worn sprockets.

31 Assessing wear in the chain tensioner is not easy. Particularly if the tensioner is known to have covered a very high mileage, and/or if a new chain is being fitted, it is recommended that an old tensioner is not re-used.

32 Examine the tensioner arm and front guide for scoring or wear ridges, and renew if necessary. If a new timing chain is being fitted, the guide arms and tensioner should always be replaced.

Refitting

33 Check that the crankshaft is set to TDC – in this position, a punched mark on one of the crankshaft sprocket teeth will be aligned with an arrowhead marking on the engine block. The woodruff key slot will be in the 12 'clock position.

34 The camshaft should also be set to TDC – in this position, the word UP should be uppermost, and the two horizontal lines should align with the top of the cylinder head. If the marks are not aligned, turn the camshaft sprocket only very slightly, as turning it by more than a few degrees could bend the valves. If the camshaft must be turned significantly, turn the crankshaft approximately 90° first, so the pistons are down the bores – reset the camshaft, then bring the crankshaft back to TDC.

35 It should be possible to fit the chain with the crankshaft and camshaft sprockets in position. However the easy way is to remove the camshaft and crankshaft sprockets and fit the chain to them on the bench.

36 Find a clean working area, to lay out the timing chain and the two sprockets.

37 Fit the chain around the camshaft sprocket. The coloured link should sit just to the right of the word UP on the sprocket **(see illustration)**.

38 Now fit the timing chain around the crankshaft sprocket, so that the single coloured link sits exactly over the sprocket tooth with the punched mark on it – this is in the 7 o'clock position in relation to the woodruff key way **(see illustration)**.

39 With the chain in place, again check that the two sprockets are correctly aligned.

40 Fit the chain front guide, and tighten the bolts to the specified torque **(see illustration)**.

41 Fit the curved tensioner arm in position on the rear run of the chain, then oil the pivot bolt, and tighten it to the specified torque.

42 Apply a little engine oil to the tensioner's sliding surface (where it contacts the curved tensioner arm). Fit the tensioner and tighten the bolts to the specified torque.

43 Remove the locking pin from the tensioner and allow the plunger to to take up the slack in the chain.

44 Using an open-ended spanner on the camshaft flats provided, hold the camshaft in

5.37 The camshaft chain and sprocket correctly aligned. Note the uses of a tie wrap to secure the chain in position

5.38 The crankshaft sprocket and chain correctly alighned

5.40 Fit the fixed chain guide

5.44 Tighten the camshaft sprocket bolt

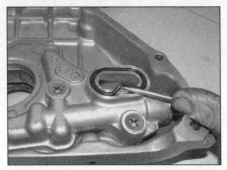
5.49 Replace the oil pump O-ring seals

5.50 Apply sealant to the cover

position. Tighten the camshaft sprocket bolt to the specified torque **(see illustration)**.

45 Temporarily refit the crankshaft pulley bolt, and use a spanner or socket to slowly turn the engine through two complete revolutions. Check that the TDC marks are correctly aligned. If the crankshaft binds or seems to hit something, do not force it, as the valves may be hitting the pistons. If this happens, the chain is incorrectly fitted. If necessary, reset the engine to TDC, then remove the chain and repeat the refitting procedure.

46 Remove the crankshaft pulley bolt.

47 Before refitting the timing cover, check the condition of the crankshaft oil seal which is fitted to it. This seal is much easier to renew when the cover is removed – see Section 14 for details.

48 Clean off all traces of old sealant from the cover, engine faces, cover bolts and bolt holes. Take care not to mark the mating faces. Wash the cover and engine mating faces with suitable solvent, and dry them before continuing.

49 Fit new O-rings to the oil pump **(see illustration)**.

50 Apply a bead of RTV sealant (Honda Liquid Gasket, part number 08C70-K0334M, or equivalent) to the timing cover mating faces on the engine block and cylinder head, as shown. The bead should be approximately 2.5 mm diameter all round **(see illustration)**. Run the sealant inside the bolt holes – try not to get any down the holes themselves, as this may affect the bolt tightening. Once the

sealant has been applied, the cover should be fitted within 5 minutes.

51 A further bead of sealant must also be applied along the base of the cover – where it meets the sump. Once the sealant has been applied, the cover should be fitted within 5 minutes.

52 Offer the cover over the end of the crankshaft, taking care not to damage the oil seal in the cover. Fit the base of the cover on the sump and tip the cover upright. Do not be tempted to simply slide the cover over the crankshaft and into position as this will disturb the sealant on the base of the cover **(see illustration)**.

53 Fit all the cover bolts and loosely tighten them. Tighten the 8 mm bolts first and then the 6 mm bolts. Tighten the bolts evenly, and finally to their respective torques.

54 Refit the engine right-hand mounting with reference to Section 17. Also refit the earth strap in front of the mounting.

55 The remainder of refitting is a reversal of removal, noting the following points:
a) *Refit the crankshaft pulley as described in Section 6.*
b) *Refit the cylinder head cover as described in Section 4.*
c) *Refit the alternator as described in Chapter 5A.*
d) *Refit the water pump pulley, with the bolts hand-tight to begin with (it will be easier to tighten them to the specified torque once the auxiliary drivebelt has been refitted and tensioned, as described in Chapter 1A).*

e) *Wait a minimum of 30 minutes before filling the engine with oil and a minimum of 3 hours before starting the engine.*
f) *Carry out the idle learn procedure as described in Chapter 5A, Section 3.*

6 Crankshaft pulley – removal and refitting

Removal

1 Remove the auxiliary drivebelt as described in Chapter 1A.

2 The crankshaft pulley has a paint TDC marking on its outer rim (there is also another paint mark, indicating the BTDC ignition timing point). The engine does not have to be set to TDC if just the pulley is being removed, but if other work is to be carried out requiring the engine to be at TDC, the engine should be set in this position as described in Section 3 before the pulley is removed.

3 The crankshaft pulley must now be held stationary while the bolt is loosened. Honda specify a special tool that engages with the pulley and allows a socket to pass through the tool and onto the crankshaft pulley bolt. The procedure described below allows the bolt (and pulley) to be removed without the special tool.

4 Jack up the front of the car, and support it on axle stands (see *'Jacking and vehicle support'* in the Reference chapter) and then remove the engine undershield. Remove the metal cover plate on the base of the transmission bellhousing – this gives access to the flywheel ring gear **(see illustration)**.

5 Because the pulley bolt is so tight, we felt that jamming a screwdriver blade in the ring gear would not be sufficient (or safe). We slackened the bolt by fitting a nut and bolt into one of the holes in the flywheel and then jamming a prybar between the bolt and the transmission casing. Whilst this method worked it did not feel secure, so we fabricated a suitable locking tool. The tool worked very well, and it can also be used to hold the

5.52 Rotate the cover into position – do not slide it

6.4 Remove the cover plate

6.5a Locking the flywheel with a bolt and prybar might work...

6.5b...however a fabricated tool that uses one of the bell housing bolts to secure the tool and lock the flywheel is a better solution

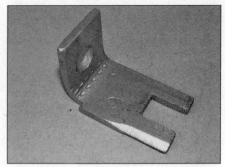

6.5c The fabricated flywheel locking tool

flywheel for tightening the pulley bolt **(see illustrations)**.

6 Before loosening the pulley bolt, ensure that the car is securely supported. Only use good-quality, close-fitting tools for this job – if something slips, it may result in injury. For extra leverage, use a long-handled breaker bar.

7 Unscrew and remove the bolt (which has an integral washer), and slip off the pulley **(see illustration)**. Note which way up the pulley fits – it engages on a keyway. Where applicable, the Woodruff key which sits in the crankshaft may be loose – it's best to recover it, and store it with the pulley.

8 If the engine had to be set to TDC before the pulley was removed (see paragraph 2), loosely refit the pulley and bolt, and reset the engine to TDC, as it is likely that the pulley

may have turned during removal. Once the setting is conformed, remove the bolt and pulley again.

Refitting

9 Wipe clean the pulley and the mating surfaces of the crankshaft and its sprocket. Also clean the pulley bolt and washer. Though not specifically required by Honda, consider using a new bolt when refitting – this should be done in any case if the bolt appears damaged.

10 Offer up the pulley and fit it over the crankshaft. Slide the woodruff key into position. Lightly oil the bolt threads and the underside of the bolt head, then tighten the bolt by hand, and check that the pulley is properly seated **(see illustrations)**.

11 Using the same method as for removal,

prevent the crankshaft pulley from turning as the bolt is tightened.

12 Tighten the bolt to the specified torque, then through the angle (which is equivalent to a quarter-turn). A quarter-turn can be made easier to judge by painting a mark on the bolt and the pulley **(see illustrations)**.

13 Refit and tension the auxiliary drivebelt as described in Chapter 1A.

| **7** | **Rocker shaft and VTEC control** – removal and refitting | |

Removal – Rocker shaft

1 Remove the cylinder head cover as described in Section 4.

6.7 Remove the crankshaft pulley bolt

6.10a Fit the pulley...

6.10b...and slide the woodruff key into position

6.10c Lubricate the bolt threads and the washer

6.12a Torque the bolt to the first stage...

6.12b...and then fit an angle gauge and tighten to the second stage

7.3a Unbolt and then...

7.3b...remove the rocker shaft assembly

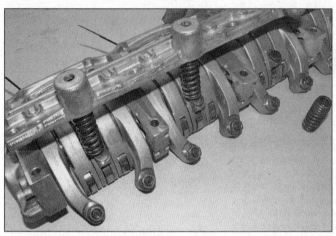
7.4a Lift off the plate and...

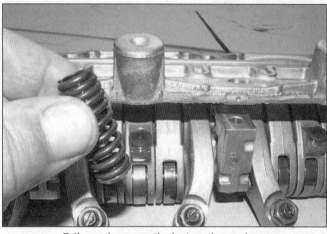
7.4b...and recover the lost motion springs

2 Work along the rocker shaft, release the lock nuts and slacken off the rocker arm adjusting screws. With all the adjusting screws backed off secure the rocker arms together with cable ties.

3 Working in reverse order to that shown below (see illustration 7.8b) slacken the lost motion holder bolts two turns at a time in sequence. Remove the holder and rocker shaft as a single assembly (see illustrations).

4 Lift off the lost motion spring retaining plate from the rocker assembly (see illustrations). Where they have been disturbed recover the locating dowels.

5 If required the shaft assembly can now be dismantled. Prepare a clean work area where the shaft can be dissembled and the components laid out in order. Leave the rocker shaft bolt in position on the end shaft holder and slide the rocker arms in turn from the shaft (see illustrations).

7.5a Remove the rocker arms in sequence...

7.5b...and note the order of the components

7.8a Secure the lost motion springs in place

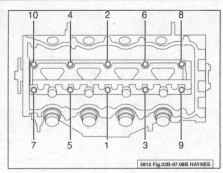

7.8b Tighten the bolts in the order shown

5913 Fig.02B-07.08B HAYNES

7.13 The VTEC oil control solenoid

7.14 Always fit a new gasket

Refitting

6 Check that all the dowels are firmly located in the cylinder head and in the lost motion spring retainer.

7 Lower the rocker shaft assembly onto the cylinder head, ensuring that the rocker arms align with the valves.

8 Refit the lost motion springs. Hold them in place with blob of grease and then refit the lost motion cover. Fit the bolts and working in the order show tighten the bolt 2 turns at a time in sequence (see illustrations).

9 Remove the cable ties and adjust the valve clearances as described in Chapter 1A.

10 Refit the cylinder head cover as described in Section 4.

VTEC control valve

Removal

11 Remove the windscreen cowl panels as described in Chapter 12 Section 12 and then remove the lower cowl panel.

12 Disconnect the wiring plug from the solenoid and then disconnect the wiring plug from the oil pressure switch (some models only).

13 Remove the mounting bolts and withdraw the control unit assembly.

Refitting

14 Refitting is a reversal of removal, but fit a new gasket, as this incorporates an oil filter (see illustration).

8 Camshaft – removal, inspection and refitting

Removal

1 There are no camshaft bearing caps to remove – therefore, the camshaft can only be withdrawn by sliding it out of the head, at the transmission end.

2 In theory, on the 1.8 petrol engine the camshaft can only be removed after the cylinder has has been removed. However by removing the battery and ECM we removed the camshaft without removing the cylinder head.

3 Remove the cylinder head cover as described in Section 4, and then remove the rocker shaft assembly as described in Section 7.

4 Remove the battery (as described in Chapter 5A) and then remove the air filter housing as described in Chapter 4A. Finally remove the ECM (see illustrations).

5 Disconnect the wiring plug from the camshaft sensor. Unbolt the sensor and remove it.

6 At the left-hand end of the cylinder head disconnect the coolant temperature sensor and then remove the wiring loom.

7 Drain the coolant (as described in Chapter 1A) so that the coolant level is below the cylinder head. Remove the coolant hoses and then remove the coolant distribution housing from the end of the cylinder head.

8 Remove the two camshaft thrust cover bolts, and withdraw the cover. It's likely that the cover will prove difficult to remove, as there is a large O-ring seal inside – take care not to damage the mating faces if the cover has to be prised off (see illustrations). Recover the O-ring seal – a new one should be used when refitting.

8.4a Remove the cover and then...

8.4b...unbolt and unplug the ECM

8.8a Remove the end (thrust) cover bolts...

8.8b...and then remove the cover

8.10 Support the camshaft sprocket

8.11a Slide out and...

8.11b...and remove the camshaft

8.15 Oil the camshaft lobes and bearing surfaces

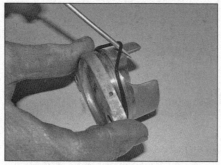

8.17 Fit a new O-ring to the cover

8.19 Fit a new blanking plug

9 Position the engine at TDC if not already done so (as described in Section) and remove the blanking plug from the timing chain cover. Hold the camshaft on the flats provided and slacken the camshaft sprocket bolt – but do not remove it. Secure the timing chain to the camshaft sprocket with a cable tie.

10 A suitable method of holding the camshaft sprocket and chain in position must now be devised. We used a screwdriver through one of the holes in the sprocket **(see illustration)** but there is no reason why self locking pliers could not be used. A suitable block of wood will be needed to avoid damaging the cylinder head.

Caution: If tension is lost from the chain, the chain will drop off the crankshaft sprocket and there is no way of knowing if the coloured link is still positioned correctly on the crankshaft sprocket. In this case the timing chain cover will have to be removed to reposition the timing chain correctly.

11 Carefully slide out the camshaft, keeping it as horizontal as possible **(see illustrations)**. If the shaft catches as it is withdrawn, slide it back in and try to free it by turning it slightly – there is a danger of damaging the cam lobes if the shaft is roughly handled. Once it is completely removed, rest the shaft on clean newspaper or rags, to protect the lobes.

Inspection

12 Examine the camshaft lobes for score marks, pitting, galling (wear due to rubbing) and evidence of overheating (blue,

discoloured areas). Look for flaking away of the hardened surface layer of each lobe. Renew the camshaft if any of these conditions are apparent.

13 If any of the lobes is damaged, check the corresponding rocker finger's surfaces for similar signs – it probably wouldn't be wise to fit a new camshaft and re-use the old rocker shaft assembly, as both would have suffered wear. Seek the advice of an engine rebuilding specialist if in doubt.

14 As far as possible, examine the condition of the camshaft bearing surfaces in the cylinder head. If the head bearing surfaces are worn excessively, the cylinder head will need to be renewed.

Refitting

15 Liberally oil the camshaft lobes and the camshaft bearings in the cylinder head **(see illustration)**.

16 Slide the camshaft into the head, keeping it horizontal to avoid catching the lobes, which might cause damage. Turn the camshaft so that the sprocket locating keyway is in the TDC position (12 o'clock), as noted before removal.

17 Fit a new (lightly oiled) O-ring seal to the thrust cover, then press the cover into position and secure with the two bolts, tightened to the specified torque **(see illustration)**.

18 Carefully refit the camshaft sprocket to the camshaft and tighten the camshaft sprocket bolt to the specified torque. Remove the spark plugs and rotate the engine several times in

the normal direction, checking that the timing marks are correctly aligned at TDC (Top Dead Centre).

19 Fit a new blanking plug to the timing chain cover **(see illustration)**.

20 Refit the camshaft position sensor to the back of the engine, with a new, lightly-oiled O-ring. Tighten the sensor mounting bolt to the specified torque.

21 Refit the rocker shaft assembly as described in Section 7 and adjust the valve clearances as described in Chapter 1A. Refit the spark plugs.

22 Refit the cylinder head cover as described in Section 4.

23 Refit the remaining components in the reverse order of removal. Refill the cooling system as described in Chapter 1A.

---

9 Cylinder head – removal, inspection and refitting

Removal

Note: *To avoid the possibility of warping the cylinder head, the cylinder head bolts should only be loosened when the engine has cooled down completely.*

1 Remove the number 2 fuse (fuel pump) from the interior fusebox and run the engine until it stops.

2 Disconnect the battery as described in Chapter 5A.

9.4 Remove the support bracket

9.5 Remove the inlet manifold

9.7 Remove the coolant hoses

3 Refer to Chapter 1A and drain the cooling system.

4 Remove the air cleaner assembly as described in Chapter 4A and then remove the support bracket from the cylinder head **(see illustration)**.

5 Remove the inlet manifold as described in Chapter 4A **(see illustration)**.

6 Release the spring clip and remove the crankcase ventilation hose.

7 Release the spring clips, and disconnect the radiator top hose from the thermostat housing **(see illustration)**. Similarly, disconnect the heater hose at the rear of the housing.

8 Remove the auxiliary drivebelt as described in Chapter 1A.

9 Disconnect the wiring plugs from the following components around the engine:

a) *The camshaft position (TDC) sensor, from the rear of the head, at the transmission end.*

b) *The coolant temperature sensor* **(see illustration)**

c) *The oxygen sensor*

d) *The fuel injectors*

e) *The oil pressure switch*

f) *The exhaust gas recirculation connector (EGR)*

g) *The rocker oil control solenoid* **(see illustration)**

h) *The rocker arm oil pressure switch (some models only)*

10 Unbolt and remove the ignition coils.

11 Unbolt the wiring loom support bolts from the end of the cylinder head and move the wiring loom to the side.

12 Remove the cylinder head cover as described in Section 4.

13 With reference to Chapter 4A, remove the catalytic converter **(see illustration)**.

14 Remove the remaining coolant hoses from

the thermostat housing and then remove the EGR by-pass pipe from the EGR valve. Unbolt and remove the complete thermostat housing.

15 Set the engine to TDC on No 1 cylinder, as described in Section 3. As the cylinder head cover has been removed, check that the camshaft sprocket UP mark and horizontal lines are correctly aligned.

16 With reference to Section 5, remove the timing chain.

17 Remove the rocker shaft as described in Section 7.

18 Working in the reverse of the tightening sequence shown later in this Section, loosen each head bolt by a quarter-turn each time, repeating the sequence until all bolts are completely loose, and can be removed **(see illustration)**. If new bolts are not being fitted (this is not something we would recommend), lay the old bolts out in their fitted order, so they can be refitted in the same place.

19 Carefully lift off the head, and place it on a clean surface – do not allow the lower face to be damaged, or even a new gasket will not seal properly. If the head is stuck, try rocking it backwards to free it, using a blunt lever (such as a wooden hammer handle) in the exhaust ports on the front. Once the gasket seal has been broken, the head should come off. Hitting the head is not advisable, as the alloy is easily damaged. Also note that the head is located on two dowels.

20 Recover the old head gasket **(see illustration)**. It must not be re-used, but it will be useful to hold onto it for now, to compare with the new one as verification.

9.9a Disconnect the coolant temperature sensor

9.9b Disconnect the wiring plug from the VTEC control solenoid

9.13 Remove the catalytic converter

9.18 Remove the cylinder head bolts

9.20 Remove the cylinder head gasket

9.22 Remove the coolant seperator

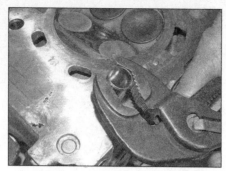

9.23 Remove the locating dowels

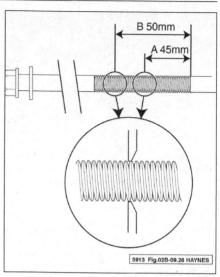

9.28 Measure the diameter at 'A' (45 mm from the end) and at 'B' (50 mm from the end). If the diameter is less than 10.6 mm replace the bolts

21 If the head is to be dismantled for overhaul, remove the camshaft as described in Section 7, then refer to Part 2D of this Chapter.
22 Remove and dispose of the coolant separator – Honda recommend this is replaced **(see illustration)**.

Preparation for refitting

23 The mating faces of the cylinder head and cylinder block/crankcase must be perfectly clean before refitting the head. Remove the two dowels (note their positions) and use a hard plastic or wood scraper to remove all traces of gasket and carbon; also clean the piston crowns **(see illustration)**.
24 Take particular care during the cleaning operations, as aluminium alloy is easily damaged. Also make sure that carbon is not allowed to enter the oil and water passages – this is particularly important for the lubrication system, as carbon could block the oil supply to the engine's components. Using adhesive tape and paper, seal the water, oil and bolt holes in the cylinder block/crankcase.
25 Take care that as little debris as possible gets onto the timing chain (and that the supported chain is not disturbed during cleaning) – anything more than a little dirt will risk getting caught up in the crankshaft sprocket, and may cause damage to the timing chain.
26 Check the mating surfaces of the cylinder block/crankcase and the cylinder head for nicks, deep scratches and other damage. If slight, they may be removed carefully with a file, but if excessive, machining may be the only alternative to renewal.
27 If warpage of the cylinder head gasket surface is suspected, use a straight-edge to check it for distortion. Refer to Part 2D of this Chapter if necessary.
28 Honda suggest that if the head bolts are within specification, they can be re-used **(see illustration)**. If there is any doubt about the condition of the head bolts then replace them.
29 Although not essential, if a suitable tap-and-die set is available, it's worth running the correct-size tap down the bolt threads in the cylinder block. This will clean the threads of any debris, and go some way to restoring any damaged threads. Make absolutely sure the tap is the right size and thread pitch, and lightly oil the tap before starting. Failing this, choose one

of the old head bolts, clean its threads with a wire brush, then lightly oil it, and run it fully into each bolt hole, cleaning it between each one.
30 If possible, clean out the bolt holes in the block using compressed air, to ensure no oil or water is present. Screwing a bolt into an oil- or water-filled hole can (in extreme cases) cause the block to fracture, due to the hydraulic pressure created.

Refitting

31 Ensure the two locating dowels are refitted to their original positions on the block top surface and check that the coolant separator is in position in the engine block. Check that the new cylinder head gasket is the same type as the original, and that any TOP or UP marking is facing upwards, then locate it onto the top face of the cylinder block and over the dowels. Ensure that it is correctly aligned with the coolant passages and oilways **(see illustration)**.

9.31 Fit the new head gasket

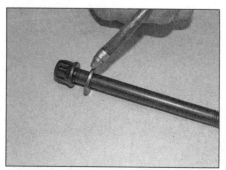

9.33 Lubricate both side of the washer – and the bolt threads

32 Lower the head onto the block, taking care not to disturb the supported timing chain, and making sure the gasket does not move. Locate the head on the two dowels **(see illustration)**.
33 Lightly oil the threads and heads of the head bolts before fitting them **(see illustration)**.
34 Following the tightening sequence, first tighten the bolts to the specified Stage 1 torque **(see illustration)**. **Note:** *If any bolt*

9.32 Lower the cylinder head into position

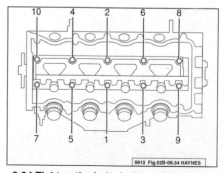

9.34 Tighten the bolts in the order shown

9.35a A torque wrench and...

9.35b...and angle gauge are essential

starts creaking during tightening, Honda suggest loosening it completely, and start tightening again. If the bolts are lubricated as stated in the previous paragraph, no creaking should be evident.

35 Now the head bolts should be tightened further, to their specified Stage 2 angle. It is strongly recommended that an angle gauge is used for this task – these are not expensive, and are available from any good car accessory shop or motor factors **(see illustrations)**. Again, follow the tightening sequence.

36 After completing stage 2, further tighten the bolts to the stage 3 setting.

37 After completing stage 3 and ONLY where new bolts are fitted complete stage 4.

38 If any bolt is tightened beyond the specified angle, then it is permissible to fully slacken the individual bolt and follow the tightening procedure again. Whilst Honda do not restrict this to only new bolts, if the old bolts are being used then careful consideration should be given to replacing all the bolts.

39 Refit the camshaft sprocket, the timing chain and timing chain cover as described in Section 5.

40 Refit the engine right-hand mounting with reference to Section 17.

41 Refit the rocker shaft assembly and adjust the valve clearances (Chapter 1A). Fit the cylinder head cover, coils, fuel injectors and wiring loom.

42 Refit the thermostat housing. Use a new seal and consider replacing the thermostat.

Install the thermostat with the jiggle pin upper most.

43 Refit the EGR valve and by-pass pipe using new gaskets.

44 The remainder of refitting is a reversal of removal, noting the following points:

a) Refit the fuel rail and inlet manifold as described in Chapter 4A. On completion, switch the ignition on and off a few times, to run the fuel pump, then check for signs of fuel leakage.

b) When all the coolant pipes and hoses have been reconnected, refill the cooling system as described in Chapter 1A.

c) Check the oil level and run the engine up to temperature whilst watching carefully for fuel, oil and coolant leaks.

10 Sump – removal and refitting

Removal

1 Jack up the front of the car, and support it on axle stands (see 'Jacking and vehicle support' in the Reference chapter). Remove the engine undershieled.

2 Drain the engine oil as described in Chapter 1A, then refit the drain plug. Remove the oil filter. It makes sense to fit a new oil filter on completion, but this is not essential.

3 Remove the axillary drivebelt as described in Chapter 1A.

> ⚠️ **Warning: Do not disconnect the air conditioning pipes. It is an offence to knowingly discharge refrigerant to the atmosphere.**

4 On models with air conditioning, the compressor is bolted to the sump's front face. Disconnect the compressor wiring plug. Remove the four bolts, then move the compressor forwards, clear of the sump. Support the compressor using wire or cable-ties, so that the refrigerant hoses (which must not be disturbed) are not strained.

5 Unbolt the AC compressor mounting bracket from the side of the sump **(see illustrations)**.

6 Remove the front section of the exhaust system. Dispose of the gaskets – they must be replaced.

7 With reference to Section 17, unbolt and remove the lower torque rod.

8 Remove the cover from the oil level sensor, disconnect the wiring plug **(see illustrations)** and remove the bolt securing the sensor wiring loom. On models fitted with automatic transmission remove the cover plate from the gear shift cable.

9 Where the sump meets the transmission, remove the bolts and take off the small cover plate from below the flywheel.

10.5a Remove the compressor mounting bracket bolts and then...

10.5b...remove the bracket

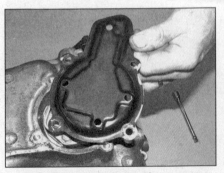

10.8a Remove the protective cover...

10.8b...and disconnect the wiring plug

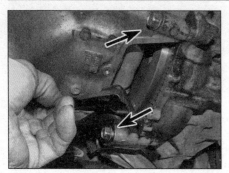

10.10 Remove the cover plate and the bolts

10.14 Fit new O-rings to the sump

10.15a Apply the sealant...

10 Remove the two large sump to transmission bolts **(see illustration)**.

11 Prise the sump down at the four corners and nowhere else. Because the sump is bonded to the engine block with a sealant and not a gasket, removing it can be difficult. An alternative method is to remove the drain plug and use a tool such as a screwdriver inserted in the drain hole as a lever to prise the sump free (take care not to damage the drain hole threads). Keep the sump level as it is lowered, to prevent spillage of any remaining oil in it. Also be prepared for oil drips from the crankcase when the sump is removed.

12 Recover the O-rings fitted to the oil filter supply passage. New O-rings must be used when refitting.

13 Clean any sealant from the sump and engine mating faces – care must be taken not to damage the soft aluminium of the sump. Wipe the mating faces with a suitable solvent, and allow to dry. While the sump is off, check that the oil pick-up/strainer on the base of the engine is clear, cleaning it if necessary.

Refitting

14 If removed refit the dowels – or check that they are firmly in place. Replace the two O-rings **(see illustration)**.

15 Apply a 2.5 mm bead of RTV sealant (Honda Liquid Gasket, part number 08C70-K0334M, or equivalent) to the sump's mating face. The sealant must run all round the perimeter of the sump and inside the

10.15b...and lower the sump into position

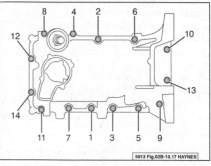

10.17 Tighten the bolts in the order shown

bolts holes. Lower the sump into position – or raise it if the engine is still in the vehicle **(see illustrations)**.

16 Fit the sump bolts and hand tighten them.

17 Working in sequence, and in three stages, tighten the nuts and bolts to the specified torque **(see illustration)**.

18 Remove any surplus sealant from the sump before it fully hardens.

19 Fit the two sump to transmission bolts and tighten them to the specified torque.

20 Refit the small cover plate from below the flywheel and secure with the three bolts.

21 Connect the wiring plug and then refit the oil level sensor cover. Refit the bolt securing the wiring loom bracket.

22 On models with air conditioning, refit the compressor support bracket and then refit the

compressor. Tighten the bolts to the specified torque. Reconnect the compressor wiring plug.

23 Refit the axillary drivebelt.

24 Fit the oil filter, tightening it by hand only – do not use any tools.

25 Fit new gaskets to the exhaust pipe and refit it. Tighten the bolts to the specified torque.

26 Refit the engine undershield and lower the vehicle to the ground.

27 Allow at least 30 minutes (and preferably, several hours) for the sealant used on the sump to cure, then refill the engine with oil as described in Chapter 1A.

28 Wait at least 3 hours before starting the engine. Start the engine and check for oil leaks.

11.2a Remove the screws...

11.2b...and remove the cover

11 Oil pump – removal and refitting

Removal.

1 The oil pump is integral to the timing chain cover and is removed with the timing chain cover as described in Section 5.

2 With the timing chain cover on the bench remove the oil pump cover plate **(see illustrations)**.

3 Useing feeler gauges first measure the inner rotor to the outer rotor clearance and compare

11.3 Measure the inner to outer rotor clearance

11.4 Measure the outer rotor to the housing clearance

11.5 Measure the free play across the face of the pump

the measurement obtained in Specifications **(see illustrations)**.

4 Next measure the housing to the outer rotor clearance and compare the measurement obtained in the Specifications **(see illustrations)**.

5 Finally place a straight edge across the pump and measure the free play (axial clearance) across the face of the pump.

6 If any of the measurements are not within specification the oil pump should be replaced.

Refitting

7 Apply thread locking compound to the oil pump cover screws and refit the oil pump cover. Note that no torque figures are available for these screws.

8 Clean the sealant from the face of the timing chain cover, apply sealant and refit it as described in Section 5.

9 Wait a minimum of 30 minutes and then refill the engine with oil. If the oil pump has been replaced the oil and oil filter must be changed – see Chapter 1A.

10 Wait an minimum of 3 hours before starting. Run the engine up to temperature and check for coolant leaks. Perform the idle learn procedure as described in Chapter 5A, Section 3.

12 Oil pressure switch – removal and refitting

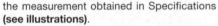

1 The oil pressure switch is a vital early warning of low oil pressure. The switch operates the oil warning light on the instrument

panel – the light should come on with the ignition, and go out almost immediately when the engine starts.

2 If the light does not come on, there could be a fault on the instrument panel, the switch wiring, or the switch itself. If the light does not go out, low oil level, worn oil pump (or sump pick-up blocked), blocked oil filter, or worn main bearings could be to blame – or again, the switch may be faulty.

3 If the light comes on while driving, the best advice is to turn the engine off immediately, and not to drive the car until the problem has been investigated – ignoring the light could mean expensive engine damage.

Removal

4 The oil pressure switch is located on the front face of the engine close to the transmission.

5 Remove the protective cover and then disconnect the wiring plug from the switch **(see illustrations)**.

6 Unscrew the switch from the block and remove it – a deep socket or large spanner will be required. There should only be a very slight loss of oil when this is done.

Refitting

7 Refitting is the reverse of the removal procedure, noting the following points:

a) *If the same switch is being refitted, clean any old sealant from the switch threads.*

b) *Apply a little RTV sealant to the switch threads, then tighten the switch to the specified torque.*

c) *Reconnect the switch connector, making sure it clicks home properly. Ensure that the wiring is routed away from any hot or moving parts.*

d) *Check the engine oil level and top-up if necessary (see Weekly checks).*

e) *Check for signs of oil leaks once the engine has been restarted and warmed-up to normal operating temperature.*

13 Camshaft oil seals – renewal

1 There are no conventional camshaft oil seals on this engine, but O-ring seals are fitted to covers at either end of the camshaft.

Timing chain end

2 If an oil leak has been noted from the timing chain end of the engine, it may be coming from the cylinder head cover (Section 4) or the timing chain cover (Section 5).

3 However, there is a small plastic plug fitted to the timing chain cover, in line with the camshaft. If oil is weeping from this plug, the seal can be renewed as follows.

4 Support the engine from below, as the right-hand mounting must be removed. Use a large piece of wood between the jack head and the sump, to spread the load, and just take the weight of the engine.

5 Where applicable, unbolt the earth strap in front of the right-hand mounting, and move it clear.

6 On models with air conditioning, one of the refrigerant hoses passes close to the right-hand mounting, and is secured to the inner wing by a support bracket. It may be useful to remove the hose support bracket bolt, to give some movement in the hose.

7 With the engine supported from below, loosen the bolts securing the right-hand mounting to the inner wing. The mounting upper bracket is secured to the engine by two nuts – one on top, and the other removed from below. Remove the two nuts, then unscrew the mounting-to-wing bolts, and lift out the mounting assembly, manoeuvring it past the refrigerant hose where applicable.

8 Prise out the large plastic plug from the

12.5a Remove the cover and...

12.5b...disconnect the wiring plug

13.9 Fit a new plug to the timing chain cover

13.15 Remove the bolts

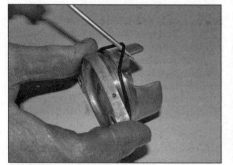

13.16a Remove the old O-ring and fit a new one and then...

13.16b...refit the cover to the cylinder head

end of the head, which covers the camshaft sprocket bolt.

9 Clean the location in the timing chain cover, then fit a new plug, pressing the plug home firmly **(see illustration)**.

10 Refit the engine right-hand mounting with reference to Section 17. Also refit the earth strap in front of the mounting, and (where removed) the refrigerant hose mounting bracket bolt.

Transmission end

11 If an oil leak has been noted from the transmission end of the engine, it may be coming from the cylinder head cover (Section 4).

12 However, the thrust cover fitted over the transmission end of the camshaft could be responsible. If oil is weeping from this cover, the seal can be renewed as follows.

13 Remove the air cleaner as described in Chapter 4A.

14 Remove the two bolts from above, and take off the air cleaner mounting bracket at the transmission end of the cylinder head. Remove the lower bolt securing the wiring harness to the end of the head, and also unbolt the earth strap from the camshaft thrust cover. Release the wiring harness from the support bracket at the rear.

15 Remove the two camshaft thrust cover bolts, and withdraw the cover. It's likely that the cover will prove difficult to remove, as there is a large O-ring seal inside – take care not to damage the mating faces if the cover has to be prised off **(see illustration)**.

16 Fit a new (lightly oiled) O-ring seal to the thrust cover, then press the cover into position and secure with the two bolts, tightened to the specified torque **(see illustrations)**.

17 Refit the wiring harness to the mounting bracket, then refit the earth strap and lower bolt. Refit the air cleaner mounting bracket, and tighten the two bolts to the specified torque.

18 Refit the air cleaner as described in Chapter 4A.

14 Crankshaft oil seals – renewal

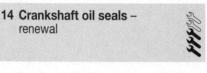

Timing chain end

1 Remove the crankshaft pulley as described in Section 6.

2 Using a suitable claw tool, extract the oil seal, but take care not to damage the seal housing **(see illustration)**. Alternatively a self-tapping screw can be screwed into the seal and a pair of self locking pliers can be used to pull out the seal. As it is removed, note the fitted orientation of the seal in the cover.

3 Clean the seal location in the timing cover as far as possible. Also, check for any sharp edges which may damage the new seal, either during fitting or in service.

4 Genuine Honda seals are supplied pre-greased, so there is no need to lubricate the seal beforehand. If fitting a non-genuine seal the seal should be oiled before fitting.

5 Offer the new seal into position and drive it home until it bottoms out on the oil pump. If the timing cover has been removed, the seal can be tapped home easily using a tube or socket of roughly the same outside diameter as the seal **(see illustrations)**. If the timing cover is still fitted, there is limited working room to tap the seal home, and it may have to be pressed in with a suitable blunt instrument.

6 Refit the crankshaft pulley as described in Section 6.

Transmission end

7 Remove the flywheel as described in Section 15.

8 Using a suitable claw tool, extract the oil seal, but take care not to damage the seal housing. Alternatively, carefully drill a small hole in the seal, then fit a self-tapping screw

14.2 Removing the seal with the timing chain cover removed

14.5a Start by firmly pressing the seal into position and then...

14.5b...and then tap the seal fully home

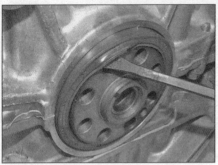

14.8 With care a small prybar can be used to remove the seal

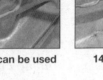

14.11a Offer the seal into position...

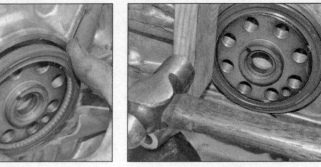

14.11b...and tap it home using a block of wood

and pull out the seal **(see illustration)**. As it is removed, note the fitted orientation of the seal, and its fitted depth.

9 Clean the seal location as far as possible. Also, check for any sharp edges which may damage the new seal, either during fitting or in service.

10 Genuine Honda seals are supplied pre-greased, so there is no need to lubricate the seal beforehand. If fitting a non-genuine seal the seal should be oiled before fitting.

11 Offer the new seal into position, and tap it home to the fitted depth noted previously (Honda specify the seal should be 0.2 mm to a maximum of 1.2 mm below the surface of the engine block). If possible, use a tube or socket of roughly the same outside diameter as the seal – failing this, work around the seal, tapping it progressively home with a

blunt instrument to make sure the seal isn't damaged **(see illustrations)**.

12 Refit the flywheel described in Section 15.

15 Flywheel/driveplate – removal, inspection and refitting

Removal

1 Remove the transmission as described in Chapter 7A or Chapter 7B.

2 On manual transmission models remove the clutch assembly as described in Chapter 6.

3 Mark the position of the flywheel/driveplate in relation to the crankshaft and then jam a

suitable tool into the ring gear teeth to prevent the flywheel/crankshaft from rotating as the bolts are removed **(see illustration)**.

4 Unscrew the retaining bolts and remove the flywheel from the rear flange of the crankshaft – take care not to drop the flywheel, as it is heavy **(see illustrations)**. On automatic transmission models recover the large washer.

Inspection

5 If on removal, the flywheel bolts are found to be in poor condition (stretched threads, etc) they must be renewed.

6 Inspect the starter ring gear on the flywheel or driveplate for any broken or excessively-worn teeth. If evident, the ring gear must be renewed. Honda do not supply the ring gear for either manual or automatic transmission models as a separate part, although they maybe available in the aftermarket.

7 On manual transmission models, the clutch friction surface on the flywheel must be carefully inspected for grooving or hairline cracks (caused by overheating). If these conditions are evident, it may be possible to have the flywheel surface-ground, however this work must be carried out by an engine overhaul specialist. If surface-grinding is not possible, the flywheel must be renewed.

Refitting

8 Check that the mating faces of the flywheel/driveplate and crankshaft are clean before refitting. Lubricate the threads of the retaining bolts with engine oil before they are screwed into position.

9 Locate the flywheel or driveplate onto the crankshaft, then insert and hand-tighten the bolts.

10 Prevent the flywheel/driveplate from turning as for removal. Tighten the bolts diagonally and progressively to the specified torque **(see illustration)**.

11 If removed, refit the starter motor as described in Chapter 5A. On manual transmission models, refit the clutch as described in Chapter 6, then refit the transmission as described in Chapter 7A or Chapter 7B.

15.3 Using a home made tool to lock the flywheel ring gear

15.4a Unscrew the flywheel bolts...

15.4b...and take off the flywheel

15.10 Tighten the bolts to the specified torque

16 Pilot bearing – renewal

1 The pilot bearing is located in the end of the crankshaft on manual transmission models. It supports the end of the transmission input shaft. Whenever the transmission is removed (such as when the clutch is being renewed), the pilot bearing should be checked for wear.

2 Remove the transmission as described in Chapter 7A.

3 The pilot bearing can be accessed through the centre of the flywheel (see illustration). Turn the bearing by hand, and check it for roughness, excess play, or any other sign of wear.

4 The bearing is press-fitted into the end of the crankshaft, and the only way to remove it is by using a suitable slide hammer and blind bearing puller (see illustration).

5 The new bearing should be lightly oiled, then tapped home to the shoulder inside the crankshaft, using a socket or tube which bears on the new bearing's outer race.

6 Refit the transmission as described in Chapter 7A.

17 Engine/transmission mountings – inspection and renewal

General

1 The engine/transmission mountings seldom require attention, but broken or deteriorated mountings should be renewed immediately, or the added strain placed on the driveline components may cause damage or wear.

2 While separate mountings may be removed and refitted individually, if more than one is disturbed at a time – such as if the engine/transmission unit is removed from its mountings – they must be reassembled and their fasteners tightened in the position marked on removal.

3 On reassembly, the complete weight of the engine/transmission unit must not be taken by the mountings until all are correctly aligned with the marks made on removal. Tighten the engine/transmission mounting fasteners to their specified torque wrench settings.

Inspection

4 During the check, the engine/transmission unit must be raised slightly, to remove its weight from the mountings.

5 Raise the front of the vehicle, and support it securely on axle stands. Position a jack under the sump, with a large block of wood between the jack head and the sump, then carefully raise the engine/transmission just enough to take the weight off the mountings.

 Warning: DO NOT place any part of your body under the engine when it is supported only by a jack.

16.3 The pilot bearing

6 Check the mountings to see if the rubber is cracked, hardened or separated from the metal components. Sometimes the rubber will split right down the centre.

7 Check for relative movement between each mounting's brackets and the engine/transmission or body (use a large screwdriver or lever to attempt to move the mountings). If movement is noted, lower the engine and check that the mounting bolts are secure.

Renewal

Note: *If the mountings are removed as part of another procedure – transmission removal for example – then the upper and lower torque rods should only be fully tightened when all the other mountings are in position.*

Right-hand mounting torque rod

8 Remove the refrigerant line bracket bolt and move it to the side.

17.9a Remove the body bolt and then remove the...

17.9c Note the location of the bolt with the damper weight fitted and then...

16.4 Removing the pilot bearing

9 Unbolt and remove the main torque rod to body bolt and then remove the two torque rod to engine bolts (see illustrations). Dispose of the bolts – they must be replaced.

10 Refit the mounting with new bolts. Tighten the torque rod to engine bolts to the specified torque first and then tighten the main torque rod to body bolt to the specified torque.

Right-hand mounting

11 Remove the upper torque rod as described above.

12 Jack up and support the front of the vehicle (see *'Jacking and vehicle support'* in the Reference chapter). Remove the engine undershield.

13 Support the weight of the engine from below. Use a large piece of wood between the jack head and the sump, to spread the load, and just take the weight of the engine.

17.9b... engine bolts

17.9d...remove the torque rod

17.14a Unbolt the earth connection

17.14b Remove the bolts...

17.14c...and lift off the mounting

17.15a Remove the bolts and...

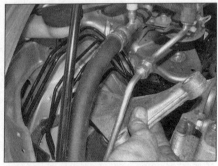

17.15b...and remove the stiffener bracket

14 Unbolt the earth strap in front of the mounting, and move it clear. Remove the single nut and the two bolts – dispose of the nut and bolts as they must be replaced **(see illustrations)**.

15 Unbolt the main body mounting stiffener **(see illustrations)**. Manoeuvre the stiffener around the brake lines and AC hoses – there is just enough room available. Dispose of the bolts they must be replaced.

16 Remove the two bolts and then remove the main flexible mounting from the body **(see illustration)**.

17 Refit the main flexible body mounting and support bracket. If marks were made prior to removal, align the mounting and then tighten the mounting and bracket to the specified torque.

18 Refit the mounting bracket loosely, using new nuts where specified. If alignment marks were made prior to removal, lower the engine and align the mounting with the marks. Tighten the nuts/bolt to the specified torque on completion.

19 Refit the torque rod, using new bolts and tighten the bolts to the specified torque.

20 The remainder of refitting is a reversal of removal.

Left-hand mounting

21 Jack up and support the front of the vehicle (see 'Jacking and vehicle support' in the Reference chapter). Remove the engine undershield.

22 Support the weight of the transmission from below **(see illustration)**. Use a large piece of wood between the jack head and the transmission, to spread the load, and just take the weight of the engine.

23 Remove the air cleaner assembly as described in Chapter 4A.

24 Disconnect the battery as describe in Chapter 5A Section 3.

25 Remove the cover from the engine control unit (ECU) disconnect the wiring plugs and then unbolt and remove the ECU.

26 Unbolt and then remove the ECU mounting bracket.

27 Release the fusebox from the support bracket.

28 Unbolt and remove the stiffener form the top of the flexible mounting **(see illustration)**.

29 Make alignment marks between the mounting and the body and between the mounting and the transmission. Where fitted unbolt the earth cable and then remove the

17.16 Remove the main flexible mounting bolts

17.22 Support the engine/transmission from below

17.28 Remove the stiffener plate

17.30 Remove the bolts and lift off the mounting

17.31 Removing the bracket from the transmission

the two nuts and single bolt from the top of the transmission. Dispose of the nuts – they must be replaced.

30 Remove the flexible mounting to body bolts. Lift the mounting from the studs on the transmission and remove it **(see illustration)**. Dispose of the bolts – they must be replaced. Alternatively the main bracket can be unbolted from the flexible mounting if required.

31 If required the bracket base (on the transmission) can now be unbolted and removed **(see illustration)**. If removed, dispose of the bolts – they must be replaced.

32 Where removed refit the bracket base to the transmission, using new bolts tightened to the specified torque. Refit the mounting loosely and align it with the previously made marks. Tighten the bolts to the specified torque and lower the transmission using the jack.

33 The remainder of refitting is a reversal of removal.

Rear mounting (torque rod)

34 To remove the engine rear mounting, apply the handbrake, then jack up the front of the car and support it on axle stands (see '*Jacking and vehicle support*' in the Reference chapter). Remove the engine undershield.

35 Removing the rear mounting will only allow the engine to move on its remaining mountings, so providing they are in sound condition, removing the rear mounting will not leave the engine dangerously unsupported.

36 To separate the mounting, unscrew and remove the through bolt and then remove the two mounting bolts from the transmission **(see illustration)**. Dispose of the bolts – they must be replaced.

37 If required the transmission mounted bracket can now be unbolted and removed. Remove the three bolts and dispose of them – they must be replaced.

38 Refitting is a reversal of removal, but fully tighten the mounting to transmission bolts before tightening the subframe bolt to the specified torque.

17.36a Remove the bolts and...

17.36b...remove the torque rod

Chapter 2 Part C
2.2 litre diesel engine in-car repair procedures

Contents

Section number

Balancer shafts – removal, inspection and refitting 14
Balancer/oil pump drive chain – removal, inspection and refitting . . 13
Camshaft, followers and hydraulic tappets – removal, inspection and
   refitting 9
Compression and leakdown tests – description and interpretation. . 2
Crankshaft oil seals – renewal 17
Crankshaft pilot bearing – removal and refitting 16
Crankshaft pulley – removal and refitting. 5
Cylinder head – removal and refitting. 10
Cylinder head cover – removal and refitting. 4
Engine/transmission mountings – inspection and renewal 20

Section number

Flywheel – removal and refitting. 15
General Information 1
Oil cooler – removal and refitting 18
Oil filter/oil cooler/water pump housing – removal and refitting. . . . 19
Oil pump – removal, inspection and refitting 12
Sump – removal and refitting 11
Timing chain – removal, inspection and refitting 7
Timing chain case – removal and refitting 6
Timing chain tensioner and sprockets – removal, inspection and
   refitting 8
Top Dead Centre – Locating. 3

Degrees of difficulty

Easy, suitable for novice with little experience ✎	**Fairly easy,** suitable for beginner with some experience ✎	**Fairly difficult,** suitable for competent DIY mechanic ✎	**Difficult,** suitable for experienced DIY mechanic ✎	**Very difficult,** suitable for expert DIY or professional ✎

Specifications

General

Engine code	N22A
Capacity	2.204 cc
Bore	85 mm
Stroke.	97.1 mm
Direction of crankshaft rotation	Clockwise (viewed from the right-hand side of vehicle)
Firing order.	1-3-4-2 (No. 1 cylinder at the timing chain end)
Output:	
Maximum power.	103 kW @ 4000 rpm
Maximum torque	340 Nm @ 2000 rpm
Compression ratio	16.7 : 1
Compression pressure:	
Minimum	24 bar
Maximum difference between any two cylinders	2 bar

Camshaft

	Standard	Maximum
Endfloat:		
Standard.	0.05 to 0.15 mm	
Maximum	0.16 mm	
Camshaft to carrier clearance:	**Standard**	**Maximum**
No 1 journal	0.0012 to 0.0027 mm	0.08 mm
Nos 2, 3, 4 and 5 journals.	0.0020 to 0.0035 mm	0.10 mm
Total runout:		
Standard.	0.03 mm	
Maximum	0.04 mm	
Cam lobe height:		
Inlet A	36.433 mm	
Inlet B	35.362 mm	
Exhaust.	35.539 mm	

Balancer shafts

Shaft endfloat.	0.07 to 0.14 mm (standard)	0.15 mm (maximum)

Lubrication system

Oil pump output (@ 4000 rpm)	52.2 litres per minute	
Minimum oil pressure at 80°C:		
Idle speed.	1.1 bar	
3000 rpm	4.1 bar	
Piston cooling jets open at.	1.2 bar	
Oil pump:	**Standard**	**Service limit**
Inner to outer rotor clearance.	0.02 to 0.14 mm	0.19 mm
Pump housing to outer rotor clearance	0.15 to 0.21 mm	0.23 mm
Pump housing to to rotor endfloat	0.020 to 0.055 mm	0.10 mm

Valves

Clearance	Hydraulic – self adjusting	
Valve to guide clearance:	**Standard**	**Service limit**
Inlet	0.020 to 0.050 mm	0.08 mm
Exhaust.	0.050 to 0.080 mm	0.11 mm
Valve spring length (inlet and exhaust).	43.54 mm	

Cylinder head

Height	114.95 to 115.05 mm	
Maximum warpage.	0.05 mm	

Cylinder block

Maximum warpage.	0.07 mm	
Bore diameter (nominal)	84.976 to 85.027 mm	
Bore diameter service limit	85.050 mm	

Piston and piston rings

	Standard	**Service limit**
Piston diameter (14 mm from base of the piston)		
Type A (marked on top of piston)	84.950 to 84.980 mm	84.920 mm
Type B (marked on top of piston)	84.940 to 84.970 mm	84.910 mm
Piston ring end gap (installed)	**Standard**	**Service limit**
Top ring.	0.15 to 0.25 mm	0.47 mm
Second ring.	0.50 to 0.65 mm	0.87 mm
Oil control ring	0.20 to 0.40 mm	0.62 mm
Piston ring groove clearance		
Top ring.	0.07 to 0.11 mm	0.12
Second ring	0.04 to 0.08 mm	0.10 mm
Oil control ring	0.02 to 0.06 mm	0.08 mm

Gudgeon pin

	Standard	**Service limit**
Pin to piston clearance.	0.0005 to 0.016 mm	0.026 mm
Pin diameter	29.995 to 30.000 mm	29.985 mm

Crankshaft and bearings

	Standard	**Service limit**
Crankshaft endfloat	0.15 to 0.35 mm	0.45 mm
Main bearing to journal clearance	0.021 to 0.045 mm	0.050 mm

Connecting rods

	Standard	**Service limit**
Big end free play	0.15 to 0.30 mm	0.40 mm
Big end bearing clearance	0.021 to 0.051 mm	0.060 mm

Torque wrench settings

	Nm	**lbf ft**
Baffle plate (lower engine block)	12	9
Balancer assembly (upper to lower clamp bolts)		
6 mm.	12	9
8 mm**	27	20
Balancer shaft/oil pump bolts	44	32
Balancer shaft/oil pump drive chain:		
Sprocket bolt**	83	61
Rear fixed guide bolts.	12	9
Tensioner blade pivot bolt	22	16
Tensioner mounting bolts	12	9
Camshaft bearing cap bolts:		
6 mm.	12	9
8 mm	22	16
Camshaft carrier (to cylinder head) bolts	12	9
Camshaft sprocket (exhaust) bolt**	118	87
Camshaft drive gear (exhaust)**	78	58

Torque wrench settings

	Nm	lbf ft
Camshaft drive gear (inlet) bolt**	78	58
Camshaft position sensor rotor (inlet) bolt	12	9
Connecting rod big-end cap bolts: **		
Stage 1	20	15
Stage 2	Angle tighten a further 90°	
Crankshaft position sensor pick up ring bolts	9	7
Crankshaft pulley bolt: **		
Stage 1 (new bolt or new crankshaft only)	34	25
Stage 1 (used bolt)	29	21
Stage 2 (all bolts)	Angle-tighten a further 90°	
Cylinder head M6 bolts	12	9
Cylinder head bolts (new block only): **		
Stage 1	49	36
Stage 2	Angle-tighten a further 100°	
Stage 3	Angle-tighten a further 100°	
Stage 4	Loosen all bolts and then follow new or old bolt sequence	
Cylinder head bolts (used bolts): **		
Stage 1	49	36
Stage 2	Angle-tighten a further 90°	
Stage 3	Angle-tighten a further 90°	
Stage 4	Angle-tighten a further 90°	
Cylinder head bolts (new bolts): **		
Stage 1	49	36
Stage 2	Angle-tighten a further 110°	
Stage 3	Angle-tighten a further 100°	
Stage 4	Angle-tighten a further 100°	
Cylinder head cover	12	9
Dipstick tube bolt	12	9
Engine-to-transmission bolts	64	47
Engine mountings:		
Left-hand mounting (transmission)		
Flexible mounting to body*	74	54
Mounting on transmission (nut/bolt)*	74	54
Rear mounting (torque rod)		
Subframe bolt*	103	76
Engine bracket bolts*	64	47
Right-hand mounting		
Torque rod to body bolt*	64	47
Torque rod to bracket bolt*	93	69
Torque rod stiffener plate bolts*	59	43
Bracket to engine nuts/bolts*	103	76
Stiffener plate*	59	43
Flexible mount to body*	64	47
Flywheel bolts**	118	87
Fuel pump driveshaft bolts:		
6 mm	12	9
8 mm	22	16
Lower engine block main bearing ladder:		
8 mm bolts	22	16
10 mm (main bearing cap bolts):		
Stage 1	29	21
Stage 2	Angle-tighten a further 58°	
Oil cooler bolts	12	9
Oil filter/oil cooler/waterpump housing bolts	44	32
Oil pump housing bolts	12	9
Oil pressure relief valve	39	29
Piston cooling jet bolts	22	16
Sump drain plug	39	29
Sump bolts	12	9
Timing chain cover bolts	12	9
Timing chain tensioner:		
Pivot bolt**	22	16
Cover plate bolts	12	9
Mounting bolts	12	9

* Use new nuts/bolts

** Oil the threads and under the head of the bolt

1 General Information

How to use this Chapter

1 This Part of Chapter 2 describes the repair procedures that can reasonably be carried out on the engine while it remains in the vehicle. If the engine has been removed from the vehicle and is being dismantled as described in Part D, any preliminary dismantling procedures can be ignored.

2 Note that, while it may be possible physically to overhaul items such as the piston/connecting rod assemblies while the engine is in the car, such tasks are not usually carried out as separate operations. Usually, several additional procedures are required (not to mention the cleaning of components and oilways); for this reason, all such tasks are classed as major overhaul procedures, and are described in Part D of this Chapter.

3 Part D describes the removal of the engine/transmission from the car, and the full overhaul procedures that can then be carried out.

Engine description

4 The 2.2 i-CTDi is Honda's first in-house developed diesel engine. The engine is a water-cooled four-stroke compression-ignition (diesel) unit, of four-cylinder in-line DOHC (Double Over Head Camshaft) layout with four valves per cylinder, mounted transversely at the front of the vehicle, with the clutch and transmission on its left-hand end. Pendulum-type engine mountings, an acoustic engine cover and a full engine compartment undershield minimise engine noise.

5 All major engine housings and covers are castings of aluminium alloy, care being taken to design an engine in which each of these components is as rigid as possible in the interests of smooth and quiet operation with minimal friction, while still being compact and light in weight. Cast-iron cylinder liners are cast into the closed-deck cylinder block/crankcase, offset in the interests of further reducing noise and vibration.

6 The crankshaft runs in five shell-type main bearings, thrustwashers to control crankshaft endfloat being fitted on each side of No. 4 main bearing's upper half. Instead of individual caps securing each of the main bearings, a single large cast aluminium alloy lower crankcase/bearing ladder is bolted to the underside of the cylinder block/crankcase. The connecting rods rotate on horizontally-split bearing shells at their big-ends.

7 High strength 'cracked' connecting rods are used in which rod and cap are forged as a single unit during the manufacturing process, and then cracked apart so that rod and cap align precisely, one way only, without the need for locating dowel pins. This minimises connecting rod weight and size, while also increasing rigidity and long-term durability thanks to increased fatigue resistance.

8 The pistons are attached to the connecting rods by gudgeon pins which are secured by circlips in the connecting rod small-end eyes. The aluminium alloy pistons are fitted with three piston rings: two compression rings and an oil control ring, and have low-friction coatings on the thrust faces of their skirts. After manufacture, the cylinder bores and piston skirts are measured and classified into two grades which must be carefully matched together to ensure the correct piston/cylinder clearance; oversizes are available to permit reboring.

9 The intake and exhaust valves – two of each per cylinder – are closed by coil springs; they operate in guides which are shrink-fitted into the cylinder head, as are the valve seat inserts. The exhaust ports in the cylinder head are siamesed, each pair of valves serving a single port. A passage in the exhaust manifold and through the cylinder head left-hand end allows exhaust gases to be fed to the EGR system components at the front of the cylinder head without using bulky external conduits and associated heat shielding.

10 The inlet manifold has a continuously-variable swirl control valve fitted. The inlet manifold's lower (swirl) tract (the only one to which the EGR valve is connected) supplies air to the intake valves opened by the higher-lift A-cam lobes through ports whose tangential orientation is designed to maximise axial swirl in the combustion chamber. The intake manifold's upper (secondary) tract, supplying those intake valves opened by the milder B-cam lobes, is opened and closed by vacuum acting on the butterfly-type valve, controlled by the engine management system Electronic Control Unit (ECU) via the solenoid valve acting on information from the swirl valve position sensor. The combination of different port geometry, dissimilar cam lobes and the enhanced swirl generated by the swirl valve system provides very high swirl in the combustion chamber at low engine speeds, reducing gradually as engine speed increases to give the ideal combustion environment at all times. This, referred to by Honda as the 'intelligent combustion control system', improves combustion efficiency so that the engine can use a relatively low compression ratio (and thus escape the friction, vibration and noise penalties of higher compression pressures) while still producing power outputs comparable with sales rivals.

11 Driven from the crankshaft right-hand end by a single-row (simplex) roller timing chain, the exhaust camshaft drives the intake camshaft by gears on the right-hand end of each; a spring-loaded anti-backlash gear in the exhaust camshaft drive gear minimises noise due to any backlash in the gear teeth. The entire length of the timing chain is supported by fixed guides along its front and upper rear runs and it is tensioned by a pivoting tensioner blade on its lower rear run; both guide and tensioner blades incorporate plastic bearing surfaces to minimise noise. A tensioner assembly acting on the tensioner blade's free end uses the lubrication

system's hydraulic pressure automatically to tension the chain, while a spring-loaded ratchet prevents the tensioner plunger from retracting when the engine is switched off and oil pressure is relaxed.

12 Each camshaft operates eight valves via finger followers; a roller in each follower minimises losses due to friction at the point of contact with the cam lobe. Each follower bears on the tip of the valve stem at its inner end and on a hydraulic tappet at its outer end, thus using the lubrication system's hydraulic pressure to automatically take up any free play in the components between each camshaft lobe and its respective valve stem and so eliminating the need for routine checking and adjustment of the valve clearances. Each camshaft rotates in five bearings that are line-bored directly in the camshaft carrier and the (bolted-on) bearing caps; this means that the bearing caps are not available separately from the camshaft carrier and must not be interchanged with caps from another engine. The use of a single, separate, bolted-on camshaft carrier (as opposed to five pairs of separate bearing caps) adds to the rigidity of the cylinder head assembly. Camshaft endfloat is controlled by the No. 4 bearing caps.

13 The Lanchester harmonic balancer assembly mounted in the sump uses two bobweights on each of two counter-rotating shafts mounted below and equidistant from the crankshaft axis which rotate at twice crankshaft speed to cancel out the unbalanced secondary inertia forces inherent in any in-line four-cylinder engine. Driven from the crankshaft right-hand end by a single-row (simplex) roller chain, the rear shaft drives the front by gear teeth to ensure that the two are always exactly correctly timed in relation to the movement of the crankshaft and pistons. The oil pump is mounted on the right-hand end of the front (driven) shaft, the load this imposes ensuring that noise due to backlash in the gear teeth is minimised. The shafts rotate in bearings machined in the oil pump housing at their right-hand ends and next to the drive gears, and in horizontally-split bearing shells located between their bobweights. Similarly to the camshaft drive/timing chain, the balancer/oil pump drive chain is supported along its rear run by a fixed plastic guide and by a plastic-faced tensioner blade along its front run. A tensioner assembly acting on the tensioner blade's free end uses the lubrication system's hydraulic pressure to tension the chain, while a spring-loaded ratchet prevents the tensioner plunger from retracting when the engine is switched off and oil pressure is relaxed.

14 The flywheel is of the dual-mass type, to further reduce noise and vibration in the driveline, especially during cruising and under acceleration. The assembly consists of an inner and an outer flywheel joined by high and low torsion springs to form a torsional vibration damper which protects the transmission gear teeth and synchro-rings from torque fluctuations, to which diesel engines are particularly prone.

15 The common-rail injection system's fuel pump is mounted on the left-hand end of the cylinder head and driven by gear from the exhaust camshaft. A spring-loaded anti-backlash gear in the camshaft drive gear minimises noise due to any backlash in the gear teeth.

16 The braking system vacuum pump is bolted to the left-hand face of the timing chain case, at the rear right-hand end of the cylinder block. It is driven by the timing chain from the crankshaft.

17 The water pump is mounted in the oil filter/oil cooler housing bolted to the front right-hand end of the cylinder block and is driven with the steering pump, alternator and air conditioning compressor by a flat 'polyvee' type auxiliary drivebelt from the crankshaft pulley. An automatic spring-loaded tensioner eliminates any need for drivebelt maintenance beyond a periodic check of its condition.

Lubrication system

18 The forced, wet-sump lubrication system uses an eccentric-rotor trochoid pump, which is mounted on the right-hand end of the front (driven) balancer shaft and draws oil through a strainer located in the sump. The pump forces oil through a full-flow paper element-type filter located in the oil filter/oil cooler housing bolted to the front right-hand end of the cylinder block – an oil cooler is fitted to the oil filter mounting, so that clean oil entering the engine's galleries is cooled by the main engine cooling system. From the filter, the oil is pumped into a main gallery in the cylinder block/crankcase, from where it is distributed to the crankshaft (main bearings) and cylinder head. Pressure is controlled by a spring-loaded pressure relief valve located in the pump housing.

19 The big-end bearings are supplied with oil via internal drillings in the crankshaft. Each piston crown is cooled by a spray of oil directed at its underside by a jet. These jets are fed by passages off the crankshaft oil supply galleries, with spring-loaded valves to ensure that the jets open only when there is sufficient pressure to guarantee a good oil supply to the rest of the engine components.   The cylinder head is provided with extensive oil galleries to ensure constant oil supply to the camshaft bearings and hydraulic tappets. An oil control orifice is inserted into the cylinder block's top surface, at the rear, on the timing chain end, to control the flow of oil to those components.   While the crankshaft, camshaft and balancer shaft bearings and the hydraulic tappets receive a pressurised supply, the camshaft lobes and valves are lubricated by splash, as are all other engine components.

Valve clearances – general

20 This engine employs hydraulic tappets which use the lubricating system's oil pressure to automatically take up the clearance in the components between each camshaft lobe and its respective valve stem. Therefore, there is no need for regular checking and adjustment

of the valve clearances, but it is essential that only good-quality oil of the recommended viscosity and specification is used in the engine and that this oil is always changed at the recommended intervals.

21 On starting the engine from cold, there will be a slight delay while full oil pressure builds-up in all parts of the engine, especially in the tappets; the valve components, therefore, may well 'rattle' for about 10 seconds or so and then quieten. This is a normal state of affairs and is nothing to worry about, provided that all tappets quieten quickly and stay quiet.

22 After the vehicle has been standing for several days, the valve components may 'rattle' for longer than usual, as nearly all the oil will have drained away from the engine's top end components and bearing surfaces. While this is only to be expected, care must be taken to avoid high speed running until all the tappets are refilled with oil and operating normally. With the vehicle stationary, hold the engine at no more than a fast idle speed (maximum 2000 rpm) for 10 to 15 seconds, or until the noise ceases. Do not run the engine at more than 3000 rpm until the tappets are fully recharged with oil and the noise has ceased.

Repair operations precaution

23 When working on this engine, read through the entire procedure first, look at the car and engine at the same time, and establish whether you have the necessary tools, equipment, skill and patience to proceed. Allow considerable time for any operation, and be prepared for the unexpected.

24 Because of the limited access, many of the engine photographs appearing in this Chapter were, by necessity, taken with the engine removed from the vehicle.

⚠️ **Warning: It is essential to observe strict precautions when working on the fuel system components of the engine, particularly the high-pressure side of the system. Before carrying out any engine operations that entail working on, or near, any part of the fuel system, refer to the special information given in Chapter 4B.**

25 Operations with engine in vehicle
a) *Removal and refitting of the timing chain, sprockets and tensioner components.*
b) *Removal and refitting of the camshafts, cam followers and hydraulic tappets.*
c) *Removal, refitting and overhaul of the cylinder head.*
d) *Removal and refitting of the sump.*
e) *Removal and refitting of the oil pump, drive chain, sprockets and tensioner components.*
f) *Removal and refitting of the balancer shafts.*
g) *Renewal of the crankshaft oil seals.*
h) *Removal and refitting of the connecting rods and pistons.*
i) *Renewal of the engine mountings.*
j) *Flywheel – removal, inspection and refitting.*

2 Compression and leakdown tests – description and interpretation

Compression test

Note: *A compression tester specifically designed for diesel engines must be used for this test. The aid of an assistant will be required.*

1 When engine performance is down, or if misfiring occurs which cannot be attributed to a fault in the fuel system, a compression test can provide diagnostic clues as to the engine's condition. If the test is performed regularly it can give warning of trouble before any other symptoms become apparent.

2 A compression tester is connected to an adapter which screws into the glow plug hole or is fitted to the injector seating. It is unlikely to be worthwhile buying such a tester for occasional use, but it may be possible to borrow or hire one – if not, have the test performed by a garage.

3 Observe the following points:
a) *The battery must be in a good state of charge.*
b) *The air filter must be clean.*
c) *The engine must be at normal operating temperature.*

4 Switch off the ignition.

⚠️ **Warning: Before disconnecting any part of the high-pressure side of the fuel system, read the warnings concerning de-pressurising the fuel system given in Chapter 4B.**

5 If the compression tester adapter fits the injector seatings, all four injectors should be removed and the sealing washer recovered. Note that the sealing washers and the high-pressure pipes must also be renewed if the injectors are removed (Chapter 4B). The simplest way to perform a compression test is to remove the glow plugs (Chapter 5C). If the glow plugs are removed the injectors must be disabled to prevent them spraying fuel into the combustion chamber as the test is carried out. Honda specify the use of the Honda Diagnostic System (HDS) tester to switch off the injectors. The obvious alternative is simply to disconnect the injector wiring connectors and to reconnect them afterwards. This, however, will almost certainly cause a fault code to be logged so that the engine management Malfunction Indicator warning Lamp (MIL) will illuminate, and/or the glow plug warning lamp will flash. Several drive cycles should clear the fault once the vehicle is running again. However there is always the possibility that the vehicle will need to be taken to a Honda dealer or suitably equipped garage for the fault code to be erased. Another alternative is to connect a remote starter switch to the starter motor. These are widely available.

6 With the injectors or glow plugs removed and the injectors disabled, as applicable, fit the compression tester to No. 1 cylinder.

7 Have the assistant crank the engine on the starter motor; there is no need to hold the accelerator pedal down because a diesel engine's air intake is not throttled. After one or two revolutions, the compression pressure should build-up to a maximum figure and then stabilise. Record the highest reading obtained.

8 Repeat the test on the remaining cylinders, recording the pressure in each.

9 All cylinders should produce very similar pressures, greater than the minimum specified. The actual compression pressures measured are not as important as the balance between cylinders; a difference of more than 2 bars between any cylinder(s) and the others indicates a fault. Note that the compression should build-up quickly in a healthy engine; low compression on the first stroke, followed by gradually-increasing pressure on successive strokes, indicates worn piston rings. A low compression reading on the first stroke, which does not build-up during successive strokes, indicates leaking valves or a blown head gasket (a cracked head could also be the cause). Deposits on the undersides of the valve heads can also cause low compression.

10 The cause of poor compression is less easy to establish on a diesel engine than on a petrol one. Introducing oil into the cylinders ('wet' testing) is not recommended because of the much smaller volume of the combustion chamber (risk of hydraulic lock).

11 A low reading from two adjacent cylinders is almost certainly due to the head gasket having blown between them; the presence of coolant in the engine oil will confirm this.

12 If the compression reading is unusually high, the combustion chambers are probably coated with carbon deposits.

13 On completion of the test, refit the glow plugs and re-enable the injectors or refit the injectors, using new high-pressure pipes and copper sealing washers, as applicable (Chapter 4B or Chapter 5C).

Leakdown test

14 A leakdown test measures the rate at which compressed air fed into the cylinder is lost. It is an alternative to a compression test, and in many ways it is better, since the escaping air provides easy identification of

2.15 A cylinder leakage test will require a suitable compressed air supply

where pressure loss is occurring (piston rings, valves or head gasket).

15 The equipment needed for leakdown testing is unlikely to be available to the home mechanic. If poor compression is suspected, have the test performed by a suitably-equipped garage **(see illustration)**.

3 Top Dead Centre – Locating

General

1 Top Dead Centre (TDC) is the highest point in its travel up-and-down its cylinder bore that each piston reaches as the crankshaft rotates. While each piston reaches TDC both at the top of the compression stroke and again at the top of the exhaust stroke, for the purpose of timing the engine, TDC refers to the No. 1 piston position at the top of its compression stroke.

2 No. 1 piston and cylinder are at the right-hand (timing chain) end of the engine. Note that the crankshaft rotates clockwise when viewed from the right-hand side of the car. There are no timing marks on the exterior of the engine.

Locating TDC

3 Remove the glow plugs (Chapter 5C) to make the engine easier to turn.

4 It is best to rotate the crankshaft using a spanner applied to the crankshaft pulley bolt;

however, it is possible also either to select top gear and (with the front of the vehicle jacked up) to turn the right-hand front roadwheel, or to use the starter motor to bring the engine close to TDC, then finish with a spanner.

5 Remove the cylinder head cover (Section 4) so that the timing marks on the exhaust camshaft sprocket and the two camshaft drive gears can be seen. Rotate the crankshaft until the camshaft timing marks align as described in Section 6, paragraph 2. No. 1 cylinder will then be at TDC on the compression stroke.

6 TDC for any of the other cylinders can now be located by rotating the crankshaft clockwise 180° at a time and following the firing order.

4 Cylinder head cover – removal and refitting

Note: *The removal of the cylinder head cover is in itself a very simple and easy procedure. However, the fuel injectors must be removed first; not only is this difficult, but all four fuel injector high-pressure pipes and copper sealing washers must be renewed. The cover gaskets must also be renewed and liquid gasket (Honda Part No. 08C70-K0334M or equivalent) must be available on reassembly.*

Removal

1 Remove the air filter assembly as described in Chapter 4B, and then unscrew the four retaining nuts and remove the engine cover.

⚠️ *Warning: Before disconnecting any part of the high-pressure side of the fuel system, read the warnings concerning depressurising the fuel system in Chapter 4B.*

2 Remove the fuel injectors (see Chapter 4B). Take precautions to prevent dirt falling into the combustion chambers.

3 From the front left-hand end of the cylinder head unscrew the bolt securing the fuel supply pipe and then unscrew the two bolts securing the fuel return line to the cylinder head **(see illustrations)**.

4 Unbolt the turbocharger boost control solenoid valve from the left-hand end of the cylinder head cover **(see illustration)**.

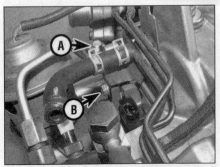

4.3a Remove the bolt (A) and then remove the upper bolt (B), followed by...

4.3b...the lower bolt form the fuel return line

4.4 Unbolt the turbocharger boost control solenoid

4.5 Remove the vacuum line retaining bolts

4.6 Remove the breather hose

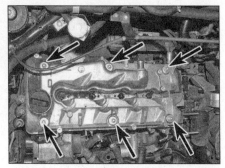

4.8 Remove the retaining nuts and lift off the cover

5 From the rear of the cylinder head cover unscrew the two bolts securing the vacuum line assembly to the rear of the cylinder head cover **(see illustration)**.

6 Disconnect the breather hose from the rear of the cylinder head cover **(see illustration)**.

7 Release the large wiring conduit from its mountings and secure all wiring, hoses and fuel lines clear of the cylinder head cover so that it can be withdrawn.

8 Unscrew the retaining nuts and remove the cylinder head cover **(see illustration)**. Peel off and discard the gaskets. Check the condition of the sealing washers under each of the cover retaining nuts and renew as necessary.

Refitting

9 Thoroughly clean the mating surfaces of the cylinder head and cover. Clean any oil or old gasket material and sealant from the cover grooves. Thoroughly clean the injector wells and the passages around the injector clamp mountings in the cover and the injector wells in the cylinder head. Be careful not to allow dirt and debris to fall into the combustion chambers.

10 Fit the new gaskets, ensuring that each is correctly seated in the cover grooves **(see illustration)**.

11 Apply liquid gasket to the points shown, to ensure that there are no oil leaks from the cylinder head cover/timing chain case/cylinder head intersection **(see illustration)**. The cylinder head cover must be installed within five minutes of applying the liquid gasket; if this time limit is exceeded, the sealant must

be wiped off completely and new liquid gasket applied.

12 Ensuring that the gaskets are not dislodged, place the cover on the cylinder head, slide the cover very slightly back-and-forth to settle the gaskets, then refit the sealing washers and nuts. Tighten the nuts by hand only at first.

13 Working in a diagonal sequence from the centre outwards and in two or three stages, tighten the cover retaining nuts to the specified torque **(see illustration)**.

14 Refit the wiring conduit to its mountings and reconnect any wiring or hoses that were disconnected on removal.

15 Reconnect the breather hose and refit the vacuum line assembly to the rear of the cylinder head cover and tighten the bolts.

16 Refit the turbocharger boost control solenoid valve. Tighten its mounting bolts to their specified torque.

17 Refit the fuel return line and high-pressure pipe clamp. Tighten the mounting bolts to their specified torques.

18 Refit the fuel injectors as described in Chapter 4B.

19 Make a final check that all hoses, pipes and wiring have been reconnected and secured. Refit the acoustic engine cover and securely tighten its retaining nuts.

20 When Honda's own liquid gasket has been used to seal a joint, note the following:
a) Where applicable, wait at least 30 minutes before filling the engine with oil.
b) Do not run the engine for at least three hours.

5 Crankshaft pulley – removal and refitting

Note: *The crankshaft pulley retaining bolt is extremely tight; the aid of an assistant will be required. Be very careful to avoid the risk of personal injury through trapped fingers, etc.*

Removal

1 Apply the handbrake, jack up the front of the vehicle and support it on axle stands (see 'Jacking and vehicle support' in the Reference chapter). Remove the right-hand road wheel and then remove the engine undershield.

2 Remove the auxiliary drivebelt as described in Chapter 1B.

3 Slacken the crankshaft pulley retaining bolt. This is extremely tight; first, ensure that the vehicle is securely supported. Only use good-quality, close-fitting tools for this job – if something slips, it may result in injury. For extra leverage, use a long-handled breaker bar (knuckle bar). Use one of the following methods to prevent crankshaft rotation:
a) *The Honda service tools for this task are a pulley holder (Part No. 07JAB-0010400) which has a 50 mm hexagon to engage with the centre of the pulley, a long handle (Part No. 07JAB-001020B) to fit over the holder and a deep 19 mm socket (Part No. 07JAA-001020A) slim enough to fit through the holder. These tools can be purchased from Honda or from an after market tool supplier.*

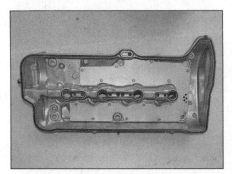

4.10 Seat the new gaskets in the grooves in the cover

4.11 Apply liquid gasket at the points shown

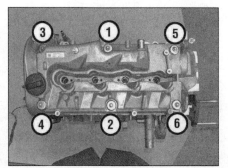

4.13 Tighten the cover bolts to the specified torque

5.4 Note the crankshaft woodruff key

5.5a Clean both surfaces

5.5b Apply clean oil to the threads...

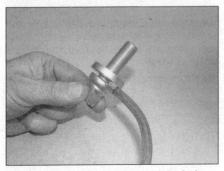

5.5c...and under the head of the bolt

b) *Remove the starter motor (Chapter 5A) and have an assistant insert a wide-bladed screwdriver in the teeth of the starter ring gear.*

c) *If the engine is removed from the vehicle, a home-made holding tool can be fabricated to lock the flywheel (see Section 15).*

4 Unscrew the pulley bolt and washer, then remove the pulley from the crankshaft. Note the locating key; this should not be loose in its keyway, as it also locates the camshaft drive/ timing chain and balancer/oil pump drive chain drive sprocket **(see illustration)**. Be careful not to dislodge it as the pulley is removed.

Refitting

5 Check that the woodruff key is firmly in place in the crankshaft keyway. Wipe clean the lips of the crankshaft hand oil seal, then clean the boss on the pulley's inboard face which passes through the oil seal lips; polish away any burrs or raised edges which might damage the seal lips. Similarly clean the pulley retaining bolt thread in the crankshaft, the pulley's central bore which fits over the crankshaft and the seating for the retaining bolt washer in the pulley's outboard face. Clean the retaining bolt washer's seating face, then apply a film of clean oil to the threads and under the head of the retaining bolt **(see illustrations)**.

6 Fit the pulley to the crankshaft, aligning the pulley keyway with the locating key and being careful not to damage the seal lips as the pulley enters them, then refit the retaining bolt and washer.

7 Lock the crankshaft using the method used on removal, and tighten the pulley retaining bolt to the specified first stage torque.

Note: *A different torque applies if a new bolt or crankshaft is being used – see the Specifications at the begining of this Chapter.*

8 Once the bolt has been tightened to the Stage 1 torque, tighten it through its specified Stage 2 angle, using a socket and extension bar **(see illustrations)**.

9 Fit a new auxiliary drivebelt (Chapter 1B Section 20).

10 The remainder of refitting is a reversal of removal.

6 Timing chain case – removal and refitting

Note: *Liquid gasket (Honda Part No. 08C70-K0334M or equivalent) must be available on reassembly.*

Removal

1 Remove the windscreen cowl panel and then remove the lower cowl panel as described in Chapter 12.

2 Remove the cylinder head cover (Section 4).

3 If further dismantling, such as removal/ refitting of the timing chain, valve gear and/ or cylinder head, is intended, bring the engine to TDC. No. 1 cylinder is correctly positioned when all four cam lobes are pointing away from No. 1 cylinder's valves and when the UP marks on the exhaust camshaft sprocket and the intake camshaft driven gear are both in the twelve o'clock position. The four double-line marks etched in both drive gear

5.8a Tighten the bolt to the stage 1 setting and then make two marks 90° apart and tighten...

5.8b...the bolt until the marks align

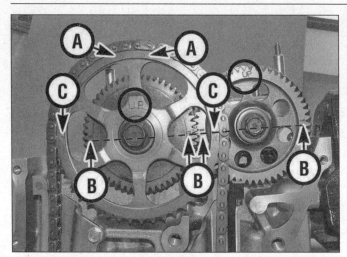

6.3 No. 1 cylinder is at TDC on the compression stroke when the UP marks and punch marks (A) are both at the top, while the double line marks (B) and the lines (C) are are aligned through the bolt centres

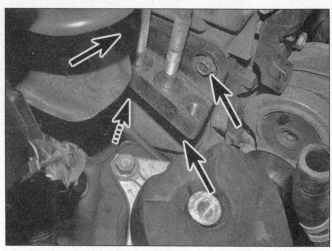

6.8 Remove the bracket from the chain cover

rims must be lined up through the drive gear retaining bolt centres, with, at the centre, the punch-marked tooth on the exhaust camshaft drive gear aligned exactly between the two punch-marked teeth on the intake camshaft driven gear. The two punch marks in the rim of the exhaust camshaft sprocket must also be in the twelve o'clock position **(see illustration)**. Rotate the crankshaft clockwise (see Section 3) until the marks are aligned.

4 If not already done, jack up the front of the vehicle and support it securely on axle stands (see '*Jacking and vehicle support*' in the Reference chapter) and then remove the right-hand road wheel. Remove the engine compartment undershield.

5 Remove the auxiliary drivebelt as described in Chapter 1B.

6 The engine right-hand mounting must now be removed. Support the weight of the engine using a trolley jack and block of wood beneath the sump. Remove the torque rod and then remove the mounting as described in Section 20.

7 Remove the crankshaft pulley as described in Section 5.

8 Unscrew the four bolts, then remove the bracket from the chain cover **(see illustration)**.

9 Unscrew the seventeen bolts – three along the bottom, five up the front edge and nine up the rear edge – securing the timing chain case **(see illustration)**. Note that certain bolts are shouldered to locate the case as well as retaining it.

10 Remove the timing chain case **(see illustration)**. Use a hammer and a block of wood or a soft-faced mallet to try and break the seal by tapping all around the edge of the timing chain case, then carefully prise it away. It is a thin and delicate casting, easily damaged or even broken if carelessly handled, and the

liquid gasket used on assembly sticks tight. Do not lever between the mating surfaces; these are easily scratched or gouged and will leak oil if badly marked. Leverage points are provided at the top and bottom of the front edge and at the rear next to the turbocharger oil feed union and braking system vacuum pump. Insert a large flat-bladed screwdriver and gently prise the timing chain case away at these points first. At the same time, a hammer and a block of wood can be used to jar the cases apart. As soon as the case is removed, cover the sump opening to keep dirt out.

11 Renew the crankshaft right-hand oil seal (Section 17) if any oil leakage is evident.

Refitting

12 Thoroughly clean the mating surfaces of the timing chain case, the cylinder head, the cylinder block and the sump. Clean any oil or old gasket material and sealant from the

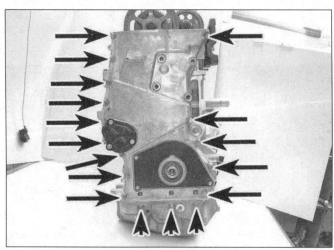

6.9 The timing chain cover bolts

6.10 Removing the timing chain cover

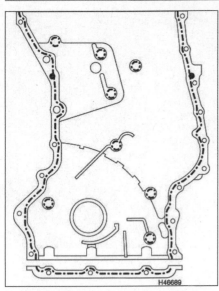

6.14 Apply a 3 mm bead of sealant as shown.

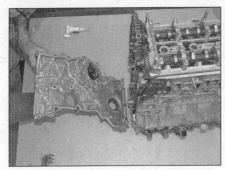

6.15a Refit the timing chain cover...

6.15b...and insert the shouldered bolts to locate it correctly

mating surfaces and from the bolt holes and threads. Be careful not to allow dirt to fall into the sump. Degrease the surfaces completely before applying sealant.

13 The timing chain case must be installed within five minutes of applying the liquid gasket – if this time limit is exceeded, the sealant must be wiped off completely and new liquid gasket applied.

14 Apply liquid gasket in a continuous thin bead (3 mm diameter approx) evenly along the length of the chain case's front, rear and bottom mating surfaces so that the bead goes around the inside edges of the bolt holes **(see illustration)**. Also apply a bead to the eight supporting bosses on the inside of the chain case. Also apply liquid gasket to the four points on the cylinder head/block/lower crankcase mating surfaces. Apply a small blob of liquid gasket to those bolt holes in the cylinder head/block/lower crankcase which pass through to the outside, and to the three bolt holes along the bottom edge of the timing chain case, to ensure that there are no oil

leaks from the threads. Do not apply sealant to blind holes in the castings.

15 Offer up the timing chain case so that the crankshaft end passes through the oil seal and align the bottom outer edge of the timing chain case on that of the sump while the upper end is tilted back clear of the cylinder block and head to avoid spreading sealant everywhere. Carefully tilt the chain case into place and refit the shouldered bolts to hold it **(see illustrations)**.

16 Refit all the bolts, tightening them by hand only at first until the timing chain case is correctly settled in position. Tighten first the three bolts along the bottom edge, then, working in a diagonal sequence from the centre outwards and in two or three stages, tighten the retaining bolts to the specified torque **(see illustration)**. Wipe off any excess sealant from the sump and chain case mating surfaces.

17 Refit the engine right-hand mounting's timing chain case/cylinder head and block bracket, tightening the four bolts to the specified torque.

18 Refit the crankshaft pulley (Section 5).

19 Refit the engine right-hand mounting intermediate bracket and torque rod as described in Section 20, using new nuts and bolts where specified and tightening the bolts and nuts to the torques specified.

20 Fit a new auxiliary drivebelt (Chapter 1B).

21 Refit the cylinder head cover (Section 4)

22 The remainder of reassembly is the reverse of the removal procedure.

23 When Honda's own liquid gasket has been used to seal a joint, note the following:

a) *Where applicable, wait at least 30 minutes before filling the engine with oil.*

b) *Do not run the engine for at least three hours.*

7 Timing chain – removal, inspection and refitting

Note: The timing chain is to be kept away from magnetic fields to prevent any chance of interference in the operation of the crankshaft position sensor.

Removal

1 Remove the timing chain case (as described in Section 6).

2 Loosely refit the crankshaft pulley and rotate it anti-clockwise to compress the tensioner until the lockplate moves back far enough for a 2.5 mm diameter pin to be inserted into the holes in the lockplate and tensioner body. We used a Torx key **(see illustrations)**.

3 Rotate the crankshaft pulley clockwise again to hold the pin in place and lock the tensioner, then unscrew its two mounting bolts and withdraw the timing chain tensioner. Remove the pulley.

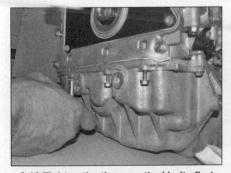

6.16 Tighten the three vertical bolts first

7.2a Rotate the crankshaft pulley anti-clockwise to compress the timing chain tensioner until the hole in the lockplate aligns with the hole in the tensioner body...

7.2b... and then insert a 2.5 mm diameter pin through the plate and into the tensioner, to lock it in the compressed position

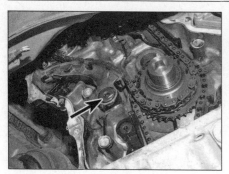

7.4 Remove the pivot bolt and then remove the tensioner blade

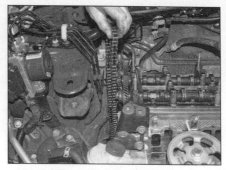

7.5 Removing the timing chain

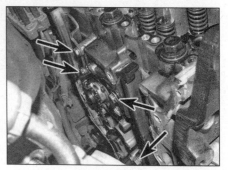

7.6 Unscrew the bolts and withdraw the fixed guides

4 Unscrew the pivot bolt and withdraw the tensioner blade **(see illustration)**.

5 Disengage the timing chain from the sprockets and withdraw it **(see illustration)**.

6 If the cylinder head is to be removed, the timing chain's fixed guides must first be removed from its upper rear (two bolts) and front (two bolts) **(see illustration)**.

Inspection

7 Make a careful examination of the links of the chain, looking for signs of wear or

7.11a Refit the timing chain's fixed guides to the upper rear...

damage on the sideplates as well as on the rollers. Check the whole length of the chain looking for links that are looser or tighter than the others, or kinked. If there is any sign of binding, excessive side play or kinking in the chain, it must be renewed.

8 Renew the timing chain regardless of its apparent condition if the engine has covered a high mileage, or if the chain has sounded noisy with the engine running. It is good practice to renew the chain and sprockets as a matched set.

9 Examine the teeth on the camshaft and crankshaft sprockets for any sign of wear or damage such as chipped or hooked teeth. If there is any such sign on any of the sprockets, all sprockets and the timing chain should be renewed as a set.

10 Examine the chain guides and tensioner blade for signs of wear or damage to their contact faces, renewing any that are badly marked.

Refitting

11 If removed, refit the timing chain's fixed guides. Tighten the mounting bolts securely **(see illustrations)**.

12 Check that No. 1 cylinder is at TDC on

the compression stroke by ensuring that the timing marks are aligned as described below. Temporarily refit the crankshaft pulley, if necessary, to rotate the crankshaft; rotate the camshafts by means of an open-ended spanner applied to the hexagons formed between the lobes of Nos. 1 and 4 cylinders. If either camshaft has to be rotated very far to bring its marks into alignment, first rotate the engine 45° backwards (anti-clockwise) using a spanner or socket on the crankshaft pulley. This positions the pistons half-way up the bores, ensuring there is no danger of accidental valve-to-piston contact. Once the camshafts are correctly positioned, return the crankshaft to TDC. The marks must be as follows:

a) *The punch mark stamped on the crankshaft sprocket must align with the arrow mark cast on the cylinder block; the keyway in the crankshaft end will point straight up, in the twelve o'clock position* **(see illustration)**.

b) *The timing marks on the camshaft sprockets and gears must align as described in Section 6, paragraph 2.*

13 One side of the timing chain has three gold-coloured sideplates, two of which are on

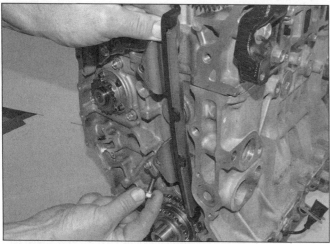

7.11b ...and front runs. Tighten the bolts securely

7.12 The punch mark on the crankshaft sprocket must align with the mark cast on the block. Note that the keyway in the crankshaft will point straight up in the twelve o'clock position

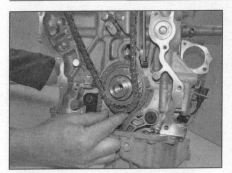

7.13a Refit the timing chain so that, with the chain's front run taut and...

7.13b...ensuring that the coloured link fits over the punch mark on the tooth of the crankshaft drive sprocket

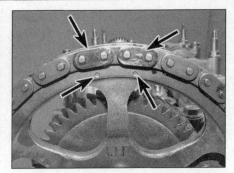

7.13c The coloured links must fit over the punch marked teeth on the exhaust camshaft sprocket

7.14 Oil the pivot bolt when refitting the timing chain tensioner blade

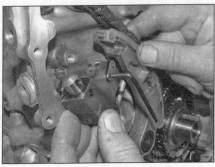

7.15a Engage the tensioner plunger on the blade...

7.15b...and then refit and tighten the mounting bolts

adjacent links while the third is some distance away. Fit the timing chain to the crankshaft sprocket so that the single coloured sideplate fits over the punch-marked tooth, then, keeping the chain taut on its front run, fit it first to the exhaust camshaft sprocket, so that the coloured sideplates fit over the punch-marked teeth, then to the braking system vacuum pump sprocket **(see illustrations)**.

14 Refit the tensioner blade to the timing chain's lower rear run. Apply a film of clean oil to the threads of the blade's pivot bolt, then tighten the pivot bolt to the specified torque **(see illustration)**.

15 Refit the tensioner, engaging its plunger on the tensioner blade's free end. Tighten the

mounting bolts to the specified torque **(see illustrations)**.

16 Hold the tensioner blade against the tensioner plunger and remove the locking pin from the tensioner **(see illustration)**. Check that the timing marks and coloured sideplates are correctly aligned and that the tensioner plunger has taken up any slack in the chain.

17 Temporarily refit the crankshaft pulley and rotate the crankshaft two full turns (720°) clockwise and check that the crankshaft and camshaft timing marks come back into alignment as previously described. If not, repeat the procedure until the timing chain is correctly refitted.

18 Refit the timing chain case as described in Section 6.

8 Timing chain tensioner and sprockets – removal, inspection and refitting

Tensioner – chain case in situ

Note: *Liquid gasket (Honda Part No.08C70-K0334M or equivalent) must be available on reassembly.*

Removal

1 Jack up the front of the vehicle and support it securely on axle stands (see '*Jacking and vehicle support*' in the Reference chapter Section 5). Release the two securing clips and prise back the wheel arch liner section of the engine compartment undershield to reach the timing chain tensioner cover plate.

2 In theory, the tensioner can be removed without disturbing any component other than its cover plate. However, in practice, it would be best to remove the cylinder head cover and bring the engine to TDC, No 1 firing (see Section 6, paragraph 2) before removing the tensioner. This permits checking on reassembly that the valve timing has not jumped a tooth while the tensioner has been removed.

3 Unscrew its three retaining bolts and withdraw the tensioner's cover plate **(see illustration)**. Use a hammer and a block of wood or a soft-faced mallet break the seal by tapping the cover plate, then carefully prise

7.16 Hold the tensioner blade against the plunger and remove the locking pin to release the tensioner

8.3 Unscrew the retaining bolts and remove the timing chain tensioner's cover plate

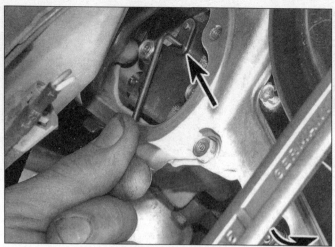

8.4 Rotate the crankshaft pulley anti-clockwise to compress the timing chain tensioner, until the hole in lockplate aligns with the hole in the tensioner body

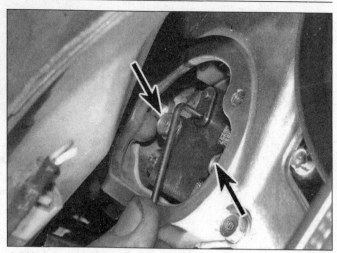

8.5 Unscrew the mounting bolts to remove timing chain tensioner

it away from the timing chain case; the liquid gasket used on assembly sticks tight. Do not lever between the mating surfaces; these are easily scratched or gouged and will leak oil if badly marked.

4 Rotate the crankshaft pulley anti-clockwise to compress the tensioner until the lockplate moves back far enough for a 2.5 mm diameter pin to be inserted into the holes in the lockplate and tensioner body **(see illustration)**.

5 Rotate the crankshaft pulley clockwise again to hold the pin in place and lock the timing chain tensioner, then unscrew its two mounting bolts and withdraw the tensioner **(see illustration)**.

Caution: Do not rotate the crankshaft while the tensioner is removed, or the timing chain may drop clear of the crankshaft sprocket and so lose correct valve timing. This will necessitate the removal of the timing chain.

6 Thoroughly clean the mating surfaces of the timing chain case and the tensioner's cover plate. Clean any oil or old gasket material and sealant from the mating surfaces and from the bolt holes and threads. Be careful not to allow dirt and debris to fall into the engine. Degrease the surfaces completely before applying sealant.

Inspection

7 Check that the tensioner is undamaged and that its oilways are clear. Compress the plunger by hand until the locking pin can be withdrawn and press in the exposed end of the ratchet, against its spring pressure, to enable the plunger to be moved in and out through its full range of movement. It should move smoothly, with no sticking or jerkiness. Do not allow the plunger to fly out uncontrolled, or the assembly may be damaged.

8 With the ratchet released, check that the plunger can extend but cannot be compressed back into the tensioner body.

Check also that there is no sign of wear along the plunger's length.

9 If there is any evidence of wear or damage, the tensioner must be renewed.

Refitting

10 Disengage the ratchet and compress the plunger as far as possible into the tensioner, then release the ratchet and fit the locking pin into the holes in the lockplate and tensioner body.

11 Carefully release the plunger to hold the pin in place and lock the tensioner.

12 Refit the tensioner, engaging its plunger on the tensioner blade's free end.

13 Tighten the mounting bolts to the specified torque.

14 Hold the tensioner blade against the tensioner plunger and remove the locking pin from the tensioner. Rotate the crankshaft two full turns (720°) clockwise until the timing marks align again. Check that the timing marks are correctly aligned as described in Section 7 and that the tensioner plunger has taken up any slack in the chain.

15 Apply a continuous thin bead of liquid gasket evenly around the cover plate's mating surface so that the bead is around the inside edges of the bolt holes. Also apply a small blob of liquid gasket to the bolt holes in the timing chain case to ensure that there are no oil leaks from the threads. The cover plate must be installed within five minutes of applying the liquid gasket – if this time limit is exceeded, the sealant must be wiped off completely and new liquid gasket applied.

16 Refit the cover plate, tightening its bolts to the specified torque.

17 The remainder of reassembly is the reverse of the removal procedure.

18 When Honda's own liquid gasket has been used to seal a joint, note the following:
a) *Where applicable, wait at least 30 minutes before filling the engine with oil.*
b) *Do not run the engine for at least three hours.*

Tensioner – chain case removed

Removal

19 Proceed as described in Section 7, paragraphs 1 to 3.

Inspection

20 Check that the tensioner is undamaged and that its oilways are clear. Compress the plunger by hand until the locking pin can be withdrawn and press in the exposed end of the ratchet, against its spring pressure, to enable the plunger to be moved in and out through its full range of movement. It should move smoothly, with no sticking or jerkiness. Do not allow the plunger to fly out uncontrolled, or the assembly may be damaged.

21 With the ratchet released, check that the plunger can extend but cannot be compressed back into the tensioner body. Check also that there is no sign of wear along the plunger's length.

22 If there is any evidence of wear or damage, the tensioner must be renewed.

Refitting

23 Proceed as described in Section 7.

Exhaust camshaft sprocket

Note: *Great care must be taken to keep the timing chain taut during this procedure. If it is allowed to drop clear of the crankshaft sprocket, valve timing will be lost and it will be necessary to remove the timing chain case in order to restore it.*

Removal

24 Remove the cylinder head cover as described in Section 4.

25 Jack up the front of the vehicle and support it securely on axle stands (see 'Jacking and vehicle support' in the Reference chapter). Depending on the work about to be undertaken, remove the right-hand or both front roadwheels. Remove the engine compartment undershield.

26 Bring the engine to TDC, No. 1 firing. (See Section 3).

27 Use a marker pen to mark the timing chain's sideplate that fits over either (or both) of the punch-marked teeth at the top of the exhaust camshaft sprocket.

28 Remove the tensioner as described in paragraphs 3 to 6 above.

29 Hold the camshaft by means of an open ended spanner applied to the hexagons formed between the lobes of Nos. 1 and 4 cylinders, then slacken the sprocket retaining bolt. Unscrew the bolt and withdraw the sprocket from the camshaft, noting the locating Woodruff key; this should not be slack, as it still locates the camshaft drive gear, but if loose it should be secured with sticky tape.

30 Use a length of wire to fix the timing chain on to the sprocket, and secure the sprocket and chain to an adjacent component to hold the sprocket out of the way and the timing chain taut, especially on the front run, to prevent it from dropping off the crankshaft sprocket.

Inspection

31 See Section 7.

Refitting

32 If the timing chain was separated from the sprocket, refit it so that the marked sideplate(s) fit(s) over the punch-marked teeth. Fit the sprocket to the camshaft end, engaging it on the key and keeping the timing chain's front run as taut as possible. Check that the valve timing marks are aligned as described in Section 6.

33 Apply a film of clean oil to the threads and under the head of the sprocket retaining bolt. Hold the camshaft with an open-ended spanner and tighten the bolt to the specified torque.

34 Refit the timing chain tensioner as described above.

35 The remainder of reassembly is the reverse of the removal procedure.

Crankshaft sprocket

Caution: The removal of the timing chain and balancer/oil pump drive chain's crankshaft drive sprocket requires the removal first of the timing chain case and of the sump, the latter entailing the removal of the front suspension subframe. This leaves the engine/transmission unit hanging on the hoist in the engine compartment and located only by its left-hand mounting. The home mechanic may prefer to consider removing the engine/transmission complete and then removing the sump.

Removal

36 Remove the timing chain (Section 7).

37 Bolt a lifting eye to the right-hand end of the cylinder head. Support the timing chain

8.42 The crankshaft drive sprocket locating key has a tapered end which must point inwards

end of the engine from above, with an engine hoist or crane.

38 Remove the sump as described in Section 11.

39 Remove the balancer/oil pump drive chain (Section 13). As the drive sprocket slides off the crankshaft, note the locating key; remove this it and keep it with the sprocket.

Inspection

40 See Section 7.

Refitting

41 The keyway in the crankshaft end must point straight up, in the twelve o'clock position; temporarily refit the crankshaft pulley, if necessary, to rotate the crankshaft into position.

42 Refit the balancer/oil pump drive chain (Section 13). As the drive sprocket slides on to the crankshaft, ensure that the locating key is refitted with its tapered end pointing inwards and that the sprocket is pressed firmly back against the shoulder on the crankshaft end **(see illustration)**.

43 The remainder of reassembly is the reverse of the removal procedure.

---

9 Camshaft, followers and hydraulic tappets – removal, inspection and refitting

Camshafts, followers and hydraulic tappets

Note: *If the exhaust camshaft sprocket, either camshaft's drive gear or the camshaft position sensor rotor is to be removed, minimise the risk of damage by slackening its retaining bolt before unbolting the camshaft bearing caps, when the camshaft is easier to hold.*

Note: *In theory it is possible to proceed by removing the exhaust camshaft sprocket (Section 8) and then removing the camshafts. However, such a method carries a high risk of losing the valve timing if the timing chain comes off the crankshaft sprocket. We recommend the procedure below; although*

9.6 Withdraw each follower and tappet in turn and place them in a marked container filled with clean engine oil

apparently longer, it is far more certain of correct reassembly.

Removal

1 Remove the timing chain as described in Section 7.

2 Working in the reverse of the tightening sequence, slacken the camshaft bearing cap bolts two turns at a time, to relieve the pressure evenly and in several gradual stages **(see illustration 9.18)**.

Caution: If the bearing cap bolts are slackened carelessly, a cap may break. If any of the caps are broken, the complete cam carrier assembly must be renewed, with the cylinder head. The caps are matched to the carrier, which is not available separately from the cylinder head.

3 Withdraw the camshaft bearing caps, noting how they are numbered (intake or exhaust and bearing number) and marked with arrows pointing to the timing chain end. Note also the correct fitted positions of the locating dowels. If the dowels are loose, remove them and store them with their bearing caps.

4 Carefully lift out the camshafts.

5 Unscrew the four retaining bolts (intake camshaft side) and withdraw the camshaft carrier from the cylinder head. Again, note the correct fitted positions of the locating dowels.

6 Obtain sixteen small, clean plastic containers, and label them for identification. Alternatively, divide a larger container into compartments. Withdraw each follower and hydraulic tappet in turn and place it in its respective container, which should then be filled with clean engine oil **(see illustration)**. Do not interchange the followers and tappets, and do not allow the hydraulic tappets to lose oil, or they will take a long time to refill with oil on restarting the engine.

Inspection

7 Examine the camshaft bearing surfaces and cam lobes for signs of wear ridges and scoring. Check that the lobes are not significantly worn below the height specified; when checking the intake camshaft, note the locations of the higher-lift A-cam lobes and

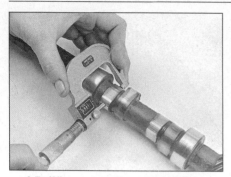

9.7a When measuring camshaft lobe height...

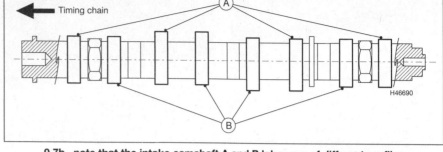

9.7b...note that the intake camshaft A and B lobes are of different profiles

the milder B-cam lobes (see illustrations). Renew the camshaft if any of these conditions are apparent.

8 To check camshaft runout and endfloat, first remove the camshaft carrier assembly, remove the followers and hydraulic tappets, then refit the carrier, the camshafts and their bearing caps to the cylinder head. Tighten the camshaft bearing cap bolts to the specified torque, as described below. Check the camshaft endfloat with a dial gauge bearing on the sprocket end of the camshaft. Push the camshaft fully away, then zero the gauge. Push the camshaft fully the other way, and check the endfloat; Honda state that if it is beyond the service limit specified, the cylinder head must be renewed and the endfloat rechecked. If it is still excessive, then the camshaft must be renewed.

9 Use a Plastigauge to check the camshaft bearing journal-to-bearing clearance. Unbolt the bearing caps, wipe clean the camshafts and refit them. Lay a strip of Plastigauge on each bearing journal, refit the bearing cap and tighten the camshaft bearing cap bolts to the specified torque. Unbolt the bearing caps again and measure the width of each strip at its widest point to determine the clearance. If any of the clearances are beyond the specified service limit then the worn components – either the camshaft or the camshaft carrier/cylinder head assembly must be renewed.

10 Examine the condition of the bearing surfaces both on the camshaft journals and in the camshaft carrier. If any of the bearing

9.12 Hydraulic tappets must be primed in clean engine oil before refitting

surfaces are worn or damaged, the components concerned will need to be renewed.

11 Examine the follower rollers and their tips which bear on the camshaft lobes and valve stems; look for any sign of wear and scoring, and for rollers which do not rotate easily and smoothly when spun. Check the hydraulic tappets and their bores in the cylinder head for signs of wear or damage. If the engine's valvegear has sounded noisy, particularly if the noise persists after initial start-up from cold, then there is reason to suspect a faulty hydraulic tappet. If any hydraulic tappet is thought to be faulty or is visibly worn it should be renewed.

Refitting

12 On reassembly, disengage each tappet from its follower, place the tappet in a container of clean engine oil of the recommended viscosity and specification and pass a slim rod through

9.13 Liberally oil the hydraulic tappets and cam followers on refitting

the hole in its ball end. Press down on the check ball in the tappet's valve assembly, then release; carry on pumping until no more air bubbles (or dirty oil) emerge and the tappet is fully-charged with clean engine oil (see illustration).

13 Carefully refit the tappet to its follower, liberally oil the cylinder head tappet bore and the follower and refit them; some care will be required to enter the tappets squarely into their bores (see illustration). Ensuring that each tappet is refitted to its original bore and is the correct way up, repeat on the remaining tappets to charge and refit all the tappets and followers to the cylinder head.

14 Refit the locating dowels (if removed), and refit the camshaft carrier to the cylinder head, engaging it on the dowels and noting the arrow mark which must point to the timing chain end. Refit the four retaining bolts and tighten them to the specified torque (see illustrations).

9.14a When refitting the camshaft carrier to the cylinder head, ensure that the locating dowels fit correctly...

9.14b...and that the arrow mark points to the timing chain end

9.14c Tighten the camshaft carrier to cylinder head bolts

9.15 The camshaft bearing journals and lobes MUST be properly lubricated on reassembly. A special assembly (paste shown here) is available

9.16a When refitting the camshafts...

9.16b...note the identifying IN or EX marks to ensure correct location and...

15 Wipe clean the camshaft bearing journals and lobes and the bearing surfaces in the cam follower assembly supports. Liberally oil all bearing surfaces, the camshaft lobes and the followers **(see illustration)**. If any components were removed from either camshaft, they should now be refitted; their retaining bolts should be tightened fully only once the camshaft has been bolted down securely.
Caution: Failure to adequately lubricate the camshafts and related components can cause serious damage to shaft journals and bearing surfaces during the first few seconds after engine start-up.

16 Refit the camshafts to the cylinder head; the camshafts are clearly identified by being marked IN or EX, as appropriate **(see illustrations)**. The UP marks on the exhaust camshaft sprocket and the intake camshaft driven gear must both be in the twelve o'clock position, while the four double-line marks etched in both drive gear rims must line up through the drive gear retaining bolt centres, with, at the centre, the punch-marked tooth on the exhaust camshaft drive gear aligned exactly between the two punch-marked teeth on the intake camshaft driven gear; two punch marks in the rim of the exhaust camshaft sprocket must also be in the twelve o'clock position **(see illustration)**.

17 Lubricating their bearing surfaces with clean engine oil and ensuring that the locating dowels are in position, refit the camshaft bearing caps and their bolts, tightening the bolts by hand only at this stage. Check

9.16c...align the punch marked tooth on the exhaust camshaft drive gear between the two punch marked teeth on the intake camshaft driven gear, with the UP marks and punch marks at the top

9.17a Lubricate the bearing surfaces and do not forget the locating dowels (A) when refitting the camshaft bearing caps...

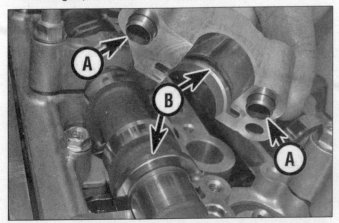

9.17b...ensure the No. 4 bearing caps fit over the endfloat control flange (B) on the camshafts

9.17c Use identifying marks and arrows to ensure the correct location of the bearing caps

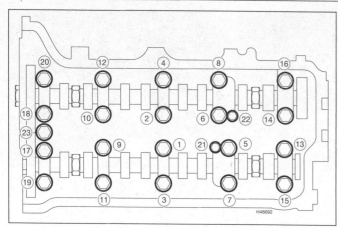

9.18 The camshaft bearing caps TIGHTENING sequence

9.21 Hold the camshaft with an open-ended spanner to unscrew the exhaust camshaft left-hand drive gear bolt

carefully that the locating dowels enter squarely into their respective bores. Each intake camshaft cap is numbered I1 to I5 in ascending order from timing side to flywheel end, the exhaust camshaft caps are similarly numbered E1 to E5 and each cap is marked with an arrow which must point towards the timing chain end **(see illustrations)**.

18 Working in sequence, evenly and progressively tighten the retaining bolts to draw the bearing caps and camshafts squarely down into place. Once the bearing caps are in contact with the head, go around in sequence and tighten the retaining bolts to the specified torque **(see illustration)**. As the camshafts are drawn down into place, check that the sprocket/driven gear timing marks remain in alignment. Once the camshaft bearing cap/carrier bolts are all fully and correctly tightened, tighten the bolts securing the exhaust camshaft sprocket, either camshaft's drive and driven gears and the camshaft position sensor rotor (as applicable).
Caution: If the bearing cap bolts are carelessly tightened, a cap might break.
19 Refit the timing chain (Section 7).

Camshaft drive gears

Removal

20 Remove the cylinder head cover (Section 4).
21 Hold the camshaft with an open-ended

spanner, then slacken the drive gear retaining bolt **(see illustration)**.
22 Remove the camshafts, as described above. Remove the drive gear (and the sprocket, in the case of the exhaust camshaft right-hand gear). Recover the Woodruff key if applicable.

Inspection

23 Renew the drive gear if its teeth are marked or damaged in any way. Do not attempt to dismantle the exhaust camshaft drive gears in the event of suspected wear or damage to the spring-loaded anti-backlash mechanism; they are available only as a complete components.

Refitting

24 Refit the drive gear to the camshaft end.
25 Refit the camshafts, as described above. Once the camshaft bearing cap/carrier bolts are all fully and correctly tightened, apply a film of clean oil to the threads and under the head of the drive gear retaining bolt, hold the camshaft with an open-ended spanner and tighten the bolt to the specified torque. Proceed with refitting the timing chain (Section 7).
26 Refit the cylinder head cover (Section 4).

Fuel pump driveshaft

Removal

27 Remove the fuel pump (Chapter 4B).

28 Remove the camshafts, as described above.
29 Unscrew the three mounting bolts and withdraw the driveshaft assembly, noting the arrow mark pointing to the timing chain end **(see illustrations)**.

Inspection

30 Renew the driveshaft if its teeth are marked or damaged in any way or if its bearing shows signs of free play or rough and jerky rotation when spun. Do not attempt to dismantle the driveshaft; it is available only as a single component.

Refitting

31 Refit the driveshaft assembly to the cylinder head so that the arrow mark points towards the timing chain end. Tighten the mounting bolts to the specified torques.
32 Refit the camshafts, as described above.
33 Refit the fuel pump (Chapter 4B).

Intake camshaft position sensor rotor

Removal

34 Remove the cylinder head cover (Section 4).
35 Hold the camshaft by means of an open-ended spanner applied to the hexagon formed over No. 4 cylinder, then slacken the rotor retaining bolt **(see illustration)**. Unscrew the bolt and withdraw the rotor from the camshaft, noting the locating key.

9.29a Note the arrow mark pointing to the timing chain end. Unscrew three bolts...

9.29b...and remove the fuel pump driveshaft assembly

9.35 Hold the camshaft with an open-ended spanner and unscrew the inlet camshaft position sensor rotor bolt

Inspection

36 Renew the rotor if it is marked or damaged in any way.

Refitting

37 Refit the rotor to the camshaft end, engaging its locating key in the camshaft keyway. Hold the camshaft with an open ended spanner and tighten the rotor retaining bolt to the specified torque.

38 Refit the cylinder head cover (Section 4).

10 Cylinder head –
removal and refitting

Note: *Allow the engine to cool completely before beginning this procedure.*

Removal

1 Disconnect the battery negative lead, and position the lead away from the battery (see *Disconnecting the battery* 5A).

2 Unscrew the four retaining nuts and remove the acoustic engine cover.

3 Remove the air cleaner assembly (Chapter 4B).

4 Remove the engine undershield.

5 Drain the cooling system (Chapter 1B).

6 Remove the auxiliary drivebelt (Chapter 1B).

7 Disconnect the fuel feed hose from the fuel pump. Plug the hose and cap the pump union to prevent the loss of fuel and the entry of dirt **(see illustrations)**.

10.7a Disconnect fuel feed hose from the fuel pump...

10.7b...and then plug the hose and cap the pump union to prevent entry of dirt into system

8 From the rear left-hand end of the cylinder head cover disconnect the fuel return hose. Plug the hose and cap the pipe union. Disconnect the braking system vacuum servo hose from the vacuum line assembly to the rear of the cylinder head cover **(see illustrations)**.

9 Disconnect the radiator top hose from the outlet at the left-hand front of the cylinder block **(see illustration)**.

10 From the rear left-hand end of the cylinder head cover disconnect the heater hoses **(see illustration)**. Mark the hoses and unions so that they can be reconnected correctly.

11 Remove the inlet manifold (Chapter 4B). (If no work is to be carried out on the cylinder head, the head can be removed complete

with manifold once the preliminary operations have been carried out).

12 Remove the exhaust manifold (Chapter 4B). (If no work is to be carried out on the cylinder head, the head can be removed complete with manifold once the preliminary operations have been carried out).

13 Remove the EGR cooler bypass valve (Chapter 4C).

14 Disconnect its wiring and unbolt the fuel pump (Chapter 4B).

15 From the left-hand end of the cylinder head, disconnect the wiring from the engine coolant temperature sensor and the camshaft position sensor, then disconnect the wiring from the turbocharger boost control solenoid valve **(see illustrations)**.

10.8a Disconnect the fuel return hose...

10.8b...and the vacuum hose

10.9 Disconnect the radiator top hose

10.10 Mark the heater hoses and unions so that they are reconnected correctly, and not swapped over, on refitting

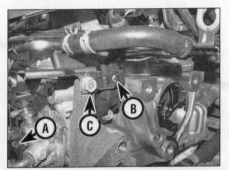

10.15a Undo the coolant temperature sensor (A) and the camshaft position sensor (B), then undo the vacuum line assembly mounting bolt (C)...

10.15b...and disconnect the wiring from the turbocharger boost control solenoid valve

10.16 Undo the vacuum line assembly mounting bolt on the rear of the cylinder head

10.21 Cylinder head bolt SLACKENING sequence. Note the 6 mm bolts (A)

16 Unbolt the vacuum line assembly mounting bolts from the left-hand end and rear of the cylinder head and cover **(see illustration)**. Ensure that hoses, wiring and pipes are secured clear of the cylinder head and cannot hinder its removal.

17 Remove the cylinder head cover (Section 4).

18 Remove the timing chain case (Section 6).

19 Remove the timing chain (Section 7).

20 Remove the camshafts, followers and hydraulic tappets (Section 9).

21 Unscrew the two 6 mm bolts (A) from the right-hand end of the cylinder head. Working in sequence, progressively slacken the cylinder head bolts by a one-third of a turn at a time until all ten are fully slackened **(see illustration)**.

22 Lift the cylinder head off the engine, noting that two dowels are used at the front. If resistance is felt, don't prise between the head and block gasket mating surfaces. Instead, try to rock the head free, by inserting a blunt lever (such as a hammer handle) into the intake or exhaust ports **(see illustration)**.

23 Remove the head from the engine, and set it down on a clean, flat surface, supported on two wooden blocks so that the gasket surface does not touch – remember at all times to avoid damage to the gasket sealing surfaces and to the protruding valves and glow plug tips **(see illustrations)**. Recover the gasket but do not discard it yet – a new one must be fitted on reassembly and the original will serve to check that the correct thickness gasket has been supplied. Recover also the oil control orifice from the cylinder block's top surface, at the rear. Remove and discard its sealing O-ring – a new one must be fitted on reassembly.

24 Cylinder head dismantling and inspection procedures are covered in detail in Chapter 2D.

Preparation for refitting

25 The mating faces of the cylinder head and cylinder block/crankcase must be perfectly clean before refitting the head. Use a hard plastic or wood scraper to remove all traces of gasket and carbon. Also clean the piston crowns. Take particular care, as the soft aluminium alloy is damaged easily. Also, make sure that the carbon is not allowed to enter the oil and water passages – this is particularly important for the lubrication system, as carbon could block the oil supply to any of the engine components. Using adhesive tape and paper, seal the water, oil and bolt holes in the cylinder block/crankcase. To prevent carbon entering the gap between the pistons and bores, smear a little grease in the gap. After cleaning each piston, use a small brush to remove all traces of grease and carbon from the gap, then wipe away the remainder with a clean cloth. Clean all the pistons in the same way.

26 Check the mating surfaces of the cylinder block/crankcase and the cylinder head for nicks, deep scratches and other damage. If the damage is light, it may be possible to have the cylinder head refaced (see Chapter 2D).

27 If warpage of the cylinder head gasket surface is suspected, use a straight-edge to check it for distortion.

28 Clean the threads in the cylinder head bolt holes. Dirt, corrosion, sealant and damaged threads will affect torque values. Ensure that there is no water or oil in the bolt holes in the block – if this is not either sucked up or blown out, the resulting hydraulic pressure when the bolts are fitted may crack the block.

29 Check the cylinder head bolts for obvious signs of wear or damage; renew them all as a set if any such signs are visible. Measure the diameter of the threads of each bolt 50 mm and 55 mm from the tip; if a bolt has stretched so that its diameter is less than 12.5 mm at either of these points, it must be renewed

10.22 The oil filter/oil cooler/water pump housing racket provide good leverage points when removing cylinder head

10.23a Remove the cylinder head from the engine...

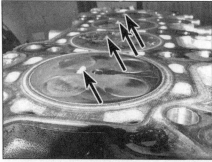

10.23b...but be careful of the protruding valves and glow plug tips when setting it down

10.29a Measure the diameter of the threads of each cylinder head bolt at 50 mm...

10.29b...and 55 mm from base. Renew the bolts if the diameter 12.5 mm or less

(see illustrations). Although Honda are happy to have bolts re-used as long as they pass this test, it is good practice to renew highly-stressed fasteners such as cylinder head bolts as a matter of course, irrespective of their apparent condition, whenever they are disturbed. These bolts are subject to significant pressure, and if one should fail during retightening, considerable extra expense and inconvenience will be incurred.

30 If new bolts are not being fitted, clean the threads of the old ones thoroughly.

Cylinder head gasket selection

31 On this engine, the cylinder head-to-piston clearance is controlled by fitting different thickness head gaskets. The piston protrusion is represented by the identifying letter and/or number of notches in the gasket next to the timing chain area **(see illustrations).** Select the new gasket which has the same thickness/ letter/number of notches as the original, unless new piston and connecting rod assemblies have been fitted or either gasket surface has been machined. In that case, the correct thickness of gasket required is selected by measuring the piston protrusions as follows

32 Mount a dial test indicator securely on the block so that its pointer can be easily pivoted between the piston crown and the block mating surface.

33 Ensure the piston is at exactly TDC, then zero the dial test indicator on the gasket surface of the cylinder block. Carefully move the indicator over No. 1 piston. Measure the piston protrusion on both the left- and right-hand sides **(see illustration).** Repeat this procedure on No. 4 piston.

34 Rotate the crankshaft 180° to bring Nos. 2 and 3 pistons to TDC. Measure the protrusions of Nos. 2 and 3 pistons, again taking two measurements for each piston. Once both pistons have been measured, rotate the crankshaft 180° to bring Nos. 1 and 4 pistons back to TDC.

35 Take the average of each piston's measurements and record the highest average protrusion found. Use the table below to select the appropriate gasket.

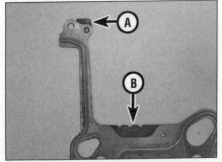

10.31a The cylinder head gasket thickness is shown by an identifying letter (A) and/or number of notches at (B)

Largest piston protrusion	Gasket letter	Notch in gasket	Gasket part number
0.485 to 0.535 mm	A	1	12251-RBD-E01
0.535 to 0.585 mm	B	2	12252-RBD-E01
0.585 to 0.635	C	0	12253-RBD-E01
0.635 to 0.685	D	3	12254-RBD-E01
0.685 to 0.735	E	4	12255-RBD-E01

10.31b Record the original gasket letter...

10.31c... along with the number of notches and part number

10.33 Measuring the piston protrusion

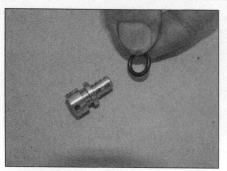

10.37a Fit a new sealing O-ring to the cleaned oil control orifice...

10.37b...and refit it in the cylinder block

10.38 Fit the new cylinder head gasket over the locating dowels

Refitting

36 Check that the crankshaft is positioned so that Nos. 1 and 4 cylinders are at TDC.

37 Use a clean rag soaked in gasket remover or cellulose thinners to remove any traces of oil or dirt from the mating surfaces. Clean carefully the oil control orifice and refit it, with a new sealing O-ring, to its location in the cylinder block's top surface, at the rear, on the timing chain end **(see illustrations)**.

38 Place a new gasket on the cylinder block, and locate it over the two dowels at the front **(see illustration)**. The gasket will fit only one way.

39 Place the cylinder head onto the block, and locate it on the two dowels.

40 Lightly oil the threads and the underside of the heads of the cylinder head bolts, then refit them. Tighten the bolts in the recommended sequence, in stages, to the torque listed in this Chapter's Specifications **(see illustrations)**. Because of the critical function of cylinder head bolts, the manufacturer specifies the following conditions for tightening them:

a) *A beam-type or dial-type torque wrench is preferable to a preset (click-stop) torque wrench. If you use a preset torque wrench, tighten slowly and be careful not to overtighten the bolts.*

b) *If a bolt makes any sound while you're tightening it (creaking, clicking, etc), slacken it completely and tighten it again in the specified stages.*

41 Refit the hydraulic tappets, followers and camshafts (Section 9).

42 Refit the timing chain (Section 7).

43 Refit the timing chain case (Section 6).

44 Refit the cylinder head cover (Section 4).

45 Refit the EGR system components (Chapter 4C), and the fuel pump, exhaust manifold and turbocharger (as applicable) (Chapter 4B).

46 Refit the inlet manifold (where removed) or reconnect the manifold hoses and wiring (Chapter 4B).

47 Refit the remaining parts in the reverse order of removal.

48 Refill the cooling system and check all fluid levels.

49 Reconnect the battery negative.

50 Run the engine until normal operating temperature is reached. Check for leaks and proper operation.

11 Sump – removal and refitting

Removal

1 Disconnect the battery (see 'Disconnecting the battery' in Chapter 5A ').

2 Jack up and support the front of the vehicle (see "Jacking and vehicle support' in the Reference chapter ') and then remove the engine undershield.

3 Drain the engine oil and remove the oil filter (Chapter 1B).

10.40a Refit the cylinder head and TIGHTEN the bolts in the sequence shown

10.40b Oil the threads...

10.40c...and under the heads of the bolts

10.40d Tighten to the first stage with a torque wrench...

10.40e...and then use an angle-tightening gauge for the succeeding stages of tightening

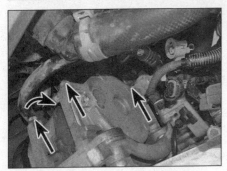

11.5 Unbolt the air conditioning compressor

11.12a Remove the engine bellhousing to gearbox bolts which pass through the sump at the front...

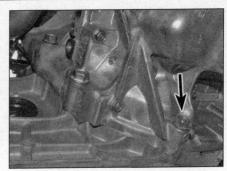

11.12b...and at the rear of the engine

4 Remove the auxiliary drivebelt (Chapter 1B) and then remove the alternator, as described in Chapter 5A.

5 Unscrew the air conditioning compressor's four mounting bolts **(see illustration)**. With the compressor unbolted, secure it clear of the working area without disconnecting or straining its wiring and pipes.

6 Slacken the hose clamps at each end and unbolt the turbocharger to intercooler pipe. Pack the turbocharger opening with clean rag to prevent anything falling in.

7 Unbolt and remove the intercooler mounting bracket.

8 Unscrew the dipstick tube mounting bolt and withdraw the dipstick and tube. Recover and discard the sealing O-ring – a new one must be fitted on reassembly.

9 Remove the torque rod (dog bone) from the rear of the engine and then unbolt the support bracket. Finally unbolt the mounting bracket from the sump.

10 Unbolt the air conditioning compressor mounting bracket from the lower crankcase/main bearing ladder/sump.

11 Remove the oil pressure switch and then remove the cover from the oil level sensor. Disconnect the wiring plug from the level sensor and then unbolt the wiring loom from the sump.

12 Unscrew the two engine bellhousing-to-

gearbox bolts which pass through the sump **(see illustrations)**.

13 Progressively slacken and remove the eighteen bolts securing the sump to the lower crankcase/main bearing ladder. Check that all sump retaining bolts have been removed before trying to prise the sump down.

14 Breaking the grip of the sealant used as gasket material is not easy; the liquid gasket used on assembly sticks very tight. Try to break the seal by tapping all around the edge of the sump with a hammer and a block of wood or a soft-faced mallet, then use the three leverage points provided, two at the front and one at the rear, to prise the sump off the lower crankcase/main bearing ladder and carefully pull it down **(see illustrations)**. Do not try to tap the sump forwards or backwards; it is located by a large dowel at the front, next to the gearbox. Do not lever between the mating faces with metal tools or force a blade into the gap as a starting point for levering, as this will damage the mating faces.

Preparation for refitting

15 Whenever the sump is removed, take the opportunity to clean the filter screen on the oil pump pick-up using solvent and a brush **(see illustration)**. Also check the balancer/oil pump drive chain for wear or damage (Section 13).

16 Thoroughly clean the sump, inside and out. Check the drain plug threads for signs of damage. Check the mating surface for distortion, particularly around the bolt holes,

using a straight-edge to ensure that the mating surface is completely flat before refitting the sump.

17 Using a gasket scraper and/or a brass wire brush, remove all traces of old sealant from the lower crankcase/main bearing ladder and the sump mating surfaces; be very careful not to mark or scratch either surface. Note that the crankshaft main bearing bore diameter code letters or numbers are marked on the bottom surface of the lower crankcase/main bearing ladder at the rear of the flywheel end; be careful not to scrub so hard that these are erased.

Refitting

18 Thoroughly clean the mating surfaces of the lower crankcase/main bearing ladder and the sump. Clean any oil or old sealant from the mating surfaces and from the bolt holes and threads. Degrease the surfaces completely before applying sealant and wipe down the inside of the engine with a clean, lint-free rag to prevent any drips of oil from contaminating the new sealant on reassembly.

19 The liquid gasket recommended by Honda (Part No: 08C70-K0234M or 08C70-K0334M) requires that the sump be installed within five minutes of applying the liquid gasket – if this time limit is exceeded, the sealant must be wiped off completely and new liquid gasket applied. A 'dry' practice run before applying liquid gasket is recommended.

20 Apply liquid gasket in a continuous thin bead (3mm diameter approx) evenly around

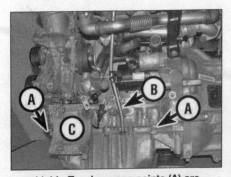

11.14a Two leverage points (A) are provided at the front of the sump/block joint. The dipstick tube (B) and air conditioning compressor mounting bracket (C) must be unbolted from the cylinder block/sump

11.14b The leverage point at the rear of the sump/block joint

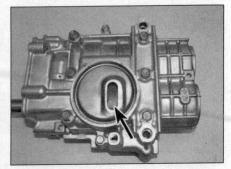

11.15 Clean the oil pump pick-up filter screen whenever the sump is removed

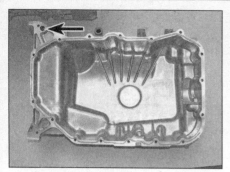

11.20 Apply a continuous bead of liquid gasket evenly around the sump's mating surface. Note the locating dowel

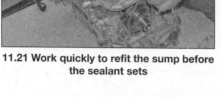

11.21 Work quickly to refit the sump before the sealant sets

11.22 Tighten the sump bolts to the specified torque setting

the sump's mating surface so that the bead goes around the inside edges of the bolt holes **(see illustration)**. Also apply a small blob of liquid gasket to those bolt holes in the lower crankcase/main bearing ladder which pass through to the outside and to the three bolt holes along the bottom edge of the timing chain case to ensure that there are no oil leaks from the threads. Do not apply sealant to blind holes in the castings. Do not apply excess sealant, as this will end up inside the engine.

21 Offer up the sump and carefully, ensuring that you do not smear the sealant bead by sliding it, fit the sump into place on its locating dowel, press it into position and refit one or two bolts to hold it **(see illustration)**.

22 Refit all the bolts, tightening them by hand only at first until the sump is correctly settled in position. Working in a diagonal sequence from the centre outwards and in two or three stages, tighten the retaining bolts to the specified torque **(see illustration)**. Check that an even bead of sealant is visible all the way round the edge of the sump; wipe off any excess.

23 The remainder of refitting is a reversal of removal, noting the following points:

a) Use a new O-ring on the dipstick tube.
b) Wait at least 30 minutes (or as instructed by the sealant manufacturer) before filling the engine with oil.
c) Do not run the engine for at least three hours (or as instructed by the sealant manufacturer).

12 Oil pump – removal, inspection and refitting

Removal

1 Bring the engine to TDC, as described in Section 3.

2 Remove the sump as described in Section 11.

3 Prevent the balancer shafts from rotating by inserting an 8 mm diameter pin punch (or equivalent) through the hole in the rear of the balancer/oil pump assembly and into the hole in the rear balancer shaft. A pin punch is the best tool for the job (a drill bit might be

too brittle and shear off, while a cheap 8 mm bolt might bend), but we found a high-tensile bolt which made a good substitute **(see illustrations)**.

4 Rotate the crankshaft pulley anti-clockwise to compress the balancer/oil pump drive chain tensioner until the lockplate moves back far enough for a 2.5 mm diameter pin to be inserted into the holes in the lockplate and tensioner body **(see illustration)**.

5 Rotate the crankshaft pulley clockwise again to hold the pin in place and lock the tensioner, then unscrew the two bolts and withdraw the balancer/oil pump drive chain tensioner.

6 Unscrew and remove the driven sprocket retaining bolt. Wipe the chain and look for

12.3a Prevent the balancer shafts from rotating by inserting an 8 mm diameter locking pin through the housing...

12.4 Rotate the crankshaft anti-clockwise (or rear balancer shaft clockwise, as here) to compress the chain tensioner so a 2.5 mm locking pin can be inserted

the gold-coloured sideplates (there should be two on adjacent links and one at the other end); note where they are in relation to the sprocket's timing marks.

7 Unscrew the four bolts and withdraw the balancer/oil pump assembly, noting the two locating dowels, and withdraw the sprocket from the rear balancer shaft, disengaging it from the drive chain **(see illustration)**. Note the locating Woodruff key; if this is loose it should be removed and kept with the sprocket.

Inspection

8 Undo the oil pump housing mounting bolts, withdraw the housing from the balancer assembly, noting the two locating dowels,

12.3b...and into the hole in the balancer shaft

12.7 Withdrawing the balancer/oil pump assembly – note the locking pin

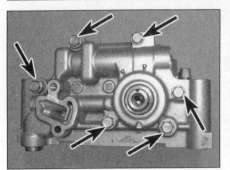

12.8a Undo the oil pump housing mounting bolts...

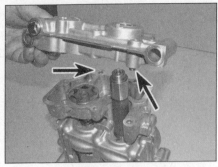

12.8b...and withdraw the housing from the balancer assembly, noting the two locating dowels

12.8c Mark one surface of the outer rotor with a felt-tip pen or similar so that it can be refitted the same way round

and dismantle the oil pump. Note any marks identifying either surface of the outer rotor; if none can be seen, make your own **(see illustrations)**. Thoroughly clean the rotors

12.9a Measuring the pump housing to outer rotor clearance

and housing. If there is any obvious sign of wear or damage, the pump must be renewed. Note that, except for the pressure relief valve components, the pump is only available as a

12.9b Measuring the inner to outer rotor tip clearance

complete assembly, including the balancer assembly housing halves.

9 Refit the rotors to the pump housing and, using feeler blades of the appropriate thickness, measure the clearance between the outer rotor and the pump housing, then between the inner rotor tip and the outer rotor **(see illustrations)**.

10 Using feeler blades and a straight-edge placed across the top of the pump housing and the rotors, measure the rotor endfloat **(see illustration)**.

11 If any measurement is outside the specified limits, the complete pump assembly must be renewed.

12 Unscrew the pressure relief valve threaded plug and extract the spring and plunger from the pump housing **(see illustrations)**. Check the spring for distortion and the plunger for scoring; if the plunger does not slide freely in the pump housing bore, then it must be renewed.

13 Check the oil pump drive chain, sprocket and tensioner as described in Section 13.

14 Lubricate the pump rotors with clean engine oil and refit them, using the marks made or noted on removal to ensure that the outer rotor is refitted the original way round **(see illustrations)**. Check that the pump rotates freely, then prime it by injecting oil into its passages and rotating it. If a long time elapses before the pump is refitted to the engine, prime it again before installation. Packing the spaces between the rotors with petroleum jelly will also prime the pump.

12.10 Measuring the pump housing to rotor axial clearance (rotor endfloat)

12.12a Unscrew the threaded plug...

12.12b...and remove the oil pressure relief valve spring and plunger

12.14a Refitting the oil pump inner rotor

12.14b Ensure the oil pump outer rotor is refitted the original way round

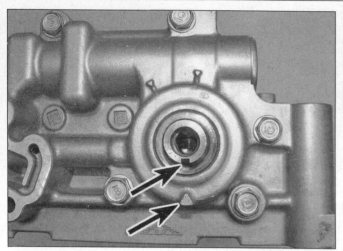

12.17 The keyway in the rear balancer shaft must align with the single arrow mark cast on the pump housing

12.19 Tightening the four balancer/oil pump assembly mounting bolts

15 Refit the oil pump housing to the balancer assembly, aligning it on the two locating dowels and engaging the pump inner rotor on the front balancer shaft's drive tongue, then refit the housing mounting bolts and tighten them to the torque specified. Lubricate and refit the oil pressure relief valve plunger and spring, then refit the plug, and tighten to the specified torque.

Refitting

16 Check again that No. 1 cylinder is at TDC on the compression stroke.
17 Rotate the balancer shafts until the keyway in the rear balancer shaft aligns with the single arrow mark cast on the pump housing **(see illustration)**. Insert the 8 mm diameter pin into the hole in the rear of the balancer/oil pump assembly to lock the balancer shafts in this position and secure it with a rubber band or similar. Position the driven sprocket on the rear balancer shaft, engaging it on the Woodruff key; note that the two punch-marked teeth will align with the arrow marks cast on the pump housing.
18 Refit the balancer/oil pump assembly, engaging the driven sprocket on the chain

and aligning the assembly on the two locating dowels. The sprocket must be fitted to the chain so that the chain's rear run is kept taut and so that the gold-coloured sideplates are restored to the relationship with the sprocket timing marks noted on removal.
19 Tighten the four balancer/oil pump assembly mounting bolts to the torque specified **(see illustration)**.
20 Lightly oil its threads, refit the driven sprocket retaining bolt and tighten it to the specified torque. Remove the locking pin.
21 Refit the chain tensioner, engaging its plunger on the tensioner blade's free end. Tighten its bolts to the specified torque, then hold the tensioner blade against the tensioner plunger and withdraw the locking pin to release the tensioner against the chain **(see illustration)**. Check that the timing marks and coloured sideplates are correctly aligned and that the tensioner plunger has taken up any slack in the chain.
22 Rotate the crankshaft two full turns (720°) clockwise and check that when the camshaft sprocket TDC marks align again, the balancer/oil pump sprocket timing marks align again with the arrow marks cast on the pump housing. If

not, repeat the procedure until the balancer/oil pump assembly is correctly timed.
23 Refit the cylinder head cover (Section 2B Section 4).
24 Refit the sump (Section 11).

13 Balancer/oil pump drive chain – removal, inspection and refitting

Caution: The removal of the timing chain and balancer/oil pump drive chain's crankshaft drive sprocket requires the removal of the timing chain case and of the sump. Depending on the skills and equipment available and the nature of the work being undertaken, the home mechanic may prefer to consider removing the engine and transmission as a complete assembly and then removing the sump.

Removal

1 Remove the timing chain (Section 7).
2 Support the timing chain end of the engine from above, with an engine hoist or crane. Bolt a lifting eye to the right-hand end of the cylinder head.
3 Remove the sump (Section 11).
4 Before proceeding any further, assess the chain's state of wear by measuring the protrusion of the tensioner plunger from the tensioner body **(see illustration)**. If the tensioner plunger protrudes more than 8 mm, the balancer/oil pump drive chain is worn out and must be renewed. Because the timing chain will have suffered an equivalent degree of wear, it too must be renewed if the balancer/oil pump drive chain fails this test.
5 Prevent the balancer shafts from rotating by inserting an 8 mm diameter pin punch (see Section 12). Unscrew and remove the sprocket retaining bolt.
6 Rotate the crankshaft anti-clockwise and

12.21 Hold the tensioner blade against the plunger and withdraw the locking pin to release the tensioner

13.4 If the tensioner plunger protrudes more than 8 mm, then the balancer/oil pump drive chain is worn out and must be renewed

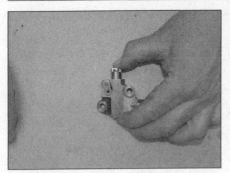

13.11a When checking chain tensioner, don't allow the plunger to fly out

13.11b Check that the plunger moves smoothly through the full range of movement...

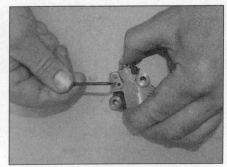

13.11c... and then compress the plunger and re-insert the locking pin for refitting

insert a locking pin into the chain tensioner (see Section 12).

7 Rotate the crankshaft pulley clockwise again to hold the pin in place, then unscrew the two bolts and withdraw the tensioner assembly.

8 Undo the two bolts and withdraw the fixed guide from its rear run.

9 Unscrew the pivot bolt and withdraw the tensioner blade.

10 Remove the chain with the drive and driven sprockets. Note the locating keys as the drive sprocket slides off the crankshaft and as the driven sprocket slides off the rear balancer shaft; if either key is loose it should be removed and kept with its sprocket.

Inspection

11 Check the chain wear as described in Section 7. With the ratchet released, check that the plunger extends smoothly and that there is no sign of wear on the plunger or ratchet assembly **(see illustrations)**.

Refitting

12 The keyway in the crankshaft end must point straight up (twelve o'clock position), so that the punch mark stamped on the drive sprocket aligns with the arrow mark cast on the cylinder block **(see illustration)**. Check that the locking pin is still in place in the balancer shaft assembly.

13 Fit the balancer/oil pump drive chain to the drive sprocket so that the single-coloured sideplate fits over the punch-marked tooth, then fit it to the driven sprocket so that the links with the coloured sideplates fit on each of the punch-marked teeth **(see illustrations)**.

14 Refit the drive chain and sprockets, keeping the chain taut on its rear run. As the sprockets slide on, ensure that the keyway of each sprocket engages with its key and that the crankshaft drive sprocket is pressed firmly back against the shoulder on the crankshaft end. Note also that the crankshaft drive sprocket locating key is fitted with its tapered end pointing inwards **(see illustrations)**.

15 Lightly oil its threads, refit the driven

13.12 The keyway must point straight up and the punch mark on the drive sprocket must align with the arrow mark cast on the cylinder block

13.13a Fit the drive chain to the crankshaft sprocket so that single-coloured link fits over the punch marked tooth

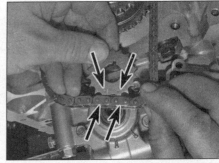

13.13b Fit the drive chain to the rear balancer shaft drive sprocket so that two coloured links fit over the punch marked teeth

13.14a Ensure that the sprocket keyway, coloured links and timing marks align correctly

13.14b Refit the drive sprocket Woodruff key as shown...

13.14c...and then ensure that the tapered end of the crankshaft drive sprocket locating key points inwards

13.15a Tighten the drive sprocket retaining bolt to the specified torque wrench setting...

13.15b...and then remove the locking pin

13.16a Check that the Woodruff key, coloured links and timing marks are all aligned...

sprocket retaining bolt and tighten it to the specified torque. Remove the locking pin **(see illustrations)**.

16 Refit the fixed guide to the chain's rear run and the tensioner blade to the front run. Tighten the mounting and pivot bolts to the specified torques **(see illustrations)**.

17 Refit the chain tensioner, engaging its plunger on the tensioner blade's free end. Tighten its bolts to the specified torque, then hold the tensioner blade against the tensioner plunger and withdraw the locking pin to release the tensioner against the chain **(see illustrations)**. Check that the timing marks and coloured sideplates are correctly aligned and that the tensioner plunger has taken up any slack in the chain.

18 Refit the timing chain (Section 7). Temporarily refit the crankshaft pulley and rotate the crankshaft two full turns (720°) clockwise, then check that all the timing marks align exactly, as described, for both chains. If not, repeat the procedure until both chains are correctly refitted.

19 The remainder of reassembly is the reverse of the removal procedure.

13.16b...and then refit the fixed guide to the drive chain's rear run...

13.16c...and the tensioner blade to the frontrun

Inspection

2 Mount a dial gauge so that its tip bears on the sprocket end of the rear balancer shaft. Push the shaft fully away, then zero the gauge. Push the shaft fully the other way, and check the endfloat; repeat to check the front shaft's endfloat. If the endfloat of either shaft is beyond the service limit specified, then the shaft must be renewed and the endfloat rechecked; if it is still excessive the balancer/ oil pump assembly must be renewed.

3 While there is no need to remove the oil pump housing in order to dismantle the balancer assembly, there is little point in not dismantling, cleaning and checking the oil pump while the opportunity presents itself. Unscrew the clamp bolts and separate the two halves of the balancer assembly, noting the two locating dowels. The bearing shells

are identical, but if disturbed must be refitted in their original locations. Make identifying marks or notes before removing any of the bearing shells.

4 Unscrew the clamp bolts and separate the two halves of the balancer assembly, noting the two locating dowels. The bearing shells are identical, but if disturbed must be refitted in their original locations. Make identifying marks or notes before removing any of the bearing shells.

5 Clean the shafts and housing halves; check particularly the bearing surfaces on the balancer shaft bearing journals and bearing shells. If there is any obvious sign of wear or damage, the component concerned must be renewed. Note that while the shafts and bearing shells are available separately, if either of the housing halves are found to be

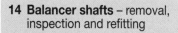

14 Balancer shafts – removal, inspection and refitting

Removal

1 Remove the balancer/oil pump assembly as described in Section 13.

13.17a Refit the locked tensioner to the blade...

13.17b... and then refit the longer bolt...

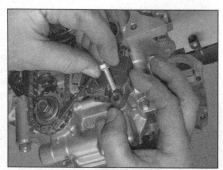

13.17c...folowed by the shorter bolt

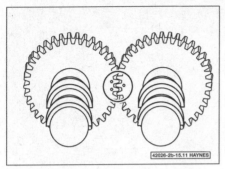

14.9 The punch marks must align

worn or damaged, they are available only as a matched pair, with the oil pump.

6 Use a Plastigauge to check the balancer shaft bearing journal to bearing clearance. Wipe clean the balancer shafts and refit them to the housing lower half. Lay a strip of Plastigauge on each bearing journal, refit the housing upper half and tighten the clamp bolts to the specified torque. Unbolt the housing upper half again and measure the width of each strip at its widest point to determine the clearance. If any of the clearances are beyond the specified service limit then the worn components must be renewed.

7 If the necessary equipment is available, the balancer shaft bearing journals and bearing bores can also be checked for wear by direct measurement.

8 On reassembly, clean the backs of the bearing shells and the bearing locations in both housing halves. Press the bearing shells into their locations, ensuring that each is refitted in its original location if the originals are being re-used, and that the tab on each shell engages in the notch in the housing location. Take care not to touch any shell bearing surface with your fingers.

9 Lubricate each bearing shell in the housing lower half, then match the balancer shafts together so that the punch-marked

tooth on the rear shaft fits between the two punch-marked teeth on the front shaft. Lower the shafts into position **(see illustration)**.

10 Lubricate each bearing shell in the housing upper half, then lower it into place, engaging it on the two locating dowels. Lightly oil the threads of the 8 mm clamp bolts, then refit them and tighten them to the specified torque. Refit the 6 mm clamp bolts with the baffle plate and tighten them to the specified torque. If removed, refit the two locating dowels to their locations in the top surface of the balancer assembly.

11 Refit the oil pump housing to the balancer assembly as described in Section 14.

Refitting

12 Refit the balancer/oil pump assembly as described in Section 14.

---

15 Flywheel – removal and refitting

Removal

1 Raise the vehicle and support it on axle stands (see 'Jacking and vehicle support' in the Reference chapter), then remove the transmission (Chapter 7A).

2 Remove the clutch assembly (Chapter 6).

3 Prevent the flywheel from turning by locking the ring gear teeth with a similar arrangement to that shown **(see illustration)**. Alternatively, bolt a strap between the flywheel and the cylinder block. Make alignment marks between the flywheel and crankshaft using paint or a marker pen.

4 Remove the bolts that secure the flywheel to the crankshaft. **Note:** *Do not use an impact wrench to slacken or tighten the bolts because of the likelihood of damage to the flywheel. Since the flywheel is heavy, be sure to support it while removing the last bolt. Remove the flywheel from the crankshaft* **(see illustration)**.

Inspection

Note: *Due to the amount of work necessary to remove and refit flywheels and clutch components, it is worth considering the renewal of the clutch components on a preventative basis if the engine and/or transmission have been removed for some other reason. Also note that it is sometimes recommended to renew the dual-mass flywheel at the same time as the clutch. This, however, is an extremely expensive course of action; seek expert advice if in doubt.*

5 Most problems with dual-mass flywheels will be evident from the sudden onset of knocking or rattling noises when the engine is idling, from the development of juddering, jerkiness and noise on taking up the drive and pulling away, and from difficulties with gear selection, etc. The fact that it may be possible to stop or change the noise and other symptoms by depressing and releasing the clutch pedal may lead one to suspect the clutch. Early symptoms of a failing dual-mass flywheel may be similar to a slipping clutch. In such cases, the only way to be sure is to remove the gearbox and clutch so that the clutch and flywheel can be physically checked for signs of wear or damage.

6 Clean the flywheel to remove clutch dust, grease and oil. Try to rotate the outer rim against the inner; while it should be possible to rotate one against the other for a short distance, the movement should be smooth and well-controlled by the torsion springs. If there is any sign of free play, of jerkiness or roughness in the motion or if any undue noises are heard, the flywheel is faulty and must be renewed. Check also that there is no sign of axial movement between the inner and outer parts of the flywheel. If any sign of wear or damage is found, the flywheel must be renewed.

7 Inspect the surface for cracks, rivet grooves, burned areas and score marks. Light scoring can be removed with emery cloth.

15.3 Homemade tool fabricated to lock flywheel

15.4 Note the alignment of the flywheel on the crankshaft before removing it. Make your own marks if none can be seen

Check for cracked and broken ring gear teeth. Lay the flywheel on a flat surface and use a straight-edge to check for warpage. If any sign of wear or damage is found, the flywheel must be renewed.

8 Clean and inspect the mating surfaces of the flywheel and the crankshaft. If the oil seal is leaking, renew it before refitting the flywheel (see Section 17).

9 Check the pilot bearing as described in Section 16.

10 Clean the bolt threads and check their condition before re-using them. These bolts are subject to significant stress, and it is good practice to renew them whenever they are disturbed.

Refitting

11 Position the flywheel against the crankshaft using the marks made on removal to ensure that it is refitted in its original location. Some engines have an alignment dowel or staggered bolt holes to ensure correct refitting.

12 Prevent the flywheel from turning. Lightly oil under the bolt heads and refit the flywheel mounting bolts, then working in a diagonal pattern and in several stages, tighten the bolts to the specified torque **(see illustrations)**. Wipe away any surplus oil.

13 The remainder of refitting is the reverse of the removal procedure.

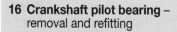

16 Crankshaft pilot bearing – removal and refitting

Inspection

1 The pilot bearing is fitted into the flywheel, and provides support for the free end of the gearbox input shaft. It can only be examined once the clutch (Chapter 6) has been removed. The bearing should rotate smoothly and quietly and should be firmly fixed in the flywheel. Check the bearing by rotating its inner race and feeling for rough or jerky rotation and any signs of free play, also of any looseness of its fit in the flywheel. If any of these conditions are evident, the bearing must be renewed.

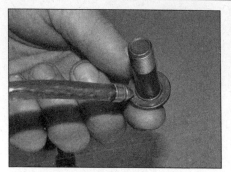

15.12a Lightly oil under the heads of the flywheel mounting bolts...

Removal

2 Remove the flywheel as described in Section 15.

3 Measure and record the depth from a straight-edge placed across the face of the flywheel to the bearing's outer edge. Drive out the bearing using a hammer and suitable drift.

Refitting

4 Smear a thin coat of oil on the bearing outer race. Using a suitable socket that bears only on the outer diameter of the bearing, drive the new bearing squarely into the flywheel until its outer edge is the depth from the flywheel face that was noted on removal. Wipe away all traces of oil from the bearing and flywheel.

5 Degrease the flywheel friction surface, using solvent and a clean rag.

6 Apply a thin smear of grease to the inner race of the bearing and to the gearbox input shaft; Honda recommend Urea Grease UM264 (Part No. 41211-PY5-305), before refitting the gearbox as described in Chapter 7A.

17 Crankshaft oil seals – renewal

Right-hand (timing chain end)

1 Remove the crankshaft pulley as described in Section 5.

2 Measure and record the depth from a straight-edge placed across the boss on the

15.12b...then refit the flywheel and tighten the bolts in criss-cross sequence to the specified torque wrench setting

timing chain case surrounding the oil seal to the seal's outer edge. If the timing chain case is removed from the engine, measure the depth from the seal's outer edge to a straight-edge placed across the case mating surface **(see illustration)**. This should be in the range 17.3 to 18.0 mm.

3 Carefully punch or drill two small holes opposite each other in the oil seal. Screw a self-tapping screw into each and pull on the screws with pliers to extract the seal. If the timing chain case is removed from the engine, either drive the seal out or lever it out using a screwdriver or similar; take care not to scratch the seal housing **(see illustration)**.

4 Clean the seal housing and polish off any burrs or raised edges which may have caused the seal to fail in the first place.

5 Lubricate the lips of the new seal with clean engine oil and ease it into position in the timing chain case, ensuring that the seal lips face inwards. Press the seal squarely into position as far as possible by hand. Use a suitable tubular drift, such as a socket, which bears only on the hard outer edge of the seal to tap the seal into position to the depth noted on removal **(see illustration)**.

6 Wash off any traces of oil, then refit the crankshaft pulley as described in Section 5, taking great care not to damage the seal lips during fitting.

Left-hand end (transmission end)

7 Remove the flywheel (see Section 15).

8 Measure and record the depth from a

17.2 Measure the fitted depth to mating surface

17.3 Drive the seal out of the timing chain housing

17.5 Driving the new seal into the timing chain housing

17.11a Apply a film of clean oil to the crankshaft seal journal and the lip of the new crankshaft seal...

17.11b...and then tap the seal into place until correctly seated

Removal

1 Drain the engine coolant, engine oil, and remove the oil filter element (Chapter 1B).
2 Remove the engine compartment undershield.
3 Remove the thermostat housing (Chapter 3).
4 Unscrew the four bolts and remove the oil cooler from the oil filter/oil cooler/water pump housing **(see illustration)**. Be prepared for fluid spillage. Recover and discard the sealing O-rings – new ones must be fitted on reassembly.

Refitting

5 Ensure the mating surfaces of the oil cooler and housing are clean and dry. Using new sealing O-rings, fit the cooler to the housing **(see illustrations)**. Tighten the bolts to the specified torque.
6 Refit the thermostat housing (Chapter 3).
7 Replenish the engine coolant, fit a new oil filter element, and fill the engine with new engine oil.
8 Refit the components removed for access.

straight-edge placed across the boss on the cylinder block and lower crankcase/main bearing ladder surrounding the oil seal to the seal's outer edge.
9 Carefully punch or drill two small holes opposite each other in the oil seal. Screw a self-tapping screw into each and pull on the screws with pliers to extract the seal.
10 Clean the seal housing and polish off any burrs or raised edges which may have caused the seal to fail in the first place.
11 Apply a film of clean oil to the crankshaft seal journal and the lip of the new seal, and carefully tap the seal into place with a seal driver. If a seal driver isn't available, use a large socket or piece of pipe, with an outside diameter which bears only on the hard outer edge of the seal, to tap the seal into position

until it seats on the shoulder in the seal housing; check that this corresponds to the depth noted on removal **(see illustrations)**.
12 The remaining steps are the reverse of removal.

18 Oil cooler – removal and refitting

Note: *The oil cooler is mounted on the front of the engine, behind the alternator and underneath the EGR equipment. Access is extremely awkward; short of removing the intake manifold and all the EGR equipment (see Chapters 4B 4B and 4C 4C), the most direct access is therefore from underneath, as detailed below.*

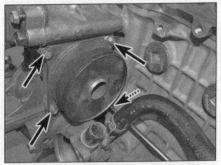

18.4 Unscrew the bolts and remove the oil cooler from the oil filter/oil cooler/water pump housing

18.5a Renew all four sealing O-rings on reassembly...

19 Oil filter/oil cooler/water pump housing – removal and refitting

Note: *The housing is mounted at the front right-hand end of the engine; the alternator must be removed and the air conditioning compressor must be unbolted to reach it. The most direct access is therefore from the front, as detailed below. When carrying out this procedure, be careful not to damage the radiator and air conditioning condenser by leaning on them; they are very delicate.*

Removal

1 Disconnect the battery negative lead (see *Disconnecting the battery* 5A).
2 Remove the engine compartment undershield.
3 Drain the cooling system (Chapter 1B).
4 Drain the engine oil and remove the oil filter element (Chapter 1B).
5 Remove the auxiliary drivebelt and its tensioner (Chapter 1B).
6 Remove the alternator (Chapter 5A).
7 Unscrew the air conditioning compressor's four mounting bolts. With the compressor unbolted, secure it out of the way without disconnecting or straining its wiring and pipes.
8 Remove the thermostat, the thermostat housing and the water pump (Chapter 3).
9 Remove the oil cooler as described in the previous Section.
10 Check that all coolant hoses, wiring harnesses and their support brackets have been removed from the housing.
11 Unscrew the bolts securing the housing to the cylinder block, then remove the housing; note the two locating dowels. Remove and discard the sealing O-rings – these must be renewed **(see illustration)**.

18.5b...and ensure the mating surfaces of the oil cooler and oil filter/oil cooler/water pump housing are clean and dry

19.11 Remove and discard the O-rings from oil filter/oil cooler/water pump housing mating surface grooves

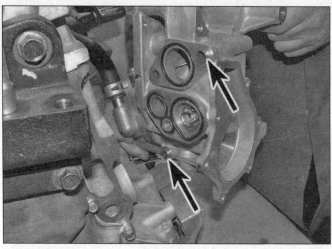

19.13a Refit the housing to the cylinder block. Note the locating dowels

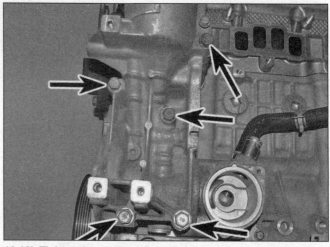

19.13b Tighten the oil filter/oil cooler/water pump housing bolts to the specified torque wrench setting

Refitting

12 Thoroughly clean the mating surfaces of the housing and the cylinder block. Clean any oil, coolant or sealant from the mating surfaces and from the oil and coolant passages, bolt holes and threads. Be careful not to allow dirt and debris to fall inside the engine. Degrease the surfaces completely before reassembly.

13 With the new O-rings fitted to their grooves, refit the housing, engaging its two locating dowels in their respective bores, then tighten the bolts to the specified torque **(see illustrations)**.

14 The remainder of reassembly is the reverse of the removal procedure.

20 Engine/transmission mountings – inspection and renewal

Inspection

1 Raise the front of the vehicle and support it securely on axle stands (see 'Jacking and vehicle support' in the Reference chapter). Remove the engine compartment undershield to reach the engine rear mounting, the cooling system expansion tank to reach the engine right-hand mounting, and the air cleaner assembly (Chapter 4B) and/or the battery and battery tray (Chapter 5A) to reach the engine/transmission left-hand mounting.

2 Check the mounting rubber to see if it is cracked, hardened or separated from the metal at any point; renew the mounting if any such deterioration is evident.

3 Check that all the fasteners are securely tightened.

4 Using a large screwdriver or prybar, check for wear in the mounting by carefully levering against it to check for freeplay. While some freeplay is to be expected even from new components, excessive wear should be obvious. If excessive freeplay is found,

check first that the fasteners are correctly secured, then renew any worn components as described below.

Renewal

Note: Before slackening any of the engine/transmission mounting bolts and nuts, note that the majority must be renewed whenever they are disturbed (see Specifications) and that a specific sequence must be followed to ensure correct alignment upon refitting.

Engine rear mounting (torque rod)

5 Jack up and support the front of the vehicle – see 'Jacking and vehicle support' in the Reference chapter. Remove the engine undershield.

6 The rear mounting does not support the engine. It is designed to stop the fore and aft movement of the engine – hence it is more accurately described as a 'torque rod' or more commonly known as as a 'dog bone' mounting.

7 Unbolt the engine rear mounting torque rod from the front suspension subframe and from the bracket on the engine and then withdraw the torque rod **(see illustrations)**. Check the torque rod's rubber sections for signs of perishing, cracks, or deterioration of the metal-to-rubber bonding.

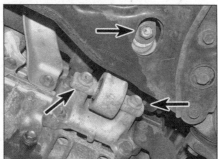

20.7 Remove the bolts

8 Unbolt the bracket from the engine **(see illustration)**.

9 On reassembly, refit the bracket to the engine, fit the new bolts and tighten them to the torque specified.

10 Refit the torque rod to the bracket on the engine and the front subframe. At this point only fit the subframe bolt loosely. Honda recommend that all the engine flexible mounting bolts are now slackened and/or replaced, to allow the engine and transmission to settle and align itself without any strain on the flexible mountings.

11 Slacken the upper torque rod to body bolt and the transmission flexible mounting (two nuts and a single bolt). Rock the engine slightly to settle the mountings and then tighten all the fixings to the specified torque. Note that Honda recommend the replacement of the bolts and nuts if the mounting is removed, however there does not seem to be any requirement to replace them if the mountings are simply adjusted or aligned.

12 Refit the engine compartment undershield and lower the vehicle to the ground.

Engine right-hand (timing end) mounting

Note: Most of the mounting's nuts and bolts must be renewed whenever they are

20.8 Remove the bracket bolts

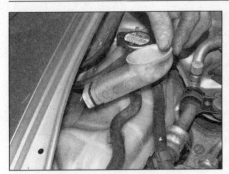

20.13a Remove the filler neck

20.13b Unclip and remove the coolant expansion bottle

20.16a Unbolt and then...

20.16b...remove the stiffener plate

20.16c Removing the torque rod

disturbed. *Obtain new nuts and bolts before starting work.*

13 Pull out the screen washer bottle neck and then remove the coolant expansion tank **(see illustrations)**. Secure the expansion tank to one side without disconnecting or straining the hoses.

14 To provide more room to access the mounting unbolt the refrigerant lines from the inner wing.

Note: *If only the upper torque rod is to be removed then there is no need to support the engine.*

15 Jack up and support the front of the vehicle (see '*Jacking and vehicle support*' in

the Reference chapter) and then remove the engine undershield. Support the weight of the engine/transmission under the sump using a trolley jack with a block of wood placed on its head.

16 Remove the bolts from the stiffener plate and then remove the main torque rod bolts **(see illustrations)**.

17 Unscrew and discard the bolts securing the side bracket to the main mounting on the engine and to the inner wing **(see illustration)**.

18 Remove the two nuts and single bolt **(see illustration)** from the engine side of mounting and then remove the bolts from the body side of the mounting. Manoeuvre

the mounting past the refrigerant lines and remove it from the vehicle.

19 Refitting is a reversal of removal, but replace the mounting bolts/nuts and before fully tightening the upper torque rod follow the procedure outlined in paragraphs 10 to 11 above.

Engine/transmission left-hand mounting

20 Jack up and support the front of the vehicle (see '*Jacking and vehicle support*' in the Reference chapter) and then remove the engine undershield. Support the weight of the transmission under the sump using a trolley jack with a block of wood placed on its head.

21 Remove the air cleaner assembly (Chapter 4B) the battery and the battery tray (Chapter 5A).

22 Make sure the gearbox is adequately supported, then unscrew the bracket mounting bolts from the transmission and then the bolts from the body. Note that one bolt is hidden below the mounting on the inner side of the inner wing **(see illustration)**. Withdraw the mounting bracket.

23 Refitting is a reversal of removal, but replace the mounting nuts/bolts. Before fully tightening the mounting, follow the procedure outlined in paragraphs 10 to 11 above and then fully tighten the mounting nuts/bolts.

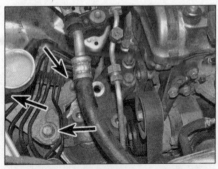

20.17 Remove the side bracket bolts (one bolt hidden)

20.18 Remove the nuts and bolt

20.22 Remove the mounting bolts

Chapter 2 Part D
Engine removal and overhaul procedures

Contents

Section number

Crankshaft – inspection 14
Crankshaft – refitting 18
Crankshaft – removal 11
Cylinder block/crankcase – cleaning and inspection. 12
Cylinder head – dismantling. 7
Cylinder head – reassembly 9
Cylinder head and valves – cleaning and inspection 8
Diesel engine – removal, separation and refitting 5
Engine initial start-up after overhaul. 20
Engine overhaul – dismantling sequence. 6

Section number

Engine overhaul – general information. 2
Engine overhaul – reassembly sequence. 16
Engine/transmission removal – methods and precautions 3
General Information 1
Main and big-end bearings – inspection 15
Petrol engine – removal, separation and refitting. 4
Piston rings – refitting. 17
Piston/connecting rod assembly – inspection 13
Piston/connecting rod assembly – removal 10
Pistons/connecting rods – refitting. 19

Degrees of difficulty

Easy, suitable for novice with little experience	Fairly easy, suitable for beginner with some experience	Fairly difficult, suitable for competent DIY mechanic	Difficult, suitable for experienced DIY mechanic	Very difficult, suitable for expert DIY or professional

Specifications

Engine overhaul and torque wrench settings
Refer to the specifications in Chapter 2A, 2B or 2C

1 General Information

1 Included in this Part of Chapter 2 are details of removing the engine/transmission from the car and general overhaul procedures for the cylinder head, cylinder block/crankcase and all other engine internal components.

2 The information given ranges from advice concerning preparation for an overhaul and the purchase of parts, to detailed step-by-step procedures covering removal, inspection, renovation and refitting of engine internal components.

3 After Section 8, all instructions are based on the assumption that the engine has been removed from the car. For information concerning in-car engine repair, as well as the removal and refitting of those external components necessary for full overhaul, refer to Part A, B or C of this Chapter (as applicable) and to Section 6. Ignore any preliminary dismantling operations described in Part A, B or C that are no longer relevant once the engine has been removed from the car.

4 Apart from torque wrench settings, which are given at the beginning of Part A, B or C (as applicable), all specifications relating to engine overhaul are at the beginning of this Part of Chapter 2.

2 Engine overhaul – general information

1 It is not always easy to determine when, or if, an engine should be completely overhauled, as a number of factors must be considered.

2 High mileage is not necessarily an indication that an overhaul is needed, while low mileage does not preclude the need for an overhaul. Frequency of servicing is probably the most important consideration. An engine which has had regular and frequent oil and filter changes, as well as other required maintenance, should give many thousands of miles of reliable service. Conversely, a neglected engine may require an overhaul very early in its life.

3 Excessive oil consumption is an indication that piston rings, valve seals and/or valve guides are in need of attention. Make sure that oil leaks are not responsible before deciding that the rings and/or guides are worn. Perform a compression test, as described in Part A, B or C of this Chapter, to determine the likely cause of the problem.

4 Check the oil pressure with a gauge fitted in place of the oil pressure switch, and compare it with that specified. If it is extremely low, the main and big-end bearings, and/or the oil pump, are probably worn out.

5 Loss of power, rough running, knocking or metallic engine noises, excessive valve gear noise, and high fuel consumption may also point to the need for an overhaul, especially if they are all present at the same time. If a complete service does not cure the situation, major mechanical work is the only solution.

6 An engine overhaul involves restoring all internal parts to the specification of a new engine. During an overhaul, the pistons and the piston rings are renewed. New main and big-end bearings are generally fitted; if necessary, the crankshaft may be renewed to restore the journals. The valves are also serviced as well, since they are usually in less-than-perfect condition at this point. While the engine is being overhauled, other components, such as the distributor, starter and alternator, can be overhauled as well. The end result should be an as-new engine that will give many trouble-free miles.

Note: *Critical cooling system components such as the hoses, thermostat and coolant pump should be renewed when an engine is overhauled. The radiator should be checked carefully, to ensure that it is not clogged or leaking. Also, it is a good idea to renew the oil pump whenever the engine is overhauled.*

7 Before beginning the engine overhaul, read through the entire procedure, to familiarise yourself with the scope and requirements of the job. Overhauling an engine is not difficult if you follow carefully all of the instructions, have the necessary tools and equipment, and pay close attention to all specifications. It can, however, be time-consuming. Plan on the car being off the road for a minimum of two weeks, especially if parts must be taken to an engineering works for repair or reconditioning. Check on the availability of parts and make sure that any necessary special tools and equipment are obtained in advance. Most work can be done with typical hand tools, although a number of precision measuring tools are required for inspecting parts to determine if they must be renewed. Often the engineering works will handle the inspection of parts and offer advice concerning reconditioning and renewal.

8 Always wait until the engine has been completely dismantled, and until all components (especially the cylinder block/crankcase and the crankshaft) have been inspected, before deciding what service and repair operations must be performed by an engineering works. The condition of these components will be the major factor to consider when determining whether to overhaul the original engine, or to buy a reconditioned unit. Do not, therefore, purchase parts or have overhaul work done on other components until they have been thoroughly inspected. As a general rule, time is the primary cost of an overhaul, so it does not pay to fit worn or sub-standard parts.

9 As a final note, to ensure maximum life and minimum trouble from a reconditioned engine, everything must be assembled with care, in a spotlessly-clean environment.

3 Engine/transmission removal – methods and precautions

1 If you have decided that the engine must be removed for overhaul or major repair work, several preliminary steps should be taken.
2 Cleaning the engine compartment and engine/transmission before beginning the removal procedure will help keep tools clean and organised.

3 An engine hoist will also be necessary. Make sure the equipment is rated in excess of the combined weight of the engine and transmission. Safety is of primary importance, considering the potential hazards involved in removing the engine/transmission from the car.
4 The help of an assistant is essential. Apart from the safety aspects involved, there are many instances when one person cannot simultaneously perform all of the operations required during engine/transmission removal.
5 Plan the operation ahead of time. Before starting work, arrange for the hire of, or obtain all of the tools and equipment you will need. Some of the equipment necessary to perform engine/transmission removal and installation safely (in addition to an engine hoist) is as follows: a heavy duty trolley jack, complete sets of spanners and sockets as described in the rear of this manual, wooden blocks, and plenty of rags and cleaning solvent for mopping-up spilled oil, coolant and fuel. If the hoist must be hired, make sure that you arrange for it in advance, and perform all of the operations possible without it beforehand. This will save you money and time.
6 Plan for the car to be out of use for quite a while. An engineering machine shop or engine reconditioning specialist will be required to perform some of the work which cannot be accomplished without special equipment. These places often have a busy schedule, so it would be a good idea to consult them before removing the engine, in order to accurately estimate the amount of time required to rebuild or repair components that may need work.
7 During the engine/transmission removal procedure, it is advisable to make notes of the locations of all brackets, cable ties, earthing points, etc, as well as how the wiring harnesses, hoses and electrical connections are attached and routed around the engine and engine compartment. An effective way of doing this is to take a series of photographs of the various components before they are disconnected or removed; the resulting photographs will prove invaluable when the engine/transmission is refitted.
8 Always be extremely careful when removing and refitting the engine/transmission. Serious injury can result from careless actions. Plan ahead and take your time, and a job of this nature, although major, can be accomplished successfully.
9 On all Civic models, the engine must be removed complete with the transmission as an assembly. There is insufficient clearance in the engine compartment to remove the engine leaving the transmission in the vehicle. The assembly is removed by raising the front of the vehicle, and lowering the assembly from the engine compartment.

Note: *Such is the complexity of the power unit arrangement on these vehicles, and the variations that may be encountered according to model and optional equipment fitted, that the following should be regarded as a guide to*

the work involved, rather than a step-by-step procedure. Where differences are encountered, or additional component disconnection or removal is necessary, make notes of the work involved as an aid to refitting.

4 Petrol engine – removal, separation and refitting

Note: *The engine and transmission are removed as a single unit from below. This requires the vehicle to be raised high enough to allow the engine and transmission to be remove from below. For the home mechanic the simple solution is to lower the engine and transmission onto an old carpet – or ideally a wheeled trolley. Remove the engine crane and lifting brackets from the engine and reposition them on the the inner wings – we used the engine mounting bolt holes to fit the brackets. With care the front of the vehicle can now be raised sufficiently to allow the engine and transmission to be dragged out from underneath the vehicle. The help of an assistant will be required.*

Note: *The recommend Honda procedure is to remove the subframe and all the steering components, however for the home mechanic this is an awkward undertaking. The method outlined here does not require removal of the subframe, but does require degassing and removal of the AC compressor and radiator.*

Removal

1 Remove the fuel pump fuse from the interior fuse box and run the engine until it stops.
2 Disconnect and then remove the battery as described in Chapter 5A.
3 Remove the air intake duct from the front of the engine and then remove the air filter housing. Remove the air filter housing support bracket (Chapter 4A).
4 With reference to Chapter 12 and Chapter 11, remove the windscreen wiper arms and windscreen cowl panels.
5 Disconnect the battery cables from the fusebox **(see illustration)** and release them from the support clamp and then remove the earth cable (where fitted) from the engine mounting.

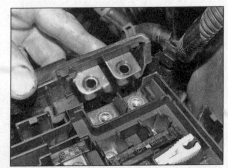

4.5 Remove the main positive cable from the fusebox

4.7 Work around the engine bay disconnecting the various wiring plugs as required

4.8 Remove the protective cover from the fuel line connector

4.15 Remove the exhaust (1.8 model shown)

6 Remove the cover form the Engine Control Unit (ECU) and then remove the mounting bolts. Disconnect the wiring plugs and then remove the ECU from the vehicle.

7 Release the ECU wiring loom from the retaining brackets and then release the wiring connectors from the engine **(see illustration)**.

8 Remove the crash cover from the fuel line connector **(see illustration)** and then disconnect the fuel lines. Anticipate some fuel spillage as the fuel lines are disconnected.

9 At the throttle body remove the brake servo hose and the EVAP hose.

10 On manual transmission models, remove the gear change cables as described in Chapter 7A.

11 Unbolt the clutch slave cylinder and the clutch hose support bracket. Carefully remove the slave and hose assembly and secure it to the side.

12 Jack up and support the front of the vehicle (see '*Jacking and vehicle support*' in the Reference chapter). Remove both front wheels and the engine undershield.

13 Remove the radiator cap and then with reference to Chapter 1A, drain the coolant.

14 Drain the engine oil (Chapter 1A) and then drain the transmission fluid (Chapter 7A).

15 Disconnect the wiring plugs from the Oxygen sensors and then remove the catalytic converter (Chapter 4C). On 1.8 engines remove the front section of the exhaust system **(see illustration)**.

16 Unbolt and remove the heat shield from the driveshaft.

17 On models fitted with air conditioning remove the auxiliary drive belt.

Warning: It is an offence to knowingly discharge an AC system to the atmosphere.

18 If not already done so, have the AC system degassed, Disconnect the refrigerant lines from the compressor and then immediately seal all the openings. Disconnect the wiring plug from the AC compressor, then unbolt the compressor from the support bracket. Remove the compressor from the vehicle.

19 Remove both driveshafts as described in Chapter 8.

20 Unbolt and remove the lower rear torque rod (Chapter 2A or Chapter 2B).

21 Disconnect the radiator hoses and the heater hoses. Remove the radiator as described in Chapter 3.

22 Engine lifting brackets are not fitted to the engine. To enable the engine to be removed lifting brackets must be fabricated. Install the brackets at the front left-hand end of the engine and at the right-hand rear of the engine.

23 Install the engine crane, with the jib raised to it's highest point – the engine will be lowered, not raised to remove it.

24 Support the weight of the engine with the crane and then remove the left and right-hand engine mountings.

25 Slowly lower the engine **(see illustrations)** checking that all hoses and connectors have been released as the engine is lowered to the ground.

26 Remove the engine crane and remove the engine from beneath the vehicle.

Separation

27 Support the engine/transmission assembly on blocks of wood, on a workbench (or failing that, on a clean area of the workshop floor).

28 On models with manual gearboxes:

a) *Unbolt and remove the flywheel cover plate.*

b) *Unscrew the bellhousing-to-gearbox bolts.*

c) *Carefully pull the gearbox away from the engine, ensuring that the weight of the transmission is not allowed to hang on the*

4.25a Install the chains and...

4.25b...and lower the engine and transmission assembly to the ground

4.28 Removing the transmission from the engine

input shaft while it is still engaged with the clutch. If necessary, carefully prise the gearbox away at first, to release the alignment dowels. **(see illustration)**

29 On models with automatic transmission:

a) Unbolt and remove the torque converter cover plate.

b) Mark the relationship of the torque converter to the driveplate.

c) Unscrew and remove the eight torque converter-to-driveplate bolts, turning the engine to bring each of the bolts into view.

d) Unbolt and remove the stiffener fitted between the engine and transmission.

e) Unscrew the bellhousing-to-transmission bolts.

f) Carefully pull the transmission away from the engine until the transmission is clear of the locating dowels. If necessary, push the torque converter back into the transmission – take care that it does not fall out as the transmission is lowered.

g) Either remove the torque converter or devise a method of keeping it inside the housing (such as bolting a metal strip across the bellhousing).

h) Recover the two locating dowels, noting their fitted locations

Reassembly

30 On models with manual transmission:

a) If removed, fit the clutch components and lightly oil the input shaft splines.

h) Make sure the two locating dowels are installed in the bellhousing mating face.

c) Slide the gearbox onto the engine so that the gearbox shaft enters the clutch. It may be necessary to 'wiggle' the gearbox slightly, to align the shaft splines with those of the clutch – if difficulty is experienced, it may mean that the clutch friction plate has not been centred (see Chapter 6). With the splines aligned, the gearbox should slide onto the two dowels, and fully up to the engine.

d) While an assistant holds the gearbox in place, insert two or three bellhousing-to-gearbox bolts and tighten them by hand.

e) Insert and tighten all the bellhousing-to-gearbox bolts to the specified torque, then refit the flywheel cover plate.

31 On models with automatic transmission:

a) If the torque converter was removed, refit it using a new O-ring seal. Have an assistant ready to keep the converter pressed into the housing as the transmission is refitted.

b) Make sure the two locating dowels are installed in the transmission mating face.

c) Slide the transmission onto the engine so that the torque converter seats against the driveplate; align the marks made on removal. It may be necessary to 'wiggle' the transmission slightly to align the two dowels with their locations in the engine bellhousing – with the dowels aligned, the transmission should slide fully up to the engine.

d) While an assistant holds the transmission in place, insert two or three bellhousing-to-transmission bolts and tighten them by hand.

e) Insert and tighten all the bellhousing-to-transmission bolts to the specified torque, then refit the stiffener and the torque converter cover plate.

Refitting

32 Where removed installed the engine/transmission mounting brackets.

33 Raise the front of the vehicle and with the aid of an assistant, slide the engine and transmission under the vehicle.

34 Lower the vehicle over the engine/transmission assembly and connect the engine crane to the engine lifting brackets.

35 Raise the engine and transmission assembly and connect first the engine (right-hand side) engine mounting and then the left-hand side (transmission side) mounting using new nuts and bolts. Tighten the fittings to the specified torque as described in Chapters 2A, 2B.

36 Remove the engine crane and if necessary raise the vehicle higher on the axle stands.

37 Remove the engine lifting brackets.

38 On models fitted with air conditioning refit the AC compressor.

39 Fit new circlips to the driveshafts and with reference to Chapter 8, refit the driveshafts and install the driveshaft heatshield.

40 Reconnect the control arms to the swivel hubs and then connect the track rod ends to the swivel hubs.

41 Refit the anti-roll bar drop links and where fitted the headlight adjustment control (Xenon headlight models only).

42 Install the catalytic converter using new gaskets and self locking nuts. On 1.8 models refit the front section of the exhaust system using new gaskets and fixings.

43 Reconnect the oxygen sensor wiring plugs and then on AC equipped models refit the auxiliary drivebelt.

44 Refit the engine undershield and the front wheels. Remove the axle stands and lower the vehicle to the ground.

45 Reconnect the coolant hoses and refit the radiator.

46 On manual transmission models refit the gear selector cables and clutch slave assembly.

47 Refit the brake vacuum hose, the EVAP hose and the fuel lines.

48 Install the ECU bracket and the ECU. Reconnect the wiring plugs and fit the protective cover.

49 Install the battery cables to the fusebox.

50 Refit the air filter housing support bracket and then fit the air filter housing and inlet duct..

51 Refit the battery.

52 Refit the windscreen cowl panels and the wiper arms.

53 Fill the radiator with fresh coolant/anti-freeze mix.

54 Fill the engine and transmission with oil and reconnect the battery.

55 Start the engine and allow it to run up to normal operating temperature whilst watch for oil, coolant and fuel leaks. Perform the idle learn procedure and the power window reset procedure as described in Chapter 5A.

56 On models fitted with Zenon (HID) headlights the headlights must be checked and adjusted using suitable diagnostic equipment.

5 Diesel engine – removal, separation and refitting

Note: The recommend Honda procedure is to remove the subframe and all the steering components, however for the home mechanic this is an awkward undertaking. The method outlined here does not require removal of the subframe, but does require degassing and removal of the AC compressor and radiator.

Removal

1 Disconnect and then remove the battery **(see illustration)** and battery tray as described in Chapter 5A.

2 With reference to Chapter 12 Section 12, remove the windscreen cowl panels.

5.1 Remove the battery

5.3 Remove the engine cover

5.4 Remove the air filter assembly

3 Remove the four bolts and remove the engine cover **(see illustration)**.

4 Remove the air filter assembly **(see illustration)** as described in Chapter 4B and then unbolt and remove the air filter mounting bracket.

5 Release the wiring loom and then unbolt the clutch pipes from the inner wing.

6 Disconnect the main supply cable from the fusebox (two bolts) and then disconnect the wiring plugs from the engine.

7 Release the hose clips and remove the intercooler outlet hose.

8 Unbolt the clutch slave cylinder and move it to the side. Secure the cylinder and pipe work to the side, out of harms way.

9 Remove the gear change cables as described in Chapter 7A and then remove the cable support bracket.

10 At the rear of the engine remove the fuel flow and return hoses. Plug the fuel lines and the pipes as soon as they are disconnected.

11 Disconnect the brake servo vacuum hose.

12 Jack up and support the front of the vehicle (see "*Jacking and vehicle support*' in the Reference chapter ') and then remove the engine undershield.

13 Drain the engine coolant and then drain the engine oil as described in Chapter 1B.

14 Drain the transmission oil and then with reference to Chapter 8, remove both driveshafts.

15 Where a Diesel Particulate Filter (DPF) is fitted disconnect the differential pressure pipes and then disconnect the exhaust gas temperature sensor. Remove the DPF, or where a catalytic converter is fitted remove the converter.

16 Slacken the hose clips and then unbolt and remove the intercooler inlet pipe from beneath the engine.

17 Remove the radiator and cooling fan assembly as described in Chapter 3.

18 Remove the auxiliary drivebelt as described in Chapter 1B. At this point the AC compressor must be removed, as it will foul the front lower cross member as the engine is lowered. To avoid any damage to the compressor or associated pipework, degassing of the AC system by a suitable equipped mobile air conditioning specialist is recommended. It may be possible to

proceed by leaving the AC system intact and just unbolting the AC compressor, but given the relatively low cost of degassing (and re-gassing) the AC system this is not recommended.

> ⚠ **Warning: It is an offence to knowingly discharge an AC system to the atmosphere.**

19 Remove the AC compressor (after degassing) from the vehicle. Immediately seal all open AC pipe work.

20 At the bulkhead disconnect the heater matrix supply and return hoses and then remove the coolant by-pass hose from the top of the engine **(see illustration)**.

21 Remove the rear torque rod (dog bone) and support bracket from the rear of the engine as described in Chapter 2C.

22 Slacken, but DO NOT remove the left and right-hand engine mounting bolts.

23 As the engine will be lowered from the vehicle, the vehicle must be raised high enough to allow the engine and transmission to be remove from beneath the front lower cross member. Check that the vehicle is raised sufficiently to allow this.

24 The engine must now be supported with chains or slings from a suitable engine crane. Note that lifting eyes are not provide and these will have to be fabricated. Attach the brackets to one of the bell housing bolts at the rear of the engine and to the front of the of the cylinder head **(see illustration)**. Full raise the engine crane and manoeuvre it into position.

25 Attach the chains or slings to the lifting brackets and take the weight of the engine/

transmission assembly on the crane. Remove both upper engine mountings as described in Chapter 2C.

26 With the aid of an assistant, lower the engine and transmission assembly slightly and check that all wiring connectors and all pipe work has been disconnected. Have the assistant slowly lower the assembly whilst constantly checking that the engine and transmission assembly do not catch any components or bodywork as they are lowered. Note that the assemble is a tight fit and certain amount of manoeuvring will be required to clear the subframe and lower front cross member.

27 Where the vehicle has been raised sufficiently the assembly can be lowered onto a suitable wheeled dolly. If space is limited then lower the assembly onto a section of old carpet. Disconnect the engine crane and drag (or wheel) the engine and transmission assembly out from under the vehicle. Note it is always possible to raise the front of the vehicle by attaching the engine crane to the front chassis legs and using the crane to safely raise the front of the vehicle.

Separation

28 Support the assembly on suitable blocks of wood, on a workbench (or failing that, on a clean area of the workshop floor).

29 Unscrew the engine bellhousing to gearbox bolts.

30 Carefully withdraw the gearbox from the engine, ensuring that the weight of the gearbox is not allowed to hang on the input shaft. If necessary, carefully prise the gearbox away at first, to release the alignment dowels.

31 Recover the two locating dowels, noting their fitted locations.

Reassembly

32 If removed, fit the clutch components (Chapter 6).

33 Lightly oil the gearbox input shaft splines – do not use multi-purpose grease.

34 Make sure the two locating dowels are installed in the bellhousing mating face.

35 Raise the gearbox on a jack, then slide it onto the engine so that the gearbox shaft enters the clutch. It may be necessary to 'wiggle' the gearbox slightly, to align the

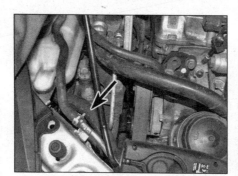

5.20 Release the bypass hose

5.24 A suitable mounting point for the front lifting eye

shaft splines with those of the clutch – if difficulty is experienced it may mean that the clutch friction plate has not been centred (see Chapter 6). With the splines aligned, the gearbox should slide onto the two dowels, and fully up to the engine.

36 While an assistant holds the gearbox in place, insert two or three engine bellhousing-to-gearbox bolts and tighten them by hand.

37 Insert and tighten all the engine bellhousing-to-gearbox bolts to the specified torque setting.

Refitting

38 Position the engine and transmission assembly under the engine bay and then lower the engine crane jib into place. Re-attach the lifting eyes, if not already done so and then attach the chains (or slings).

39 With the aid of an assistant, carefully lift the unit it into position in the engine compartment, manipulating the crane and lifting tackle as necessary, taking care not to trap or damage any components.

40 Raise the engine sufficiently so that the engine mountings can be bolted into place. Using new bolts where specified, tighten the engine mountings as described in Chapter 2C.

41 Remove the lifting chains and lifting eyes.

42 The remainder of the refitting procedure is a reversal of the removal sequence, noting the following points:

a) Ensure that all wiring is correctly routed and retained and that all connectors are correctly reconnected.

b) Ensure that all disturbed hoses are correctly reconnected and securely retained.

c) Tighten all nuts/bolts to the specified torque.

d) Lightly grease the gearchange cable end fittings and slave cylinder pushrod end when refitting.

e) Refill the gearbox with fluid (Chapter 1B).

f) Refill the engine with oil and fit a new filter (Chapter 1B).

g) Refill the cooling system (Chapter 1B).

h) Prime the fuel system when the fuel feed and return hoses have been reconnected (Chapter 4B).

i) Honda recommend that the idle speed is checked after an engine overhaul. If the idle speed is incorrect than a Honda dealer (or suitable equipped specialist) will need to adjust it using suitable diagnostic equipment.

j) If the Malfunction Indicator warning Lamp (MIL) illuminates after starting the vehicle check all the electrical connections and complete several drive cycles. The fault code should clear. If the fault code does not clear then the vehicle must be taken to a Honda dealer or suitably equipped specialist for the fault codes to be checked.

k) If the front subframe was removed, have the front wheel alignment checked.

6 Engine overhaul – dismantling sequence

1 It is much easier to dismantle and work on the engine if it is mounted on a portable engine stand. These stands can often be hired from a tool hire shop. Before the engine is mounted on a stand, the flywheel/driveplate should be removed, so that the stand bolts can be tightened into the end of the cylinder block/crankcase.

2 If a stand is not available, it is possible to dismantle the engine with it blocked up on a sturdy workbench, or on the floor. Be extra careful not to tip or drop the engine when working without a stand.

3 If you are going to obtain a reconditioned engine, all the external components must be removed first, to be transferred to the new engine (just as they will if you are doing a complete engine overhaul yourself). These components include the following:

a) Engine wiring harness and support brackets.

b) Alternator, power steering pump and air conditioning compressor mounting brackets (as applicable).

c) Coolant inlet and outlet housings.

d) Dipstick tube.

e) Fuel system components.

f) All electrical switches and sensors.

g) Inlet and exhaust manifolds and, where fitted, the turbocharger.

h) Oil filter and oil cooler.

i) Flywheel.

Note: When removing the external components from the engine, pay close attention to details that may be helpful or important during refitting. Note the fitted position of gaskets, seals, spacers, pins, washers, bolts, and other small items.

4 If you are obtaining a short engine (which consists of the engine cylinder block/crankcase, crankshaft, pistons and connecting rods all assembled), then the cylinder head, sump, oil pump, and timing belt will have to be removed also.

5 If you are planning a complete overhaul, the engine can be dismantled, and the internal components removed, in the order given below, referring to Part A, B or C of this Chapter unless otherwise stated.

a) Inlet and exhaust manifolds (Chapter 4A).

b) Timing chain, sprockets and tensioner.

c) Coolant pump (Chapter 3).

d) Cylinder head.

e) Flywheel.

f) Sump.

g) Oil pump.

h) Pistons/connecting rods (Section 10 of this Chapter).

i) Crankshaft (Section 11 of this Chapter).

6 Before beginning the dismantling and overhaul procedures, make sure that you have all of the correct tools necessary. See Tools and working facilities for further information.

7 Cylinder head – dismantling

Note: New and reconditioned cylinder heads are available from the manufacturer, and from engine overhaul specialists. Be aware that some specialist tools are required for the dismantling and inspection procedures, and new components may not be readily available. It may therefore be more practical and economical for the home mechanic to purchase a reconditioned head, rather than dismantle, inspect and recondition the original head.

1 On petrol engines remove the rocker shaft assembly (Chapter 2A or Chapter 2B) then remove the cylinder head from the engine. Remove the spark plugs.

2 On diesel engines, remove the glow plugs (Chapter 4C) and injectors (Chapter 4B). Remove the camshafts, camshaft carrier and cam followers and hydraulic tappets from the cylinder head, then remove the cylinder head from the engine.

3 On all engines, using a valve spring compressor, compress each valve spring in turn until the split collets can be removed. Release the compressor, and lift off the spring retainer and spring. Using a pair of pliers, carefully extract the valve stem oil seal from the valve guide (see illustrations).

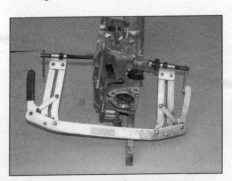
7.3a Fit the valve spring compressor...

7.3b...and compress the valve spring. Recover the collets

7.3c Remove the collet retainer and valve spring and...

7.3d...then remove the valve guide oil seal using pliers or...

7.3e...or a pair of special oil seal pliers

4 If, when the valve spring compressor is screwed down, the spring retainer refuses to free and expose the split collets, gently tap the top of the tool, directly over the retainer, with a light hammer. This will free the retainer.
5 Pull the valve out of the head through the combustion chamber. If the valve binds in the guide (won't pull through), push it back into the head and deburr the edge of the collet groove with a fine file or fine emery cloth. It is essential that each valve is stored together with its collets, retainer, spring and spring seat **(see illustration)**. The valves should also be kept in their correct sequence, unless they are so badly worn that they are to be renewed.

8 Cylinder head and valves – cleaning and inspection

1 Thorough cleaning of the cylinder head and valve components, followed by a detailed inspection, will enable you to decide how much valve service work must be carried out during the engine overhaul.
Note: *If the engine has been severely overheated, it is best to assume that the cylinder head is warped – check carefully for signs of this.*

Cleaning
2 Scrape away all traces of old gasket material from the cylinder head.
3 Scrape away the carbon from the combustion chambers and ports, then wash the cylinder head thoroughly with paraffin or a suitable solvent.
4 Scrape off any heavy carbon deposits that may have formed on the valves, then use a power-operated wire brush to remove deposits from the valve heads and stems.

Inspection
Note: *Be sure to perform all the following inspection procedures before concluding that the services of a machine shop or engine overhaul specialist are required. Make a list of all items that require attention.*

Cylinder head
5 Inspect the head very carefully for cracks, evidence of coolant leakage, and other damage. If cracks are found, a new cylinder

head should be obtained. Use a straight-edge and feeler blade to check that the cylinder head gasket surface is not distorted **(see illustration)**. If it is, it may be possible to have it machined, provided that the cylinder head height is not significantly reduced.
6 Examine the valve seats in each of the combustion chambers. If they are severely pitted, cracked, or burned, they will need to be renewed or recut by an engine overhaul specialist. If they are only slightly pitted, this can be removed by grinding-in the valve heads and seats with fine valve-grinding compound, as described below. If in any doubt, have the cylinder head inspected by an engine overhaul specialist.
7 Check the valve guides for wear by inserting the relevant valve, and checking for side-to-side motion of the valve. A very small amount of movement is acceptable. If the movement seems excessive, remove the valve. Measure the valve stem diameter and renew the valve if it is worn. If the valve stem is not worn, the wear must be in the valve guide, and the guide must be renewed. The renewal of valve guides is best carried out by an engine overhaul specialist, who will have the necessary tools available.
8 If renewing the valve guides, the valve seats should be recut or reground only after the guides have been fitted.

Valves
9 Examine the head of each valve for pitting, burning, cracks, and general wear. Check the valve stem for scoring and wear ridges.

8.5 Check the cylinder head gasket surface for distortion

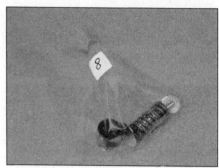

7.5 If the components are to be refitted, place each valve and its associated components in a labelled polythene bag or similar container, and mark the bag/container with the relevant number to ensure that it is refitted in its original position.

Rotate the valve, and check for any obvious indication that it is bent. Look for pits or excessive wear on the tip of each valve stem. Renew any valve that shows any such signs of wear or damage.
10 If the valve appears satisfactory at this stage, measure the valve stem diameter at several points using a micrometer **(see illustration)**. Any significant difference in the readings obtained indicates wear of the valve stem. Should any of these conditions be apparent, the valve must be renewed.
11 If the valves are in satisfactory condition, they should be ground (lapped) into their respective seats, to ensure a smooth, gas-tight seal. If the seat is only lightly pitted,

8.10 Measure the valve stem diameter with a micrometer

8.13 Grinding-in a valve

8.16a Measure the valve spring length

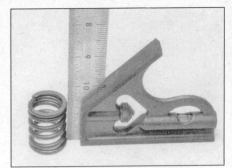

8.16b Check the valve spring for squareness

or if it has been recut, fine grinding compound only should be used to produce the required finish. Coarse valve-grinding compound should not be used, unless a seat is badly burned or deeply pitted. If this is the case, the cylinder head and valves should be inspected by an expert, to decide whether seat recutting, or even the renewal of the valve or seat insert (where possible) is required.

12 Valve grinding is carried out as follows. Place the cylinder head upside-down on a bench.

13 Smear a trace of (the appropriate grade of) valve-grinding compound on the seat face, and press a suction grinding tool onto the valve head **(see illustration)**. With a semi-rotary action, grind the valve head to its seat, lifting the valve occasionally to redistribute the grinding compound. A light spring placed under the valve head will greatly ease this operation.

14 If coarse grinding compound is being used, work only until a dull, matt even surface is produced on both the valve seat and the valve, then wipe off the used compound, and repeat the process with fine compound. When a smooth unbroken ring of light grey matt finish is produced on both the valve and seat, the grinding operation is complete. Do not grind-in the valves any further than absolutely necessary, or the seat will be prematurely sunk into the cylinder head.

15 When all the valves have been ground-in, carefully wash off all traces of grinding compound using paraffin or a suitable solvent, before reassembling the cylinder head.

Valve components

16 Examine the valve springs for signs of damage and discoloration. The condition of each spring can be judged by measuring its free length. Stand each spring on a flat surface, and check it for squareness **(see illustrations)**.

If any of the springs are less than the specified free length or are damaged or distorted, obtain a complete new set of springs.

17 Renew the valve stem oil seals regardless of their apparent condition.

9 Cylinder head – reassembly

1 Working on the first valve assembly, refit the spring seat then dip the new valve stem oil seal in fresh engine oil. Locate the seal on the valve guide and press the seal firmly onto the guide using a suitable socket. Note that some genuine Honda seals are colour coded – black for the exhaust and white for the inlet **(see illustrations)**.

2 Lubricate the stem of the first valve, and insert it in the guide **(see illustration)**.

9.1a Fit the spring seat first

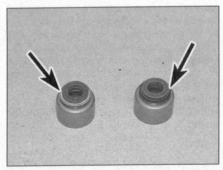

9.1b Some valve stem oil seals may be colour coded

9.1c Locate the valve stem oil seal on the valve guide...

9.1d ...and press the seal firmly onto the guide using a suitable socket

9.2a Lubricate the stem of the valve...

9.2b...and insert it into the guide

9.4 Fit the collets. A small blob of grease will help to locate the collets

9.5 Lightly tap the end of each valve stem to settle the components

3 Locate the valve spring on top of its seat, then refit the spring retainer.

4 Compress the valve spring, and locate the split collets in the recess in the valve stem **(see illustration)**. Release the compressor, then repeat the procedure on the remaining valves. Ensure that each valve is inserted into its original location. If new valves are being fitted, insert them into the locations to which they have been ground.

5 With all the valves installed, support the cylinder head and, using a hammer and interposed block of wood, tap the end of each valve stem to settle the components **(see illustration)**.

6 On petrol engines, working as described in Chapter 2A (1.4 litre engines) or Chapter 2B (1.8 litre engines), refit the cylinder head to the engine and install the cam follower assembly and camshafts. Refit the spark plugs loosely to prevent dirt or small objects dropping into the combustion chamber (see Chapter 1A)

7 On diesel engines, working as described in Chapter 2C, refit the cylinder head to the engine and install the cam followers and hydraulic tappets, camshaft carrier, and camshafts. Refit the injectors and glow plugs as described in Chapters 4B and 4C.

10 Piston/connecting rod assembly – removal

1 Referring to Part A, B or C of this Chapter, remove the cylinder head and sump.

2 Where fitted unbolt the baffle plates and oil pick up pipe from the main bearing ladder **(see illustrations)**.

3 If not already done so, remove the oil pump. On diesel engines remove the oil pump and balancer shaft assembly as described in Chapter 2C.

4 Use feeler blades to measure the gap between the machined surface on the web of the crankpin and the side of the connecting rod big-end bearing **(see illustration)**. If the connecting rod endfloat is greater than the specified service limit, the connecting rod or crankshaft must be renewed.

5 The pistons and connecting rods can be removed with the main bearing ladder in position on the 1.8 petrol and the diesel engines On the 1.4 petrol engines the main bearing cap ladder must be removed first. However in most cases inspection of the main bearings should always be carried out if the piston and connecting rods are being removed.

6 Using a hammer and centre punch, paint or similar, mark each connecting rod big-end bearing cap with its respective cylinder number on the flat, machined surface provided; make the marks in such a way that there is no possibility of fitting the caps the wrong way around on refitting **(see illustrations)**. If the engine has been dismantled before, note carefully any identifying marks made previously, but note that the number or marking etched across each connecting rod and

10.2a Remove the baffle plate on the 1.8 petrol engine...

10.2b...and on the 2.2 diesel engine

10.4 Measuring the connecting rod end float

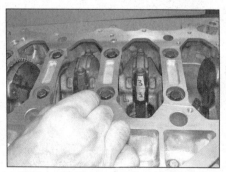

10.6a Use paint, or correction fluid, to mark each connecting rod big-end bearing cap...

10.6b...and the connecting rod big-end bearing cap with its respective cylinder number prior to removal

10.6c Note the big-end bearing bore diameter class marking etched across front face of each connecting rod and bearing cap on some engines

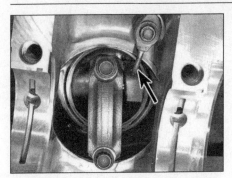

10.10 Take care not to damage the piston cooling oil jets (where fitted) when removing or refitting the piston/connecting rod

bearing cap (and facing to the front, on the engines dismantled for the workshop project) is the big-end bearing bore diameter class marking, not a cylinder-identifying number. Note that No. 1 cylinder is at the timing chain end of the engine.

7 On the 1.4 petrol engines remove the bearing ladder before marking up the connecting rods and bearing caps. Slacken the bolts in the reverse order to that shown in Section 18. Remove the bearing ladder and recover the main bearing shells, keeping them in the correct order and orientation.

8 On all other engines either remove the bearing ladder first – as described in Section 11 – or rotate the crankshaft and remove the connecting rods by lowering the pistons to bottom dead centre (BDC) individually.

9 If there is a pronounced wear ridge at the top of any bore, it may be necessary to remove it with a scraper or ridge reamer, to avoid piston damage during removal. Such a ridge indicates excessive wear of the cylinder bore. Note however that if the ridge is pronounced then it is reasonable to assume the engine will require a re-bore and new pistons.

10 Unscrew and remove the big-end bearing cap bolts in order, rotating the crankshaft as required. Withdraw the cap, complete with bearing shell, from the connecting rod. Note that on petrol engines, the big-end caps are located on the connecting rods by dowels. Do not tap the caps sideways in an attempt to remove them. On diesel engines, 'cracked' connecting rods are used in which rod and cap align precisely, one way only, without the need for locating dowel pins. If the bearing shells are to be re-used, tape the cap and the shell together. If only the bearing shells are being attended to, push the connecting rod up and off the crankpin, ensuring that the connecting rod big-ends do not mark the cylinder bore walls and that the piston-cooling oil jets (where fitted) are not bent or damaged, then remove the upper bearing shell **(see illustration)**. Keep the cap, bolts and bearing shells together in their correct sequence.

11 Using a hammer handle, push the piston up through the bore, and remove it from the top of the cylinder block. Recover the bearing shell, and tape it to the connecting rod for safe-keeping.

12 Loosely refit the big-end cap to the connecting rod, and secure with the nuts/bolts – this will help to keep the components in their correct order.

13 Remove the No 4 piston assembly in the same way and then turn the crankshaft through 180° to bring pistons 2 and 3 to BDC. Remove pistons 2 and 3 in the same way.

11 Crankshaft – removal

Note: *The 1.8 litre petrol engines and the diesel engines have a main bearing ladder (retainer) that is part of the lower engine block. The sump is bolted directly to the bearing ladder. 1.4 litre petrol engines have a smaller bearing ladder that does not form part of the lower engine block. On these engines the sump bolts directly to the main engine block (see illustration).*

1 Referring to Part A, B or C of this Chapter, remove the sump and flywheel/driveplate. On diesel engines unbolt the balancer shaft assembly and oil pump from the lower crankcase/main bearing ladder. If no work is to be done on the pistons and connecting rods, the cylinder head can be left in position; if they are to be removed, then the cylinder head must be removed first.

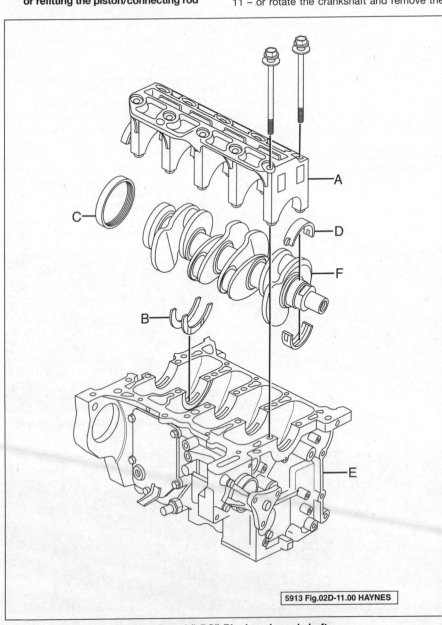

5913 Fig.02D-11.00 HAYNES

11.0 1.4 Petrol (i-DSI) Block and crankshaft

A Bearing bridge (Ladder)
B Trust washers
C Oil seal
D Main bearings
E Engine block
F Crankshaft

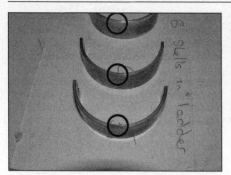

11.6 Remove the bearing shells and store them in their correct fitted order – note the colour coding (diesel model shown)

11.7a Remove the crankshaft

11.7b Where fitted remove the crankshaft position sensor pulse plate.

2 Where fitted unbolt the baffle plate from the cylinder block and if not already done so remove the oil pump pick-up pipe.

3 Check the crankshaft endfloat as described in Section 14.

4 Working in the reverse of the sequence shown in Section 18, progressively unscrew the lower crankcase/main bearing ladder-to-cylinder block 8 mm bolts by a turn at a time – diesel and 1.8 petrol engines only. Remove all the bolts, keeping them in the correct fitted order.

5 Working in the reverse of the sequence shown in Section 18, progressively unscrew the lower crankcase/main bearing ladder main bearing cap bolts by a one-third of a turn at a time. Remove all the bolts, keeping them in the correct fitted order.

6 Withdraw the lower main bearing ladder. Note the two locating dowels at each bearing location, plus the large single dowel, and the main bearing shells, which should be removed from the ladder and stored in their correct fitted order **(see illustration)**.

7 Carefully lift out the crankshaft, taking care not to displace the upper main bearing shells and being careful not to mark or damage the journals or damage the crankshaft position sensor pick-up plate (1.8 litre petrol and diesel engines only). Remove and discard the oil seal. If necessary, the pick-up plate can be unbolted **(see illustrations)**.

8 Withdraw the two thrustwashers from the No. 4 main bearing upper location. Noting

the position of the grooved shells, remove the upper main bearing shells, which must be kept with their correct respective partners from the main bearing ladder so that all shells can be identified and (if necessary) refitted in their original locations.

12 Cylinder block/crankcase – cleaning and inspection

Cleaning

1 Remove all external components and electrical switches/sensors from the block.

2 Remove the oil filter/oil cooler/water pump housing on diesel engines.

3 Remove all oil gallery and coolant passage core plugs fitted. Most are threaded, with square or hexagon apertures so that they can be unscrewed using the appropriate key. The plugs are usually very tight – use only good-quality tools to remove and refit them and discard the sealing washers – these must be renewed whenever the plugs are disturbed. For complete cleaning, the punched-in core plugs should also, ideally, be removed. Drill a small hole in the plug, then insert a self-tapping screw into the hole. Pull out the plug by pulling on the screw with a pair of grips, or by using a slide hammer. Carefully clean the plug threads and recesses in the casting.

4 On diesel engines and 1.8 petrol engines,

undo the retaining bolts and remove each piston-cooling oil jet from inside the cylinder block. Wash each jet thoroughly in solvent to clean its passages. On the 1.8 petrol engines Honda recommend that the the oil cooling jets are replaced.

Diesel engine piston cooling jets

5 Check the piston-cooling oil jets **(see illustrations)**. If any has a damaged or bent nozzle, it must be renewed. Check that a 3.1 mm drill bit can be inserted into the oil intake (nominal diameter 3.2 mm) and that the check ball moves smoothly through a stroke of about 2 mm. If the necessary equipment is available apply air pressure and check that the check ball opens at the specified pressure (see the Specifications in Chapter 2C). Check that a 1.7 mm drill bit can be inserted into the jet itself (nominal diameter 1.8 mm).

Caution: Wear eye protection when using compressed air.

Petrol engine piston cooling jets

6 Check the piston-cooling oil jets. Honda recommend that the actual jets are discarded if removed. Check that a 1.1 mm drill bit can be inserted into the oil intake (nominal diameter 1.2 mm) and that the check ball moves smoothly through a stroke of about 4 mm. If the necessary equipment is available apply air pressure and check that the check ball opens at the specified pressure (see the Specifications in Chapter 2B).

All engines

7 On all engines, thoroughly clean the mating surfaces of the cylinder block/crankcase and the lower crankcase/main bearing ladder, taking care not to damage the surfaces. Clean any oil or old sealant from the mating surfaces and from the bolt holes and threads. Note that the crankshaft main bearing bore diameter code letters or numbers are marked on the bottom surface of the lower crankcase/main bearing ladder at the rear of the flywheel end; be very careful not to scrub so hard that these are erased. Similarly, do not scrub out the cylinder bore diameter size group markings stamped on the top of the timing chain end of the cylinder block, at the front (petrol engines) or rear (diesel engines).

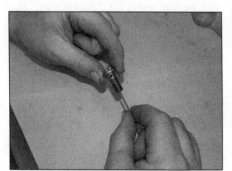

12.5a Check the piston cooling oil jets – ensure the intake is clear and that the check ball is free to move correctly

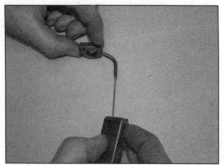

12.5b Check that the nozzle is clear

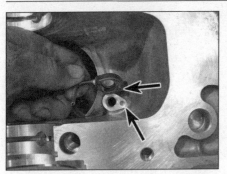

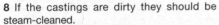

12.13 Align the piston cooling oil jet locating dowel with hole in cylinder block (diesel engine shown)

12.15 All bolt holds should be cleaned and restored with a tap

8 If the castings are dirty they should be steam-cleaned.

9 If the castings are not very dirty, you can do an adequate cleaning job with hot water, detergent and a stiff brush. Take plenty of time, and do a thorough job. Regardless of the cleaning method used, be sure to clean all oil holes and galleries very thoroughly, and to dry all components well. Lightly oil the cylinder bores to prevent rusting.

10 All threaded holes must be clean, to ensure accurate torque readings during reassembly. To clean the threads, use an old toothbrush, a small bottle brush or a small wire brush. Remove deposits of sludge and plugs and beads of old sealant using a finely-pointed instrument, but take care not to scratch the casting. If possible, use compressed air to clear the holes of debris produced by this operation. A good alternative is to inject aerosol-applied water-dispersant lubricant into each hole, using the long spout usually supplied.

11 After the castings are returned from any resurfacing, reboring or other machining work, clean all oil holes and oil galleries one more time. Flush all internal passages with warm water until the water runs clear. Dry thoroughly, and apply a light film of oil to all mating surfaces, to prevent rusting. Also oil the cylinder bores. If you have access to compressed air, use it to speed up the drying process, and to blow out all the oil holes and galleries.

12 Refit all oil gallery and coolant passage core plugs that were removed. Fit new sealing

washers to the threaded plugs and tighten them securely to the torque wrench settings specified. Similarly, apply suitable sealant to new core plugs and drive them into the casting with a close-fitting tube or socket.

13 On diesel engines, refit the piston-cooling oil jets to the cylinder block, so that the locating peg on the jet engages in the hole in the cylinder block **(see illustration)**. On 1.8 litre petrol engines fit new oil cooling jets if they have been removed. Refit the retaining bolts, tightening them carefully to the specified torque wrench setting.

14 If the engine is not going to be reassembled right away, cover it with a large plastic bag to keep it clean; protect all mating surfaces and the cylinder bores as described above, to prevent rusting. When you do rebuild the engine, remember to degrease completely all mating surfaces before applying sealant.

Inspection

Note: *On all engines, have the cylinder block inspected by an engine reconditioning specialist. They will be able to determine if the cylinder block is re-usable, carry out any machining work, and supply the correct new pistons, etc.*

15 Visually check the castings for cracks and corrosion. Look for stripped threads in the threaded holes. If there has been any history of internal water leakage, it may be worthwhile having an engine overhaul specialist check the cylinder block/crankcase

with special equipment. If defects are found, have them repaired if possible, or renew the assembly. Damaged threads, or threads that are heavily rusted or corroded, or fouled with old thread-locking compound, must be restored by running the correct size tap into each of the holes until the thread is clear and the fastener concerned can be run in and out to its full depth by hand **(see illustration)**. Broken threads and castings are a matter for an engine reconditioning specialist.

16 Check each cylinder bore for scuffing and scoring. Check for signs of a wear ridge at the top of the cylinder, indicating that the bore is excessively worn.

17 Measure the inside diameter of each cylinder bore **(see illustration)**. Take two measurements, one parallel with the crankshaft axis and the other at right-angles to it. Compare the results with the figures given in the Specifications. Note that there are two bore diameter size groups to allow for manufacturing tolerances; the size group marking is stamped on the top of the timing chain end of the cylinder block, at the front (petrol engines) or rear (diesel engines) **(see illustration)**. No. 1 cylinder's code is the closest to the timing chain end, No. 4's closest to the flywheel.

18 Oversize pistons are available, and it should be possible to have the cylinder block rebored and fit the oversize pistons. Seek the advice of a Honda dealer or engine reconditioning specialist on the best course of action.

19 If the bores are in reasonably good condition and not worn to the specified limits, then the piston rings should be renewed. If this is the case, the bores should be honed to allow the new rings to bed in correctly and provide the best possible seal. The conventional type of hone has spring-loaded stones, and is used with a power drill. You will also need some paraffin (or honing oil) and rags. The hone should be moved up-and-down the bore to produce a crosshatch pattern, and plenty of honing oil should be used. Ideally, the crosshatch lines should intersect at approximately a 60° angle. Do not take off more material than is necessary to produce the required finish. If new pistons are being fitted, the piston manufacturers may specify a finish with a different angle, so their instructions should be followed. Do not withdraw the hone from the bore while it is still being turned – stop it first. After honing a bore, wipe out all traces of the honing oil. If equipment of this type is not available, or if you are not sure whether you are competent to undertake the task yourself, an engine overhaul specialist will carry out the work at moderate cost.

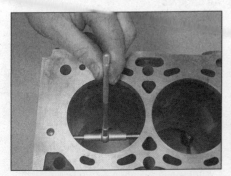

12.17a Use an internal micrometer to measure the cylinder bore diameter

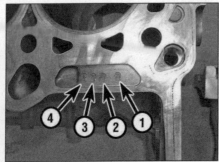

12.17b The cylinder bore diameter size group codes are stamped on top of the timing chain end of the block

13 Piston/connecting rod assembly – inspection

1 Before the inspection process can begin, the piston/connecting rod assemblies must be cleaned, and the piston rings removed from the pistons.

13.2 Using a feeler blade to remove a piston ring

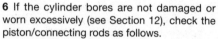

13.4a The piston ring grooves can be cleaned with a special tool, as shown here...

13.4b...or a section of a broken ring, if available

2 Carefully expand the old rings over the top of the pistons. The use of two or three old feeler blades will be helpful in preventing the rings dropping into empty grooves **(see illustration)**. Be careful not to scratch the piston with the ends of the ring. The rings are brittle, and will snap if they are spread too far. They're also very sharp – protect your hands and fingers. Note that the third (oil control) ring may consist of a spacer and two side rails, or a one-piece ring. Always remove the rings from the top of the piston. Keep each set of rings with its piston if the old rings are to be re-used.

3 Scrape away all traces of carbon from the top of the piston. A hand-held wire brush (or a piece of fine emery cloth) can be used, once the majority of the deposits have been scraped away. The piston identification markings should now be visible.

4 Remove the carbon from the ring grooves in the piston, using either one of the purpose-built tools available, or an old ring **(see illustrations)**. Break the ring in half to do this (be careful not to cut your fingers – piston rings are sharp). Be careful to remove only the carbon deposits – do not remove any metal, and do not nick or scratch the sides of the ring grooves.

5 Once the deposits have been removed, clean the piston/connecting rod assembly with paraffin or a suitable solvent, and dry thoroughly. Make sure that the oil return holes in the ring grooves are clear.

6 If the cylinder bores are not damaged or worn excessively (see Section 12), check the piston/connecting rods as follows.

7 Carefully inspect each piston for cracks around the skirt, around the gudgeon pin holes, and at the piston ring lands (between the ring grooves).

8 Look for scoring and scuffing on the piston skirt, holes in the piston crown, and burned areas at the edge of the crown. If the skirt is scored or scuffed, the engine may have been suffering from overheating, and/or abnormal combustion which caused excessively high operating temperatures. The cooling and lubrication systems should be checked thoroughly. Scorch marks on the sides of the pistons show that blow-by has occurred. A hole in the piston crown, or burned areas at the edge of the piston crown, indicates that abnormal combustion (pre-ignition, knocking, or detonation) has been occurring. If any of the above problems exist, the causes must be investigated and corrected, or the damage will occur again. The causes may include incorrect ignition/injection timing (as applicable), or a faulty injector.

9 Corrosion of the piston, in the form of pitting, indicates that coolant has been leaking into the combustion chamber and/or the crankcase. Again, the cause must be corrected, or the problem may persist in the rebuilt engine.

10 Measure the piston diameter at the places given in the Section 0 and compare the results **(see illustrations)**. Note that on diesel engines there are two piston size groups to allow for manufacturing tolerances; the size group marking is stamped on the piston crown.

11 To measure the piston-to-bore clearance, measure the bore diameter as described in Section 12. Calculate the clearance by subtracting the piston diameter from the bore measurement. Alternatively, insert each piston into its original bore, then select a feeler blade and slip it into the bore along with the piston. The piston must be aligned exactly in its normal attitude, and the feeler blade must be between the piston and bore, on one of the thrust faces, with the piston at the top, middle, and bottom of the bore. If the clearance is excessive at any point, a rebore and new pistons may be required. If the piston binds at the lower end of the bore and is loose towards the top, the bore is tapered. If tight spots are encountered as the piston/feeler blade is rotated in the bore, the bore is out-of-round.

12 Repeat this procedure for the remaining pistons and cylinder bores. Any piston which is worn beyond the specified limits must be renewed.

13 Examine each connecting rod carefully for signs of damage, such as cracks around the big-end and small-end bearings. Check that the rod is not bent or distorted. Damage is highly unlikely, unless the engine has been seized or badly overheated. Detailed checking of the connecting rod assembly can only be carried out by an engine repair specialist. Connecting rod endfloat is checked when the connecting rod is assembled on its crankshaft journal, as described in Section 10.

14 Check the big-end bearings as described in Section 13 and Section 14.

15 On the diesel engine and the 1.8 litre petrol engine the gudgeon pins are held in place by circlips. On the 1.4 petrol engines the pins are an interference fit and a hydraulic press will be required to remove them. To avoid confusion on reassembly always mark the relation of the piston to the connecting rod.

16 Using a small screwdriver, remove the circlips from the piston (note the location of the circlip end gaps) then push out the

13.10a Measure the piston diameter at right angles to the gudgeon pin axis

13.10b The piston size group code is stamped on the piston crown (diesel engines)

13.16a Use a small screwdriver to remove the circlips from the piston...

13.16b...and push out the gudgeon pin to separate the piston from the connecting rod

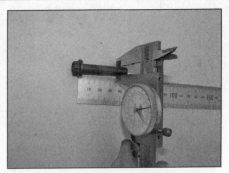

13.18 Measure the diameter of the threads. Do not allow the vernier to drop into the thread grooves

gudgeon pin **(see illustrations)**. Honda are careful to stress that the circlips should be oiled before being moved round to a position from which they can be removed, ie, with a free end in the cut-out in the piston boss. Hand pressure should be sufficient to remove the pin on diesel engines, but it may be necessary to heat the piston and connecting rod assembly of petrol engines to about 70ºC to remove the pin. Identify the piston and rod to ensure correct reassembly. Discard the circlips – new ones must be used on refitting.

17 Where interference gudgeon pins are fitted then special tooling will be required to push out the pin using a hydraulic press. It is important that the piston is not damaged during this procedure, so the task is best left to a suitable equipped machine shop.

18 Inspect the connecting rod big-end bearing cap bolts closely for signs of wear or damage and check that they screw easily into the connecting rods. Renew any bolt which shows visible signs of damage or does not screw easily into position. On the diesel and 1.8 litre petrol engines measure the diameter of the threads of each bolt at 35 mm (diameter A) and 20 mm (diameter B) from the underside of the head, then subtract B from A. If the difference in diameter is greater than 0.1 mm then it must be replaced **(see illustration)**. If working on the 1.4 litre petrol engine follow the same procedure, but check the bolt at 30 mm and 15 mm. If the difference in diameter

is greater than than 0.05 mm them the bolt must be replaced. Although Honda are happy to have bolts re-used as long as they pass this test, it is good practice to renew highly-stressed fasteners such as these as a matter of course, irrespective of their apparent condition, whenever they are disturbed.

19 Examine the gudgeon pin and connecting rod small-end bearing for signs of wear or damage. Wear will require the renewal of both the pin and connecting rod. If the necessary measuring equipment is available, measure the inside diameter of each piston bore and connecting rod small end eye, and the outside diameter of the gudgeon pin at the appropriate points; subtract one from the other to establish gudgeon pin-to-rod and piston clearances. Compare the results with the figures given in the Specifications.

20 Examine all components, and obtain any new parts from your Honda dealer or engine parts supplier. If any machining is required then the machine shop should supply the necessary parts.

21 Assemble the piston and connecting rod so that the arrow (where visible) on the piston crown is pointing in the same direction as the embossed mark on the flank of the connecting rod **(see illustration)**.

22 Apply a smear of clean engine oil to the gudgeon pin and to the piston bores and connecting rod small end eye. Slide the gudgeon pin into the piston and through the

connecting rod small-end. If necessary on 1.8 litre petrol engines, heat the piston and rod to about 70ºC to allow the gudgeon pin to be refitted. Check that the piston pivots freely on the rod, then secure the gudgeon pin with two new circlips, ensuring that each circlip is correctly located in its groove in the piston. Honda state that the circlips must be turned until their end gaps are at the bottoms of the pistons, but on the engines dismantled for the project, all the end gaps were found at the tops of the pistons **(see illustration)**.

14 Crankshaft – inspection

Checking endfloat

1 If the crankshaft endfloat is to be checked, this must be done when the crankshaft is still installed in the cylinder block, but is free to move (see Section 11).

2 Check the endfloat using a dial gauge in contact with the end of the crankshaft. Push the crankshaft fully one way, and then zero the gauge. Push the crankshaft fully the other way, and check the endfloat **(see illustration)**. The result can be compared with the specified amount, and will give an indication as to whether new thrustwashers are required. Thrustwashers are supplied in one thickness only; if endfloat is excessive

13.21 Assemble the piston and connecting rod so that the arrow on the piston crown is pointing in the same direction as the embossed mark on the connecting rod flank

13.22 Gudgeon pin circlip end gaps should all be at the bottom of the piston – ensure each circlip is correctly located in its groove

14.2 Check the endfloat using a dial gauge in contact with the end of the crankshaft

and new thrustwashers do not bring it back within tolerances, the crankshaft must be renewed.

3 If a dial gauge is not available, feeler blades can be used. First push the crankshaft fully towards the flywheel end of the engine, then use feeler blades to measure the gap between the web of the crankpin and the side of the thrustwasher fitted to the flywheel side of the No. 4 main bearing upper location.

Inspection

4 Clean the crankshaft using paraffin or a suitable solvent, and dry it, preferably with compressed air if available. Be sure to clean the oil holes with a pipe cleaner or similar probe, to ensure that they are not obstructed. *Warning: Wear eye protection when using compressed air.*

5 Check the main and big-end bearing journals for uneven wear, scoring, pitting and cracking.

6 Big-end bearing wear is accompanied by distinct metallic knocking when the engine is running (particularly noticeable when the engine is pulling from low speed) and some loss of oil pressure.

7 Main bearing wear is accompanied by severe vibration and rumble – getting progressively worse as engine speed increases – and again by loss of oil pressure.

8 Check the bearing journal for roughness by running a finger lightly over the bearing surface. Any roughness (which will be accompanied by obvious bearing wear) indicates that the crankshaft requires regrinding (where possible) or renewal.

9 Check for burrs around the crankshaft oil holes (the holes are usually chamfered, so burrs should not be a problem unless regrinding has been carried out carelessly). Remove any burrs with a fine file or scraper, and thoroughly clean the oil holes as described previously.

10 Have the crankshaft inspected and measured by an engine overhaul specialist. They will be able to determine whether the crankshaft is re-usable or not. If the crankshaft is damaged or if it has worn beyond the specified limits, it will have to be renewed.

11 At the time of writing, it appeared that Honda do not produce undersize bearing shells. If the main or big-end bearing shell-to-journal clearances, checked using Plastigauge, are beyond the service limit specified and cannot be brought back within tolerances using new bearing shells of the same colour-coding, or shells of different thicknesses from within the range provided by Honda, then the crankshaft must be renewed. Consult an engine overhaul specialist for further information on parts availability from other sources, as this will govern whether or not the crankshaft can be reground.

12 Carefully inspect the lower crankcase/main bearing ladder-to-cylinder block bolts (main bearing cap bolts) and renew any which show signs of damage.

15 Main and big-end bearings – inspection

1 Even though it is normal to renew the main and big-end bearing shells during the engine overhaul, the old shells should be retained for close examination, as they may reveal valuable information about the condition of the engine.

2 Bearing failure can occur due to lack of lubrication, the presence of dirt or other foreign particles, overloading the engine, or corrosion **(see illustration)**. Regardless of the cause of bearing failure, the cause must be corrected (where applicable) before the engine is reassembled, to prevent it from happening again.

3 When examining the bearing shells, remove them from the cylinder block, the lower crankcase/main bearing ladder, the connecting rods and the connecting rod big-end bearing caps. Lay them out on a clean surface in the same general position as their location in the engine. This will enable you to match any bearing problems with the corresponding crankshaft journal. Check the colour code on the edge of each bearing shell and record them carefully; a mark of Red, Pink, Yellow, Green, Brown, Black, or Blue (in ascending order of shell thickness) should be found **(see illustration 11.6)**. On petrol engine connecting rod big-end bearings, both shells should have the same colour code; on petrol engine main bearings and both sets of bearings on diesel engines, it is possible to have two shells of different colour codes fitted to the same bearing.

4 Dirt and other foreign matter gets into the engine in a variety of ways. It may be left in the engine during assembly, or it may pass through filters or the crankcase ventilation

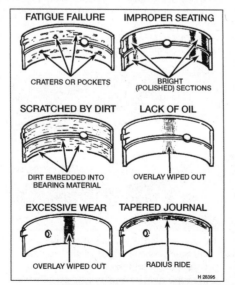

15.2 Typical bearing shell failures

system. It may get into the oil, and from there into the bearings. Metal chips from machining operations and normal engine wear are often present. Abrasives are sometimes left in engine components after reconditioning. Whatever the source, these foreign objects often end up embedded in the soft bearing material, and are easily recognised. Large particles will not embed in the bearing, and will score or gouge the bearing and journal. The best prevention for this cause of bearing failure is to clean all parts thoroughly, and keep everything spotlessly clean during engine assembly. Frequent and regular engine oil and filter changes are also recommended.

5 Lack of lubrication (or lubrication breakdown) has a number of interrelated causes. Excessive heat (which thins the oil), overloading (which squeezes the oil from the bearing face) and oil leakage (from excessive bearing clearances, worn oil pump or high engine speeds) all contribute to lubrication breakdown. Blocked oil passages, which usually are the result of misaligned oil holes in a bearing shell, will also oil-starve a bearing, and destroy it. When lack of lubrication is the cause of bearing failure, the bearing material is wiped or extruded from the steel backing of the bearing. Temperatures may increase to the point where the steel backing turns blue from overheating.

6 Driving habits can have a definite effect on bearing life. Full-throttle, low-speed operation (labouring the engine) puts very high loads on bearings, tending to squeeze out the oil film. These loads cause the bearings to flex, which produces fine cracks in the bearing face (fatigue failure). Eventually, the bearing material will loosen in pieces, and tear away from the steel backing.

7 Short-distance driving leads to corrosion of bearings, because insufficient engine heat is produced to drive off the condensed water and corrosive gases. These products collect in the engine oil, forming acid and sludge. As the oil is carried to the engine bearings, the acid attacks and corrodes the bearing material.

8 Incorrect bearing installation during engine assembly will lead to bearing failure as well. Tight-fitting bearings leave insufficient bearing running clearance, and will result in oil starvation. Dirt or foreign particles trapped behind a bearing shell result in high spots on the bearing, which lead to failure.

9 As mentioned earlier, bearing shells should be renewed as a matter of course during engine overhaul; to do otherwise is false economy.

Selection of bearing shells

10 To ensure precise bearing fits and close control of tolerances in mass production, the crankshaft, cylinder block and lower crankcase/main bearing ladder and connecting rod big-end bearings are graded into size groups, each identified by a code letter or number. Big-end bores and journal diameters are divided into four groups, or

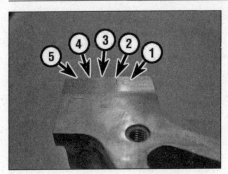

15.11 The main bearing bore diameter size group codes are marked on the bottom rear of the flywheel end of the lower crankcase/main bearing ladder

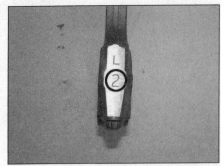

15.12 The big-end bearing bore diameter class markings are etched across the front face of each connecting rod and bearing cap

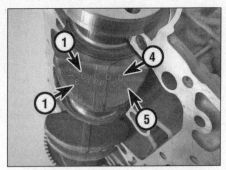

15.13 The main and big-end bearing journal diameter codes are marked across the face of the crankshaft web nearest the flywheel

classes, as are main bearing bore diameters, while main bearing journal diameters are divided into six classes and seven thicknesses of bearing shell are provided for each bearing. Cross-referencing a bearing's bore diameter code letter or number against the journal diameter code letter or number gives the colour code of the bearing shells required for that bearing location. Where bearing shells of two colours are called for, Honda state that it does not matter which colour is used in the top or bottom shell location.

11 For crankshaft main bearings, the main bearing bore diameter code letters or numbers are marked on the bottom surface of the lower crankcase/main bearing ladder at the rear of the flywheel end **(see illustration)**. No. 1 (timing chain end) main bearing's mark is the one nearest the timing chain end, No. 5 (flywheel end) main bearing's mark is nearest the flywheel end.

12 For connecting rod big-end bearings, the connecting rod big-end bearing bore diameter code number or class marking is etched across each connecting rod and bearing cap **(see illustration)**.

13 For main and big-end bearings, the journal diameter codes are marked either on the edges of the adjacent crankshaft web,

or across the face of the web nearest the flywheel **(see illustration)**. For either set of codes, from left to right, the codes are for No. 1 (timing chain end) on the left, through to No. 4 (big-end) or No. 5 (flywheel end main bearing).

14 Whenever new bearing shells are being ordered, or the existing ones checked, note and record all the relevant codes along with the colour codes of the existing shells, a Honda dealer or engine specialist will be able to supply correct new parts.

15 As mentioned earlier, Honda do not supply undersize bearing shells.

16 The only way of assessing the amount of wear that has taken place, if neither crankshaft journal nor bearing shells show visible signs of wear or damage, is to use Plastigauge **(see illustrations)**. If this shows any main or big-end bearing shell-to-journal clearance to be excessive, first fit new bearing shells of the same colour code(s). Recheck the clearance. If it is still incorrect, fit new shells of the next size and check the clearance again.

17 If any of the main or big-end bearing shell-to-journal clearances are beyond the service limit specified and cannot be brought back within tolerances using new bearing shells of the same colour coding, or shells of different

thicknesses from within the range provided by Honda, then the crankshaft must be renewed. In that case, all new bearing shells must be ordered, cross-referencing the bearings' bore diameter code letters or numbers against the new crankshaft's journal diameter code letters or numbers.

16 Engine overhaul – reassembly sequence

1 Before reassembly begins, ensure that all new parts have been obtained, and that all necessary tools are available. Read through the entire procedure to familiarise yourself with the work involved, and to ensure that all items necessary for reassembly of the engine are at hand. In addition to all normal tools and materials, thread-locking compound will be needed. A suitable tube of liquid sealant will also be required for the joint faces that are fitted without gaskets. It is recommended that Honda's own products are used, which are specially formulated for this purpose.

2 In order to save time and avoid problems, engine reassembly can be carried out in the following order:
a) Crankshaft (Section 18).
b) Piston/connecting rod assemblies (Section 19).
c) Oil pump (see Chapter 2A, B or C – as applicable).
d) Sump (see Chapter 2A, B or C – as applicable).
e) Flywheel (see Chapter 2A, B or C – as applicable).
f) Cylinder head (see Chapter 2A, B or C – as applicable).
g) Timing belt tensioner and sprockets, and timing belt (see Chapter 2A, B or C – as applicable).
h) Engine external components.

3 At this stage, all engine components should be absolutely clean and dry, with all faults repaired. The components should be laid out (or in individual containers) on a completely clean work surface.

15.16a To check the bearing clearances, lay Plastigauge strip (arrowed) on the bearing journals, parallel to the crankshaft centre-line...

15.16b... and then reassemble, dismantle and compare the width of the crushed Plastigauge on the scale provided to determine the bearing clearance (always take measurement at the widest point of the Plastigauge strip)

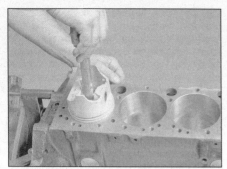

17.3 Position the piston ring using the piston as described in the text

17.4 Measure the end gap using feeler blades

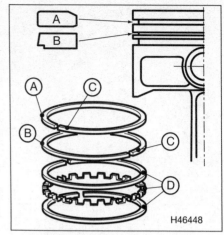

17.9 The piston ring fitting details

A First compression ring
B Second compression ring
C Manufacturer's markings (R1 and R)
D Oil control rings and expander

17 Piston rings – refitting

1 Before fitting new piston rings, the ring end gaps must be checked as follows.
2 Lay out the piston/connecting rod assemblies and the new piston ring sets, so that the ring sets will be matched with the same piston and cylinder during the end gap measurement and subsequent engine reassembly.
3 Insert the top ring into the first cylinder, and push it down the bore using the top of the piston. This will ensure that the ring remains square with the cylinder walls. Push the ring down into the bore until it is positioned 15 to 20 mm from the bottom of the bore **(see illustration)**. Withdraw the piston.
4 Measure the end gap using feeler blades, and compare the measurements with the figures given in the Specifications **(see illustration)**.
5 If the gap is too small (unlikely if genuine Honda parts are used), it must be enlarged, or

the ring ends may contact each other during engine operation, causing serious damage. Ideally, new piston rings providing the correct end gap should be fitted; check carefully that the correct items have been ordered and supplied. As a last resort, the end gap can be increased by filing the ring ends very carefully with a fine file. Mount the file in a vice with soft jaws, slip the ring over the file with the ends contacting the file face, and slowly move the ring to remove material from the ends. Take care, as piston rings are sharp, and are easily broken.
6 With new piston rings, it is unlikely that the end gap will be too large. If the gaps are too large, check that you have the correct rings for your engine and for the particular cylinder bore size.
7 Repeat the checking procedure for each ring in the first cylinder, and then for the rings in the remaining cylinders. Remember to keep rings, pistons and cylinders matched up.
8 Once the ring end gaps have been checked and if necessary corrected, the rings can be fitted to the pistons as follows, using the same technique as for removal.

Petrol engines

9 Fit the oil control ring expander first (it will be easier if the end gap is correctly positioned at this point), then fit the side rails, which have no identification markings and can be fitted either way up **(see illustration)**. The second and top compression rings are of a similar cross-section but are different and can be distinguished by the identification

markings on their top surfaces, near the end gaps (see Specifications 2C Section 0); fit the rings ensuring that each ring is fitted the correct way up with its identification mark uppermost. **Note:** *Always follow any instructions supplied with the new piston ring sets – different manufacturers may specify different procedures. Do not mix up the top and second compression rings.*
10 Check that each ring is free to rotate easily in its groove, then measure the ring-to-groove clearance of each ring, using feeler blades. If the clearance is within the specified range, position the ring end gaps as shown **(see illustration)**.

Diesel engine

11 Fit the oil control ring expander first, then fit the ring to the piston; the ring has no identification marking and can be fitted either way up **(see illustrations)**.
12 The second and top rings are different (the top ring having a tapered cross-section, while the second is rectangular, with an undercut in its bottom surface) and can be distinguished by the identification markings (see Specifications) on their top surfaces, near the

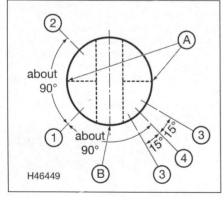

17.10 Piston ring end gap positioning

A Piston thrust surfaces (front/rear) – do not position ring gaps here
B Gudgeon pin axis – do not position ring gaps here
1 Top ring gap position
2 Second ring gap position
3 Oil ring gap positions
4 Oil ring spacer gapposition

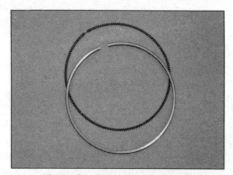

17.11a On diesel engines the oil control ring is in two pieces

17.11b Engage the oil control ring correctly over the expander

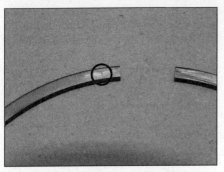

17.12a The top compression ring top surface marking (T)

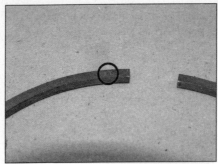
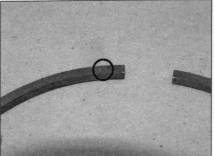

17.12b The second compression ring top surface marking (2T or FTE)

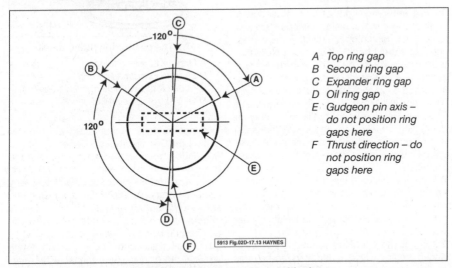

A Top ring gap
B Second ring gap
C Expander ring gap
D Oil ring gap
E Gudgeon pin axis – do not position ring gaps here
F Thrust direction – do not position ring gaps here

17.13 Diesel piston ring gap positioning

18.3 Fit the connecting rod bearing shells

18.4 Fit the upper main bearing shells

18.5a Apply grease to the back of the thrust washers to help locate them...

18.5b... and then lay them in place either side of No 4 bearing

18.6a Lubricate the main...

end gaps **(see illustrations)**. Fit the second and top compression rings ensuring that each ring is fitted the correct way up with its identification mark uppermost. **Note:** *Always follow any instructions supplied with the new piston ring sets – different manufacturers may specify different procedures. Do not mix up the top and second compression rings.*

13 Check that each ring is free to rotate easily in its groove, then measure the ring-to-groove clearance of each ring, using feeler blades. If the clearance is within the specified range, space the ring end gaps at 120° intervals **(see illustration)**.

18 Crankshaft – refitting

Note: *On the 1.4 litre petrol engines the pistons and connecting rods must be fitted to the crankshaft before the main bearing ladder is fitted.*

1 If removed, fit a new crankshaft pilot bush or bearing (Chapter 2A, 2B or 2C).

1.4 litre petrol engines

2 Fit the pistons and connecting rods as described in Section 19.

3 Fit the connecting rod bearing shells in place, making sure the shell's locating tab engages correctly **(see illustration)**.

4 Wipe clean the main bearing shell seats in the crankcase, and clean the backs of the bearing shells. Insert the respective upper shells (dry) into position in the crankcase. Note that the upper shells have grooves and oil holes in them (the lower shells are plain). The shell oil holes must align with the oil supply holes in the crankcase. Where the old main bearings are being refitted, ensure that they are located in their original positions. Make sure that the tab on each bearing shell fits into the notch in the block **(see illustration)**.

5 Place the crankshaft thrustwashers into position in the crankcase, either side of No 4 bearing, so that their oil grooves are facing outwards (away from the web). Hold them in position with a little grease **(see illustrations)**.

6 Lubricate the main and big-end bearings with clean engine oil **(see illustrations)**.

18.6b...and big-end bearings with engine oil

18.8 Carefully lay the crankshaft into position

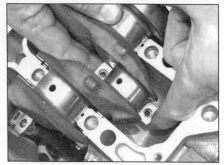

18.9a Guide the connecting rods onto the crankshaft

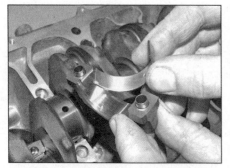

18.9b Fit the big-end shells to the caps...

18.9c...then apply engine oil...

18.9d...and fit them using the locating dowels

7 Adjust the position of the connecting rods to allow the crankshaft to be fitted – for instance, by moving all the pistons close to the top of the bores.

8 Make sure the crankshaft journals are clean, then lay the crankshaft back in place in the block **(see illustration)**.

9 Guide each connecting rod onto the crankshaft. Fit the shells to the big-end caps, then lubricate them and fit them **(see illustrations)**. Note that each cap has two dowels to ensure correct positioning – refit the dowels if they were removed earlier.

10 Lightly oil the threads and heads of the new bearing cap bolts, then tighten them to the specified Stage 1 torque **(see illustrations)**.

11 Now tighten the bolts to the specified Stage 2 angle **(see illustration)**.

12 Refit the remaining connecting rods and big-end caps, turning the crankshaft as little as possible.

13 Clean all traces of sealant from the main bearing cap bridge. Apply fresh RTV sealant (Honda part number 08C70-K0334M, or equivalent) to the oil seal end of the bridge, as

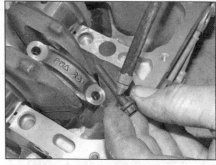

18.10a Lightly oil the new bolt threads...

18.10b... then fit and tighten them to the Stage 1 torque

18.11 Tighten the bolts through the second stage using an angle gauge

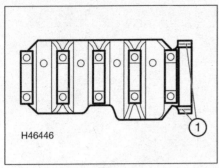

18.13a Apply sealant to the main bearing cap bridge before fitting

1 Bead of sealant, 1.5 mm diameter

18.13b Applying sealant to the oil seal end of the bridge

18.14 Oil the bearing shells in the main bearing bridge

18.15a Fit the main bearing bridge into position and...

18.15b...then oil and fit the new bolts

shown **(see illustrations)**. Once the sealant has been applied, the bridge should be fitted within 5 minutes.

1 Bead of sealant, 1.5 mm diameter

14 Clean the bearing surfaces of the shells in the bearing cap bridge, then lubricate them with oil **(see illustration)**.

15 Fit the bearing cap bridge into position. Fit the new bolts, with their threads and heads lightly oiled. Working in sequence, tighten the bridge bolts to the Stage 1 setting **(see illustrations)**.

16 With all the main bearing bolts tightened to the Stage 1 setting, go round again in the same sequence and tighten them further to the Stage 2 angle **(see illustration)**. Once this is done, clean off any excess sealant.

1.8 litre petrol and diesel engines

17 Where removed, refit the crankshaft position sensor pulse plate, engaging it on its locating dowel; tighten its bolts to the specified torque. A drop of thread-locking compound on each bolt's threads would provide additional security against their working loose.

18 Clean the backs of the bearing shells and the bearing locations **(see illustration)**.

19 Press the bearing shells into their locations, ensuring that the tab on each shell engages in the notch in the cylinder block or main bearing ladder **(see illustration)**. Take care not to touch any shell bearing surface

18.15c The main bearing cap bridge bolts tightening sequence

18.15d Tighten the main bearing bolts to the Stage 1 torque

18.16 Tighten the bolts to the second stage using an angle gauge

18.18 Clean the backs of the bearing shells and bearing locations in the cylinder block and the lower crankcase/main bearing ladder

18.19 Press the bearing shells into their locations, ensuring that the tab on each shell engages in the notch

18.20a Use grease to locate the crankshaft thrust washers in place...

18.20b...ensuring that the grooves are on the outside and that the oil ways all line up

18.21 Liberally lubricate each bearing shell in the cylinder block and then refit the crankshaft

18.22 Carefully lubricate each (plain) bearing shell in the lower crankcase/main bearing ladder and check that the locating dowels are in place

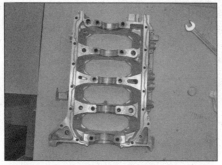

18.23 Apply sealant as shown to the lower crankcase/main bearing ladder mating surface

18.24 Refitting the lower crankcase/main bearing ladder – take care not to smear the sealant bead

with your fingers. The grooved shells must be fitted in the cylinder block bearing locations, to match the oilways in the block, while the plain shells must be fitted in the main bearing ladder. Where bearing shells of two colours are called for on any one bearing location, it does not matter which colour is used in the top or bottom location.

20 Using a little grease, stick the thrustwashers to each side of the No. 4 main bearing upper location. Ensure that the oilway grooves on each thrustwasher face outwards **(see illustrations)**.

21 Liberally lubricate each bearing shell in the cylinder block, then lower the crankshaft into position, being careful not to mark or damage the journals or damage the crankshaft position sensor pulse plate **(see illustration)**.

22 The liquid gasket recommended by Honda requires that the lower crankcase/main bearing ladder must be installed within five minutes of applying the liquid gasket – if this time limit is exceeded, the sealant must be wiped off completely and new liquid gasket applied. A 'dry' practice run before applying liquid gasket is recommended. Degrease the mating surfaces. Liberally lubricate each crankshaft main bearing journal and the lower bearing shells; apply as much oil as possible without risking drips onto the mating surfaces **(see illustration)**.

23 Apply liquid gasket in a continuous thin

bead (diameter 3 mm approx) evenly along the lower crankcase/main bearing ladder's mating surface so that the bead goes around the inside edges of the front 8 mm bolt holes and around the outside edges of the rear 8 mm bolt holes **(see illustration)**. Also apply a small blob of liquid gasket to those 8 mm bolt holes in the cylinder block which pass through to the outside. Do not apply sealant to blind holes in the castings. Do not apply excess sealant, as this will end up inside the engine.

24 Offer up the lower crankcase/main bearing ladder and very carefully, ensuring that you do not smear the sealant bead by sliding

the casting in any direction, fit the lower crankcase/main bearing ladder into place on its locating dowels, press it into position and refit one or two 10 mm bolts to hold it **(see illustration)**. Check that the crankshaft is free to rotate smoothly.

25 Refit all the 10 mm bolts, tightening them by hand only at first until the lower crankcase/main bearing ladder is correctly settled in position. Working in sequence and in two or three stages, tighten the 10 mm bolts to the specified Stage 1 torque **(see illustrations)**.

26 Tighten the 10 mm bolts again, in sequence, through their specified Stage 2 angle, using a socket and extension bar. It

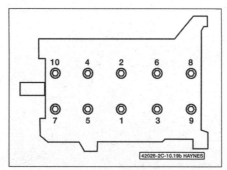

18.25a The lower crankcase/main bearing ladder 10 mm (crankshaft main bearing cap) bolts tightening sequence

18.25b Tighten the 10 mm bolts to first stage with a torque wrench...

18.26...and then use an angle-tightening gauge to fully tighten to the second stage

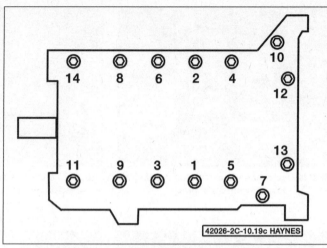

18.27 The lower crankcase/main bearing ladder 8 mm bolts tightening sequence

is recommended that an angle-measuring gauge is used during this stage of tightening, to ensure accuracy **(see illustration)**.

27 Refit all the 8 mm bolts, tightening them by hand only at first. Working in sequence and in two or three stages, tighten the 8 mm bolts to the specified torque **(see illustration)**.

28 Check that an even bead of sealant is visible all the way round the edge of the lower crankcase/main bearing ladder; wipe off any excess.

29 Check that the crankshaft is free to rotate smoothly, without any sign of binding or tight spots; if excessive pressure is required to turn the crankshaft, investigate the cause before proceeding further.

30 Check the crankshaft endfloat as described in Section 11.

31 Refit and reconnect the piston connecting rod assemblies to the crankshaft as described in Section 19.

32 Refit the baffle plate(s) to the cylinder block. Tighten their bolts to the specified torque.

33 Working as described in Part B or C of this Chapter, carry out the following procedures in order:

a) *Fit a new left-hand oil seal to the crankshaft.*
b) *Refit the balancer assembly/oil pump (diesel engine)*
c) *Refit the sump.*
d) *Refit the flywheel.*

19 Pistons/connecting rods – refitting

1 On the 1.8 petrol and diesel engines the crankshaft can be fitted first and then the pistons and connecting rods fitted. On the 1.4 petrol engines the pistons and connecting rods must be in position before the crankshaft is fitted.

2 Clean the backs of the bearing shells and the bearing recesses in the connecting rods and the big-end bearing caps. Ensure that all traces of any protective grease are cleaned off using paraffin. Wipe dry the shells and connecting rods with a lint-free cloth.

3 Press the bearing shells into their locations, ensuring that the tab on each shell engages in the notch in the connecting rod or big-end

bearing cap and taking care not to touch any shell's bearing surface with your fingers **(see illustration)**. Where bearing shells of two colours are called for on any one bearing location (diesel engines only), it does not matter which colour is used in the top or bottom shell location.

4 Lubricate the cylinder bores, the pistons and piston rings, then lay out each piston/connecting rod assembly in its respective position.

5 Starting with assembly No. 1, make sure that the piston rings are still correctly spaced (see Section 17) then clamp them in position with a piston ring compressor **(see illustration)**. Rotate the crankshaft so that No. 1 cylinder big-end bearing journal is at Bottom Dead Centre (BDC).

6 Insert the piston/connecting rod assembly into the top of cylinder No. 1, ensuring that the arrow marking on the piston crown is pointing towards the timing chain end of the engine. The big-end bearing bore diameter class number or marking etched across each connecting rod and bearing cap should face the front of the engine **(see illustration)**.

7 Using a block of wood or hammer handle

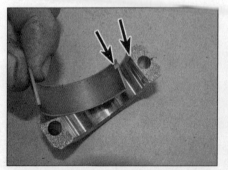

19.3 Ensure the tab on each shell engages in the notch in the connecting rod and big-end bearing cap

19.5 Using a piston ring compressor to refit a piston/connecting rod assembly

19.6 The arrow on the piston crown must point to the timing belt end of the engine

19.7 Tap the piston/connecting rod assembly into the cylinder

19.8a Oil the big-end bearing shells before refitting the connecting rod to the crankshaft...

19.8b... and then refit the big-end bearing cap so that the marks made on removal correspond...

19.8c...and the big-end bearing bore diameter class marking aligns exactly at the front

against the piston crown, tap the assembly into the cylinder until the piston crown is flush with the top of the cylinder **(see illustration)**. Where fitted, take care that the end of the connecting rod is well clear of the piston-cooling oil jet.

8 Liberally lubricate the crankpin and both bearing shells, then pull the piston/connecting rod assembly down the bore and guide it on to the crankpin. Refit the big-end bearing cap, making sure it is fitted the correct way around **(see illustrations)**.

9 Lubricate the threads of the bolts with clean engine oil then screw them into position in the connecting rod, tightening them both by hand. Evenly and progressively tighten the bolts to the specified Stage 1 torque, then tighten each bolt through the specified Stage 2 angle **(see illustrations)**.

10 Refit the remaining three piston and connecting rod assemblies in the same way.

19.9a Lightly oil the threads of the connecting rod big-end bearing cap bolts

19.9b Tighten the big-end bearing cap bolts to the specified Stage 1 torque...

19.9c...and then through the specified second stage

11 Rotate the crankshaft, and check that it turns freely, with no signs of binding or tight spots.

12 Where fitted, refit the baffle plate to the cylinder block. Tighten their bolts to the specified torque.

13 Working as described in Part A, B or C of this Chapter, carry out the following procedures in order:

a) *Refit the balancer assembly/oil pump.*

b) *Refit the sump.*

c) *Refit the cylinder head.*

d) *Refit the rocker shaft assembly (petrol engine).*

e) *Refit the cam followers and hydraulic tappets, camshaft carrier and camshafts (diesel engine).*

f) *Refit the timing chain sprockets, chain and tensioner.*

20 Engine initial start-up after overhaul

1 With the engine refitted in the vehicle, double-check the oil and coolant levels.

Make a final check that everything has been reconnected, and that there are no tools or rags left in the engine compartment.

2 On petrol engined-models, disable the ignition system by removing all four ignition coils and spark plugs (Chapter 1A Section 22). Turn the engine on the starter until the oil pressure warning light goes out, then refit the spark plugs and the coils.

3 On diesel engined-models, if you do not have access to the Honda Diagnostic System (HDS) tester to disable the injectors, turning the engine over without starting it requires the removal of the injectors (but this requires the renewal of the copper sealing washers and the high-pressure pipes), or the disabling of the injectors by disconnecting their wiring connectors and reconnecting them afterwards. The easiest way to crank the diesel engine over without starting it is to use a remote starter switch connrcted directly to the starter motor. These are widely available form most motor factors. Whichever method is adopted, turn the engine on the starter until the oil pressure warning light goes out, then stop and re-enable or refit the injectors, as applicable.

4 On all models, start the engine as normal noting that this may take a little longer than usual, due to the fuel system components having been disturbed. Prime the diesel engine fuel system if necessary (Chapter 4B).

5 While the engine is idling, check for fuel, water and oil leaks. Don't be alarmed if there are some odd smells and smoke from parts getting hot and burning off oil deposits.

6 Assuming all is well, keep the engine idling until hot water is felt circulating through the top hose, then switch off the engine. On diesel engined-models, Honda state that if any big-end or crankshaft main bearing shells have been renewed then the engine must be run at idle until it reaches normal operating temperature and then run for another 15 minutes to bed in the new components.

7 Allow the engine to cool then recheck the oil and coolant levels and top-up as necessary.

8 If new pistons, rings or crankshaft bearings have been fitted, the engine must be treated as new, and run-in for the first 500 miles. Do not operate the engine at full throttle, or allow it to labour at low engine speeds in any gear. It is recommended that the oil and filter be changed at the end of this period.

Chapter 3
Cooling, heating and air conditioning systems

Contents

Section number

Air conditioning system components – removal and refitting 10
Cooling system hoses – disconnection and renewal 2
Cooling system sensors and switches – removal and refitting 8
Expansion tank – removal and refitting 6
General Information 1
Heater/ventilation system components – removal and refitting 9

Section number

Radiator – removal, inspection and refitting. 5
Radiator and condenser cooling fans – testing, removal and
  refitting 4
Thermostat – removal, testing and refitting 3
Water pump – inspection, removal and refitting. 7

Degrees of difficulty

Easy, suitable for novice with little experience	**Fairly easy,** suitable for beginner with some experience	**Fairly difficult,** suitable for competent DIY mechanic	**Difficult,** suitable for experienced DIY mechanic	**Very difficult,** suitable for expert DIY or professional

Specifications

Coolant
Mixture type . . . .   See *Lubricants and fluids*
Cooling system capacity . . . .   See Chapter 1A or 1B

System pressure
Pressure test . . . .   1.3 to 1.75 bar approximately – see cap for actual value

Thermostat – opening temperature
1.4 Petrol engine (L13A):
  Starts to open. . . . .   76 – 80 °C
  Fully open. . . . .   90 °C
1.4 Petrol engine (L13Z):
  Starts to open. . . . .   86 – 90 °C
  Fully open . . . .   100 °C
1.8 Petrol engine (R18A):
  Starts to open. . . . .   80 – 84 °C
  Fully open . . . .   95 °C
2.2 Diesel engine:
  Starts to open. . . . .   86 – 90 °C
  Fully open . . . .   100 °C

Air conditioning system
Compressor clutch air gap. . . . .   0.35 – 0.65 mm
Compressor field coil resistance . . . .   3.15 – 3.45 Ohms at 20°C
Refrigerant type R134a
Refrigerant quantity 440-490g
Refrigerant oil type:
  Sanden compressor. SP-10
  Denso compressor ND--Oil8
Refrigerant oil capacity (when refilling after a system flush):
  When renewing the condenser. . . . .   20 ml
  When renewing the evaporator . . . .   35 ml
  When renewing the compressor. . . . .   75 ml
  When replacing a line or hose . . . .   10 ml

Torque wrench settings

	Nm	lbf ft
Air conditioning accumulator/dehydrator-to condenser bolt	10	7
Air conditioning compressor mounting bolts	22	16
Air conditioning compressor clutch centre bolt	25	19
Air conditioning high-pressure cut-off switch	10	7
Coolant pump pulley bolts	14	10
Drivebelt automatic tensioner:		
M10 bolt	54	40
M8 bolt	24	17
Idler pulley (diesel models):		
Upper bolt.	45	33
Lower bolts.	22	16
Refrigerant line to compressor	10	7
Refrigerant line to evaporator.	10	7
Thermostat housing bolts:		
1.4 litre petrol engine (L13A)	10	7
1.4 litre petrol engine (L13Z)	12	9
1.8 litre petrol engine	10	7
2.2 litre diesel engines	12	9
Water pump bolts (all engines):	12	9

1 General Information

 Warning: DO NOT attempt to remove the expansion tank filler cap, or to disturb any part of the cooling system, while it or the engine is hot, as there is a very great risk of scalding. If the expansion tank filler cap must be removed before the engine and radiator have fully cooled down (even though this is not recommended) the pressure in the cooling system must first be released. Cover the cap with a thick layer of cloth, to avoid scalding, and slowly unscrew the filler cap until a hissing sound can be heard. When the hissing has stopped, showing that pressure is released, slowly unscrew the filler cap further until it can be removed; if more hissing sounds are heard, wait until they have stopped before unscrewing the cap completely. At all times, keep well away from the filler opening.

Warning: Do not allow coolant to come in contact with your skin, or with the painted surfaces of the vehicle. Rinse off spills immediately with plenty of water. Never leave coolant lying around in an open container, or in a puddle in the driveway or on the garage floor. Children and pets are attracted by its sweet smell, but coolant is fatal if ingested.

Warning: If the engine is hot, the electric cooling fan may start rotating even if the engine is not running, so be careful to keep hands, hair and loose clothing well clear when working in the engine compartment.

**Warning: Warning: The refrigerant is potentially dangerous, and should only be handled by qualified persons. If it is splashed onto the skin, it can cause frostbite – do not allow it to come in contact with skin or eyes. It is not itself poisonous, but in the presence of a naked flame (including a cigarette) it forms a poisonous gas. Uncontrolled discharging of the refrigerant is dangerous, illegal and damaging to the environment.

Engine cooling system

1 All models covered by this manual employ a pressurised engine cooling system with a thermostatically controlled coolant circulation. The water pump is mounted in a housing bolted to the front right-hand end of the cylinder block and is driven with the alternator and air conditioning compressor by an auxiliary drivebelt from the crankshaft pulley. The water pump pumps coolant through the engine, around each cylinder (and the engine oil cooler on diesel-engined models) and into the cylinder head. In addition to supplying the heating system, external pipes and hoses channel coolant to the turbocharger and EGR cooler (diesel-engined models), and to the throttle body and (where appropriate) the automatic transmission fluid cooler on petrol-engined models.

2 A thermostat controls engine coolant temperature. During warm-up, the closed thermostat prevents coolant from circulating through the radiator. As the engine nears normal operating temperature, the thermostat opens and allows hot coolant to travel through the radiator, where it is cooled before returning to the engine. The thermostat is mounted in a housing low down at the front of the engine.

3 The cooling system is sealed by a radiator mounted pressure cap on petrol models. On diesel models the cap is fitted to the expansion tank on the right-hand inner wing. The pressurised cap raises the boiling point of the coolant and increases the efficiency of the radiator.

4 The operation of the cooling fans is controlled by the engine management system's Electronic Control Module (ECM), which receives engine temperature data from the engine coolant temperature sensor, in conjunction with signals from the radiator temperature sensor mounted in the bottom of the radiator. At a predetermined temperature, the ECU energises the relay which operates the cooling fan.

Heating/ventilation system

5 The heating system consists of a blower fan and heater matrix, the hoses connecting the heater matrix to the engine cooling system and the heater/air conditioning controls on the facia. Cold air enters the system through the grille at the rear of the engine compartment. Hot coolant permanently circulates (when the engine is at normal operating temperature) through the heater matrix. When the heater temperature control is turned to hot, a motor-operated flap opens to link the heater matrix chamber to the passenger compartment. When required, a fan switch on the control panel activates the blower motor, which forces air through the matrix, increasing the supply of air. Stale air is expelled through ducts at the rear of the vehicle. A recirculation switch enables the outside air supply to be closed off.

6 Diesel engined models have an electrically powered auxiliary heater fitted in front of the heater matrix to raise the cabin temperature when the engine coolant is cold.

Air conditioning system

General information

7 The air conditioning system enables the temperature of incoming air to be lowered; it also dehumidifies the air, which makes for rapid demisting and increased comfort. Two types of air conditioning are fitted – manual and automatic (climate control).

8 The cooling side of the system works in a similar way to a domestic refrigerator. Refrigerant gas is drawn into a belt-driven compressor, and passes into a condenser in front of the radiator, where it loses heat and becomes liquid. The liquid passes through an expansion valve to an evaporator, where it changes from liquid under high pressure to gas under low pressure. This change is accompanied by a drop in temperature, which cools the evaporator. The refrigerant returns to the compressor and the cycle begins again.

9 Air blown through the evaporator passes to the heater unit, where it is mixed with hot air to achieve the desired temperature in the passenger compartment. On models with climate control, the flap doors on the heater unit and blower motor housing are operated automatically by the system's control unit via electric motors to warm or cool the air as required and direct it wherever the controls are set.

Checks

10 The air conditioning system should be operated at least once a week, all year round, for at least 10 minutes at a time and at full speed, to circulate the lubricating oil around those of the system's components that require it and to prevent seals from deteriorating, to dry out the system and to prevent the build-up of bacteria in the system's components that produce odours.

11 The following checks should be performed on a regular basis:

a) Inspect the auxiliary drivebelt (Chapter 1A or 1B).

b) Inspect the system hoses. If there is any wear, damage or leakage, have them renewed.

c) Inspect the condenser cooling fins for leaves, insects, etc. Use a 'fin comb' or compressed air to remove debris.

d) If the effectiveness of the air conditioning system seems to be reduced, have the refrigerant charge checked (this includes checking for leaks) and recharged if necessary **(see illustration)**.

e) Check that the drain tube from the front of the evaporator is clear – note that it is normal to have water dripping from this while the system is in use and when the vehicle is parked.

12 If the air conditioning system is working properly, when the system is switched on with the engine running there should be an audible clunk as the compressor clutch engages. However, if the system is low on gas (low charge), the clutch will not engage.

2 Cooling system hoses – disconnection and renewal

Note: *Refer to the warnings given in Section 1 of this Chapter before starting work.*

1 If the checks described in Chapter 1A or 1B reveal a faulty hose, it must be renewed as follows.

2 First drain the cooling system (see Chapter 1A or 1B); if the coolant is not due for renewal, the drained coolant may be re-used, if it is collected in a clean container.

3 To disconnect any hose, use a pair of pliers to release the spring clamps (or a screwdriver to slacken screw-type clamps), then move them along the hose clear of the union. Carefully work the hose off its stubs **(see illustration)**. The hoses can be removed with relative ease when new – on an older car, they may have stuck.

4 If a hose proves stubborn, try to release it by rotating it on its unions before attempting to work it off. Gently prise the end of the hose with a blunt instrument (such as a flat-bladed screwdriver), but do not apply too much force, and take care not to damage the pipe stubs or hoses. Note in particular that the radiator hose unions are fragile; do not use excessive force when attempting to remove the hoses. If all else fails, cut the hose with a sharp knife, then slit it so that it can be peeled off in two pieces. While expensive, this is preferable to buying a new radiator. Check first, however, that a new hose is readily available.

5 When refitting a hose, first slide the clamps onto the hose, then work the hose onto its unions. If the hose is stiff, use soap (or washing-up liquid) as a lubricant, or soften it by soaking it in boiling water, but take care to prevent scalding.

6 Work each hose end fully onto its union, then check that the hose is settled correctly and is properly routed. Slide each clip along the hose until it is behind the union flared end, before tightening it securely.

7 Refill the system with coolant (see Chapter 1A or 1B).

8 Check carefully for leaks as soon as possible after disturbing any part of the cooling system.

3 Thermostat – removal, testing and refitting

Note: *Refer to the warnings given in Section 1 of this Chapter before starting work.*

Checking

1 As the thermostat ages, it may stick in the open or closed position. A thermostat which is stuck open will result in a very slow warm-up; a thermostat which is stuck shut will lead to rapid overheating.

2 Before assuming the thermostat is to blame for a cooling system problem, check the coolant level. If the system has not been properly filled, there may be an airlock in the system (see the coolant renewal procedure in Chapter 1A or 1B).

3 If the engine seems to be taking a long time to warm up (based on heater output), the thermostat could be stuck open or missing.

4 Don't drive the vehicle without a thermostat – the engine management system's ECU will stay in warm-up mode for longer than necessary, causing emissions and fuel economy to suffer.

5 If the engine runs hot, use your hand to check the temperature of the radiator top hose. If the hose isn't hot, but the engine is, the thermostat is probably stuck closed. But again, this problem could also be due to an airlock.

6 If the radiator top hose is hot, it means that the coolant is flowing (at least as far as the radiator) and the thermostat is open.

7 To gain a rough idea of whether the thermostat is working properly, proceed as follows:

8 With the engine completely cold, start the engine and let it idle, while checking the temperature of the radiator top hose by hand. Periodically check the temperature indicated on the coolant temperature gauge – if overheating is indicated, switch the engine off immediately.

9 The top hose should feel cold for some time as the engine warms-up, and should then get warm quite quickly as the thermostat opens.

10 Precise testing is only possible after removing the thermostat as described below.

Removal

11 Drain the cooling system as described in Chapter 1A or 1B, saving the coolant if it is fit for re-use. Note that unless the coolant is to be replaced, draining the coolant level below the height of the thermostat housing will be sufficient.

1.4 litre i-DSI engines

12 Remove the air cleaner as described in Chapter 4A.

13 Release the hose clips and then remove the coolant hoses. Remove the bolts from the wiring loom support brackets and move the loom to the side.

1.11 The AC service ports

2.3 You can buy special tools specifically designed to release spring type hose clamps

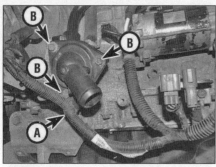

3.14 Remove the thermostat housing bolts

3.15 Note the position of the jiggle pin

3.18a Remove the bolts – 1.8 engine shown

3.18b Remove the cover and...

3.18c...pull out the thermostat

3.21a Remove the cooling fan to access the thermostat

14 Remove the bolts and remove the housing **(see illustration)**. Note that the housing is held in place by a sealing ring and liquid gasket.

15 Remove the thermostat and discard the seal **(see illustration)**.

16 Anticipate some coolant to loss as the seal is broken. Recover the seal and dispose of it – a new one must befitted.

1.4 litre and 1.8 litre i-VTEC engines

17 On the 1.4 litre engine remove the air inlet duct.

18 Remove the coolant hose – note however it can be left in place if necessary. On the 1.8 litre engine remove the bolts securing the loom support bracket to the the housing. Remove the bolts and pull off the thermostat housing **(see illustrations)**.

19 Anticipate some coolant to loss as the seal is broken. Recover the seal and dispose of it – a new one must befitted.

2.2 litre Diesel engine

20 On diesel engines the thermostat is located low down on the right-hand end of the engine, close to the rear of the starter motor.

21 Access is limited both from above and from below. If the vehicle is already raised and supported at the front then remove the thermostat from below. If the vehicle is on it's wheels then removal of the bonnet slam panel and the right-hand cooling fan provides sufficient room to remove the thermostat **(see illustrations)**.

22 Anticipate some coolant loss as the seal is broken. Note the position of the jiggle pin – it should be in the 12 o'clock position. Recover

the seal and dispose of it – a new one must befitted.

Testing

23 If the thermostat remains in the open position at room temperature, it is faulty and must be renewed.

24 Check the temperature marking stamped on the thermostat **(see illustration)**. It should correspond with one of those given in the Specifications.

25 To test the thermostat fully, suspend it on a length of string in a pan of cold water, with a thermometer beside it. Ensure that the thermostat does not touch the bottom or sides of the container **(see illustration)**.

26 Heat the water and check the temperature at which the thermostat begins to open. Compare this value with that specified.

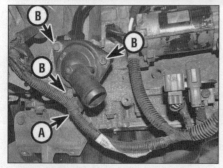

3.21b Release the wiring loom (A) and remove the housing bolts (B)

3.24 The thermostat opening (or fully open) temperature, maybe marked on the thermostat

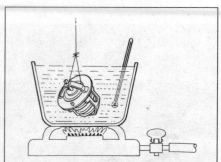

3.25 Testing the thermostat

Continue to heat the water until the thermostat is fully open; again, compare this value with that specified. When the thermostat is fully open, remove it from the water and measure the amount the valve has lifted. Allow the thermostat to cool down and check that it closes fully.

27 If the thermostat does not open and close as it should, then it must be renewed. Note also that given the relatively low cost of a replacement thermostat, if there is any doubt as to the operation of the thermostat then replace it.

Refitting

28 Refitting is a reversal of removal, but note the following additional points:
a) Clean all mating surfaces thoroughly before reassembly.
b) On L13A petrol engine models apply a 1.5 mm bead of liquid gasket (Honda 08C70-K0234M, or equivalent) as shown **(see illustration)**.
c) Fit a new O-ring or rubber seal, as applicable.
d) On models fitted with a jiggle pin, the pin is should be at the top **(see illustration)**.
e) Tighten all bolts to their specified torques.

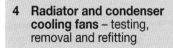

4	Radiator and condenser cooling fans – testing, removal and refitting

Testing

Note: *Models equipped with air conditioning have two complete fan circuits – one for the condenser and one for the radiator. The following procedures apply to both. Both fans are ultimately controlled through the engine management ECU.*

1 To test a fan motor, disconnect the two-pin electrical connector at the motor. Check that the fan rotates freely. If the fan rotates then

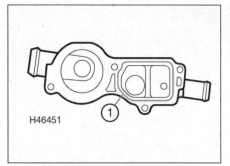

3.28a Sealant application details:
1 Bead of sealant, 1.5 mm diameter

use bridging wires to connect the fan directly to the battery. If the fan still doesn't work, renew the motor.

2 If the motor tests OK, check the fuse and relays (see Chapter 12). The fans are controlled by the coolant temperature sensors – one mounted on the cylinder head and one mounted at the base of the radiator. The sensors supply coolant temperature information to the main engine ECU. The ECU operates the fans via relays mounted in the engine compartment fusebox. Removal and refitting of the sensors is described in Section 8.

Removal

3 On all models the cooling fans can be removed without the need to drain or remove the radiator. However if the radiator has been drained for coolant replacement, then it is preferable to remove the cooling fans complete with the radiator assembly.

4 Jack up and support the front of the vehicle – see *'Jacking and vehicle support'* in the Reference chapter. Remove the engine undershield and if the fans are to be removed with the radiator, drain the coolant as described in Chapter 1A or 1B.

3.28b Applying the sealant to the thermostat housing

5 Remove the bonnet slam panel cover by releasing the trim clips and then on 1.8 petrol and diesel models remove the upper grille **(see illustrations)**. On 1.4 petrol models remove the grille only if the radiator is to be removed with the cooling fans.

6 Disconnect the battery as described in Chapter 5A and then on 1.8 petrol and diesel models remove the bonnet slam panel. The panel can be removed completely by disconnecting the bonnet release cable and the bonnet open warning light switch.

4.5a Remove the slam panel cover

4.5b Remove the bolts in each corner...

4.5c...and then remove the grille

4.6a Release the retaining clips from the cable...

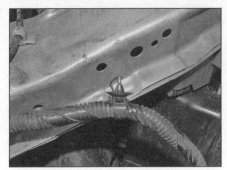

4.6b..and from the wiring loom

4.6c Remove the bolts from the radiator retaining brackets...

4.6d...and then unbolt the slam panel

Alternatively release the wiring loom and cable, turn the panel over and lay it on top of the engine **(see illustrations)**.

7 On 1.4 iVTEC models remove the air inlet duct and then remove the duct support bracket.

8 Disconnect the wiring plug from the AC compressor and then release the wiring loom from the fan shrouds. Disconnect the wiring plugs from the cooling fans and the coolant temperature sensor.

9 On 1.8 litre petrol engines remove the coolant reservoir **(see illustration)**.

10 Remove the bolts securing the condenser shroud assembly and then lift up and remove the shroud complete with the fan and motor **(see illustration)**.

11 With the condenser fan removed, unbolt the radiator fan shroud. Lift up the shroud fan

and motor assembly and remove it from the vehicle.

12 With the shrouds on the bench, remove the fans and motors from the shrouds **(see illustration)**.

13 Unusually Honda supply the all the individual parts to overhaul the fan and motor assembly.

Refitting

14 Refitting is the reverse of the removal procedure.

5 Radiator – removal, inspection and refitting

Note: *Refer to the warnings given in Section 1 of this Chapter before starting work*

Radiator removal

Note: *If leakage is the reason for removing the radiator, bear in mind that minor leaks can often be cured using a radiator sealant added to the coolant with the radiator in situ.*

1 On all models except 1.4 litre petrol models the radiator is removed complete with the cooling fans. On 1.4 litre models the fans are removed forst and then the radiator is removed.

2 On all models, ensure that the handbrake is firmly applied, then raise and support the front of the car on axle stands (see'*Jacking and vehicle support*' in the Reference chapter). Remove the engine undershield.

3 Drain the coolant system as described in Chapter 1A or Chapter 1B.

1.4 litre petrol engines

4 Disconnect the wiring plug from the coolant temperature sensor and the AC compressor clutch switch. Release the loom from the cooling fan shroud.

5 At the top of the radiator, disconnect the wiring plugs from the cooling fans and free the wiring loom from the fan shrouds.

6 Unbolt the condenser fan shroud and remove the fan and shroud assembly, as described in Section 4. Repeat the procedure for the radiator fan assembly.

7 Release the spring clips and remove the radiator upper and lower hoses at the engine end. (The hoses will be removed from the radiator once it is removed). Anticipate some coolant loss as the hoses are removed.

8 Remove the coolant reservoir hose and then unbolt the filler cap from the slam panel. Unbolt the radiator upper retaining brackets.

9 Lift up the radiator and remove it from the vehicle. Recover the lower rubber mountings from the radiator support panel.

10 With the radiator on the bench remove the coolant hoses and the filler neck extension. Unscrew the coolant temperature sensor and dispose of the O-ring seal. Remove the drain plug (if not already done so) and dispose of the seal – a new one must befitted.

1.8 petrol engines and diesel engines

11 Remove slam panel cover, the grille and the slam panel as described in Section 4.

12 On petrol models unbolt and remove

4.9 Remove the coolant reservoir (1.8 petrol models)

4.10 On all models the fan shrouds slot into brackets at the base of the radiator (shown with radiator removed)

4.12 On some models a protective bracket must be removed to access the fan motor bolts

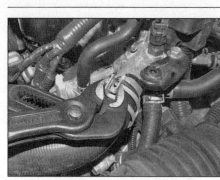

5.15 Remove the radiator hoses

5.16 Remove the radiator

the coolant reservoir tank. On diesel models remove the coolant expansion tank hoses.

13 Disconnect the wiring plugs from the cooling fans, coolant temperature sensor and on some models, the AC compressor clutch. Release the loom from the cooling fan shrouds.

14 On diesel engines, clean the area surrounding the upper and lower coolant hoses (at the radiator) and then pull out the spring clips from the quick release hose connectors. Work the hoses free from the radiator without the use of any tools. Release the spring type hose clip from the small by-pass hose and then remove it.

15 On petrol engines release the upper and lower radiator hoses at the coolant outlet on the cylinder head – the hoses will be removed from the radiator on the bench **(see illustration)**.

16 Pull up the radiator complete with the fan assemblies – the aid of a assistant is recommended – and place the assembly on the bench **(see illustration)**.

17 With the radiator on the bench remove the cooling fan shroud, complete with the cooling fans and motors. On petrol models remove the coolant hoses. Remove the coolant temperature sensor and dispose of the seal – a new one must be fitted. Repeat the procedure for the coolant drain plug.

Radiator inspection

18 With the radiator removed, it can be inspected for leaks and damage. If it leaks or is damaged the radiator should be replaced – repair is not usually an option.

19 Insects and dirt can be removed from the radiator with a garden hose or a soft brush. Take care not to damage the cooling fins as this is being done.

Radiator refitting

20 Fit new seals to the coolant drain plug and the coolant temperature sensor. On petrol models refit the coolant hoses.

21 On 1.8 petrol models and diesel models refit the cooling fans.

22 Ensure that the rubber lower supports are in position and then refit the radiator.

23 Refit the remaining components in reverse order and then refill the radiator with coolant as described in Chapter 1A or Chapter 1B.

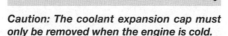

6   Expansion tank – removal and refitting

Caution: The coolant expansion cap must only be removed when the engine is cold.

Removal

Petrol models

1 On petrol models the expansion tank is a reserve coolant reservoir – the tank is not under pressure as the radiator cap is mounted on the radiator.

2 Unscrew the filler cap, or remove the coolant hose from the radiator filler neck.

Diesel models

3 Remove the slam panel cover.

4 Remove the cap and pull out the screen washer reservoir filler neck **(see illustration)**.

5 Drain the coolant. If only the expansion tank is to be removed, then it is only necessary to remove the coolant to below the level of the tank.

6 Release the spring clips and release the upper hoses **(see illustration)**.

7 Remove the single bolt (some models) or release the retaining clip. Pull up the reservoir to free it from the mounting peg. Turn the reservoir over and remove the lower coolant hoses. Remove the reservoir.

Refitting

8 Refitting is a reversal of removal. Top up the coolant level (diesel models) and fill the

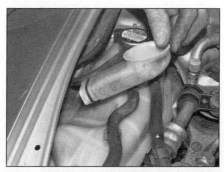

6.4 Remove the filler neck

reservoir to the 'Max' mark on petrol models. Run the engine up to operating temperature and check for coolant leaks.

7   Water pump – inspection, removal and refitting

Note: Refer to the warnings given in Section 1 of this Chapter before starting work.

Checking

1 A failure in the coolant pump can cause serious engine damage due to overheating and in the case of the diesel engine valve train damage as the coolant pump is driven by the timing belt.

2 There are three ways to check the operation of the coolant pump while it's installed on the engine. If the pump is defective, fit a new one.

3 With the engine running at normal operating temperature, squeeze the radiator top hose. If the coolant pump is working properly, a pressure surge should be felt as the hose is released.

⚠ *Warning: Keep your hands away from the radiator electric cooling fan blades.*

4 Coolant pumps are equipped with weep or vent holes. If a failure occurs in the pump seal, coolant will leak from the hole. In most cases you'll need an torch to find the hole on the coolant pump from underneath to check for leaks.

5 If the coolant pump shaft bearings fail, there may be a howling sound at the drivebelt end of the engine while it's running. Shaft wear can be felt if the coolant pump pulley is rocked up and down.

6 Don't mistake drivebelt slippage, which causes a squealing sound, for coolant pump bearing failure.

Removal

7 Loosen the right-hand front wheel nuts, then jack up the front of the car, and support it on axle stands (see *'Jacking and vehicle support'* in the Reference chapter). Remove the right-hand front wheel. Also unbolt and remove the engine undertray and right-hand front wheel arch liner (see Chapter 11).

8 Drain the cooling system as described in Chapter 1A or Chapter 1B.

6.6 Remove the upper hoses

7.11a Remove the idler pulley and...

7.11b...and then remove the tensioner

7.12a Remove the water pump pulley

7.12b Remove the automatic tensioner (shown with engine removed for clarity)

9 On petrol models, loosen (but do not yet remove) the three water pump pulley bolts – this is more easily done before the auxiliary drivebelt is removed.

10 Remove the auxiliary drivebelt as described in Chapter 1A or Chapter 1B.

11 On diesel models remove the idler pulley and the automatic tensioner **(see**

illustrations). The tensioner is retained by two bolts and a central hex headed bolt.

12 On 1.8 litre petrol models remove the drivebelt automatic tensioner **(see illustration)**. On 1.8 petrol models access can be improved if the alternator is removed, as described in Chapter 5A.

13 On 1.4 litre petrol models, unscrew the three bolts, and remove the water pump pulley. If the bolts were not previously loosened, it may be possible to hold the pulley using a tool through the pulley holes.

14 On 1.4 petrol models with air conditioning, remove the auxiliary drivebelt's idler pulley, which is secured by a single bolt **(see illustration)**. Access to the bolt is not easy, but we found it to be possible from below. Removing the pulley greatly improves access to the water pump's top mounting bolt.

15 Unscrew and remove the five or six mounting bolts, and withdraw the water pump from the engine **(see illustrations)**. Recover the pump's rubber seal – a new one should be used when refitting.

Refitting

16 Commence refitting by thoroughly cleaning the mating faces of the water pump and the cylinder block.

17 Refit the water pump, using a new rubber seal. Where fitted, refit (if necessary) the two locating dowels, and tighten the bolts to the specified torque **(see illustrations)**.

18 Further refitting is a reversal of removal, bearing in mind the following points:

a) Delay fully tightening the water pump pulley bolts until the drivebelt has been fitted.

b) On 1.8 models refit the automatic tensioner and using a spanner slowly compress and then release the tensioner. Repeat this three times to bleed the damper assembly.

c) Refit the auxiliary drivebelt as described in Chapter 1A or Chapter 1B.

d) On completion, refill the cooling system as described in Chapter 1A or Chapter 1B.

7.15 Remove the bolts (1.8 litre petrol shown)

7.17a Fit a new seal...

7.17b...offer up the pump...

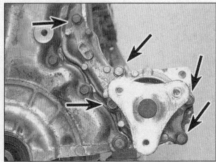

7.17c...refit the bolts and tighten them to the specified torque

8 Cooling system sensors and switches – removal and refitting

Removal

1 All models have two coolant sensors fitted – one in the cylinder head and one in the radiator. Both are critical inputs for the engine management system to control both the engine fuelling and the operation of the cooling fans.

Cylinder head sensor

2 This is the primary sensor for the engine management system. Drain the coolant to below the level of the sensor. Alternatively if you are replacing the sensor and have a new one to hand it is possible to quickly swap them over with little or no loss of coolant.

3 On 1.4 litre engines remove the air filter assembly and then on L13A engines remove the throttle body as described in Chapter 4A. On L13Z engines the sensor is accessed by unbolting the mounting bracket and moving the coolant hose to one side. Disconnect the wiring plug and unscrew the sensor. Recover the seal if necessary.

4 On the 1.8 petrol engine and diesel engines access is straight forward. Disconnect the wiring plug and unscrew the sensor. Recover the seal if necessary **(see illustration)**.

Radiator fitted sensor

5 Jack up and support the front of the vehicle – see '*Jacking and vehicle support*' in the Reference chapter.

6 Remove the engine undershield and disconnect the wiring plug from the sensor.

7 Drain the coolant as described in Chapter 1A or 1B. Alternatively if you are replacing the sensor and have a new one to hand it is possible to quickly swap them over **(see illustration)**. There will be some coolant loss. Have a clean container ready to catch the coolant in case you drop or misplace the new sensor.

Refitting

8 Refitting is a reversal of removal, but fit a new seal and top up (or refill) the engine coolant as required. Run the engine up to temperature and check for coolant leaks.

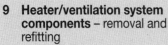
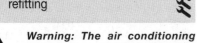

9 Heater/ventilation system components – removal and refitting

⚠ *Warning: The air conditioning system is under high pressure. Do not loosen any fittings or remove any components until after the system has been discharged. Air conditioning refrigerant should be properly discharged at a dealer service department or an automotive air conditioning repair facility capable of handling R134a refrigerant. Always wear eye protection when disconnecting air conditioning system fittings*

Caution: Always disconnect the battery before starting work on any electrical system (see disconnecting the battery in Chapter 5A). If working on, or in close proximity to any of the supplementary restraint systems (SRS) such as the seatbelts or airbags, wait a minimum of 10 minutes before starting work.

Heater/climate control panel

1 The heating, climate control and air conditioning controls are incorporated into

8.4 The coolant temperature sensor on the cylinder head (1.8 litre petrol engine)

the instrument panel binnacle. The exact function and operation of the switches varies depending on the trim level and if a navigation system (SatNav) is fitted. Removal and refitting is similar for all models.

Removal

2 Fully extend and lower the steering column.

3 Using a suitable plastic trim tool pull up the lower section of the instrument panel. Disconnect the cabin temperature sensor as the panel is removed **(see illustrations)**.

4 Remove the two screws and gently prise the instrument panel from the binnacle **(see illustrations)**. With the panel partially freed disconnect the wiring plugs from the rear of the panel.

5 Place the panel face down on a soft

8.7 The radiator mounted sensor (1.8 litre petrol engine shown)

surface, remove the mounting screws and lift out the switch panel.

Refitting

6 Refitting is a reversal of removal. Models fitted with climate control have a self test function built into the system. The self test should be performed after component replacement, or if a fault is suspected. To initiate the self test:

a) *Turn the ignition off.*
b) *Press and hold the 'Auto' and 'Recirculation' buttons.*
c) *Turn the ignition on whilst still holding the buttons.*
d) *Release the buttons.*
e) *The temperature display will light up and the test will begin.*

7 If an error is found the drivers temperature

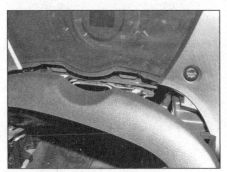

9.3a Remove the lower panel and...

9.3b and disconnect the temperature sensor

9.4a Remove the screws and...

9.4b...and remove the the panel

display will show a letter from A to P. The AUTO indicator may also illuminate depending on the fault. The table shows the associated fault codes:

Temperature segment	Fault
A	Cabin temperature sensor open circuit
B	Cabin temperature sensor short circuit
C	Ambient air sensor open circuit
D	Ambient air sensor short circuit
E	Sunlight sensor open circuit
F	Sunlight sensor short circuit
G	Evaporator temperature sensor open circuit
H	Evaporator temperature sensor short circuit
J	Drivers mixture control fault
K	Passenger mixture control fault
L	Mode control fault
M	Recirculation control fault
N	Blower motor fault
P	Control unit error
A and Auto	Control unit communication error with gauge control
B and Auto	Control unit error with gauge control
C and Auto	Control unit communication lost with recirculation control motor
D and Auto	Control unit communication lost with mode control motor
E and Auto	Control unit communication lost with gauge control module
F and Auto	Control unit communication lost with display
G and Auto	Drivers air mix motor failure
H and Auto	Passenger air mix motor failure
J and Auto	Bus error
K and Auto	Control unit communication error with all control motors
L and Auto	Control unit communication lost with drivers air mix motor
M and Auto	Control unit communication lost passengers air mix motor
N and Auto	Mode control motor failure
P and Auto	Recirculation control motor failure

8 To exit the diagnostic mode, turn the ignition off.

9.14a Remove the motor mounting screws...

Heater blower motor switch

9 The switch is part of the control panel and is removed with the panel.

Heater blower motor

Removal

10 The blower motor is located on the upper right-hand side of the main air distribution and heater housing. Access is limited, but it is possible to remove the motor without removing the facia or heater housing assembly.
11 Remove drivers side lower knee panel (below the steering column) and then remove the centre console as described in Chapter 11.
12 Remove the clutch pedal assembly as described in Chapter 6.
13 Disconnect the wiring plug from the drivers side air mixture control motor. Remove the screws and withdraw the motor.
14 Disconnect the wiring plug from the blower motor, remove the screws and remove the motor (see illustration).

Refitting

15 Refitting is a reversal of removal.

Heater blower motor resistor

Removal

16 The blower motor speed control unit (resistor pack) is located on the right-hand

9.16 The blower motor speed control unit

9.14b...and lower the motor into the footwell

side of the air distribution/heater housing (see illustration). Access is limited.
17 Remove the clutch pedal assembly as described in Chapter 6.
18 Disconnect the wiring plug, remove the fixing screws and remove the resistor pack (see illustration).

Refitting

19 Refitting is a reversal of removal.

Heater matrix

Removal

Note: *The heater matrix is located deep inside the air distribution/heater housing. Replacing the matrix is a long and complicated task, not to be undertaken lightly.*

20 Where fitted have the air conditioning system drained by a suitably equipped garage or mobile air conditioning specialist.
21 Drain the coolant as described in Chapter 1A or Chapter 1B.
22 Disconnect the battery and then remove the air filter housing as described in Chapter 4A or Chapter 4B.
23 At the bulkhead, mark (if necessary) the heater hoses and remove them.
24 Inboard of the heater matrix outlet pipes (and just above the AC evaporator supply pipes) is a single nut. Remove the nut.
25 At the bulkhead disconnect the evaporator/expansion valve pipes. Seal the pipes immediately.
26 The complete facia and cross member

9.18 Remove the control unit

9.26 The crossmember must be removed to access the heater matrix

9.28a Prise free the clips and...

(see illustration) must now be removed as described in Chapter 11.

27 Work around the air distribution housing and remove the loom and wiring plugs from:
● The recirculation motor
● The passenger side distribution motor
● The evaporator temperature sensor
● The drivers side air distribution motor
● The mode control motor
● The blower motor
● The blower motor speed control (resistor pack)

28 Prise free the clips and remove the air distribution ducts from the front of the housing **(see illustrations)**.

29 Remove the mounting nuts **(see illustrations)** and pull the complete housing into the cabin to release the evaporator and heater matrix pipes from the bulkhead. Lift up the unit and disconnect the evaporator drain pipe – or pull it up and out from the floor pan.

30 Remove the screws, release the cover and recover the gasket **(see illustration)**.

31 Remove the matrix pipe cover from the side **(see illustrations)** and then unscrew and remove the air mixture control motor on the passengers side.

32 Remove the screws and then remove the covers from the AC evaporator core. Unscrew and remove the expansion valve.

33 With all the covers removed pull out the heater matrix from the housing **(see illustration)**.

9.28b...and remove the air distribution duct

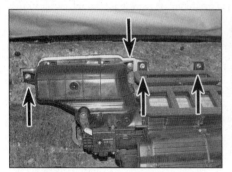

9.29a Remove the upper fixings...

9.29b...and the lower (one side shown)

9.30 Remove the pipe cover

9.31a Remove the screws...

9.31b...and then remove the cover

9.33 Removing the heater matrix

9.37 The recirculation control motor

9.48 The air mix motor

9.51 Remove the mounting screws

Refitting

34 Refitting is a reversal of removal, noting the following points:

a) *Ensure the evaporator drain pipe is correctly fitted and that it exits correctly from beneath the the vehicle.*

b) *Refill the system with engine coolant. Use new coolant as described in Chapter 1A or Chapter 1B.*

c) *Have the air conditioning recharged by a suitably equipped garage*

Heater control motors

Recirculation motor

35 Remove the glovebox as described in Chapter 11.

36 Unclip the passenger side foot well air distribution duct.

37 Disconnect the wiring plug, remove the screw and release the motor **(see illustration)**.

38 Refitting is a reversal of removal, ensuring that operating pin engages with the linkage.

Air mix motor left-hand side

Note: *The left-hand air mixture motor is only fitted to vehicles with dual climate control.*

39 Remove the glovebox as described in Chapter 11.

40 Unclip the passenger side foot well air distribution duct.

41 The mixture control motor is the lower motor, the upper motor is the recirculation motor.

42 Refitting is a reversal of removal, ensuring that operating pin engages with the linkage.

Mode control motor

43 Remove the drivers side lower (knee) panel.

44 Unclip and remove the heater duct.

45 Disconnect the wiring plug, remove the retaining screw and then remove the motor.

46 Refitting is a reversal of removal, ensuring that operating pin engages with the linkage.

Air mix motor drivers side

47 Remove the centre console as described in Chapter 11.

48 Disconnect the wiring plug, remove the retaining screws and then remove the motor **(see illustration)**.

49 Refitting is a reversal of removal, ensuring that operating pin engages with the linkage.

Facia vents

Drivers vent

50 Remove the heater control panel surround – as described in this Section.

51 Place the panel face down on a soft surface and remove the three screws **(see illustration)**. Remove the vent.

52 Refitting is reversal of removal.

Centre vent

53 The centre vent is part of the audio unit support/mounting panel. Remove the audio unit as described in Chapter 12.

54 Remove the mounting screws and prise out the vents.

55 Refitting is reversal of removal.

Passenger vent

56 If required the vent can be removed by prising it out. Protect the facia if necessary.

57 Refitting is reversal of removal.

Heater assembly

58 The facia and crossmember must be removed before the heater/air distribution housing can be removed. Most of the component parts of the housing can be removed without the removal of the facia and the crossmember, the only exceptions being the heater matrix and on diesel models the auxiliary heater. With a little ingenuity and the fabrication of new parts the advanced home mechanic may be able to able to replace both of these components without removing the facia and crossmember.

Auxilliary heater -diesel only

59 It is not possible to remove the heater without first removing the facia and crossmember **(see illustration)** as described in Chapter 12.

60 Disconnect the wiring plug, remove the mounting screws and remove the heater **(see illustration)**.

61 Refitting is reversal of removal.

Pollen filter

62 Refer to Chapter 1A or 1B.

---

10 Air conditioning system components – removal and refitting

---

9.59 The auxiliary heater. Note that the facia and crossmember must be removed to access the heater

9.60 The auxiliary heater wiring plug

⚠ *Warning: The air conditioning system is under high pressure. Do not loosen any fittings or remove any components until after the system has been discharged. Air conditioning refrigerant should be properly discharged into an approved type of container at a dealer service department or an automotive air conditioning repair facility capable of handling R134a refrigerant. Cap or plug the pipe lines as soon as they are disconnected to prevent the entry of moisture. Always wear eye protection when disconnecting air conditioning system fittings.*

10.3 Remove the upper AC hose

10.4 Remove the lower AC hose

10.5a Remove the brackets and then...

Note: *This Section refers to the components of the air conditioning system itself – refer to Sections 9 and 10 for details of components common to the heating/ventilation system.*
Note: *When any major component of the AC system is replaced the receiver drier should always be replaced. The receiver/drier should always be replaced on any AC system that has been left open to atmosphere for any length of time.*

Condenser

1 Have the air condition system discharged by a suitably equipped garage or mobile air conditioning specialist.
2 Remove the front bumper cover and the grille as described in Chapter 11. Remove the trim clips and then work free and remove the lower air deflector.
3 Disconnect the upper (discharge) AC hose **(see illustration)** and then immediately seal the hose and the condenser with suitable plugs.
4 Disconnect the lower (receiver) AC hose **(see illustration)**. Seal the hose and the condenser with suitable plugs.
5 Remove the upper mounting brackets and then lift out the condenser complete with the receiver/drier **(see illustrations)**.

10.5b...lift out the condenser

10.9 Remove the bulkhead panel

6 Refitting is a reversal of removal.

Evaporator

7 Have the system discharged by a suitably equipped garage or mobile AC specialist.
8 Working under the bonnet, disconnect the battery and then remove the air filter housing as described in Chapter 4A or Chapter 4B.
9 Remove the engine cover, the centre section of the windscreen cowls and the lower bulkhead panel **(see illustration)**.
10 Release the AC refrigerant pipes from

the retaining clips on the bulkhead **(see illustration)** and remove the bolt from the pipe clamp from the right-hand engine mounting.
11 Unbolt the AC refrigerant pipes at the expansion valve.
12 With reference to Chapter 11, remove the glovebox.
13 Where fitted remove the retaining clip and then prise free the passenger side air distribution duct **(see illustration)**.
14 Disconnect the wiring plug and then remove the passenger side air mix motor.

10.10 Release the refrigerant pipe clips

10.13 Remove the air distribution duct

10.15 Remove the lower cover

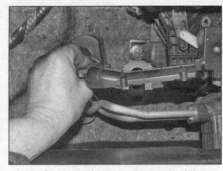

10.17a Remove the upper cover and then...

10.17b...remove the refrigerant pipes and expansion valve.

10.18 Remove the evaporator

10.21 Checking the clearance of the compressor clutch

15 Remove the screws and release the expansion valve lower cover **(see illustration)**.
16 Unclip the pollen filter cover and remove the pollen filter. Remove the screws from the evaporator cover and then remove the cover and recover the seal.
17 Remove the upper cover from the expansion valve and then remove the valve and refrigerant pipes from the evaporator **(see illustrations)**.
18 Slide the evaporator out of the housing **(see illustration)**.
19 Refitting is a reversal of removal, but fit new seals (lubricated with compressor oil) and have the system checked for leaks and recharged with refrigerant.

Compressor clutch

20 Ensure the ignition is switched off and then rotate the compressor in the normal direction of rotation – it should turn smoothly.
21 Measure the clearance between the clutch and the compressor pulley – there is no need to remove the compressor **(see illustration)**.
22 With the compressor still installed the resistance of the filed coil can also be checked. Disconnect the wiring plug and measure the resistance between the main terminal and the compressor body. Check the resistance against the specification.

23 If the clearance is not within specifcation the compressor must be removed to adjust the clearance – as described in this Section. A suitable tool will also be required to lock the clutch whilst the centre nut is removed.
24 With the clutch locked remove the armature plate and recover the shims.
25 If required remove the circlip and remove filed coil. Not however if the field coil is damaged and the clutch requires re-shimming, an exchange compressor may be the most economic solution. Compressors are usually supplied on an exchange basis.
26 Install the correct shims. Shims are available in four sizes – 0.1 mm, 0.2 mm, 0.4 mm and 0.5 mm. Tighten the bolt. Refit the compressor and check for the correct operation of the compressor.

Compressor

27 Have the system discharged by a suitably equipped garage or mobile AC specialist.
28 Disconnect the battery and then remove the bonnet slam panel cover.
29 Remove the auxiliary drive belt as described in Chapter 1A or Chapter 1B.
30 Disconnect the wiring plug and release the wiring loom from the support bracket **(see illustrations)**.
31 Jack and support the front of the vehicle

10.30a Release the wiring loom...

10.30b...and unbolt the support bracket

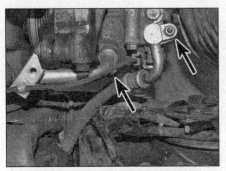

10.32 Remove the refrigerant hoses

10.33a Remove the bolts...

10.33b...and remove the compressor

10.33c Always seal all AC components to protect them from the ingress of dirt and moisture

10.36a Remove the lower mounting bolt and seal

10.36b Remove the upper bracket mounting

(see '*Jacking and vehicle support*' in the Reference chapter). Remove the engine undershield.

32 Disconnect the refrigerant hoses from the compressor **(see illustration)** and immediately seal the hoses with suitable plugs.

33 Unbolt and remove the compressor **(see illustrations)**.

34 Refitting is a reversal of removal, bearing in mind the the following points:

a) *Always fit new seals to the hose connections*

b) *Lubricate the new seals with compressor oil*

c) *Where a new compressor is being fitted check if it is supplied pre filled with oil. Add oil if necessary*

d) *Have the system checked for leaks and re-gassed by a suitably equipped garage*

Receiver/dryer

35 The receiver/drier is bolted onto the left-hand side of the condenser. Remove the condenser as described in this Section.

36 Unbolt the drier from the condenser **(see illustration)**. Remove the bracket and recover the O-ring seal from the base of the drier.

37 Refitting is a reversal of removal, but fit a new O-ring seal and lubricate it with compressor oil. Where a new drier is being fitted, only remove the blanking plugs just prior to refitting.

High- and low-pressure cut-off switch

Caution: The AC system must be degassed

before the switch is removed. Unlike many other manufacturers Honda fit the switch directly into the refrigerant line. Other manufactures often fit a Schrader type valve beneath the switch, allowing the switch to be removed without degassing the AC system.

38 Have the air condition system discharged by a suitably equipped garage or mobile air conditioning specialist.

39 The pressure switch is located close to the right-hand headlight. Remove the headlight as described in Chapter 12.

40 Disconnect the wiring plug and unscrew the sensor **(see illustrations)**.

41 Refitting is a reversal of removal, but fit a new O-ring seal and lubricate it with compressor oil. Have the system re-gassed

10.40a Disconnect the wiring plug...

10.40b...use a second spanner to counterhold the refrigerant line, unscrew the sensor...

10.40c...and recover the seal

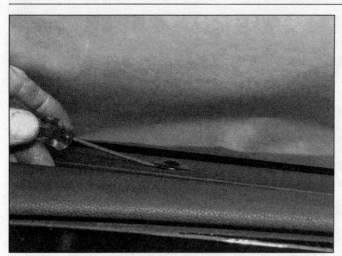

10.42 Prise out the sensor

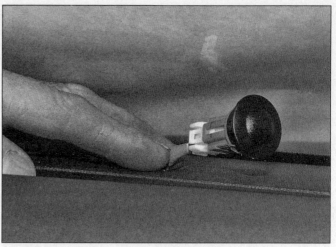

10.43 Disconnect the wiring plug

by a suitably equipped garage or mobile AC specialist.

Sensors

Sunlight sensor

42 The sensor is fitted to the centre of the facia. Protect the facia panel if necessary and then prise up the sensor **(see illustration)**.
43 Disconnect the wiring plug and remove the sensor **(see illustration)**. Attach a length of string to the wiring loom (or tape the loom to the facia) to stop the loom disappearing into the bowels of the facia.
44 Refitting is a reversal of removal.

Evaporator temperature sensor

45 The sensor is located at the front, right-hand side of the air distribution/heater housing.
46 Remove the centre console as described in Chapter 11.
47 Disconnect the wiring plug, remove the retaining screw and withdraw the sensor.
48 Refitting is a reversal of removal.

Cabin temperature sensor

49 Remove the lower section of instrument panel by prising it up.

50 Disconnect the wiring plug and remove the screws. Remove the sensor.
51 Some models also have a sensor fitted to the right-hand knee panel below the steering column. Remove the panel as described in Chapter 11, disconnect the wiring plug and remove the sensor.

Ambient temperature sensor

52 Remove front bumper as described in Chapter 11.
53 Disconnect the wiring plug from the sensor and unclip the sensor from the mounting bracket.
54 Refitting is a reversal of removal.

Chapter 4 Part A
Fuel and exhaust systems – petrol engines

Contents

Section number

Accelerator pedal – removal and refitting.................... 4
Air filter assembly – removal and refitting 5
Exhaust manifold – removal and refitting...................... 12
Exhaust system – general information, removal and refitting 13
Fuel filler flap – removal and refitting 9
Fuel injection system – checking........................... 8
Fuel injection system components – removal and refitting 10

Section number

Fuel pipes and connections................................ 3
Fuel pump/fuel gauge sender unit – removal and refitting......... 6
Fuel system – depressurisation 2
Fuel tank – removal, inspection and refitting 7
General information and precautions....................... 1
Inlet manifold – removal and refitting........................ 11

Degrees of difficulty

Easy, suitable for novice with little experience	Fairly easy, suitable for beginner with some experience	Fairly difficult, suitable for competent DIY mechanic	Difficult, suitable for experienced DIY mechanic	Very difficult, suitable for expert DIY or professional

Specifications

General

Engine codes:
    1.4 (i-DSI) L13A
    1.4 (i-VTEC)... L13Z
    1.8 (i-VTEC)... R18A
System type .... Honda PGM-FI (Programmed Fuel Injection) – Sequential multiport fuel injection
Fuel octane requirement..................................... 95 RON unleaded

Fuel system data

Fuel pump type .... Electrical – tank mounted pump
Fuel pressure:
    1.4 litre .... 47-54 psi
    1.8 litre.. 55-63 psi
Idle speed:
    1.4 .... 700 ± 50 rpm
    1.8 .... 650 ± 50 rpm
Idle CO .... 0.1% max

Torque wrench settings

	Nm	lbf ft
Accelerator pedal assembly nuts	12	9
Camshaft position sensor	12	9
Crankshaft position sensor	12	9
Exhaust heat shield bolts	10	7
Exhaust to catalytic converter bolts	93	69
Exhaust down pipe to exhaust bolts	22	16
Exhaust down pipe to sump bracket bolts	22	16
Exhaust flange self locking nuts	33	25
Fuel tank strap retaining bolts	38	28
Fuel rail mounting nuts:		
1.4 litre engines	12	9
1.8 litre engines	22	16
Inlet manifold nuts/bolts	24	17
Inlet manifold support bracket:		
M8 bolts	24	17
M6 bolts	10	7
Knock sensor	31	23
Throttle body bolts:		
1.4 (L13A)	24	17
1.4 (L13Z) and 1.8 (R18A)	22	16
Variable camshaft timing oil control valve		
1.4 (L13Z)	10	7
1.8 (R18A)	12	9

1 General information and precautions

General information

1 The fuel system consists of the fuel tank, located centrally on the underbody, a fuel pump/gauge sender unit submerged in the tank, a fuel rail supplying four injectors (one per cylinder) and a fully-electronic multipoint sequential fuel injection system.

2 All petrol-engined models are equipped with Honda's Multi-Point Programmed Fuel Injection (PGM-FI) engine management system, in which information from various sensors is supplied to the engine management system's Electronic Control Unit (ECU), to enable the unit to determine the optimum settings for both fuelling and ignition timing. On models with automatic transmission (1.8 litre engines) the system components and sensors are exactly the same, but because there are additional transmission control parameters and functions, the control unit is known by Honda as the Powertrain Control Module, or PCM. For simplicity, however, we shall refer to the control unit throughout as the ECU. The same control unit also manages aspects of the operation of the air conditioning system, especially on vehicles with automatic air conditioning (climate control) (see Chapter 3) and is linked to the ABS Electronic Control Unit (ECU) to play a part in the operation of the Vehicle Stability Assist (VSA) system (where fitted) – see Chapter 9. It also receives inputs from the power steering system and the alternator to enable it to compensate for the increased load placed on the engine – especially when cold – when the power steering system is being used or there is heavy demand from various electrical systems.

3 The ECU has a fail-safe function whereby if a signal from a sensor becomes abnormal, the ECU can ignore that signal and substitute a pre-programmed value that allows the engine to continue to run. There is also a back-up function which controls the injectors in the event of major system failure to permit minimal driving – a 'limp-home' mode. If a problem occurs with a component of the engine management system and/or transmission control system, the ECU has a self-diagnosis ability that enables it to store a code relating to that fault in its memory and to alert the driver to the fact that all is not well by illuminating the engine management Malfunction Indicator warning Lamp (MIL); for some systems (such as the automatic transmission), a supplementary warning will be given by flashing another indicator lamp. To filter out spurious indications for some self-diagnostic functions, the ECU stores the code whenever the fault occurs, but only illuminates the MIL if that fault occurs again after the ignition has been switched off and on again. If a fault ever occurs that causes a fault code to be logged so that the MIL illuminates consistently, the vehicle must be taken to a Honda dealer or other specialist so that dedicated electronic test equipment can be connected to the system via the diagnostic socket located under the driver's side of the facia. This will enable any fault codes stored to be read and, once the necessary corrective action has been taken, for the fault code(s) to be erased (refer to Section 10). **Note:** *The engine management Malfunction Indicator warning Lamp (MIL) in the instrument panel will illuminate when the ignition is first switched on as a check of its function. If the MIL lights while the vehicle is being driven, pull to the side of the road as soon as it is safe to do so and switch off the engine. Restart the engine (thus resetting the system) and watch the MIL; if it remains on, or comes back on while driving, the vehicle must be taken to a specialist as soon as possible for fault diagnosis and repair. If the vehicle has automatic transmission, the MIL's warning message may be reinforced by the instrument panel D indicator flashing as well.*

4 This Chapter deals with the fuel side of the system – refer to Chapter 5B for ignition specific details.

5 An electric fuel pump, filter gauze, pressure regulator and fuel gauge sender unit are located inside the fuel tank. Fuel is pumped from the fuel tank to the fuel rail, which is equipped with a pulsation damper to smooth out fluctuations in the flow of fuel. The system is 'returnless' – there is no return feed to the tank. Fuel vapours from the tank are stored in a canister at the rear of the tank, and supplied to the throttle body through a separate pipe.

6 Fuel delivery is by a multipoint sequential electronic fuel injection system, which essentially means it operates the four injectors separately, in firing order. Because each cylinder is equipped with its own injector, much better control of the fuel/air mixture ratio is possible. Various sensors are used to supply information relating to throttle butterfly position, engine coolant temperature, crankshaft angle, intake manifold pressure, atmospheric pressure, intake air temperature, vehicle speed and exhaust gas oxygen content. Information from these sensors is fed to the ECU, which then decides when to activate each injector. The system can alter fuel delivery to match the engine's needs under varying environmental and engine-load conditions. An Electrical Load Detector (ELD) built into the engine compartment main fuse/relay box monitors the demand on the alternator from the vehicle's other electrical systems and adjusts idle speed and fuelling accordingly to ensure smooth and consistent engine performance and response under all conditions.

Exhaust system

7 The exhaust system consists of an exhaust manifold (integrated into the cylinder head on later 1.4 models (L13Z engine codes) and all 1.8 litre engines. A three-way catalytic converter, a centre section with silencer, and a rear silencer.   The catalytic converter is an emissions control device added to the exhaust system to reduce pollutants. Refer to Chapter 4C for more information regarding the catalytic converter and other emissions control components.

Precautions

8 Before disconnecting any of the fuel injection system sensor wiring plugs, ensure at least that the ignition is switched off (ideally, disconnect the battery). If this is not done, it could result in a fault code being logged in the system memory, and may even cause damage to the component concerned.

9 Residual pressure will remain in the fuel lines long after the car was last used. When disconnecting any fuel line, first depressurise the fuel system as described in Section 2.

⚠️ *Warning: Many of the procedures in this Chapter require the removal of fuel lines and connections, which may result in some fuel spillage. Before carrying out any operation on the fuel system, refer to the precautions given in 'Safety first!' at the beginning of this manual, and follow them implicitly. Petrol is a highly-dangerous and volatile liquid, and the precautions necessary when handling it cannot be overstressed.*

2 Fuel system – depressurisation

Warning: The following procedure will merely relieve the pressure in the fuel system – remember that fuel will still be present in the system components, and take precautions accordingly before disconnecting any of them.

Note: *Refer to the warning note in Section 1 before proceeding.*

1 The fuel system referred to in this Chapter is defined as the fuel tank and tank-mounted fuel pump/fuel gauge sender unit, the fuel rail, the fuel injectors, and the metal pipes and flexible hoses of the fuel lines between these components. All these contain fuel, which will be under pressure while the engine is running and/or while the ignition is switched on.

2 The pressure will remain for some time after the ignition has been switched off, and must be relieved before any of these components is disturbed for servicing work.

3 The simplest depressurisation method is to disconnect the fuel pump electrical supply by removing the fuel pump fuse – fuse number 2 in the under facia fuse box. Allow the engine to idle until it stops through lack of fuel. Turn the engine over once or twice on the starter to ensure that all pressure is released, then switch off the ignition. Do not forget to refit the fuse when the work is complete.

4 Note that, once the fuel system has been depressurised and drained (even partially), it will take significantly longer to restart the engine – perhaps several seconds of cranking – before the system is refilled and pressure restored.

3 Fuel pipes and connections

1 Disconnect the cable from the negative battery terminal (see Chapter 5A) before proceeding.

2 The fuel supply pipe connects the fuel pump in the fuel tank to the fuel rail on the engine.

3 Whenever you're working under the vehicle, be sure to inspect all fuel and evaporative emission pipes for leaks, kinks, dents and other damage. Always replace a damaged fuel pipe immediately.

4 If you find signs of dirt in the pipes during disassembly, disconnect all pipes and blow them out with compressed air. Inspect the fuel strainer on the fuel pump pick-up unit for damage and deterioration.

Steel tubing

5 It is critical that the fuel pipes be replaced with pipes of equivalent type and specification.

6 Some steel fuel pipes have threaded fittings. When loosening these fittings, hold the stationary fitting with a spanner while turning the union nut.

Plastic tubing

⚠️ *Warning: When removing or installing plastic fuel tubing, be careful not to bend or twist it too much, which can damage it. Also, plastic fuel tubing is NOT heat resistant, so keep it away from excessive heat.*

7 When replacing fuel system plastic tubing, use only original equipment replacement plastic tubing.

Flexible hoses

8 When replacing fuel system flexible hoses, use original equipment replacements, or hose to the same specification.

9 Don't route fuel hoses (or metal pipes) within 100 mm of the exhaust system or within 280 mm of the catalytic converter. Make sure that no rubber hoses are installed directly against the vehicle, particularly in places where there is any vibration. If allowed to touch some vibrating part of the vehicle, a hose can easily become chafed and it might start leaking. A good rule of thumb is to maintain a minimum of 8.0 mm clearance around a hose (or metal pipe) to prevent contact with the vehicle underbody.

Disconnecting Fuel pipe Fittings

10 Typical fuel pipe fittings:

3.10a Two-tab type fitting; depress both tabs with your fingers, then pull the fuel pipe and the fitting apart

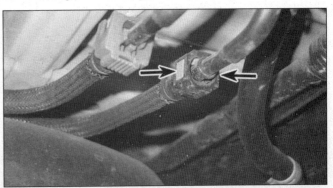

3.10b On this type of fitting, depress the two buttons on opposite sides of the fitting, then pull it off the fuel pipe

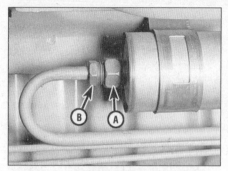

3.10c Threaded fuel pipe fitting; hold the stationary portion of the pipe or component (A) while loosening the union nut (B) with a flare-nut spanner

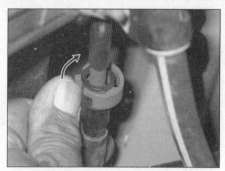

3.10d Plastic collar-type fitting; rotate the outer part of the fitting

3.10e Metal collar quick-connect fitting; pull the end of the retainer off the fuel pipe and disengage the other end from the female side of the fitting...

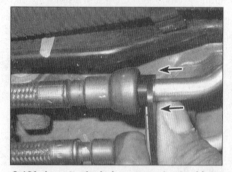

3.10f...insert a fuel pipe separator tool into the female side of the fitting, push it into the fitting and pull the fuel pipe off the pipe

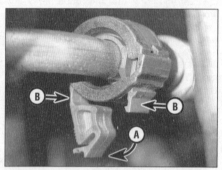

3.10g Some fittings are secured by lock tabs. Release the lock tab (A) and rotate it to the fully-opened position, squeeze the two smaller lock tabs (B)...

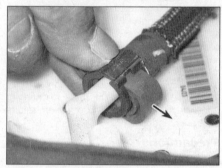

3.10h...then push the retainer out and pull the fuel pipe off the pipe

3.10i Spring-lock coupling; remove the safety cover, install a coupling release tool and close the tool around the coupling...

3.10j...push the tool into the fitting, then pull the two pipes apart

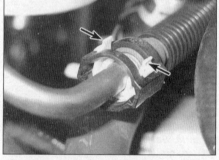

3.10k Hairpin clip type fitting: push the legs of the retainer clip together, then push the clip down all the way until it stops and pull the fuel pipe off the pipe

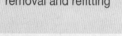

4 Accelerator pedal – removal and refitting

Removal

Note: *All models have a 'fly by wire' accelerator pedal – there is no throttle cable. Pressing the pedal sends a signal to the engine management control unit that then signals the stepper motor (on the throttle body) to open the throttle plate as required.*

1 Remove the driver's side facia lower panel, as described in Chapter 11.

2 Disconnect the battery negative lead as described in Chapter 5A.

3 Disconnect the wiring plug from the throttle position sensor, then unscrew the mounting nuts and remove the pedal/sensor assembly from the bulkhead studs **(see illustration)**.

Refitting

4 Refit in the reverse order of removal. On completion, check the action of the pedal to ensure that the throttle has full unrestricted movement, and fully returns when released.

5 Reconnect the battery as described in Chapter 5A.

4.3 Accelerator pedal/sensor assembly mounting nuts

5.1a Disconnect the MAF sensor (1.8 model shown)...

5.1b ...and release the cover retaining clips (1.4 model shown)

5.1c Remove the cover and lift out the filter

5.2a Remove the right...

5.2b...and the left-hand mounting bolts

5.2c Lift out the base of the air filter housing

5 Air filter assembly – removal and refitting

1 Disconnect the Mass Airflow Sensor (MAF) and unclip the wiring loom. Release the top cover clips and lift off the cover – note that some models require a hose clip to be slackened, before the cover can be removed. Remove the air filter **(see illustrations)**.
2 Remove the mounting bolts and lift out the air filter housing, disconnecting the inlet duct as the housing is removed **(see illustrations)**. Note that the mounting bolts are positioned differently on each model, but the housing is removed in a similar manner for all models.
3 Refitting is a reversal of removal.

6 Fuel pump/fuel gauge sender unit – removal and refitting

Note: *Refer to the warning note in Section 1 before proceeding.*

Removal

1 Unscrew the fuel filler cap – this is done to equalise the pressure in the tank.
2 Depressurise the fuel system as described in Section 2.
3 Disconnect the battery and then remove the centre console as described in Chapter 11.
4 Disconnect the handbrake warning light switch wiring plug, then remove the two handbrake lever mounting bolts and move the lever to one side, without disconnecting the cables **(see illustrations)**.
5 Unscrew the four screws securing the tank access panel to the car floor, and carefully lift it up – there's wiring attached to it **(see illustrations)**.
6 Disconnect the pump/sender unit wiring

6.4a Remove the handbrake mounting bolts

6.4b Move the wiring loom to the side

6.5a Remove the screws and...

6.5b...lift off the cover plate

6.6 Disconnect the wiring plug

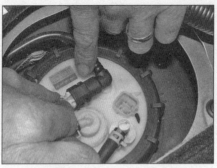

6.7 Disconnect the fuel hose

6.8 Remove the vapour hoses

6.9a Remove the collar with a fabricated tool...

6.9b...or a commercially available equivalent

6.10a Remove the locking collar

6.10b Slowly remove the pump/sender. Allow any fuel present to drain back into the tank

6.11a Unclip and disconnect the fuel gauge sender

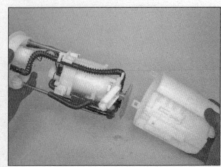

6.11b Remove the lower cover

plug inside, and move the access panel clear **(see illustration)**.

7 Release the fitting on the fuel supply hose on top of the sender unit, and disconnect it, anticipating a small amount of fuel spillage **(see illustration)**. Either plug or tape over the hose ends. The quick-release fittings are typically released by squeezing the upper and lower tabs on the plastic collar while sliding the hose off.

8 Noting their fitted positions (attach labels if necessary) disconnect the two vapour hoses on top of the unit **(see illustration)**.

9 The sender unit is secured using a threaded plastic collar, which will be tight. As access to it is limited by the hole in the car floor, Honda mechanics use a special three-legged gripping tool which engages the ribs on the collar's sides. An equivalent to this tool is available from several tool manufacturers. With care, it may be possible to unscrew the collar using large slip-joint water pump pliers, an oil filter strap wrench, or even by tapping the collar round with a screwdriver, but care must be taken not to damage either the collar or the tank. Mark the position of the collar before removing it and then unscrew and remove the collar **(see illustrations)**.

10 Carefully lift the pump and sender unit out of the tank. Lift the unit straight up, then turn it to keep the fuel level float from catching on the tank opening **(see illustrations)**. Recover the sealing ring – if this is in poor condition, a new one should be used when refitting.

11 Remove the pump/sender assembly from the vehicle and place it on the bench. Temporarily refit the collar to the fuel tank – this will stop the fuel tank threaded opening from distorting The pump can be dismantled to access the fuel filter, but note that this is not a service item as such **(see illustrations)**. Note also that Honda do not appear to list a replacement filter for all models. Check with your Honda dealer if a separate filter is available for your model.

Refitting

12 Refitting is a reversal of removal, but fit a new rubber seal and tighten the retaining ring

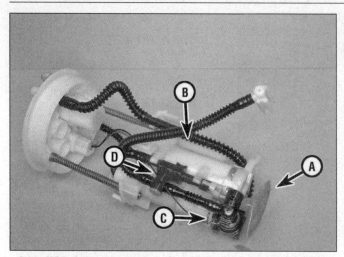

6.11c **With the lower cover removed note the component parts:**

A Fuel filter   B Fuel pump   C Fuel pressure regulator   D Check valve

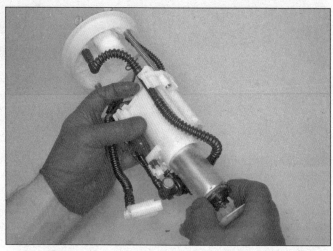

6.11d **Disconnect the wiring plug and remove the fuel pump**

securely, aligning the arrow on the top of the module with the mark on the top of the tank **(see illustration)**.

---

7 Fuel tank – removal, inspection and refitting

Note: *Refer to the warning note in Section 1 before proceeding.*

Removal

1 Disconnect the battery as described in Chapter 5A.

2 Before removing the fuel tank, all fuel must be drained from the tank. Since a fuel tank drain plug is not provided, it is therefore preferable to carry out the removal operation when the tank is nearly empty. The remaining fuel can then be syphoned or hand-pumped from the tank.

3 Unscrew the fuel filler cap – this is done to equalise the pressure in the tank. Depressurise the fuel system as described in Section 2.

4 Remove the centre console as described in Chapter 11.

5 Disconnect the handbrake warning light switch wiring plug, then remove the two handbrake lever mounting bolts and move the lever to one side, without disconnecting the cable(s).

6 Unscrew the four screws securing the tank access panel to the car floor, and carefully lift it up (see Section 6).

7 Disconnect the pump/sender unit wiring plug inside, and move the access panel clear.

8 Release the fitting on the fuel supply hose on top of the sender unit, and disconnect it, anticipating a small amount of fuel spillage. Either plug or tape over the hose ends. The quick-release fittings are typically released by squeezing the upper and lower tabs on the plastic collar while sliding the hose off.

9 Noting their fitted positions (attach labels if necessary), disconnect the two vapour hoses on top of the unit.

10 Jack up either the front or rear of the car, and support it on axle stands (see '*Jacking and vehicle support*' in the Reference chapter). Unusually, the fuel tank is mounted in the centre of the car.

11 The tank (and much of the floor) is protected by a large plastic cover. Remove the clips and bolts and manoeuvre the cover out from beneath the vehicle **(see illustrations)**.

12 Release the clips, then disconnect the filler and breather hoses from the rear of the tank – once the clips are released, twist the hoses off to avoid damage **(see illustration)**.

13 Unbolt and remove the heat shield from in front of the tank.

6.12 **Align the arrow on the top of the sender with the mark on the tank and the mark on the collar**

7.11a **Remove the clips...**

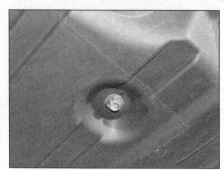

7.11b **...and bolts**

7.11c **Lower the cover**

7.12 **Release the spring clips**

7.15 Remove the tank straps (rear shown)

8.2 The Data Link Connector (DLC)

14 Position a jack (and a large flat piece of wood, to spread the load) under the tank, and just take its weight. Place the jack and wood centrally, so that the tank's support straps can be removed.

15 Taking care that the tank does not move, loosen and remove the four tank strap mounting bolts **(see illustration)**.

16 With the aid of an assistant to steady the tank on the jack, lower the jack and remove the tank out from under the car. Note that the tank may 'stick' on the underseal. Try and keep the tank as level as possible, especially if it still contains fuel – if the tank tips, the fuel will run to one end, and the tank may slide off the jack.

17 As the tank is lowered, check for any hoses which may still be attached, and disconnect them as they become accessible.

Inspection

18 Whilst removed, the fuel tank can be inspected for damage or deterioration. Removal of the fuel pump/fuel gauge sender unit (see Section 6) will allow a partial inspection of the interior. If the tank is contaminated with sediment or water, swill it out with clean fuel. Do not under any circumstances undertake any repairs on a leaking or damaged fuel tank; this work must be carried out by a professional who has experience in this critical and potentially dangerous work.

19 Whilst the fuel tank is removed from the car, it should be placed in a safe area where sparks or open flames cannot ignite the fumes coming out of the tank. Be especially careful inside garages where a natural-gas type appliance is located, because the pilot light could cause an explosion. It is strongly recommended that the fuel tank is stored in a safe location outside, if it is to remain removed for any length of time.

20 Check the condition of the lower filler pipe and renew it if necessary.

Refitting

21 Refitting is the reverse of the removal procedure, noting the following points:
a) *When lifting the tank back into position, take care to ensure that none of the hoses become trapped between the tank and body.*

b) *Refit the tank starps and tighten the bolts to the specified torque.*
c) *Ensure all pipes and hoses are correctly routed, and all hose connections securely remade.*
d) *On completion, refill the tank with a small amount of fuel, and check for signs of leakage prior to taking the car out on the road.*

8 Fuel injection system – checking

Note: *Refer to the warning note in Section 1 before proceeding.*

1 If a fault appears in the fuel injection system, first ensure that all the system wiring connectors are securely connected and free of corrosion. Then ensure that the fault is not due to poor maintenance; ie, check that the air cleaner filter element is clean, the spark plugs are in good condition, the cylinder compression pressures are correct, the ignition system wiring is in good condition and securely connected, and the engine breather hoses are clear and undamaged, referring to Chapter 1A, Chapter 2A or 2B and Chapter 5B.

2 If these checks fail to reveal the cause of the problem, the car should be taken to a Honda dealer or suitably equipped garage for testing. A diagnostic connector is fitted below the steering column, into which dedicated electronic test equipment can be plugged **(see illustration)**. The test equipment is capable of 'interrogating' the engine management system ECM (Engine Control Unit) electronically and accessing its internal fault log (reading fault codes).

3 Fault codes can only be extracted from the ECU using a dedicated fault code reader. A Honda dealer will have the official factory tool (HDS), but they are also available from other suppliers. Note that even the professional tools will not have the depth of coverage that the official factory tool will have. Code readers are becoming increasingly affordable for the home mechanic, however their scope is often limited to displaying the mandatory emissions related fault codes.

4 Using this equipment in the hands of a

skilled technician, faults can be pinpointed quickly and simply, even if their occurrence is intermittent. Testing all the system components individually in an attempt to locate the fault by elimination is a time consuming operation that is unlikely to be fruitful (particularly if the fault occurs dynamically), and carries a high risk of damage to the ECM's internal components. Note however that fault codes may be logged as symptom of the fault, not the cause of the fault.

Limited Operation Strategy

5 Certain faults, such as failure of one of the engine management system sensors, will cause the system will revert to a backup (or 'limp-home') mode, often referred to as a 'Limited Operation Strategy' (LOS). This is intended to be a 'get-you-home' facility only – the engine management warning light will come on when this mode is in operation.

6 In this mode, the signal from the defective sensor is substituted with a fixed value (it would normally vary), which may lead to loss of power, poor idling, and generally-poor running, especially when the engine is cold.

7 However, the engine may in fact run quite well in this situation, and the only clue (other than the warning light) would be that the exhaust CO emissions (for example) will be higher than they should be.

8 Bear in mind that, even if the defective sensor is correctly identified and renewed, the engine may not return to normal running until the fault code is erased. Note however that completing several drive cycles will usually clear the fault code – assuming the fault has been repaired correctly.

9 Fuel filler flap – removal and refitting

1 Open the filler door, remove the filler cap and then remove the single screw at the rear of the filler surround.

2 Remove the load area trim panel as described in Chapter 11.

3 Remove the screw and release the fuel filler latch.

4 Unclip and remove the surround and the flap together from the car.

5 Refitting is a reversal of removal. Fold the rubber surround over the filler neck as the flap is fitted.

10 Fuel injection system components – removal and refitting

Note: *Refer to the precautions in Section 1 before proceeding.*

Throttle body

Note: *There will be some coolant loss, so only remove the throttle body with a cold*

10.3 Remove the short inlet hose (1.8 models only)

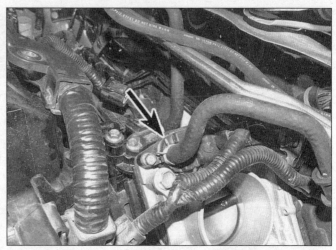

10.4 Remove the EVAP hose from the solenoid on the throttle body

engine and release the radiator cap before proceeding. There is no need to drain the cooling system as the coolant loss will be minimal.

1 Disconnect the battery before proceeding – see '*Disconnecting the battery*' in Chapter 5A.

2 Remove the centre section of the windscreen cowl panel and then remove the lower section as described in Chapter 12.

3 Remove the air filter housing as described in Section 5. On the 1.8 litre engine remove the short inlet duct **(see illustration)**.

4 Disconnect the wiring plugs and then remove the EVAP (Evaporative emissions) hose(s) from the throttle body **(see illustration)**.

5 Disconnect and then plug the coolant by-pass hoses **(see illustration)**. On the 1.4 i-VTEC engines pay particular attention to the orientation of the hoses and the position of the hose clips.

6 Remove the mounting bolts and withdraw the throttle body from the inlet manifold – we left the bolts in position and removed the body with the bolts **(see illustration)**.

7 Recover the gasket and then dispose of it – a new one must be fitted **(see illustration)**.

8 If required clean the throttle plate with a lint free cloth and a suitable cleaner. Honda list a

specific cleaner for this purpose. Do not spray the cleaner into the throttle body and avoid allowing the cleaner to penetrate the throttle plate spindles.

9 Refitting is a reversal of removal, noting the following points:

a) Use a new rubber seal, and tighten the throttle body bolts to the specified torque.

b) Ensure that the wiring plugs and hoses are correctly refitted. If any of the hoses show signs of perishing or split ends, new hoses should be obtained.

c) Check the coolant level, and top-up if necessary.

d) Turn the ignition on and wait for 3 seconds – do not press the accelerator pedal

e) If the throttle body has been cleaned carry out the idle lean procedure (Chapter 5A).

Fuel injectors

10 Disconnect the battery (see Chapter 5A) and depressurise the fuel system as described in Section 2.

11 On 1.4 litre models remove the air filter housing (Section 5) and the inlet manifold (Section 11).

12 On 1.8 litre models remove the windscreen cowl upper and lower panels as described in Chapter 12.

13 On the 1.8 litre models remove the protective cover and then disconnect the wiring pugs from the fuel injectors and the VTEC control solenoid. Remove the bolts from the wiring loom and then move the loom clear of the fuel rail **(see illustration)**.

14 On the 1.4 litre models disconnect the fuel injector wiring plugs and move the harness clear of the fuel rail.

15 On all models remove the protective cover and then – anticipating some fuel spillage – disconnect the fuel rail supply pipe (see

10.5 Remove the coolant hoses

10.6 Remove the throttle body

10.7 Note the bolts refitted to the manifold for safe keeping

10.13 Disconnect and then remove the wiring loom

10.15a Remove the fuel line connection protective cover

10.15b Releasing the fuel supply pipe quick release with a special tool...

10.15c...and immediately seal it

10.16 Remove the fuel rail complete with the injectors

10.17a Remove the clips and...

10.17b...remove the injectors from the rail with a twisting action

illustrations). Note that special tools are available for this purpose, but release is also possible without them.

16 On all models remove the fuel rail mounting bolts and then remove the rail complete with the injectors **(see illustration)**. Where fitted recover the spacers from beneath the fuel rail.

17 With the the fuel rail on a clean work surface and anticipating some fuel spillage remove the circlips from the injectors and then remove the injectors from the fuel rail (keeping them in cylinder order) **(see illustrations)**.

18 Remove the O-rings from the injectors. Note that the black O-rings fit the top of the injector and go into the fuel rail. The brown O-rings fit to the bottom of the injector and go into the cylinder head **(see illustrations)**.

19 Refitting is a reversal of removal, noting the following points:

a) *Use new O-ring seals, lightly oiled, and ensure the injectors are located in the rail the same way round as noted on removal*
b) *Where removed, fit the two spacer collars over the rail mounting studs* **(see illustration)**. *Seat the rail and injectors fully home, and tighten the mounting nuts.*
c) *Refit all hoses and wiring plugs securely.*
d) *On completion, switch on the ignition to pressurise the system, and check for leaks.*

Fuel pressure regulator

20 The pressure regulator is mounted inside the fuel tank, and forms part of the fuel pump/sender unit.

21 Remove the fuel pump assembly as described in Section 6.

Fuel filter

22 The filter unit is mounted inside the fuel

tank, and forms part of the fuel pump/sender unit.

23 Remove the fuel pump assembly as described in Section 6.

Engine control unit (ECU)

Note: *The ECU contains the immobiliser coding and model specific parameters. This information was programmed into the vehicle when the car was new. If a new ECM is fitted it must be programmed by a Honda dealer before the car will start or run properly. It is not possible to swap ECUs from car to car without the specific factory tool. A Honda dealer will have this tool, but a local garage may also have the tool if they are a Honda specialist.*

24 Disconnect and remove the battery as described in Chapter 5A.

25 Remove the protective cover and then remove the mounting bolts **(see illustrations)**.

10.18a Remove the O-rings

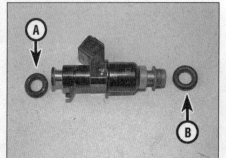

10.18b The injector O-rings:
A: Black   B: Brown

10.19 Fit the fuel rail spacers (1.4 litre models only)

10.25a Remove the cover...

10.25b...and remove the mounting bolts

10.26a Tilt the ECU forward to...

10.26b...access the wiring plugs. Lift the latch and disconnect the plugs

10.26c Always protect the ECU wiring plugs from contamination

10.30a Disconnect the wiring plug...

26 Disconnect the wiring plugs as the ECU is removed **(see illustrations)**.
27 Refitting is a reversal of removal.

Manifold Absolute Pressure Sensor

28 The MAP sensor is fitted to the inlet manifold on all models.
29 Access can be improved by removing the windscreen cowl panels as described in Chapter 12.
30 Disconnect the wiring plug, unbolt and remove the sensor. Note the O-ring **(see illustrations)**.

31 Refitting is a reversal of removal. Use a new O-ring if necessary, and tighten the mounting bolt securely.

Mass airflow sensor (MAF)

Note: *The sensor also incorporates the Inlet Air Temperature sensor (IAT). If either component is faulty the complete sensor must be replaced.*
32 On all models the sensor is mounted on the air filter housing.
33 Disconnect the wiring plug **(see illustration)** and remove the bolt (or bolts depending on the model).

10.30b...remove the mounting screw...

10.30c...and withdraw the MAP sensor – note the O-ring seal

10.33 Disconnect the wiring plug

10.37a Disconnect the wiring plug and...

10.37b...then remove the sensor

10.41a Disconnect the wiring plug
(L13A engine shown)

10.41b Remove the sensor
(1.8 litre engine shown)

10.43 Fit a new O-ring

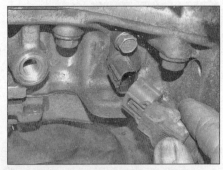

10.46a Disconnect the wiring plug
(1.8 litre)...

10.46b...and remove the bolt

10.47 Remove the sensor
(1.4 early engine shown)

34 Remove the sensor and recover the seal.

35 Refitting is a reversal of removal.

Knock sensor

36 Remove the inlet manifold as described in Section 11.

37 Disconnect the wiring plug and unscrew the sensor (see illustrations).

38 Refitting is a reversal of removal.

Camshaft position sensor

39 Remove the upper and lower windscreen cowl panels as described in Chapter 12.

40 On the 1.4 litre engines remove the air filter housing (Section 5) and then on the early 1.4 (L13A) engines only remove the throttle body as described earlier in this section.

41 Where necessary release the wiring loom and then disconnect the wiring plug from the sensor (see illustrations).

42 Remove the mounting bolt and withdraw the sensor. Recover the O-ring seal.

43 Refitting is a reversal of removal, but fit a new O-ring (see illustration).

Crankshaft position sensor

44 On all models access is best gained from below. Jack up and support the front of the vehicle – see 'Jacking and vehicle support' in the Reference chapter. Remove the engine undershield.

45 Where fitted remove the protective cover.

46 Disconnect the wiring plug and remove the single bolt (see illustrations).

47 Withdraw the sensor and remove the O-ring (see illustration).

48 Refitting is a reversal of removal, but use a new O-ring and perform the crankshaft sensor learn procedure:

a) Start the engine and run at 3,000 rpm until the radiator fan cuts in

b) On a level road (with no traffic) accelerate to 2,500 rpm in 1st gear. Slow down to 1,000 rpm (take your foot off the pedal)

c) Repeat the above procedure, but accelerate to 5,000 rpm and then slow to 3,000 rpm (take your foot off the pedal)

d) Repeat steps A and B several times

e) Turn the ignition off

f) Turn the ignition ON (do not start the vehicle) and wait 3 seconds

Coolant temperature sensor

49 Refer to Chapter 3 Section 8.

Variable camshaft timing oil control valve

50 The control valve is located at the front left-hand end of the cylinder head on 1.4 litre models and at the rear right-hand end of the cylinder head on 1.8 litre models.

51 Release the wiring loom from the support bracket and then disconnect the wiring plug.

52 Anticipate some oil spillage by placing a clean rag below the control valve and then remove the mounting bolts. Withdraw the

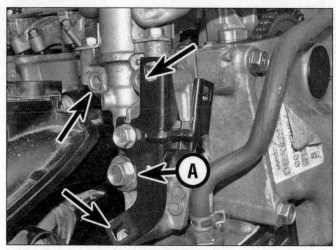

10.52a Note that some models will have a pressure switch fitted at 'A'. Remove the mounting bolts...

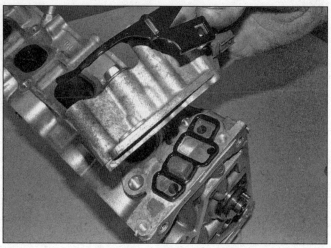

10.52b...lift off the control valve...

10.52c...and recover the gasket/filter

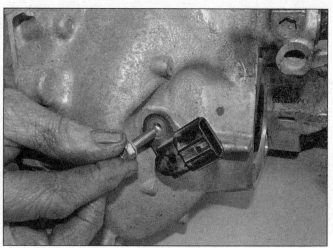

10.56 Remove the bolt

control solenoid and where necessary recover the gasket **(see illustrations)**.

53 Refitting is a reversal of removal. Ensure the valve and aperture are scrupulously clean prior to refitting and always use a new gasket. Tighten the bolts to the specified torque.

Vehicle speed sensor

54 Fitted to the rear of the transmission the Vehicle Speed Sensor (VSS) replaces the traditional speedometer drive cable.

55 The sensor is best reached from below. Jack up and support the front of the vehicle – 'see '*Jacking and vehicle support*' in the Reference chapter.

56 Disconnect the wiring plug, remove the bolt and withdraw the sensor **(see illustration)**.

57 Refitting is a reversal of removal.

Clutch pedal position switch

58 One or two position switches may be fitted, depending on the vehicle specification. Both switches are adjustable, but adjustment should only be made after checking that the clutch pedal stroke is correct – see Chapter 6 for the details of clutch pedal adjustment.

59 Remove the driver's side facia lower panel as described in Chapter 11.

60 With the ignition switched off, disconnect the wiring from the clutch switch.

61 Slacken the lock nut and unscrew the switch.

62 Refitting is a reversal of removal, but note the following:

a) *The clutch pedal travel must be correct before fitting the switch*

b) *Screw in the near vertical switch until it just contacts the clutch pedal and then screw it in another 3/4 of a turn. Tighten the lock nut*

c) *If refitting the near horizontal switch (cruise control) then depress the clutch pedal down between 35 – 38 mm and adjust the*

switch so that it contacts the pedal. Tighten the lock nut in this position

d) *Refit the remainder of the removed components*

Oxygen sensor

63 Refer to Chapter 4C.

Fuel shut-off (inertia) switch

64 The fuel shut-off switch is a safety device which automatically cuts off the fuel supply in the event of a sudden impact or collision. The switch may occasionally be triggered in normal driving, for example when driving over badly-maintained roads.

65 Remove the drivers side lower facia panel (knee) panel as described in Chapter 11.

66 Disconnect the wiring plug, remove the mounting bolts and remove the switch.

67 To reset the switch after an impact or shock, depress the button on the top of the switch.

68 Refitting is a reversal of removal.

11.3a Unscrew the two domed bolts...

11.3b...and take off the plastic cover

11.3c Disconnect the PCV hose in the centre...

11 Inlet manifold – removal and refitting

Note: *Refer to the warning note in Section 1 before proceeding.*

Inlet manifold

1 On 1.8 litre engines depressurise the fuel system (see Section 2). Disconnect the battery and then remove the upper and lower windscreen cowl panels (see Chapter 12).

2 Remove the air filter housing as described in Section 5.

1.4 litre (L13A) engines

Removal

3 Remove the plastic cover from the inlet manifold – this is secured by two domed bolts. Release the clip and disconnect the PCV hose from the centre of the manifold, and the brake servo vacuum hose just behind it **(see illustrations)**.

4 Disconnect the EVAP hose from the throttle body end of the manifold **(see illustration)**.

5 Remove the dipstick and then remove the bolts securing the wiring loom to the manifold.

6 Disconnect the wiring plugs from the throttle body, the EVAP purge valve and the MAP sensor. Release the wiring loom from the top of the manifold.

7 It is possible to remove the throttle body without draining the cooling system. Remove the bolts and move the throttle body to one side **(see illustrations)**.

8 Unbolt and remove the small support bracket from the manifold **(see illustration)**.

9 The manifold is secured at the front by three

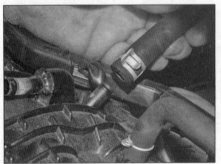

11.3d...and the servo hose behind it

11.4 Remove the EVAP hose

11.7a Remove the throttle body bolts...

11.7b...and move it to one side

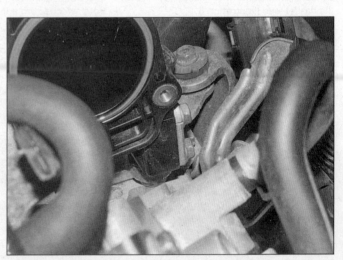

11.8 Remove the support bracket

11.10 Removing the inlet manifold

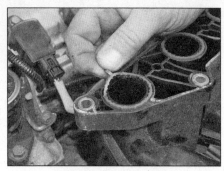

11.11 Recover the seals

11.12a Remove the EGR plate...

11.12b and the metal gasket

11.15a Fit the new EGR plate gasket...

11.15b...and then fit the EGR plate

bolts and two nuts. Unscrew the nuts/bolts – access to them is not easy, and care must be taken not to hit the radiator.

10 Support the manifold at the rear, then withdraw it forwards off its two studs. When it is clear of the studs, remove it from the engine compartment **(see illustration)**.

11 Recover the four rubber port seals from the manifold, and discard them – new ones must be used when refitting **(see illustration)**.

12 The EGR plate should also be removed from the manifold studs, so that a new plate-to-head gasket can be fitted (this should always be renewed when the manifold has been disturbed) **(see illustrations)**.

13 Clean all the mating faces prior to refitting and wipe them dry.

14 Check the manifold for any signs of splitting or cracking – this may be most evident around the mounting holes. If the manifold is damaged, a new one will be needed, although small isolated cracks may be repairable.

Refitting

15 Fit a new EGR plate-to-head gasket over the studs, then slide on the EGR plate **(see illustrations)**.

16 Fit four new port seals to the inlet manifold, then slide it onto the studs and up to the injector plate **(see illustration)**.

17 Refit the manifold nuts and bolts, and tighten them fully by hand. Once they are hand-tight, tighten the manifold nuts and bolts by a quarter-turn each at a time to the specified torque, working in a diagonal pattern from the centre outwards.

18 Further refitting is a reversal of removal.

1.4 litre (L13Z) engines

Removal

19 There are two ways to remove the inlet manifold: the manifold and induction chamber can be removed together, or the inlet manifold can be removed on by itself. Removal with the induction chamber is similar to the removal of the inlet manifold on the 1.4 litre L13A engine. Described below is the removal of the inlet manifold as a separate item.

20 Remove the bolt from the loom carrier **(see illustration)** and then move the loom to one side.

21 Remove the dipstick, the PCV hose and then disconnect the EGR valve **(see illustration)**.

11.16 Fit four new seals to the manifold

11.20 Remove the bolt

11.21 Disconnect the EGR valve

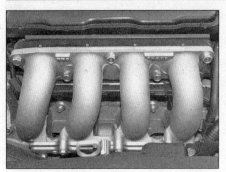

11.22 The inlet manifold

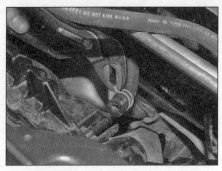

11.29 Disconnect the servo hose

11.33 Remove the manifold support bracket

22 Unbolt the inlet manifold from the cylinder head and the induction chamber (**see illustration**).

23 Recover the four seals from the induction chamber and the single gasket from the cylinder head.

Refitting

24 Fit new gaskets to the cylinder head and the induction chamber.

25 Tighten all the nuts/bolts hand tight to start and then (working in a criss cross pattern) tighten the nut/bolts to the final torque in three stages.

26 Further refitting is a reversal of removal.

11.34 The manifold mounting nuts/bolts

1.8 litre engine

Removal

27 If not removed with the air filter housing, then remove the small extension duct from the throttle body (**see illustration 10.3**).

28 Lift off and then remove the fuel injector cover.

29 Disconnect the lines from the: EVAP hose, the brake vacuum hose (**see illustration**) and the PCV hose.

30 Anticipate some fuel spillage and then disconnect the fuel line as described in Section 10.

31 Release the wiring loom form the inlet manifold and then disconnect the wiring plugs from:
a) *The throttle body*
b) *The MAP sensor*
c) *The EVAP purge valve (on the throttle body)*
d) *The inlet manifold tuning control valve*

32 Anticipating some coolant loss disconnect the coolant pipes from the throttle body. Alternatively drain the coolant below the level of the throttle body – note however there will be some coolant trapped in the throttle body. Remove the throttle body as described in Section 10.

33 Working blind remove the support bracket from the rear of the manifold. Alternatively, jack up and support the front of the vehicle, remove the engine undershield and then

remove the bracket from below (**see illustration**).

34 Again, working blind reach over the inlet manifold and remove the mounting bolts (**see illustration**).

35 Manoeuvre the manifold out from the engine bay. It is a tight fit, but removal is possible (**see illustration**).

Refitting

36 Replace all the gaskets before refitting the manifold (**see illustration**).

37 Tighten all the nuts/bolts hand tight to start and then (working in a criss cross pattern from the centre outwards) tighten the nut/bolts to the final torque in three stages.

Inlet manifold tuning valve (1.8 litre engines only)

38 The Honda 1.8 litre petrol engine has a variable length inlet manifold. The length of the manifold is varied by opening and closing a set of flaps in the manifold. When the flaps are closed there is high torque at a low engine speed and when the flaps are open there is high torque at a high engine speed. The position of the flaps is controlled by the engine management ECU.

Removal

39 Remove the inlet manifold as described in Section 11.

40 With the manifold on the bench, unscrew and remove the actuator/stepper motor (**see illustration**).

11.35 Removing the manifold

11.36 Always fit new gaskets

11.40 Remove the mounting screws

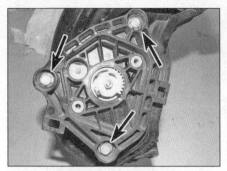

11.41a Remove the bolts...

11.41b...take off the cover...

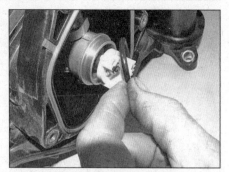

11.41c...remove the O-ring and...

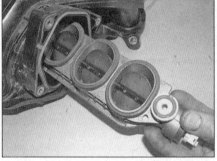

11.41d...withdraw the flap assembly

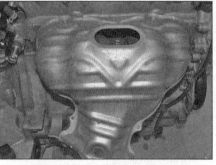

12.5a Remove the three bolts...

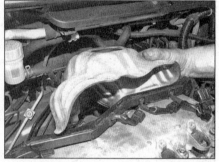

12.5b...and take off the heat shield

41 Remove the three mounting bolts and slide the assembly out of the manifold **(see illustrations)**.

Refitting

42 Refitting is a reversal of removal, but always replace the gaskets.

12 Exhaust manifold – removal and refitting

1 The 1.4 litre engines have a standard exhaust manifold. On the 1.8 litre engine the manifold is part of the catalytic converter. Removal and refitting of the catalytic converter is covered in Chapter 4C.

Removal

2 The exhaust manifold is at the rear of the cylinder head, and access is not easy – part of the job must be done from above, and the rest from below.

3 Remove the upper and lower windscreen cowl panels, as described in Chapter 12.

4 Jack up and support the front of the vehicle (see '*Jacking and vehicle support*' in the Reference chapter) and then remove the engine undershield.

5 Remove the three bolts securing the heat shield and remove it **(see illustrations)**. These bolts often suffer from corrosion, and may be difficult to remove. Use a wire brush and plenty of penetrating oil first if they appear to be rusty. If the bolts are in less-than-perfect condition, new ones should be obtained for reassembly.

6 Disconnect the wiring plug from the pre catalytic converter oxygen sensor.

7 The manifold is secured with two nuts on top, and three bolts along the bottom edge **(see illustration)**. Loosen (do not yet remove) the nuts and bolts which are accessible from above.

8 Have a support (such as an axle stand or a small jack) ready to rest the front pipe on.

9 At the manifold/downpipe joint, a support bracket is fitted. Unscrew the bracket to engine bolt, so that the bracket is removed with the manifold.

10 Undo the two bolts securing the front pipe to the manifold **(see illustration)**. Recover the springs and the gasket – it is recommended that new bolts, springs and a new gasket are used when refitting.

12.7 The exhaust manifold is held in place with two nuts and three bolts (one hidden)

12.10 The flexible manifold to catalytic converter joint

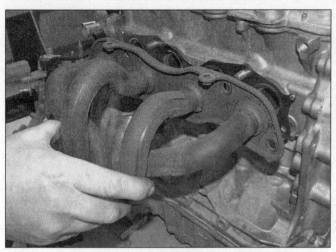

12.12 Removing the exhaust manifold

12.13 Always use a new manifold gasket

11 Do not let the front pipe hang down unsupported, as this will strain the oxygen sensor wiring (as well as the pipe itself). Place an axle stand or another jack under the pipe.
12 Unscrew any remaining manifold nuts or bolts which were not accessible from above, then remove those which were previously only loosened. Withdraw the manifold off the studs, and remove it from the engine compartment **(see illustration)**. Recover the manifold gasket from the engine – a new one should always be used when refitting.

Refitting

13 Refitting is a reversal of removal, noting the following points:
a) *Clean the manifold and cylinder head mating faces, and fit a new gasket* **(see illustration)**.
b) *If the manifold studs were removed, it's best to obtain a set of new studs and nuts, rather than try to separate the old ones. The new studs can be fitted by tightening two nuts against each other on the stud, then using them to screw the stud into place – once this is done, the nuts can be unscrewed from each other, and removed.*
c) *Apply anti-seize compound (copper grease will do) to the manifold studs before fitting the nuts, and to the bolt threads.*

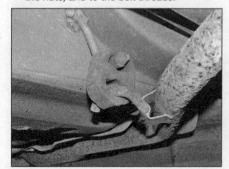

13.2 Check the condition of the exhaust rubber mountings regularly

d) *Tighten the manifold nuts/bolts to the specified torque.*
e) *Reconnect the front pipe, using a new gasket, springs and bolts. Do not apply exhaust jointing compound to the new gasket. Tighten the bolts fully by hand, then by a quarter-turn each at a time to the specified torque.*
f) *Reconnect the primary oxygen sensor wiring plug, and clip the plug back in place. Ensure that the wiring is routed clear of any hot components.*

---

13 Exhaust system – general information, removal and refitting

Caution: Any work on the exhaust system should only be attempted once the system is completely cool – this may take several hours, especially in the case of the forward sections, such as the manifold and catalytic converter.

General information

1 The exhaust system consists of three sections: the front pipe (including the catalytic converter on 1.4 litre models) the centre pipe and silencer, and the rear silencer. Como models have a twin tail pipe exhaust fitted. The system is unusual because the centre mounted fuel tank means the exhaust is routed around it.
2 The system is suspended throughout its entire length by rubber mountings **(see illustration)**.
3 If any section of the exhaust is damaged or deteriorated, excessive noise and vibration will occur.
4 Carry out regular inspections of the exhaust system, to check security and condition. Look for any damaged or bent parts, open seams, holes, loose connections, excessive corrosion, or other defects which could allow exhaust fumes to enter the car. Deteriorated

sections of the exhaust system should be renewed.
5 If the exhaust system components are extremely corroded or rusted together, it may not be possible to separate them. This often happens with the rear silencer, which rusts to the centre section – try twisting the pipes to separate them. Cut off the old components carefully with a hacksaw, and see if any corroded pipe can be removed (perhaps with a chisel) without damaging the remaining exhaust section. Wear safety glasses to protect your eyes, and wear gloves to protect your hands.
6 Here are some simple guidelines to follow when repairing the exhaust system:
a) *Work from the back to the front when removing exhaust system components.*
b) *Apply penetrating fluid to the flange nuts before unscrewing them. Wire brush any exposed threads to remove corrosion and dirt before trying to loosen the nuts*
c) *Use new gaskets and rubber mountings when installing exhaust system components*
d) *Apply anti-seize compound (copper grease will do) to the threads of all exhaust system studs/bolts during reassembly*
e) *The downpipe is secured to the manifold (or the catalytic converter on 1.8 litre models) and the rear silencer to the centre section, by two coil springs and bolts. When the bolts are tightened to the specified torque, the pressure of the springs will then be sufficient to make a gas tight seal. Do not overtighten the bolts to cure a leak, or they may shear. Renew the gasket and the springs if a leak is found.*
f) *Be sure to allow sufficient clearance between newly-installed parts and all points on the underbody, to avoid overheating the floorpan, and possibly damaging the interior carpet and insulation. Pay particularly close attention to the catalytic converter and its heat shield*

13.12 Rigid mounting (to the catalytic converter) on 1.8 litre engines

13.13a The catalytic converter rear mounting (1.4 litre engines)

Removal

7 Each exhaust section can be removed individually, or the complete system can be removed as a unit. Even if only one part of the system needs attention, in some cases it will be easier to remove the whole system and separate the sections on the bench.

8 To remove the system or part of the system, first jack up the front or rear of the car, and support it on axle stands. Alternatively, position the car over an inspection pit, or on car ramps.

Front pipe

9 The front pipe includes the catalytic converter on 1.4 litre models.

10 Trace the wiring from the secondary oxygen sensor to the wiring plug and disconnect it. Release the wiring from any clips or ties, so that it is free to be removed with the exhaust system.

11 Have a support (such as an axle stand or a small jack) ready to rest the front pipe on as required during removal.

12 Undo the two bolts securing the front pipe to the manifold (or catalytic converter on 1.8 litre models) **(see illustration)**. Recover the springs and the gasket – it is recommended

that new bolts, springs and a new gasket are used when refitting.

13 Unscrew the flange nuts from the joint behind the catalytic converter/front pipe and separate the flange from the centre section **(see illustrations)**. Recover the gasket and discard it – this and the flange nuts should be renewed.

14 Remove the front pipe or (on 1.4 litre models) the catalytic converter from underneath the car. Take care that the converter is not dropped or roughly handled.

Centre pipe and silencer

15 Slacken and remove the three flange nuts securing the centre pipe to the catalytic converter (or front pipe on 1.8 litre models) and separate the joint. Recover and discard the gasket – a new one must be used when refitting.

16 Undo the two bolts securing the rear silencer to the centre section. Recover the springs and the gasket – it is recommended that new bolts, springs and a new gasket are used when refitting.

17 Release the centre section from the mounting rubbers by pulling it forwards, then remove it from underneath the car.

13.13b Recover the gasket (1.8 litre model)

Rear silencer

18 Undo the two bolts securing the rear silencer to the centre section **(see illustrations)**. Recover the springs and the gasket – it is recommended that new bolts, springs and a new gasket are used when refitting.

19 Unhook the rear silencer from its mounting rubbers, and free it from the centre pipe.

Complete system

20 Trace the wiring from the oxygen sensor and disconnect the wiring plug. Release the

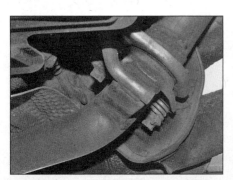

13.18a The rear flexible mounting

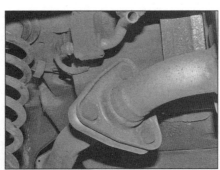

13.18b On models with a twin rear exhaust pipe, remove the short single pipe before removing the silencer

13.18c Always fit a new gasket

wiring from any clips or ties, so that it is free to be removed with the exhaust system.

21 Have a support (such as an axle stand or a small jack) ready to rest the front pipe on as required during removal.

22 Undo the two bolts securing the front pipe to the manifold (or catalytic converter on 1.8 litre models). Recover the springs and the gasket – it is recommended that new bolts, springs and a new gasket are used when refitting.

23 Free the system from its mounting rubbers, then remove it from underneath the car.

Heat shields

24 The heat shields are secured to the underside of the body by various nuts, bolts and rivets (which will have to be drilled out). Each shield can be removed once the relevant exhaust section has been removed. If a shield is being removed to gain access to a component located behind it, it may prove sufficient in some cases to remove the retaining nuts and/or bolts, and simply lower the shield, without disturbing the exhaust system.

Refitting

25 Each section is refitted by reversing the removal sequence, noting the following points:

a) *Ensure that all traces of corrosion have been removed from the flanges, and renew all necessary gaskets, bolts and springs as applicable.*

b) *The exhaust system flange nuts are all of self-locking type, and new ones should be used when refitting.*

c) *Inspect the rubber mountings for signs of damage or deterioration, and renew as necessary.*

d) *Prior to tightening the exhaust system fasteners, ensure that all rubber mountings are correctly located, and that there is adequate clearance between the exhaust system and underbody.*

e) *Tighten all flange bolts and nuts fully by hand, then by a quarter-turn each at a time to the specified torque.*

Chapter 4 Part B
Fuel and exhaust systems – diesel engines

Contents

Section number

Air filter housing – removal and refitting.	4
Common rail – removal and refitting	10
Electronic diesel control (EDC) system components – removal and refitting	8
Exhaust manifold – removal and refitting.	13
Exhaust system – general information, removal and refitting	15
Fuel gauge sender – removal and refitting.	6
Fuel injectors – removal testing and refitting	11

Section number

Fuel pipe and connectors.	3
Fuel pump – removal and refitting	9
Fuel system – depressurising, priming and bleeding.	2
Fuel tank – removal and refitting	7
General information and precautions.	1
Inlet manifold – removal and refitting.	12
Intercooler – removal and refitting	5
Turbocharger – removal, examination and refitting	14

Degrees of difficulty

Easy, suitable for novice with little experience 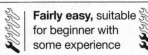	**Fairly easy,** suitable for beginner with some experience	**Fairly difficult,** suitable for competent DIY mechanic	**Difficult,** suitable for experienced DIY mechanic	**Very difficult,** suitable for expert DIY or professional

Specifications

General
System type . . . . Bosch direct injection common rail, with timing belt driven high-pressure delivery pump, variable nozzle turbocharger and intercooler

Torque wrench settings

	Nm	lbf ft
Accelerator pedal mounting nuts.	12	9
Air intake/ISV to IMRC valve nuts/bolts.	22	16
Camshaft position sensor:	12	9
Catalytic converter to exhaust nuts*	33	24
Common rail mounting bolts	22	16
Crankshaft position sensor	12	9
Exhaust front pipe to catalytic converter nuts*	33	24
Exhaust front pipe to warm up catalyist.	22	16
Exhaust manifold cover bolts.	22	16
Exhaust manifold to cylinder head nuts*	44	32
Exhaust rear silencer to centre section	22	16
Fuel high-pressure pipe union nuts**	27	20
Fuel injector clamp bolts:		
Stage 1.	5	4
Stage 2.	Angle tighten a further 90°	
Fuel injection pump mounting bolts.	22	16
Fuel tank sender unit collar	93	69
Fuel tank mounting bolts.	38	28
IMRC valve nuts and bolts.	22	16
Inlet manifold nut/bolts.	22	16
Turbocharger coolant bypass pipe banjo bolt	28	21
Turbocharger inlet pipe support bracket:		
6 mm bolts	12	9
8 mm bolts	44	32
Turbocharger oil supply banjo bolt.	44	32
Turbocharger support bracket bolt.	44	32
Turbocharger to exhaust manifold*	59	43
Warm up catalytic converter support bracket	44	32
Warm up catalytic converter to turbocharger nuts.	44	32

*Use new nuts/bolts

** The *fuel high pressure pipes must always be replaced*

1 General information and precautions

1 The fuel system consists of the centrally located fuel tank, a fuel hand primer and a filter assembly mounted at the left-hand rear of the engine compartment. The filter housing incorporates: a fuel heater, a fuel temperature sensor and a water level switch. From the filter assembly, fuel is drawn to the fuel pump which is mounted on the left-hand end of the cylinder head and driven by gears from the exhaust camshaft. This is a tandem pump, combining a gear-type low-pressure lift pump to draw fuel from the tank via the hand primer and filter assembly, and a radial-piston high-pressure side which compresses the fuel ready for injection. Fuel at a pressure of up to 1600 bars is supplied to the fuel rail, which forms a reservoir of fuel common to all four injectors (hence the name 'common rail'). Rail pressure is controlled in the first instance by a fuel rail pressure control valve mounted on the pump, which regulates the quantity of fuel to the high-pressure side of the pump; the valve being opened by the engine management system's Electronic Control Unit (ECU) in response to signals from the fuel rail pressure sensor, and excess fuel being returned to the tank. A pressure-limiting valve mounted in the end of the fuel rail opens if rail pressure rises above the maximum permissible level, excess pressure again being returned to the tank. Solenoid-valve fuel injectors are connected to the fuel rail by short high-pressure lines and are opened by the ECU to spray fuel directly into the combustion chambers. A variable-nozzle turbocharger with intercooler is fitted.

Fuel injection system

2 All diesel engined models are equipped with a second-generation version of the Bosch Electronic Diesel Control (EDC) engine management system. Information from various sensors relating to engine coolant temperature, crankshaft angle, intake manifold pressure, atmospheric pressure, intake air temperature and vehicle speed is supplied to the engine management system's Electronic Control Unit (ECU), to enable the unit to determine the optimum settings for both fuelling and injection timing. The same control unit also manages aspects of the operation of the air conditioning system, especially on vehicles with automatic air conditioning (climate control) (see Chapter 3) and is linked to the ABS Electronic Control Unit (ECU) to play a part in the operation of the Vehicle Stability Assist (VSA) system (where fitted) – see Chapter 9. It also receives inputs from the power steering system and the alternator to enable it to compensate for the increased load placed on the engine when the power steering system is being used or there is heavy demand from various electrical systems. An Electrical Load Detector (ELD)

built into the engine compartment main fuse/relay box monitors the demand on the alternator from the vehicle's other electrical systems and adjusts idle speed and fuelling to ensure smooth and consistent engine performance and response.

3 The ECU has a fail-safe function whereby if a signal from a sensor becomes abnormal, the ECU can ignore that signal and substitute a pre-programmed value that allows the engine to continue to run. There is also a back-up function which controls the injectors in the event of major system failure to permit minimal driving – a 'limp-home' mode. If a problem occurs with a component of the engine management system, the ECU has a self-diagnosis ability that enables it to store a code relating to that fault in its memory and to alert the driver to the fact that all is not well by illuminating the engine management Malfunction Indicator warning Lamp (MIL); for some systems (such as the ABS or VSA systems), a supplementary warning will be given by flashing another indicator lamp. To filter out spurious indications for some self-diagnostic functions, the ECU stores the code whenever the fault occurs, but only illuminates the MIL if that fault occurs again after the ignition has been switched off and on again. If a fault ever occurs that causes a fault code to be logged so that the MIL illuminates consistently, the vehicle must be taken to a specialist so that dedicated electronic test equipment can be connected to the system via the diagnostic socket located under the driver's side of the facia. This will enable any fault codes stored to be read and, once the necessary corrective action has been taken, erased. **Note:** *The MIL will illuminate when the ignition is switched on as a check of its function. If the MIL lights while the vehicle is being driven, pull to the side of the road as soon as it is safe to do so and switch off the engine.* Restart the engine (thus resetting the system) and watch the MIL; if it remains on, or comes back on while driving, the vehicle must be taken to a specialist as soon as possible for fault diagnosis and repair. The glow plug warning lamp may also flash while the engine is running and the MIL is on. The glow plug warning lamp may also flash after the vehicle has run out of fuel, especially if air has entered the system so that the engine will not start even after the fuel tank has been refilled. In that case, once the engine has been restarted the warning lamp can be turned off by switching off the engine and then restarting it and switching it off at least three times in succession at intervals of approximately 30 seconds.

4 The common rail injection system allows close regulation of injection pressure and timing to give optimum performance across all driving conditions. The fuel pump simply provides high-pressure fuel; the timing and duration of the injection is controlled by the ECU, based on the information received from the various sensors and is not adjustable in any way. The injection system interacts with the turbocharger to ensure optimum control over intake pressure, facilitating higher intake

pressures at a lower speed, as well as better fuel economy and fewer harmful emissions through lean burn combustion.

Intake Manifold Runner Control system

5 IMRC here is a continuously-variable swirl control valve. The intake manifold's lower (swirl) tract (the only one to which the EGR valve is connected) supplies air to the intake valves opened by the higher-lift A-cam lobes through ports whose tangential orientation is designed to maximise axial swirl in the combustion chamber. The intake manifold's upper (secondary) tract, supplying those intake valves opened by the milder B-cam lobes, is opened and closed by vacuum acting on the butterfly-type IMRC valve, controlled by the engine management system Electronic Control Unit (ECU) via the IMRC solenoid valve acting on information from the IMRC valve position sensor. The combination of different port geometry, dissimilar cam lobes and the enhanced swirl generated by the IMRC system provides very high swirl in the combustion chamber at low engine speeds, reducing gradually as engine speed increases to give the ideal combustion environment at all times. This, referred to by Honda as the 'intelligent combustion control system', improves combustion efficiency so that the engine can use a relatively low compression ratio (and thus escape the friction, vibration and noise penalties of higher compression pressures) while still producing power outputs comparable with sales rivals.

Turbocharger

6 A turbocharger increases engine efficiency by raising the pressure in the intake manifold above atmospheric pressure. Instead of the air simply being sucked into the cylinders, it is forced in. Additional fuel is supplied by the engine management system in proportion to the increased air intake.

7 Energy for the operation of the turbocharger comes from the exhaust gas. The gas flows through a specially-shaped housing (the turbine housing) and in so doing, spins the turbine wheel. The turbine wheel is attached to a shaft, at the end of which is another vaned wheel known as the compressor wheel. The compressor wheel spins in its own housing and compresses the inducted air on the way to the intake manifold.

8 The compressed air passes through an intercooler. This is an air-to-air heat exchanger, mounted next to the radiator at the front of the vehicle. The purpose of the intercooler is to remove from the inducted air some of the heat gained in being compressed. Because cooler air is denser, removal of this heat further increases engine efficiency.

9 The turbocharger shaft is pressure-lubricated by an oil feed pipe from the main oil gallery. The shaft 'floats' on a cushion of oil. A drain pipe returns the oil to the sump. Similarly, the turbocharger has its own coolant feed from the main engine cooling system.

Exhaust system

10 The exhaust system includes an exhaust manifold, turbocharger, a four-way oxidation ('warm-up') catalytic converter, a front pipe with flexible section, a NOx-reducing catalytic converter, a centre section with silencer, and a rear silencer. Some later models also have a Diesel Particulate Filter (DPF) fitted.

11 The catalytic converters are emissions control devices added to the exhaust system to reduce pollutants. Refer to Chapter 4C for more information regarding the catalytic converters and other emissions control components.

Precautions

• *When working on diesel fuel system components, scrupulous cleanliness must be observed, and care must be taken not to introduce any foreign matter into fuel lines or components.*

• *After carrying out any work involving disconnection of fuel lines, it is advisable to check the connections for leaks; pressurise the system by cranking the engine several times.*

• *Electronic control units are very sensitive components, and certain precautions must be taken to avoid damage to these units.*

• *When carrying out welding operations on the vehicle using electric welding equipment, the battery and alternator should be disconnected.*

• *Although the underbonnet-mounted modules will tolerate normal underbonnet conditions, they can be adversely affected by excess heat or moisture. If using welding equipment or pressure-washing equipment in the vicinity of an electronic module, take care not to direct heat, or jets of water or steam, at the module. If this cannot be avoided, remove the module from the vehicle, and protect its wiring plug with a plastic bag.*

• *Before disconnecting any wiring, or removing components, always ensure that the ignition is switched off.*

• *Do not attempt to improvise PCM fault diagnosis procedures using a test lamp or multimeter, as irreparable damage could be caused to the module.*

• *After working on fuel injection/engine management system components, ensure that all wiring is correctly reconnected before reconnecting the battery or switching on the ignition.*

2 Fuel system – depressurising, priming and bleeding

Depressurising the fuel system

1 The low-pressure side of the fuel system, between the fuel tank and the pump, is under negative pressure while the engine is running. The high-pressure side of the system – the pump, the fuel rail, the injectors and the rigid high-pressure fuel pipes linking these components – can attain pressures of up to 1600 bars while the engine is running. Residual pressure may persist for some time after the engine is switched off.

2 There is no convenient method of depressurising the high-pressure side of the system. Do not attempt to 'depressurise' the system by disabling the fuel pump's supply and running the engine out of fuel – the pump and injectors rely on the lubrication offered by diesel fuel and will be irreparably damaged by being run dry. The only safe method of dealing with the residual pressure is to wrap a large rag around the first high-pressure fuel pipe union to be disconnected, ready to soak up any escaping fuel. Slowly (to avoid a sudden release of pressure and to allow any fuel spray which may be expelled to be caught by the rag) unscrew the union nut. When any hissing has stopped, indicating that all residual pressure has been released, unscrew the nut completely; be prepared for some loss of fuel.

> ⚠ **Warning: Wear eye protection when disconnecting any part of the high-pressure side of the fuel system in this way.**

Priming and bleeding

> ⚠ **Warning: The following applies only to the low-pressure side of the fuel system, between the fuel tank and the pump. Do not attempt to disconnect any part of the high-pressure side of the system, between the fuel pump and the injectors, to bleed out trapped air.**

3 Since the system is designed to be self-bleeding, it is not always necessary manually to prime and bleed the fuel system after working on the system components. Just starting the engine may be sufficient (although this may take longer than usual). Operate the starter in ten-second bursts only, with five seconds rest in between each operation. When the engine starts, run it at fast idle speed for a minute or so to purge any trapped air from the fuel lines. After this time, the engine should idle smoothly at a constant speed.

4 If a significant amount of work has been carried out on the fuel system, and the engine either won't start or idles roughly, then there is still some air trapped in the system.

5 To prime the system, operate the hand primer as many times as necessary (40 or 50 strokes) until the filter and hoses as far as the fuel pump are refilled with diesel fuel and the primer becomes hard **(see illustration)**. Start the engine and keep it running at a fast idle until it is running smoothly, then allow it to idle and check for signs of fuel leakage. If the engine does not start first time – do not operate the starter for more than 30 seconds at a time, or there is a risk of damage to the starter motor and to the common-rail injection system's fuel pump – operate the hand primer

2.5 The hand primer is hidden behind a protective cover

again until it becomes hard, then try again. Note that while the hand primer does become hard when used to pump fuel into the system, under normal circumstances it will be soft to the touch, as the lift pump draws fuel through the system from the fuel tank.

6 No bleed nipples being provided, the only way of bleeding the system is to disconnect the fuel feed hose from the fuel pump (Section 10) and to operate the hand primer until diesel fuel, free from air bubbles, appears from the end of the hose – direct the hose into a clean container and place plenty of rag to prevent any fuel from being spilled on to surrounding components. Reconnect the fuel feed hose to the fuel pump, operate the hand primer until it becomes hard, then try to start the engine again. Once the engine starts, keep it running at a fast idle until it is running smoothly, then allow it to idle and check for signs of fuel leakage.

7 If you have to resort to using the hand primer when no servicing work has been carried out, or if poor starting necessitates the use of the hand primer on a frequent basis, there is an air leak in the system. Refer to Section 9.

3 Fuel pipe and connectors

1 Disconnect the cable from the negative battery terminal (see Chapter 5A) before proceeding.

2 The fuel supply pipe connects the fuel pump in the fuel tank to the fuel filter on the engine.

3 Whenever you're working under the vehicle, be sure to inspect all fuel and evaporative emission pipes for leaks, kinks, dents and other damage. Always replace a damaged fuel pipe immediately.

4 If you find signs of dirt in the pipes during disassembly, disconnect all pipes and blow them out with compressed air. Inspect the fuel strainer on the fuel pump pick-up unit for damage and deterioration.

Steel tubing

5 It is critical that the fuel pipes be replaced with pipes of equivalent type and specification.

6 Some steel fuel pipes have threaded fittings. When loosening these fittings, hold

3.10a Two-tab type fitting; depress both tabs with your fingers, then pull the fuel pipe and the fitting apart

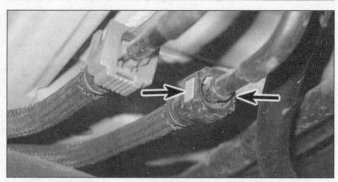

3.10b On this type of fitting, depress the two buttons on opposite sides of the fitting, then pull it off the fuel pipe

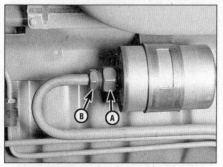

3.10c Threaded fuel pipe fitting; hold the stationary portion of the pipe or component (A) while loosening the union nut (B) with a flare-nut spanner

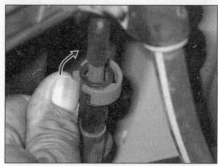

3.10d Plastic collar-type fitting; rotate the outer part of the fitting

3.10e Metal collar quick-connect fitting; pull the end of the retainer off the fuel pipe and disengage the other end from the female side of the fitting...

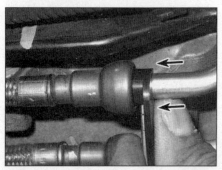

3.10f ...insert a fuel pipe separator tool into the female side of the fitting, push it into the fitting and pull the fuel pipe off the pipe

3.10g Some fittings are secured by lock tabs. Release the lock tab (A) and rotate it to the fully-opened position, squeeze the two smaller lock tabs (B)...

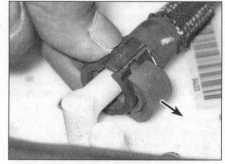

3.10h ...then push the retainer out and pull the fuel pipe off the pipe

3.10i Spring-lock coupling; remove the safety cover, install a coupling release tool and close the tool around the coupling...

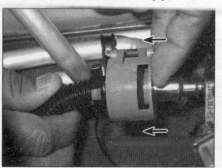

3.10j ...push the tool into the fitting, then pull the two pipes apart

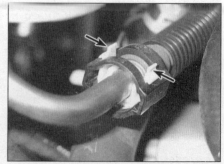

3.10k Hairpin clip type fitting: push the legs of the retainer clip together, then push the clip down all the way until it stops and pull the fuel pipe off the pipe

the stationary fitting with a spanner while turning the union nut.

Plastic tubing

Warning: When removing or installing plastic fuel tubing, be careful not to bend or twist it too much, which can damage it. Also, plastic fuel tubing is NOT heat resistant, so keep it away from excessive heat.

7 When replacing fuel system plastic tubing, use only original equipment replacement plastic tubing.

Flexible hoses

8 When replacing fuel system flexible hoses, use original equipment replacements, or hose to the same specification.

9 Don't route fuel hoses (or metal pipes) within 100 mm of the exhaust system or within 280 mm of the catalytic converter. Make sure that no rubber hoses are installed directly against the vehicle, particularly in places where there is any vibration. If allowed to touch some vibrating part of the vehicle, a hose can easily become chafed and it might start leaking. A good rule of thumb is to maintain a minimum of 8.0 mm clearance around a hose (or metal pipe) to prevent contact with the vehicle underbody.

Disconnecting fuel pipe fittings

10 Typical fuel pipe fittings are pictured on the opposite page.

4   Air filter housing – removal and refitting

Note: Whenever the air cleaner cover or the complete assembly is removed, pack the turbocharger air intake with clean rag to keep dirt out.

Air cleaner assembly

1 Disconnect and then remove the battery (**see illustrations**). Full details are given in Chapter 5A.
2 Slacken the clamp securing the air filter housing to the turbocharger. Disconnect the hose and then release the intake duct from the side of the housing (**see illustration**).

5.3a Release the hose clips...

4.1a Remove the battery and...

4.2 Slacken the hose clamp

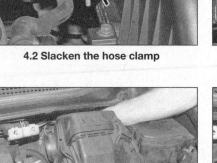
4.4a Partially remove the air filter housing...

3 Unscrew the bolt securing the assembly (**see illustration**).
4 Withdraw the air cleaner assembly, easing it off the two mounting pegs at the bottom rear (**see illustrations**).

5.3b...and remove the hoses

4.1b...then remove the battery tray

4.3 Remove the single mounting bolt

4.4b...and disconnect the MAF sensor before completely removing the housing

5 If required, remove the air filter inlet ducting can now be removed by removing the single bolt from the mounting bracket.
6 Refitting is a reversal of removal.

5   Intercooler – removal and refitting

Removal

1 Jack up and support the front of the vehicle – see '*Jacking and vehicle support*' in the Reference chapter.
2 Remove the engine undershield and then remove the front bumper cover as described in Chapter 11.
3 Slacken the hose clips and remove the intercooler outlet hose (the upper hose) and then remove the inlet hose (**see illustrations**).

5.4 Remove the bolts

5.5a Remove the mounting bolts

5.5b Remove the bracket and the intercooler...

5.5c...and then remove the intercooler from the mounting bracket

4 At the front of the intercooler unbolt and remove the air inlet duct **(see illustration)**.

5 Unbolt the intercooler support bracket and then remove bracket and intercooler **(see illustrations)**.

6 If required unbolt the outlet elbow from the intercooler. Recover the gasket and dispose of it.

Refitting

7 Refitting is a reversal of removal, but fit a new gasket if the outlet elbow has been removed.

6 Fuel gauge sender –
removal and refitting

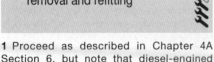

1 Proceed as described in Chapter 4A Section 6, but note that diesel-engined models will have two quick-release fuel hose fittings on the top of the fuel gauge sender unit – one feed and one return. Mark or label these so that they do not get swapped over on refitting. For diesel-engined models there is no fuel pump submerged in the tank, so there is only the fuel gauge sender unit; if this is faulty, it must be renewed complete.

7 Fuel tank –
removal and refitting

1 Proceed as described in Chapter 4A Section 7, but note that diesel-engined models do not have a charcoal canister to remove, nor a fuel vapour hose to disconnect.

8 Electronic diesel control (EDC) system components
– removal and refitting

Note: *Refer to the precautions in Section 1 before proceeding.*

Accelerator pedal position sensor

Note: *The sensor and the pedal are a single assembly. No individual parts are available.*
1 Disconnect the wiring plug.
2 Using a flat bladed screwdriver release the locking plate at the base of the pedal. Remove the upper mounting nuts and remove the pedal from the vehicle.
3 Refitting is a reversal of removal.

8.8 The camshaft position sensor

Barometric pressure sensor

4 The barometric pressure sensor is incorporated in the ECU to enable it to measure atmospheric pressure and adjust injector opening duration accordingly. The sensor is not available separately from the ECU.

Brake pedal position switch

5 Refer to Chapter 9.

Camshaft position (CMP) sensor

6 The camshaft position sensor is fitted to the left-hand end of the cylinder head, between the fuel pump and the EGR cooler bypass valve.
7 Unscrew the four retaining nuts and remove the acoustic engine cover.
8 Disconnect the sensor's electrical connector **(see illustration)**. Remove the mounting bolt, and withdraw the sensor from the cylinder head; be prepared for slight oil loss. Remove the O-ring.
9 Refitting is the reverse of the removal procedure, noting the following points:
a) *Use a new O-ring and smear it with clean engine oil*
b) *Tighten the bolt to the specified torque*
10 The camshaft position sensor's pick-up rotor is mounted on the inlet camshaft. It can be withdrawn once the cylinder head cover has been removed.

Clutch pedal position switch

Note: *The clutch pedal position switch is fitted to the clutch pedal assembly, above the clutch pedal. Some models have two switches.*
11 Refer to Chapter 4A and Chapter 6.

Crankshaft position (CKP) sensor

12 The crankshaft position sensor is fitted to the front right-hand end of the engine's lower crankcase/main bearing ladder, buried behind the air conditioning compressor mounting bracket. It is visible from beneath, but a considerable amount of preliminary dismantling is required to reach it **(see illustration)**. Its pulse plate is bolted to the crankshaft right-hand web; the engine must be dismantled completely to reach it.
13 Disconnect the battery (see *Disconnecting the battery* 5A).
14 Unscrew the four retaining nuts and remove the engine acoustic cover. Jack up

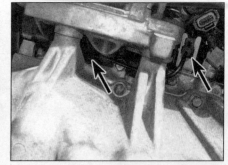

8.12 The crankshaft position sensor. Note the location of the wiring plug

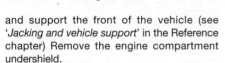

8.20a Lubricate the new O-ring with clean engine oil...

8.20b...tighten the bolt and route the wiring correctly

8.30 The hand primer bulb location

and support the front of the vehicle (see '*Jacking and vehicle support*' in the Reference chapter) Remove the engine compartment undershield.

15 Remove the auxiliary drivebelt (Chapter 1B).

16 Remove the alternator (Chapter 5A).

17 Unscrew the air conditioning compressor's four mounting bolts. With the compressor unbolted, secure it clear of the working area without disconnecting or straining its wiring and pipes.

18 Unbolt the air conditioning compressor mounting bracket from the engine.

19 Disconnect the wiring plug, then unscrew the mounting bolt and remove the sensor from the engine. Recover the O-ring.

20 Refitting is a reversal of removal. Fit a new sealing O-ring, lubricate it with clean engine oil and tighten the sensor mounting bolt to the specified torque **(see illustrations)**.

21 Refit all components removed for access.

EGR control solenoid valve

22 Refer to Chapter 4C.

Electronic Control Unit (ECU)

Note: *The ECU contains the immobiliser coding and the correct software for the vehicle. It is not possible to swap ECUs without access to suitable diagnostic equipment. If a new ECU is fitted, the new ECU will have to be programmed to the vehicle. This is only possible with the Honda factory tool – HDS.*

23 Disconnect the battery (see *Disconnecting the battery* 5A). This is essential when working

on the ECU – if the unit's wiring connector is unplugged when the battery is still connected, this will almost certainly damage the unit.

24 Remove the glovebox and the footwell kick panel as described in Chapter 11.

25 Releasing their locking catches, unplug the connectors to disconnect the wiring from the ECU.

26 Unscrew the two nuts and the bolt securing the ECU mounting bracket to the bulkhead.

27 Unscrew the ECU mounting bolts and withdraw the ECU.

28 Refitting is a reversal of removal.

Coolant temperature sensor

29 Refer to Chapter 3.

Hand primer

30 The hand primer is a rubber bulb fitted in the fuel feed line from the fuel tank to the fuel filter assembly and is hidden behind a protective cover at the rear of the engine compartment **(see illustration)**.

31 To remove the hand primer, unclip and pull the bulb forward to reach the hoses to and from the primer. Clamp the fuel hoses using brake hose clamps; if such clamps are not available, unplug each hose in turn and plug it as quickly as possible to prevent diesel fuel from contaminating other components and to prevent dirt from getting into the fuel system. Release the clips to remove the hand primer.

32 Refitting is a reversal of removal.

Fuel filter

33 Refer to Chapter 1B.

Fuel filter water level switch

34 The switch is fitted to the base of the fuel filter and is removed and refitted as part of the fuel filter renewal procedure described in Chapter 1B.

Fuel heater

35 The heater is part of the the fuel filter head, which is removed and refitted as part of the filter replacement procedure described in Chapter 1B. The filter is secured by four small Torx screws, but is only available as part of the filter assembly.

Fuel rail pressure (FRP) sensor

36 The sensor is part of the fuel rail **(see illustration)**. It is not supplied as a separate part. If it is faulty then the fuel rail must be replaced, as described in Section 10.

Fuel rail pressure control valve

Note: *Honda do not supply the control valve separately from the fuel pump. The components are of Bosch manufacture and may be available through Bosch approved diesel specialists.*

37 Unscrew the four retaining nuts and remove the acoustic engine cover **(see illustration)**. Although not strictly necessary, access is greatly improved by removing the air cleaner assembly as described in Section 4 4.

38 Disconnect the control valve wiring plug, then undo the screws and detach the valve from the fuel pump **(see illustration)**. Immediately seal the opening in the pump.

39 Refitting is a reversal of removal, tightening the retaining screws securely.

8.36 The fuel rail pressure sensor

8.37 Remove the engine cover

8.38 The fuel rail pressure control valve

8.41 The fuel temperature sensor location

Fuel shut-off (inertia) switch

40 Refer to Chapter 4A Section 10.

Fuel temperature sensor

41 The fuel temperature sensor is located in the fuel filter head and informs the ECU of the temperature of the incoming fuel; its resistance decreasing as the temperature of the incoming fuel increases. Disconnect the wiring plug from the sensor **(see illustration)**.
42 Using a suitable deep socket, unscrew the sensor from the filter head; be prepared for some loss of fuel. Plug the filter opening to prevent contamination.
43 Refitting is a reversal of removal. Fit a new sealing O-ring, lubricate it with clean diesel fuel to aid installation and tighten the sensor to the specified torque.

Glow plug control module

44 Refer to Chapter 5C.

Intake Manifold RunnerControl (IMRC) system

Solenoid valve

45 Unscrew the four retaining nuts and remove the engine cover.
46 Disconnect the valve's electrical connector and two vacuum hoses **(see illustration)**. Unscrew the mounting bolt, and withdraw the valve from the intake manifold.
47 Refitting is the reverse of the removal procedure.

Valve assembly

48 Unscrew the four retaining nuts and remove the engine cover.
49 Disconnect the intercooler outlet hose from the intake manifold air intake passage, then unscrew the mounting bolts and nuts and withdraw the air intake passage from the valve assembly **(see illustration)**.Note that on models fitted with a DPF the intake has a shutter valve fitted. Disconnect the wiring plug on these models and remove the shutter valve in the same manner. Recover and discard the gasket – a new one must be fitted on reassembly. Unscrew the bolt securing the intake manifold support bracket to the IMRC valve.
50 Disconnect the manifold absolute pressure sensor wiring plug (or remove the sensor, as described below) and the IMRC valve position sensor wiring plug **(see illustration 8.46)**.
51 Disconnect the vacuum hose from the valve.
52 Unscrew the two mounting nuts and two mounting bolts and withdraw the valve from the intake manifold **(see illustration)**. Recover and discard the gasket – a new one must be fitted on reassembly.
53 The valve is available only as a complete assembly; do not attempt to dismantle it or to remove the valve position sensor **(see illustration)**.

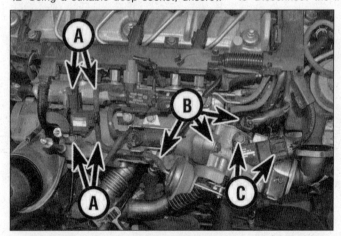

8.46 IMRC solenoid valve mounting bolt, hoses and wiring connector (A), IMRC valve upper mounting nut, hose and position sensor wiring connector (B), MAP sensor wiring connector and mounting bolt (C)

8.49 Unscrew the bolts and nuts and remove the air intake passage

8.52 IMRC valve lower mounting bolts and nut

8.53 The IMRC valve is sealed – do not attempt to dismantle or adjust

8.62 The MAF sensor mounting screws

8.65a The turbocharger boost control solenoid valve wiring connector and vacuum hoses

54 Refitting is the reverse of the removal procedure, noting the following points:
a) *Fit new gaskets to the valve and to the air intake passage.*
b) *Tighten all nuts and bolts to their specified torque wrench settings.*
c) *Ensure that all wiring plugs are securely reconnected.*

Valve position sensor

55 The position sensor is fitted to the IMRC valve butterfly's spindle, and is not available separately. In the event that a position sensor problem is suspected, the only solution is a new IMRC valve assembly.

Manifold absolute pressure and inlet air temperature sensor

56 The manifold absolute pressure sensor is located on top of the IMRC valve assembly and provides the ECU with information on pressure levels in the manifold generated by the turbocharger. The sensor also incorporates an intake air temperature sensor, the resistance of which decreases as the temperature of the incoming air increases. The ECU uses these signals to calculate the engine load, and the appropriate fuelling, further to refine injector opening duration.

57 Unscrew the four retaining nuts and remove the acoustic engine cover.

58 Disconnect the sensor wiring plug, then unscrew the mounting bolt and withdraw the sensor. Recover and discard the sealing O-ring – this must be renewed whenever the sensor is disturbed.

59 Refitting is a reversal of removal. Fit a new O-ring, lubricate it with clean engine oil to aid installation and tighten the mounting bolt securely; note the specified torque setting.

Mass airflow and inlet air temperature sensor

60 The Mass Airflow (MAF) sensor is located in the air cleaner assembly cover and incorporates a hot-wire mass airflow sensor to

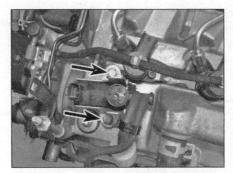

8.65b The turbocharger boost control solenoid valve mounting bolts

send the ECU a voltage signal corresponding to the volume of air passing into the engine. The sensor also incorporates an inlet air temperature sensor, the resistance of which decreases as the temperature of the incoming air increases. The ECU uses these signals to calculate the mass of air entering the engine.

61 Remove the air filter housing, as described in Section 4, disconnecting the mass airflow sensor wiring connector as the housing is removed.

62 Undo the two screws and withdraw the sensor **(see illustration)**. Examine the seal, where fitted, and renew it if worn or damaged.

63 Refitting is a reversal of removal; tighten the mounting screws to the specified torque setting.

Turbocharger boost control solenoid valve

64 Unscrew the four retaining nuts and remove the acoustic engine cover.

65 Disconnect the valve's electrical connector and two vacuum hoses. Unscrew the mounting bolts, and withdraw the valve from the cylinder head **(see illustrations)**.

66 Refitting is the reverse of the removal procedure.

Vehicle speed sensor

67 The vehicle speed sensor is located on

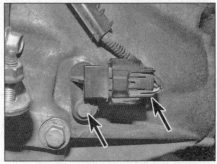

8.69 The vehicle speed sensor

the front of the gearbox, underneath the reversing light switch and behind the clutch slave cylinder hydraulic pipe. The sensor should not be confused with the reversing light switch, which does not have a separate mounting bolt. The sensor provides an electronic signal of the vehicle speed, which is used by the engine management ECU and anti-lock braking system (ABS), as well as for the speedometer itself.

68 Remove the air filter housing as described in Section 4.

69 Disconnect the wiring plug from the sensor **(see illustration)**.

70 Unscrew the sensor mounting bolt, then withdraw the sensor from the transmission, noting the spacer under the bolt – there may be some resistance, both from the O-ring seal and from the sensor drive gear. Remove and discard the sensor's sealing O-ring; this must be renewed whenever it is disturbed.

71 Refitting is a reversal of removal, noting the following points:
a) *Clean the mating faces of the sensor and transmission, and fit a new O-ring.*
b) *Tighten the sensor mounting bolt securely, and ensure that the wiring plug is securely reconnected.*

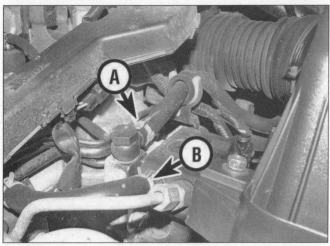

9.4a Disconnect the fuel feed hose (A) and the fuel return hose (B)...

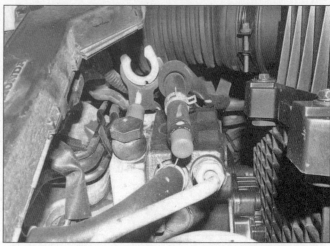

9.4b... and swiftly plug the hoses. Cap the pump unions to prevent the loss of fuel and entry of dirt into fuel system

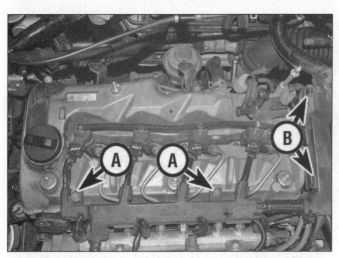

9.5a Undo two bolts securing the wiring conduit (A) and lift the conduit off the brackets on the cylinder head left-hand end (B)

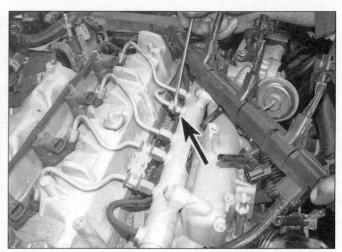

9.5b Lift the conduits sufficiently to unscrew the fuel pump to fuel rail high-pressure pipe union...

9 Fuel pump –
removal and refitting

Caution: Be careful not to allow dirt into the fuel pump, fuel rail or injectors during this procedure.
Note: *Any rigid high-pressure fuel pipes disturbed must be renewed.*

Removal

1 Disconnect the battery negative lead, and position the lead away from the battery (see *Disconnecting the battery* 5A).
2 Unscrew the four retaining nuts and remove the acoustic engine cover.
3 Remove the air filter assembly as described in Section 4.
4 Note the fitted position of the hoses. Disconnect the fuel feed and return hoses from the fuel pump. Swiftly plug the hoses and cap the pump unions to prevent the loss

of fuel and the entry of dirt into the system **(see illustrations)**.
5 Undo the two bolts securing the large square-section black plastic wiring conduit to the cylinder head cover and lift the other conduit off its brackets on the left-hand end of the cylinder head sufficiently to reach the fuel pump to fuel rail high pressure fuel pipe union nut. Disconnect the wiring for the fuel rail pressure sensor, the fuel injectors, the glow plugs and any vacuum hoses. Note their locations and do not forget to reconnect them on reassembly **(see illustrations)**.
6 Make sure the areas around the high-pressure fuel pipe unions from the fuel pump to the fuel rail and from the fuel rail to the injectors are scrupulously clean and free from debris, etc. If possible, use a vacuum cleaner and a degreaser to clean the area.

⚠ *Warning: Before disconnecting any part of the high-pressure side of the fuel system, read the precautions concerning*

depressurising the fuel system given in Section 2 and take action accordingly.
7 Place a large rag around the fuel pump to fuel rail high pressure fuel pipe union nut near the centre of the fuel rail **(see illustration 9.5b)** ready to soak up any escaping fuel. Slowly (to avoid a sudden release of pressure and to

9.5c...and then undo the high pressure pipe retaining clamp bolt

9.8 Counterhold hexagon on the union with one spanner and unscrew the fuel pipe union nut with a second spanner

9.9a Release the wiring from the retaining bracket beneath the fuel pump...

9.9b...disconnect the wiring plug...

9.9c...and unbolt the pump. Do NOT lose the connecting piece

9.11a Refit the connecting piece to the pump drive and fit a new O-ring

9.11b Lubricate the O-ring and refit the pump, aligning the connecting piece drive dogs with the fuel pump driveshaft slots

allow any fuel spray which may be expelled to be caught by the rag) unscrew the union nut. When any hissing has stopped, indicating that all residual pressure has been released, unscrew the nut from the rail. Anticipate some loss of fuel.

8 Counterhold the hexagon on the fuel pump union with one open-ended spanner and unscrew the fuel pump to fuel rail high pressure fuel pipe union nut with a second spanner **(see illustration)**. Be prepared for fuel spillage. Unscrew the high pressure pipe retaining clamp bolt **(see illustration 9.5c)** and discard the high-pressure pipe – a new one must be fitted on reassembly. Swiftly cap the pump and rail unions to prevent the entry of dirt into either.

9 Disconnect its wiring and unbolt the fuel pump from the left-hand end of the cylinder head; be careful not to lose the connecting piece between the fuel pump drive shaft and the pump drive – this is easily lost as the pump is removed **(see illustrations)**. Remove and discard the pump's sealing O-ring; this must be renewed whenever it is disturbed.

10 It appears at the time of writing that no spare parts are available for the pump, though reconditioned units may be available. Check parts availability before proceeding, and remember that the components are of Bosch manufacture and so may be available through Bosch specialists.

Refitting

11 On refitting, wipe clean the mating

surfaces of the cylinder head and fuel pump. Fit a new O-ring to the pump mating surface, lubricated with clean engine oil to aid installation. Align the drive dogs on the pump connecting piece with the slots in the end of the fuel pump driveshaft **(see illustrations)**.

12 Offer up the pump and fit its mounting bolts, but tighten them by hand only at this stage **(see illustration)**. **Note:** *The fuel pump has no timing function, so its precise position, within the range of movement provided by the mounting bolts, is not important.*

13 Fit the new fuel pump to fuel rail high pressure fuel pipe, settling it on the fuel rail union and retaining clamp bracket. Ensure that the pipe union seats correctly on that of the pump, then tighten the two union nuts as far as possible by hand **(see illustration)**.

14 Tighten the fuel pump mounting bolts to the specified torque wrench setting.

15 Using a crows-foot adapter, tighten the high pressure fuel pipe union nuts to the specified torque wrench setting, fuel pump union first (counterholding the pump's hexagon), then the fuel rail union.

16 Fit the high pressure fuel pipe retaining clamp rubber sleeve, check that the clamp fits correctly on its bracket without stressing the pipe, then refit the clamp bolt and tighten it to the specified torque wrench setting. **Note:** *If the retaining clamp strains the pipe away from its natural run, or if the retaining clamp and rubber sleeve are not fitted as described, stresses will be imposed on the pipe as the engine is running that will cause it to leak, or even break, in service.*

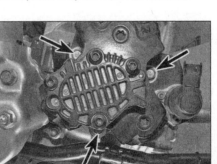

9.12 Refit the mounting bolts, but do not tighten them...

9.13...until the new fuel pump to fuel rail high pressure fuel pipe has been fitted

17 Refit the black plastic wiring conduit to the cylinder head cover and reconnect any hoses and wiring that were disconnected.

18 Reconnect the pump's wiring and the fuel feed and return hoses.

19 Refit the air filter housing and reconnect the battery.

20 Prime the fuel system and start the engine, then thoroughly check for fuel leaks from the disturbed pipes/hoses before refitting the acoustic engine cover.

10 Common rail – removal and refitting

Caution: Be careful not to allow dirt into the fuel pump, fuel rail or injectors during this procedure.

Note: *Any rigid high-pressure fuel pipes disturbed must be renewed.*

Removal

1 Disconnect the battery negative lead, and position the lead away from the battery (see *Disconnecting the battery* 5A).

2 Unscrew the four retaining nuts and remove the acoustic engine cover.

3 Undo the two bolts securing the large square-section black plastic wiring conduit to the cylinder head cover and lift the other conduit off its brackets on the left-hand end of the cylinder head sufficiently to reach the fuel rail high-pressure fuel pipe union nuts. Disconnect the wiring from the fuel rail pressure sensor, the fuel injectors and the glow plugs. If it is necessary to disconnect any other wiring, and any vacuum hoses, note them carefully and do not forget to reconnect them on reassembly.

4 Make sure the areas around the high-pressure fuel pipe unions from the fuel pump to the fuel rail and from the fuel rail to the injectors are scrupulously clean and free from debris, etc. If possible, use a vacuum cleaner and a degreaser to clean the area.

 Warning: Before disconnecting any part of the high-pressure side of the fuel system, read the precautions concerning *depressurising the fuel system given in Section 1 and take action accordingly.*

5 Place a large rag around the fuel pump to fuel rail high pressure fuel pipe union nut near the centre of the fuel rail, ready to soak up any escaping fuel. Slowly (to avoid a sudden release of pressure and to allow any fuel spray which may be expelled to be caught by the rag) unscrew the union nut. When any hissing has stopped, indicating that all residual pressure has been released, unscrew the nut from the rail; be prepared for some loss of fuel.

6 Counterhold the hexagon on the fuel pump union with one open-ended spanner and unscrew the fuel pump to fuel rail high pressure fuel pipe union nut with a second spanner. Anticipate some fuel spillage **(see illustration 9.8)**. Unscrew the high pressure pipe retaining clamp bolt and discard the highpressure pipe – a new one must be fitted on reassembly. Swiftly cap the pump and rail unions to prevent the entry of dirt into either.

7 Working in a similar fashion, first at the injector (and counterholding the injector hexagon to prevent damage to the injector), then at the rail, disconnect each fuel rail to fuel injector high pressure fuel pipe in turn and discard them – all must be renewed on reassembly **(see illustration)**. Unbolt the retaining clamp securing Nos. 1 and 2 high-pressure pipes. Swiftly cap all injector and rail unions to prevent the entry of dirt into any of them.

8 Disconnect the fuel return hose from the fuel rail.

9 Unscrew and remove the two fuel rail mounting nuts, and withdraw the rail **(see illustration)**.

10 Store the fuel rail in clean conditions – take care that no dirt enters the pipe unions.

11 As preparation for refitting, remove the fuel injectors, clean and check them as described in Section 11, fit new copper sealing washers and apply grease to their stems.

Refitting

12 On refitting, install the injectors in their original positions (see Section 11), and slacken the three fuel pump mounting bolts.

13 Wipe clean the mating surfaces of the cylinder head and fuel rail, refit the rail and tighten its mounting nuts to the specified torque wrench setting. Reconnect the fuel return hose **(see illustration)**.

14 Ensuring that each is fitted in its correct location, install the four new fuel rail to fuel injector high-pressure fuel pipes. Turn each injector as necessary to seat its pipe snugly at both end unions, then tighten both union nuts as far as possible by hand.

15 With all four pipes installed and the injectors aligned, refit the injector clamps and tighten the clamp bolts as described in Section 11. Refit the fuel return hose assembly.

16 Using a crows-foot adapter, tighten the high-pressure fuel pipe union nuts to the specified torque wrench setting, fuel injector union first (counterholding the injectors' hexagons to prevent damage), then the fuel rail union. Tighten securely the retaining clamp bolt securing Nos. 1 and 2 high-pressure pipes.

17 Fit a new fuel pump to fuel rail high pressure fuel pipe and tighten its union nuts. Tighten the pump mounting bolts and pipe retaining clamp, as described in Section 9.

18 Refit the black plastic wiring conduit to the cylinder head cover and reconnect all hoses and wiring that were disconnected.

19 Reconnect the battery, prime the fuel system and start the engine, then thoroughly check for fuel leaks from the disturbed pipes/hoses before refitting the acoustic engine cover.

11 Fuel injectors – removal testing and refitting

Caution: Be careful not to allow dirt into the fuel pump, fuel rail or injectors during this procedure.

Note: *The removal of the fuel injectors seems in itself a quite simple and straightforward procedure. However, not only is extraction of the fuel injectors quite likely to be extremely difficult, but all four fuel rail-to-injector high-pressure pipes and the four copper sealing washers must be renewed as a matter of course on reassembly, regardless of their apparent condition.*

10.7 Counterhold the hexagon on the injector body to prevent damage while slackening the high-pressure fuel pipe union nut

10.9 Withdraw the fuel rail. Note the fuel unions capped to exclude dirt

10.13 Reconnect the fuel return hose

11.2a Prise out the clips just far enough to release the unions...

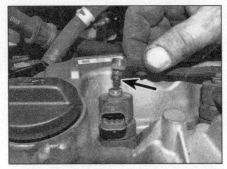

11.2b...and then disconnect the fuel return hose from the top of each injector

11.6a Unscrew the clamp bolt to release the injector...

11.6b...then lift the injector out of the cylinder head

11.6c Some persuasion will be necessary in most cases

11.8 Store the injectors upright at all times.

Removal

1 Remove the common rail as described in Section 10.

⚠️ *Warning: Before disconnecting any part of the high-pressure side of the fuel system, read the precautions concerning depressurising the fuel system given in Section 2 and take action accordingly.*

2 Prise out the clips just far enough to release the unions, and disconnect the fuel return hose from the top of each injector **(see illustrations)**. Check the sealing O-ring at each union – if any are damaged, the complete return hose assembly must be renewed. If any of the clips were removed completely, they should be replaced.

3 Place a large rag around the first fuel rail to fuel injector high pressure fuel pipe union nut, ready to soak up any escaping fuel. Slowly (to avoid a sudden release of pressure and to allow any fuel spray which may be expelled to be caught by the rag) unscrew the union nut. When any hissing has stopped, indicating that all residual pressure has been released, unscrew the nut from the rail; be prepared for some loss of fuel.

4 Counterhold the hexagon (but do not move it or the injector will be damaged) on the injector body with one open-ended spanner and unscrew the fuel rail to fuel injector high pressure fuel pipe union nut with a second spanner. Anticipate some fuel spillage. Remove and discard the high pressure pipe – a new one must be fitted on reassembly.

Swiftly cap the injector and rail unions to prevent the entry of dirt into either.

5 Working in a similar fashion, first at the injector, then at the rail, disconnect each fuel rail to fuel injector high pressure fuel pipe in turn and discard them – all must be renewed on reassembly. Unbolt the retaining clamp securing Nos. 1 and 2 high pressure pipes. Swiftly cap all injector and rail unions to prevent the entry of dirt into any of them.

6 Unscrew the Torx bolt securing each injector clamp, withdraw the clamps and remove the injectors **(see illustrations)**. If any of the injectors is found to be stuck, first try soaking it in penetrating fluid and leaving the vehicle for as long as possible for the fluid to act. If this does not work then special injector pullers are widely available. Sometimes even a special puller will not work and the cylinder head will have to be removed and taken to machine shop or diesel specialist to have the injectors removed.

7 Once the injectors are removed, recover (noting which way up each is fitted) and discard the copper sealing washer under each – these must be renewed on reassembly. As each injector is removed, cover or plug its well with clean rag or similar to prevent dirt or other objects from dropping into the combustion chambers; be very careful to keep this in place all the time the injectors are removed so as not to allow dirt and debris to fall into the engine.

8 The injectors are coded to their respective cylinders. A label affixed to the cylinder head cover lists by cylinder the individual

identification number marked on each injector's top surface. They must be refitted to their original positions – if the original number cannot be deciphered mark the injectors for identification, so they can refitted to their original locations. Keep the injectors upright and store them in cylinder order **(see illustration)**.

9 Use a rag or paper towel to wipe clean each injector's stem. DO NOT clean the smaller-diameter injector nozzle. Do not attempt to dismantle the injectors or use any stronger cleaning methods on them. If any of the injectors require attention of any sort, this is a task for a Honda dealer or specialist. Take care not to drop the injectors, nor allow the needles at their tips to become damaged.

10 Thoroughly clean the injector wells – both the tubes in the cylinder head cover and the seatings in the cylinder head. Be very careful not to allow dirt and debris to fall into the combustion chambers. Use an electric torch to examine the condition of the seatings in the cylinder head – if any are damaged, burned, corroded or marked in any way they must be resurfaced using a seat cutting tool.

Testing

11 Testing of the injectors requires the use of special equipment. If any injector is thought to be faulty have it tested and, if necessary, reconditioned by a Honda dealer or specialist.

Refitting

12 Remove the material covering or plugging the well and ensure that the injectors and

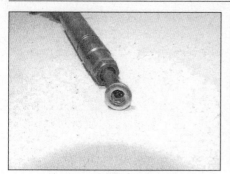

11.13a Fit a new copper sealing washer...

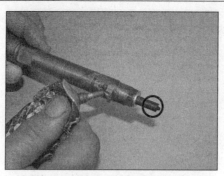

11.13b...and lubricate the injector stem to prevent sticking. Do NOT grease the smaller-diameter nozzle area indicated

11.14a To ensure the injectors are refitted to the original cylinders, check the marking on top of the injector...

11.14b...against the label on the cylinder head cover

11.15a The injector clamps must engage as shown on the flats of the injector bodies...

11.15b...with the rounded projections fitting into the locating dowels

seats in cylinder head are clean and dry. It's essential the sealing surfaces are dirt free, otherwise leakage will occur. Check that each injector's clamp bolt threads are clean and dry.

13 Fit a new copper sealing washer to each injector, using a dab of grease to stick it in place and ensuring it is fitted the same way as noted on removal. It is advisable to coat the stem of each injector with suitable grease to make easier the task of removing them in the future. Special grease is available from some suppliers, but copper grease can also be used if nothing better is available. Do NOT grease the smaller-diameter injector nozzle (see illustrations).

14 Fit each injector to its original cylinder, rotate it approximately into position and, ensuring that each is fitted in its correct location, install the new fuel rail to fuel injector high pressure fuel pipe (see illustrations). Turn each injector as necessary to seat its pipe snugly at both end unions, then tighten both union nuts as far as possible by hand.

15 When all four injectors and pipes are installed, refit the clamps. Fit each clamp bolt and tighten it to the specified Stage 1 torque wrench setting. Once the bolt has been tightened to the Stage 1 torque, tighten it through its specified Stage 2 angle. It is recommended that an angle-measuring gauge is used during this stage of tightening,

to ensure accuracy, but a good alternative is to use a felt-tip pen, paint, typists' correction fluid or similar to make alignment marks between the bolt head and the clamp, the clamp mark being 90° (one-quarter-turn) after the bolt head mark. The Stage 2 fastening can then be achieved by tightening the bolt through one-quarter of a turn so that the mark on the bolt head now aligns with the corresponding mark on the clamp (see illustrations).

16 Using a crows-foot adapter, tighten the high pressure fuel pipe union nuts to the specified torque wrench setting, fuel injector union first (counterholding the injectors' hexagons to prevent damage), then the fuel

11.15c Check that the threads are clean and dry before refitting the clamp bolts

11.15d Tighten the clamp bolts to the Stage 1 torque setting...

11.15e...and then tighten through the Stage 2 angle

11.16a Counterhold the hexagon on the injector body to prevent damage whilst tightening the high pressure fuel pipe union nut...

11.16b...then tighten the fuel rail union nut

11.16c Do not forget to refit and tighten the retaining clamp bolt securing Nos. 1 and 2 high-pressure pipes

rail union. Securely tighten the retaining clamp bolt securing Nos. 1 and 2 high pressure pipes **(see illustrations)**.

17 Fit the return hose assembly to the top of each injector and press in the clip to secure each union**(see illustrations)**.

18 Refit the black plastic wiring conduit to the cylinder head cover and reconnect all hoses and wiring that were disconnected.

19 Reconnect the battery, prime the fuel system and start the engine, then thoroughly check for fuel leaks from the disturbed pipes/

hoses before refitting the acoustic engine cover.

20 On completion the fuel injectors must be coded to the engine. This requires the use of suitable diagnostic equipment. Honda's factory tool (HDS) is obviously capable of this, but many generic scan tools are capable of injector coding. Consult a Honda dealer or suitably equipped garage. Note that if the old injectors have been removed for cylinder head work and they are replaced in the same cylinder then there should be no need to have the injectors coded to the car.

12 Inlet manifold – removal and refitting

Removal

1 Disconnect the battery negative lead, and position the lead away from the battery (see *Disconnecting the battery* 5A).

2 Unscrew the four retaining nuts and remove the acoustic engine cover.

11.17a Fit the fuel return hose assembly to the injectors...

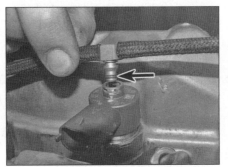

11.17b...ensuring that the O-rings are sound and properly fitted

11.17c Fit the retaining clips (new if the originals were removed completely on dismantling)...

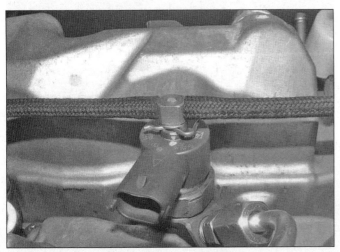

11.17d...and press into place

11.17e Reconnect the return hose to the return pipe

12.3a Disconnect the intercooler outlet hose from the manifold air inlet passage

12.3b Remove the support bracket

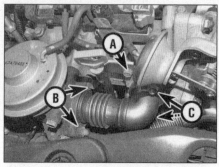

12.4 Unscrew the dipstick tube bolt (A) and the shorter EGR pipe nuts (B) and (C)

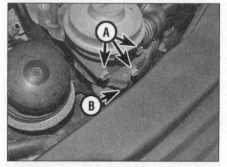

12.5a Unscrew the bolts (A) securing the EGR valve to cylinder head and nuts (B)...

12.5b ...securing the EGR valve to the long EGR pipe

12.5c Disconnect the EGR valve vacuum hose and withdraw the valve and short pipe together

3 Disconnect the intercooler outlet hose from the intake manifold air intake passage, then unscrew the bolt securing the intake manifold support bracket to the IMRC valve (see illustrations).

4 Unscrew the dipstick tube mounting bolt and the nuts securing the short EGR pipe to the EGR valve and inlet manifold (see illustration).

5 Unscrew the nuts securing the EGR valve to the long EGR pipe and the three bolts securing the EGR valve to the cylinder head. Disconnect its vacuum hose and withdraw the EGR valve and short EGR pipe together (see illustrations). Recover all EGR component gaskets and discard them – new ones must be fitted on reassembly.

6 Remove the dipstick and dipstick tube (see illustration). Recover and discard the sealing O-ring – a new one must be fitted on reassembly.

7 Disconnect the wiring for the IMRC solenoid valve, the EGR control solenoid valve, the EGR cooler bypass control solenoid valve, the manifold absolute pressure and the IMRC valve position sensor. Release the wiring from any clips or ties (see illustration).

8 Unscrew the mounting bolts for the IMRC solenoid valve, the EGR control solenoid valve, the EGR cooler bypass control solenoid valve, and the vacuum line assembly. Disconnect the vacuum hoses as necessary and remove the valve and line assembly from the intake manifold (see illustrations).

9 Disconnect the wiring for the fuel rail pressure sensor, the fuel injectors and the glow plugs, then undo the two bolts securing the square-section black plastic wiring conduit to the cylinder head cover and lift the conduit off its brackets on the left-hand end of the cylinder head (see illustrations).

12.6 Remove the dipstick and tube

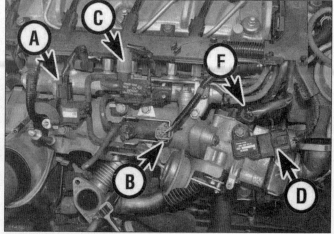

12.7 Disconnect the wiring for IMRC valve (A), EGR control valve (B), EGR cooler control valve (C), manifold absolute pressure sensor (D) and the IMRC valve position sensor (E)

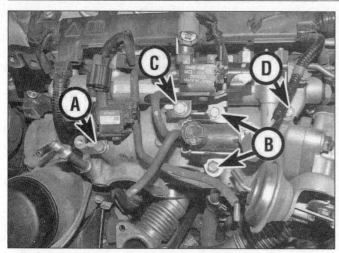

12.8a Unscrew the mounting bolts for the IMRC valve (A), EGR control valve (B), EGR cooler control valve (C), and vacuum line assembly (D)

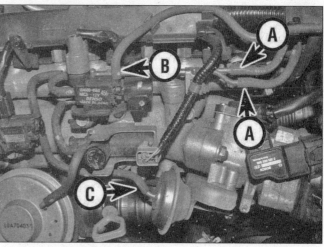

12.8b Disconnect the vacuum hoses from vacuum line assembly (A), EGR cooler control valve (B) and IMRC valve (C)

12.8c Remove the valve and line assembly from the inlet manifold

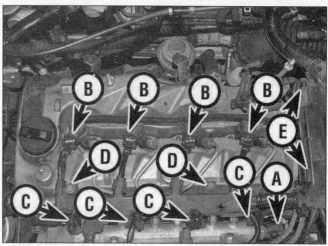

12.9a Disconnect the wiring for the fuel rail pressure sensor (A), fuel injectors (B) and glow plugs (C) and then unbolt the wiring conduit bolts (D). Release the conduit from the brackets (E)

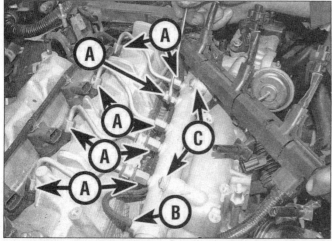

12.9b Disconnect and remove all five high-pressure fuel pipes (A). Disconnect the fuel return hose (B) and unscrew the fuel rail mounting nuts (C)

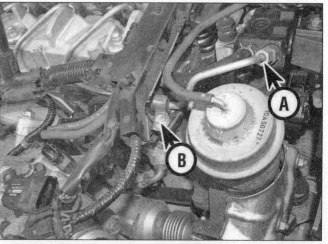

12.9c Disconnect the high pressure fuel pipe from the fuel pump (A) and unscrew the pipe support bracket bolt (B) to remove the fuel rail

12.11a Unscrew the bolts and release the coolant bypass pipe from the inlet manifold

12.11b Disconnect the hoses from each end of the bypass pipe and remove them

12.12a Unscrew three bolts from below and then the four nuts (shown here) securing manifold to cylinder head...

12.12b...and then withdraw the inlet manifold

⚠ **Warning: Before disconnecting any part of the high-pressure side of the fuel system, read the precautions concerning depressurising the fuel system given in Section 2 and take action accordingly.**

10 Disconnect and remove all five high pressure fuel pipes, disconnect the fuel

return hose from the end of the fuel rail, unscrew its mounting nuts and remove the fuel rail (see Section 11). Note that the high pressure fuel pipes must be discarded – new ones must be fitted on reassembly.

11 Disconnect the coolant bypass hoses from each end of the pipe, then unbolt the

bypass pipe from the intake manifold **(see illustrations)**.

12 Unscrew the three bolts and four nuts securing the manifold to the cylinder head and withdraw it **(see illustrations)**. Recover and discard the manifold gasket – this must be renewed whenever it is disturbed to prevent any risk of air leaks.

13 Check the manifold for any signs of cracking or other damage – this may be most evident around the mounting points. If the manifold is damaged, a new one will be needed.

Refitting

14 Clean all mating faces prior to refitting, and wipe them dry. Fit a new manifold-to-head gasket over the studs, then slide on the manifold **(see illustrations)**. Working in several stages and in a diagonal sequence from the centre outwards, tighten the mounting nuts and bolts to the specified torque wrench setting.

15 Further refitting is a reversal of removal.

12.14a Always renew the manifold gasket...

12.14b...before refitting the inlet manifold

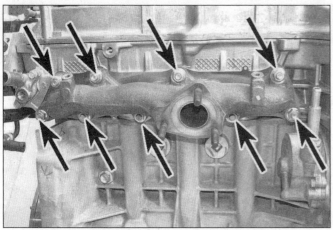

13.2 Unscrew the exhaust manifold retaining nuts

13.3 Withdraw the exhaust manifold

13 Exhaust manifold – removal and refitting

Removal

1 Remove the turbocharger as described in Section 14.

2 Unscrew and remove the nine nuts securing the manifold to the cylinder head **(see illustration)**.Discard the nuts. Use a wire brush and plenty of penetrating fluid first if they appear to be rusty.

3 Withdraw the manifold from the studs, and remove it from the engine compartment **(see illustration)**. Recover the manifold gasket – a new one should always be used when refitting.

Refitting

4 Refitting is a reversal of removal, noting the following points **(see illustration)**:

a) Clean the manifold and cylinder head mating faces, and fit a new gasket.

b) It is recommended that new nuts are used as a matter of course – even if the old ones came off without difficulty, they may not stand being retightened. New components will be much easier to remove in future, should this be necessary.

c) If any of the manifold studs were removed, it's best to obtain new studs with the new nuts, rather than try to separate the old ones. The new studs can be fitted by tightening two nuts against each other on the stud, then using them to screw the stud into place – once this is done, the nuts can be unscrewed from each other, and removed.

d) Tighten the manifold nuts to the specified torque.

e) Refit the turbocharger as described in Section 14.

14 Turbocharger – removal, examination and refitting

Note: Pack the turbocharger openings with clean rag to prevent dirt or other objects falling in.

Removal

1 Remove the upper and lower windscreen cowl panels as described in Chapter 12.

2 Unscrew the four retaining nuts and remove the acoustic engine cover.

3 Unbolt the brake fluid reservoir and move it to the side. Seal the reservoir in a plastic bag to avoid any chance of the fluid leaking.

4 Remove the air filter assembly and withdraw

13.4 Always renew the manifold gasket to prevent

the turbocharger inlet hose as described in Section 4.

5 Jack up and support the front of the vehicle – see 'Jacking and vehicle support' in the Reference chapter. Remove the engine compartment undershield.

6 Drain the cooling system (see Chapter 1B).

7 Where fitted release the AC refrigerant lines from the bulkhead bracket and (again where fitted) disconnect the diesel particulate filter (DPF) differential pressure lines.

8 Slacken the hose clamps at each end and unbolt the turbocharger to intercooler pipe, then remove the turbocharger outlet hose **(see illustrations)**.

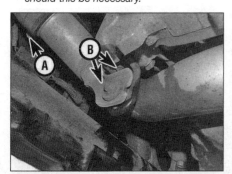

14.8a Slacken hose clamp (A) and unscrew the mounting bracket bolts (B) at the front...

14.8b...and rear of turbocharger to intercooler pipe. Remove the pipe...

14.8c...and turbocharger outlet hose. Note the raised rib to be aligned with the hose mark on refitting

14.10 Unscrew the three exhaust front pipe to catalytic converter nuts

14.13 Disconnect the breather hose from the rear of the cylinder head cover

the support bracket between the cylinder block/crankcase and the warm-up catalytic converter.

12 Unscrew the three retaining nuts and withdraw the warm-up catalytic converter.

13 Disconnect the breather hose from the rear of the cylinder head cover **(see illustration)**.

14 Unscrew the two bolts securing the vacuum line assembly to the rear of the cylinder head cover and the bracket supporting the air cleaner-to-turbocharger intake pipe, disconnect the vacuum hose from the vacuum pump and from the turbocharger, then withdraw the vacuum line assembly **(see illustrations)**.

15 Unbolt and withdraw the cover over the exhaust manifold **(see illustration)**.

16 Unscrew the turbocharger coolant line banjo union bolt and recover the sealing washers, then disconnect the coolant hose from the turbocharger union **(see illustrations)**.

9 Where fitted disconnect the exhaust gas temperature sensor and then remove the DPF – see Chapter 4C.

10 Unbolt the exhaust front pipe from the warm-up catalytic converter; recover the springs. Unscrew and discard the three front pipe to catalytic converter nuts, then withdraw the exhaust front pipe **(see illustration)**. Recover and discard both gaskets.

11 Unscrew the two bolts and withdraw

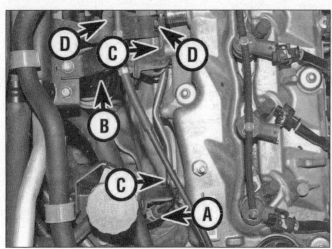

14.14a Disconnect the vacuum pump vacuum hose (A), turbocharger vacuum hose (B), undo the vacuum line assembly bolts (C) and the inlet pipe support bracket bolts (D)...

14.14b ...and withdraw the vacuum line assembly

14.15 Unbolt and withdraw the exhaust manifold cover

14.16a Unscrew the turbocharger coolant bypass pipe banjo union bolt...

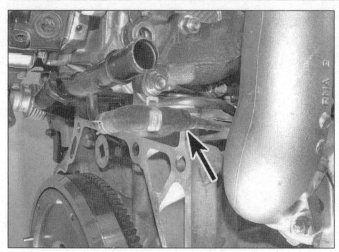

14.16b...and then disconnect the turbocharger coolant return hose

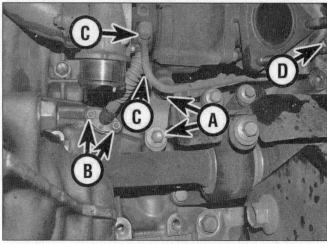

14.18 Unscrew two turbocharger support bracket bolts (A), nuts (B) and bolts (C). Undo the banjo union bolt (D) to withdraw turbocharger oil feed and return line

17 Unscrew the two bolts and withdraw the support bracket between the cylinder block/crankcase and the turbocharger.
18 Unscrew the two nuts, two bolts and the banjo union bolt (recover the gaskets and sealing washers) to withdraw the turbocharger oil feed and return line **(see illustration)**.
19 Undo the three retaining nuts and withdraw the turbocharger assembly **(see illustrations)**. Recover and discard the gasket – this must be renewed whenever it is disturbed.

Examination

20 Unscrew the two bolts and withdraw the coolant pipe. Unscrew the two nuts and withdraw the breather hose assembly and undo the two nuts to remove the intake pipe. Unscrew the two bolts securing the turbocharger outlet elbow cover, then unscrew the three nuts and remove the outlet elbow itself. Recover and discard the gasket from each of these unions – all must be renewed whenever they are disturbed **(see illustrations)**.
21 Spin the turbine or the compressor wheel to verify that the shaft is intact and to feel for excessive shake or roughness. Some play is

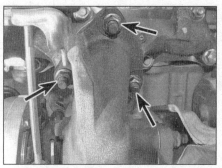

14.19a Unscrew three nuts...

14.19b...and remove the turbocharger. Note the openings taped to exclude dirt, etc

normal since in use the shaft is 'floating' on a film of oil. Check that the wheel vanes are undamaged.
22 If the exhaust or induction passages are oil-contaminated, the turbocharger shaft oil seals have probably failed. (On the induction side, this will also have contaminated the intercooler, which if necessary should be flushed with a suitable solvent.)
23 Check the turbocharger oil feed and return line and banjo union bolt; flush them with solvent if they are thought to be

clogged and blow them clear with an airline **(see illustration)**. Renew the oil feed and return line and banjo union bolt if there is the slightest doubt about their condition.
24 No DIY repair of the turbocharger is possible. A new unit may be available on an exchange basis.
25 On reassembly, refit the coolant pipe, breather, intake pipe and outlet elbow. Renew all gaskets and sealing washers and tighten all fasteners to the torque wrench settings specified. Plug or cover the turbocharger openings until

14.20a Unscrew the nuts and bolts...

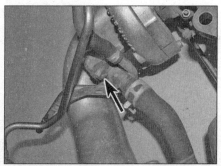

14.20b...and remove the coolant, breather and inlet pipes from the turbocharger

14.23 Check the turbocharger oil feed banjo union bolt is clear – always renew sealing washers

14.26a Always renew the turbocharger gasket

14.26b Securely fasten the turbocharger coolant return hose...

14.26c ...and always renew the sealing washers at the coolant bypass pipe banjo union

14.26d Fit a new gasket to the oil return line union on the cylinder block...

14.26e ...and to the turbocharger union

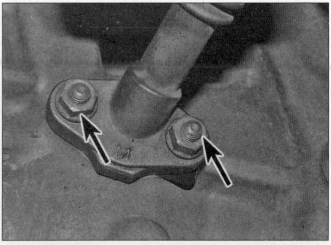

14.26f Tighten the oil bypass pipe union mounting flange nuts...

14.26g...and bolts to the specified torque setting

14.26h Prime the turbocharger lubrication system by injecting as much oil as possible into the feed line...

14.26i...and then refit the banjo union bolt with new sealing washers.Tighten to specified torque

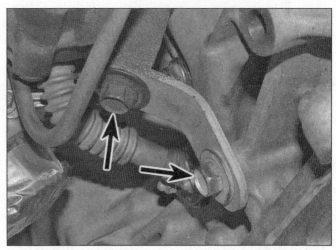

14.26j Refit the turbocharger support bracket and tighten the bolts

the intake and outlet hoses are ready to be connected during the refitting procedure.

Refitting

26 Refitting is a reversal of removal, noting the following points **(see illustrations)**:

a) *Ensure all mating surfaces are clean and dry.*

14.26k Leave the turbocharger openings covered until they are to be reconnected

b) *Renew all sealing washers and gaskets.*
c) *Tighten all fasteners to the specified torque wrench settings, where available.*
d) *When refitting the turbocharger oil feed and return line, prime the lubrication system by filling the pipe as much as possible with clean engine oil via the banjo union orifice.*
e) *When reconnecting the turbocharger outlet hose, align the mark on the hose with the raised rib on the turbocharger body (see illustration 15.5c).*
f) *Tighten all hose clips securely, to avoid air leaks.*
g) *Fit new exhaust front pipe-to-catalytic converter nuts.*
h) *Refill the cooling system (Chapter 1B).*
i) *Start the engine, then thoroughly check for exhaust, oil and coolant leaks from the disturbed pipes/hoses before refitting the acoustic engine cover and engine compartment undershield.*

15 Exhaust system – general information, removal and refitting

⚠️ *Warning: Inspection and repair of exhaust system components should be done only after the system has cooled completely. This applies particularly to the turbocharger and catalytic converters, which run at very high temperatures.*

General information

1 Downstream of the turbocharger and four-way oxidation ('warm-up') catalytic converter, the exhaust system consists of four sections: the front pipe with flexible section, a NOx-reducing catalytic converter, the centre section with silencer, and the rear silencer. On models fitted with a Diesel Particulate Filter (DPF) the second catalytic converter

15.2a The rear mounting of the centre section

15.2b On the left of the rear silencer...

15.2c...and on the right-hand side

is replaced by the DPF. The removal of the catalytic converter(s) and the DPF is covered in Chapter 4C.

2 The system is suspended throughout its entire length by rubber mountings **(see illustrations)**.

Removal and refitting

Note: *Some of the system's nuts (see Specifications) must be renewed irrespective of their apparent condition whenever they are disturbed, as must the gaskets. Obtain new nuts and gaskets before starting work.*

3 Although there are detail differences between the systems fitted to petrol and diesel engined models, basic working procedures are identical. Proceed as described in Chapter 4A Section 13, noting the torque wrench settings given in the Specifications Section of this Chapter **(see illustrations)**.

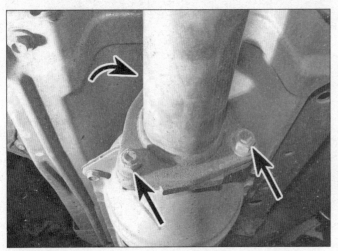

15.3a The catalytic converter nuts must be renewed whenever they are disturbed

15.3b Tighten the nuts (or bolts) evenly and let spring pressure make a leak proof connection

Chapter 4 Part C
Emission control systems

Contents

Section number

Catalytic converter –general informationand precautions 2
Crankcase emission control system – checking and component
   renewal 3
Evaporative emission control (EVAP) system – checking and
   component renewal 4

Section number

Exhaust emission control systems – checking and component
   renewal 5
General Information 1

Degrees of difficulty

Easy, suitable for novice with little experience	**Fairly easy,** suitable for beginner with some experience	**Fairly difficult,** suitable for competent DIY mechanic	**Difficult,** suitable for experienced DIY mechanic	**Very difficult,** suitable for expert DIY or professional

Specifications

Torque wrench settings	Nm	lbf ft
Catalytic converter (to exhaust nuts)	44	32
Catalytic converter to cylinder head (nuts and bolts).	31	23
Catalytic converter support bracket (petrol).	44	33
Catalytic converter heat shield.	10	7
EGR pipe	22	16
EGR valve.	22	16
Oxygen sensor	44	33

* Use new nuts

1 General Information

1 All models covered by this manual have various features built into the fuel and exhaust systems to help minimise harmful emissions. These features fall broadly into three categories; crankcase emission control, evaporative emission control (petrol engines only), and exhaust emission control. The main features of these systems are as follows.

Crankcase emission control

Petrol-engined models

2 To reduce the emissions of unburned hydrocarbons from the crankcase into the atmosphere, a Positive Crankcase Ventilation (PCV) system is used which circulates fresh air from the air cleaner through the crankcase, where it mixes with blow-by gases and is then rerouted through a PCV valve to the intake manifold. The engine is sealed, and the blow-by gases and oil vapour are drawn from inside the crankcase, through an oil separator, into the intake tract, to be burned by the engine during normal combustion.

3 Under conditions of high manifold depression (idling, deceleration) the gases will be sucked positively out of the crankcase. Under conditions of low manifold depression (acceleration, full-throttle running) the gases are forced out of the crankcase by the (relatively) higher crankcase pressure; if the engine is worn, the raised crankcase pressure (due to increased blow-by) will cause some of the flow to return under all manifold conditions.

4 The main components of the system are the PCV valve and the hoses connecting the air cleaner with the engine and the valve with the intake manifold.

Diesel-engined models

5 To reduce the emission of unburned hydrocarbons from the crankcase into the atmosphere, the engine is sealed. Blow-by gases and oil vapour are drawn from inside the crankcase, through an oil separator and the cylinder head cover into the turbocharger. From the turbocharger, the gases enter the intake manifold to be burned by the engine during normal combustion. Apart from a check valve, there are no restrictors in the system, since the minimal depression in the intake manifold remains constant during all engine operating conditions.

Evaporative emission control (EVAP)

Petrol-engined models only

6 The evaporative emission control (EVAP) system is used to minimise the escape of unburned hydrocarbons into the atmosphere. To do this, the fuel tank filler cap is sealed, and a charcoal canister is used to collect and store petrol vapours generated in the tank. When the engine is running, the vapours are cleared from the canister by an ECU-controlled electrically-operated purge valve, into the intake tract, to be burned by the engine during normal combustion. To enable this to happen, fresh air is drawn through the canister via a vent filter.

7 To ensure that the engine runs correctly when idling, the valve only opens when the coolant temperature is above 65ºC and the engine is running under load; the valve then opens to allow the stored vapour to pass into the intake tract.

8 A two-way valve, mounted behind the fuel tank, regulates fuel vapour flow from the fuel tank to the charcoal canister, based on the pressure or vacuum caused by temperature changes. A liquid/vapour separator is fitted, mounted inside the fuel tank, to ensure that no liquid fuel is passed into the system.

Exhaust emission control

Petrol engine models – catalytic converter

9 To minimise the amount of pollutants which escape into the atmosphere, all models are fitted with a catalytic converter in the exhaust system. The system is of the closed-loop type, in which two heated oxygen sensors in the exhaust system provide the engine management ECU with constant feedback on the oxygen content of the exhaust gases. This enables the ECU to adjust the mixture by altering injector opening time, thus providing the best possible conditions for the converter to operate.

10 The sensors upstream and downstream of the converter are known respectively as the 'primary' and 'secondary' sensors; the primary sensor is also referred to as the air/fuel ratio (A/F) sensor. Both function in the same way, but the ECU monitors the signals from the secondary sensor and compares them with those of the primary sensor to determine whether the catalytic converter is working properly or not. The system functions in the following way:

11 The oxygen sensors (also known as lambda sensors) have built-in heating elements, activated by the ECU to quickly bring the sensor's tip to an efficient operating temperature. The sensor's tip is sensitive to oxygen, and sends the ECU a varying voltage depending on the amount of oxygen in the exhaust gases; if the intake air/fuel mixture is too rich, the exhaust gases are low in oxygen, so the sensor sends a voltage signal proportional to the oxygen detected, the voltage altering as the mixture weakens and the amount of oxygen in the exhaust gases rises. Peak conversion efficiency of all major pollutants occurs if the intake air/fuel mixture is maintained at the chemically-correct ratio for complete combustion of petrol – 14.7 parts (by weight) of air to 1 part of fuel (the stoichiometric ratio). The sensor output voltage alters in a large step at this point, the ECU using the signal change as a reference point, and correcting the intake air/fuel mixture accordingly, by altering the fuel injector opening time.

Diesel engine models –catalytic converters

12 A close-coupled warm-up four-way oxidation catalytic converter and underfloor deNox catalytic converter contribute to low emissions performance. The warm-up catalytic converter is bolted directly to the turbocharger to ensure the quickest-possible warm-up time and maximum efficiency of its conversion of carbon monoxide and hydrocarbons to carbon dioxide and water. It also raises the temperature in the exhaust system to increase the efficiency of the underfloor catalytic converter in reducing the level of oxides of nitrogen (NOx) present in the exhaust gas.

Diesel engine models – particulate filter

13 Some later models have a Diesel Particulate Filter (DPF) fitted. The filter forms part of the secondary (main) catalytic converter. The particulate filter traps the microscopic soot particles that are a by product of the combustion process. The filter has a differential pressure sensors that allows the ECU to calculate the saturation of the filter. When the filter is full the ECU can regenerate the filter by raising the temperature of the exhaust gas. To raise the exhaust gas temperature the ECU alters the engine fueling to allow post TDC fuel injection to take place. This raises the temperature in the filter and allows the accumulated soot particles to be burnt off.

14 Regeneration always takes place at cruising speeds (typically above 40 mph). Vehicle that are used for stop/start town driving should always be taken for an extended drive to allow regeneration to take place. A instrument panel warning light is fitted to alert the driver of the need to regenerate the filter.

Exhaust Gas Recirculation (EGR) system

15 The exhaust gas recirculation (EGR) system is designed to recirculate small quantities of exhaust gas into the intake tract, and therefore into the combustion process. This lowers peak combustion temperatures at the appropriate moments and so reduces the level of oxides of nitrogen (NOx) present in the exhaust gas which is released into the atmosphere. Exhaust gas recirculation under the control of the electrically operated (petrol models) or vacuum operated (diesel models) EGR valve increases intake air volume and reduces oxides of nitrogen and particulates. Water cooling of the exhaust gases on petrol models prior to their recirculation helps to reduce the formation of oxides of nitrogen still further.

16 The volume of exhaust gas recirculated is controlled, via an electrically-operated solenoid valve, by the engine management ECU, which receives information on engine operating parameters from its various sensors.

---

2 Catalytic converter – general information and precautions

1 On petrol-engined models, a three-way catalytic converter is incorporated into the front section of the exhaust pipe, whilst on diesel-engined models, a close-coupled warm-up four-way oxidation catalytic converter is bolted directly to the turbocharger and a NOx-reducing catalytic converter is fitted between the system's front and centre sections. This part of Chapter 4 should be used in conjunction with Part A or B of Chapter 4, where details of the removal of the exhaust manifold and exhaust system will be found.

2 The catalytic converter is a reliable and simple device, which needs no maintenance in itself, but there are some facts of which an owner should be aware if the converter is to function properly for its full service life.

Petrol engined models

a) *DO NOT use leaded petrol – the lead will coat the precious metals, reducing their converting efficiency, and will eventually destroy the converter.*

b) *Always keep the ignition and fuel systems well-maintained in accordance with the manufacturer's schedule (see Chapter 1A).*

c) *If the engine develops a misfire, do not drive the vehicle at all (or at least as little as possible) until the fault is cured.*

d) *DO NOT switch off the ignition at high engine speeds, ie, do not blip the throttle immediately before switching off.*

e) *DO NOT use fuel or engine oil additives – these may contain substances harmful to the catalytic converter.*

f) *DO NOT continue to use the vehicle if the engine burns oil to the extent of leaving a visible trail of blue smoke.*

g) *Remember that the catalytic converter operates at very high temperatures. DO NOT, therefore, park the vehicle in dry undergrowth, over long grass or piles of dead leaves, after a long run.*

h) *Remember that the catalytic converter is FRAGILE. Do not strike it with tools during servicing work.*

i) *In some cases, a sulphurous smell (like that of rotten eggs) may be noticed from the exhaust. This is common to many catalytic converter-equipped vehicles. Once the vehicle has covered a few thousand miles, the problem should disappear – in the meantime, try changing the brand of petrol used.*

j) *The catalytic converter used on a well-maintained and well-driven vehicle should last for between 50 000 and 100 000 miles. If the converter is no longer effective, it must be renewed.*

Diesel-engined models

3 Refer to the information given in parts e f, g, h, i and k of the petrol engine information given above.

---

3 Crankcase emission control system – checking and component renewal

Checking

1 The components of this system require no attention other than to check that the hoses are clear and undamaged. To check the valve on petrol-engined models, pinch its hose lightly while the engine is idling; the valve should be heard to click shut. If not, check the

3.2a The PCV on early 1.4 litre engines and...

3.2b...behind the wiring loom on later 1.4 litre engines

valve's sealing grommet in the water pump housing, looking for signs of cracking, leaks or other damage. If the grommet seems sound, renew the valve.

Positive Crankcase Ventilation (PCV) valve

2 The valve is located on the oil separator on early 1.4 litre engines, close to the inlet manifold (behind the wiring loom) on later 1.4 engines and on the timing chain cover on the 1.8 litre engine **(see illustrations)**.

3 To remove the valve, disconnect its hose and unscrew it.

4 The oil vapour/separator is part of the PCV system. If it is accessible remove it to check that the oil ways are clear.

5 On a poorly serviced vehicle accumulated combustion by-products will be found here **(see illustrations)**.

6 Refitting is the reverse of removal.

3.5a Remove the oil separator cover and inspect the galleries. Note the outlet to the PCV valve

3.5b Always apply fresh sealant to the cover before refitting

---

4 Evaporative emission control (EVAP) system – checking and component renewal

Checking

1 Poor idle, stalling and poor driveability can be caused by an inoperative canister vacuum valve, a damaged canister, split or cracked hoses, or hoses connected to the wrong fittings. Check the fuel filler cap for a damaged or deformed gasket.

2 Fuel loss or fuel odour can be caused by liquid fuel leaking from fuel lines, a cracked or damaged canister, an inoperative canister vacuum valve, and disconnected, misrouted, kinked or damaged vapour or control hoses.

3 Inspect each hose attached to the canister for kinks, leaks and cracks along its entire length. Repair or renew as necessary.

4 Inspect the canister. If it is cracked or

damaged, renew it. Look for fuel leaking from the bottom of the canister. If fuel is leaking, renew the canister, and check the hoses and hose routing.

Component renewal

Charcoal canister

5 The canister is located underneath the vehicle, close to the fuel tank.

6 Chock the front wheels, select first or reverse gear (or P), then jack up the rear of

4.8 Remove the retaining clips from the protective cover

the vehicle, and support it securely on axle stands (see 'Jacking and vehicle support' in the Reference chapter).

7 Open the fuel filler cap to release any excess pressure in the fuel tank.

8 Prise free the clips **(see illustration)**, remove the bolts and then remove the underbody protective cover.

9 Unbolt the charcoal canister **(see illustration)**.

10 Disconnect the two vapour hoses and the larger-diameter air vent hose from the

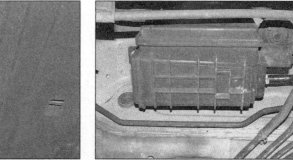

4.9 The charcoal canister

4.14a Remove the EVAP hose

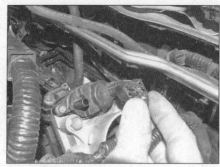

4.14b Disconnect the wiring plug...

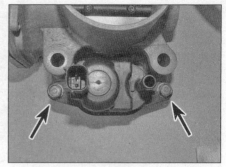

4.14c...and remove the mounting bolts

canister. Label all hoses before disconnecting, to ensure correct refitting.

11 Unscrew the two mounting bolts and lower the canister from the underbody.

12 Refitting is a reversal of removal.

Charcoal canister purge solenoid valve

13 The canister purge valve is mounted in the engine compartment, on top of the throttle body.

14 Disconnect the hose and wiring plug from the valve **(see illustrations)**.

15 Undo the mounting screws and withdraw the valve from the throttle body. Recover and discard the sealing O-ring – this must be renewed whenever the valve is disturbed.

16 Refitting is a reversal of removal. Fit a new O-ring, and tighten the mounting screws to the specified torque setting.

Charcoal canister two-way valve

17 The two-way valve is located underneath the vehicle, bolted to the canister mounting bracket, just above the canister itself.

18 Remove the charcoal canister, as described above.

19 Unbolt the canister mounting bracket from the underbody.

20 Disconnect the two vapour hoses from the valve. Label all hoses before disconnecting, to ensure correct refitting.

21 Unscrew the single mounting bolt and withdraw the valve from the mounting bracket.

22 Refitting is a reversal of removal.

5 Exhaust emission control systems – checking and component renewal

1 Checking of the system as a whole entails a close visual inspection of all hoses, pipes and connections for condition and security. Apart from this, any known or suspected faults should be attended to by a Honda dealer or specialist.

Oxygen (lambda) sensors

Note: *The sensor is delicate, and will not work if it is dropped or knocked, if its power supply is disrupted, or if any cleaning materials are used on it.*

2 Apply the handbrake, then jack up the front of the vehicle and support it on axle stands (see '*Jacking and vehicle support*' in the Reference chapter).

3 Disconnect the sensor wiring connector, and release the wiring from any clips or ties.

4 Unscrew the sensor from the exhaust, and collect the sealing washer (if fitted) **(see illustrations)**.

5 On refitting, clean the sealing washer (where fitted) and renew it if it is damaged or worn. Apply a smear of anti-seize compound to the sensor's threads, then refit the sensor, tightening it to the specified torque. Reconnect the wiring and secure with the clips or ties provided.

Catalytic converter(s)

⚠️ *Warning: Inspection and repair of exhaust system components should be done only after the system has cooled completely. This applies particularly to the turbocharger and catalytic converters, which run at very high temperatures*

6 On all models jack up and support the front of the vehicle – see '*Jacking and vehicle support*' in the Reference chapter. Remove the engine undershield.

1.4 petrol models

7 Disconnect the oxygen sensor wiring plug or remove the sensor from the converter.

8 Remove the three nuts from the junction with the exhaust system. Recover the nuts and gasket – dispose of both items as they must be replaced.

9 Separate the exhaust system from the rear of the converter – detach the front exhaust flexible mounting if necessary to do this.

10 At the exhaust manifold remove the bolts from the spring loaded coupling. Lower the converter and recover the gasket.

11 With the converter on the bench remove the heat shields and if not already done so the oxygen sensor.

12 Refitting is a reversal of removal, but use new gaskets and replace the self locking nuts.

1.8 petrol models

13 Remove the primary oxygen sensor as described in this section.

5.4a A special slotted socket will be required to remove the sensor

5.4b Remove the sensor (1.8 litre shown)

5.4c The secondary sensor on the 1.8 litre engine

5.14 Remove the heat shield

5.15 Remove the EGR pipe

14 Unbolt the upper heat shield and remove it **(see illustration)**.

15 Unbolt the EGR pick up pipe from the EGR valve. Recover the gasket **(see illustration)**.

16 Disconnect or remove the secondary oxygen sensor. Unbolt the support bracket and then unbolt the exhaust system from the converter **(see illustration)**.

17 At the cylinder head/exhaust manifold, unbolt the converter and remove it. Recover the gasket **(see illustrations)**.

18 Refitting is a reversal of removal, but use new gaskets and replace the self locking nuts.

Diesel models

19 Diesel models have a 'warm up' converter and a main (or secondary catalytic converter). On models fitted with a DPF the secondary catalytic converter is part of the DPF.

20 Have a support (such as an axle stand or a small jack) ready to rest the front pipe on as required during removal.

21 Unbolt and disconnect the exhaust front pipe from the warm-up catalytic converter. Recover the springs and the gasket, then unhook the front pipe's rubber mounting and rest the exhaust system on the support.

22 Unscrew the two bolts and withdraw the support bracket between the cylinder block/crankcase and the warm-up catalytic converter

23 Unscrew the three retaining nuts and withdraw the warm-up catalytic converter **(see illustration)**. Take care that the converter is not dropped or roughly handled.

24 With the warm up converter removed the main converter or DPF (where fitted) can be removed. Note that the main converter (or DPF) can also be removed before removing the warm up converter.

5.16 Remove the support bracket bolt and the exhaust pipe nuts

5.17a Remove the nuts/bolts (two hidden) and...

5.17b...remove the catalytic converter

5.17c Recover the gasket from the manifold/cylinder head...

5.17d...and from the EGR housing

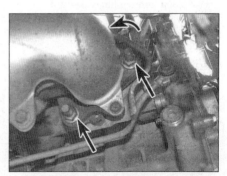

5.23 Remove the warm up converter mounting nuts

5.27a Always replace the gasket and...

5.27b...fit a new one to avoid gas leaks

5.29 Disconnect the wiring plug (1.4 litre model)

25 On models fitted with a DPF remove the support bracket and then remove the differential pressure pipes. These can be removed at the DPF or at the hose clips.

26 On all models remove the front mounting nuts and then the rear mounting nuts or bolts. Remove the catalytic converter (or DPF). Recover the gaskets and dispose of them.

27 Refitting is the reverse of removal; ensure that all traces of corrosion have been removed from the flanges, and renew the gaskets **(see illustrations)**. Tighten the nuts to the torque wrench settings specified. Inspect the rubber mounting for signs of damage or deterioration, and renew as necessary.

Exhaust Gas Recirculation

28 Both petrol and diesel models have exhaust gas recirculation.

Petrol models

Control valve

29 Disconnect the wiring plug **(see illustration)**.

30 Remove the mounting bolts, lift of the valve and recover the gasket **(see illustrations)**.

31 If required the complete housing can be removed, after the inlet pipe has been removed and the coolant drained **(see illustration)**.

32 Refitting is the reverse of the removal procedure, but always use new gaskets. If the housing has been removed, refill the cooling system and check for the system for leaks.

Diesel models

Vacuum control solenoid valve

33 Unscrew the four retaining nuts and remove the acoustic engine cover.

34 Disconnect the valve's electrical connector and two vacuum hoses. Unscrew the mounting bolts, and remove the valve.

35 Refitting is the reverse of the removal procedure.

Control valve

36 Remove the engine cover.

37 To improve access release the coolant expansion tank and then move the coolant hoses to the side.

38 Disconnect the vacuum hose from the control valve.

39 Unbolt the dipstick guide tube and move it to the side – there is no need to remove it.

40 Remove the two nuts and the two bolts and remove the control valve. Recover the gaskets and dispose of them – new ones must be used.

41 Refitting is a reversal of removal; renew all gaskets and tighten all fasteners to the torque wrench settings specified.

5.30a Remove the valve and...

5.30b...recover the gasket (1.8 litre model shown)

5.31 The EGR cooler housing on 1.8 litre models – this is also the thermostat housing

Chapter 5 Part A
Starting and charging systems

Contents

Section number

Alternator – removal and refitting 5
Battery – disconnecting, removal, refitting and reconnecting 3
Battery – testing and charging 2
Charging system – testing 4

Section number

General information and precautions 1
Starter motor – removal and refitting 7
Starting system – testing 6

Degrees of difficulty

Easy, suitable for novice with little experience 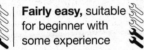	**Fairly easy,** suitable for beginner with some experience	**Fairly difficult,** suitable for competent DIY mechanic	**Difficult,** suitable for experienced DIY mechanic	**Very difficult,** suitable for expert DIY or professional

Specifications

System type . . . . 12 volt, negative earth

Battery

Type . . . . Low-maintenance or maintenance-free sealed for life
Capacity:
    1.4 litre litre petrol . . . . 28 Ah or 35 Ah
    1.8 litre petrol . . . . 36 Ah or 45 Ah
    2.2 litre diesel . . . . 59 Ah or 74 Ah
Charge condition:
    Poor . . . . 12.5 volts
    Normal . . . . 12.6 volts
    Good . . . . 12.7 volts

Alternator

Output at 13.5v (at operating temperature):
    1.4 (L13A) engine 75A
    1.4 (L13Z) engine 95A
    1.8 (R18A) engine 90A
    2.2 (N22A) engine 105A

Brush length	Standard	Minimum
1.4 (L13A) engine	19.0 mm	5.0 mm
1.4 (L13Z) engine	23.0 mm	18.0 mm
1.8 (R18A) engine	19.0 mm	5.0 mm
2.2 (N22A) engine	10.5 mm	1.5 mm

Torque wrench settings	Nm	lbf ft
Alternator bolts (diesel engines)	22	16
Alternator bolts (petrol engines)	24	17
Alternator main cable nut	12	9
Starter motor mounting bolts:		
M12 bolts	64	47
M10 bolts	44	33

1 General information and precautions

General information

1 The engine electrical system consists mainly of the charging and starting systems. Because of their engine-related functions, these components are covered separately from the body electrical devices such as the lights, instruments, etc (which are covered in Chapter 12). Information on the ignition system (petrol engines only) is covered in Part B of this Chapter.

2 The electrical system is of the 12 volt negative earth type.

3 The factory fitted battery is a maintenance free (sealed for life) type and is charged by the alternator, which is belt-driven from the crankshaft pulley.

4 The starter motor is of the pre-engaged type, incorporating an integral solenoid. On starting, the solenoid moves the drive pinion into engagement with the flywheel ring gear before the starter motor is energised. Once the engine has started, a one-way clutch prevents the motor armature being driven by the engine until the pinion disengages from the flywheel.

5 Diesel engines have glow plugs fitted to aid starting in cold conditions. The removal and refitting of the glow plugs is covered in Chapter 5C.

6 Further details of the various systems are given in the relevant Sections of this Chapter. While some repair procedures are given, the usual course of action is to renew the component concerned.

Precautions

⚠️ *Warning: It is necessary to take extra care when working on the electrical system to avoid damage to semi-conductor devices (diodes and transistors), and to avoid the risk of personal injury. In addition to the precautions given in Safety first 0 2 !, observe the following when working on the system:*

• *Always remove rings, watches, etc, before working on the electrical system. Even with the battery disconnected, capacitive discharge could occur if a component's live terminal is earthed through a metal object. This could cause a shock or nasty burn.*

• *Do not reverse the battery connections. Components such as the alternator, electronic control units, or any other components having semi-conductor circuitry could be irreparably damaged.*

• *Never disconnect the battery terminals, the alternator, any electrical wiring or any test instruments when the engine is running.*

• *Do not allow the engine to turn the alternator when the alternator is not connected.*

• *Never test for alternator output by 'flashing' the output lead to earth.*

• *Always ensure that the battery negative lead is disconnected when working on the electrical system.*

• *If the engine is being started using jump leads and a slave battery, connect the batteries positive-to-positive and negative-to-negative (see Jump starting). This also applies when connecting a battery charger.*

• *Never use an ohmmeter of the type incorporating a hand-cranked generator for circuit or continuity testing.*

• *Before using electric-arc welding equipment on the car, disconnect the battery, alternator and components such as the electronic control units (where applicable) to protect them from the risk of damage.*

2 Battery – testing and charging

Note: *A sealed for life maintenance free battery is the original factory fitted battery on all models. Where the battery has been replaced it may be of the low maintenance, standard type or equally another maintenance free type.*

Testing

Standard and low-maintenance battery

1 If the vehicle covers a small annual mileage, it is worthwhile checking the specific gravity of the electrolyte every three months to determine the state of charge of the battery. Use a hydrometer to make the check, and compare the results with the following table. Note that the specific gravity readings assume an electrolyte temperature of 15°C; for every 10°C below 15°C subtract 0.007. For every 10°C above 15°C add 0.007.

	Ambient temperature	
	Above 25°C	Below 25°C
Fully-charged	1.210 to 1.230	1.270 to 1.290
70% charged	1.170 to 1.190	1.230 to 1.250
Discharged	1.050 to 1.070	1.110 to 1.130

2 If the battery condition is suspect, first check the specific gravity of electrolyte in each cell. A variation of 0.040 or more between any cells indicates loss of electrolyte or deterioration of the internal plates.

3 If the specific gravity variation is 0.040 or more, the battery should be renewed. If the cell variation is satisfactory but the battery is discharged, it should be charged as described later in this Section.

Maintenance-free battery

4 All models are be fitted with a maintenance free battery, with a built-in charge condition indicator. The indicator is located in the top of the battery casing, and indicates the condition of the battery from its colour **(see illustration)**. The charge conditions denoted by the colour of the indicator should be printed on a label attached to the battery – if not, consult a suitably equipped garage or automotive electrician for advice.

All types

5 If testing the battery using a voltmeter, connect the voltmeter across the battery and note the voltage. The test is only accurate if the battery has not been subjected to any kind of charge for the previous six hours. If this is not the case, switch on the headlights for 30 seconds, then wait four to five minutes before testing the battery after switching off the headlights. All other electrical circuits must be switched off, so check that the doors and tailgate are fully shut when making the test.

6 If the voltage reading is less than 12.2 volts, then the battery is discharged, whilst a reading of 12.2 to 12.4 volts indicates a partially-discharged condition.

7 If the battery is to be charged, remove it from the vehicle and charge it as described later in this Section.

Charging

Note: *The following is intended as a guide only. Always refer to the manufacturer's recommendations (often printed on a label attached to the battery) before charging a battery.*

Standard and low-maintenance battery

8 Charge the battery at a rate equivalent to 10% of the battery capacity (eg, for a 45 Ah battery charge at 4.5 A) and continue to charge the battery at this rate until no further rise in specific gravity is noted over a four-hour period.

9 Alternatively, a trickle charger charging at the rate of 1.5 amps can safely be used overnight.

10 Specially rapid boost charges which are

2.4 The battery charge indicator

claimed to restore the power of the battery in 1 to 2 hours are not recommended, as they can cause serious damage to the battery plates through overheating. If the battery is completely flat, recharging should take at least 24 hours.

11 While charging the battery, note that the temperature of the electrolyte should never exceed 38°C.

Maintenance-free battery

12 This battery type takes considerably longer to fully recharge than the standard type, the time taken being dependent on the extent of discharge, but it can take anything up to three days.

13 A constant voltage type charger is required, to be set, when connected, to 13.9 to 14.9 volts with a charger current below 25 amps. Using this method, the battery should be useable within three hours, giving a voltage reading of 12.5 volts, but this is for a partially-discharged battery and, as mentioned, full charging can take far longer.

14 If the battery is to be charged from a fully-discharged state (condition reading less than 12.2 volts), have it recharged by your Honda dealer or local automotive electrician, as the charge rate is higher, and constant supervision during charging is necessary.

---

3 Battery – disconnecting, removal, refitting and reconnecting

Note: *Wait at least 5 minutes after turning off the ignition switch before disconnecting the battery. This is to allow sufficient time for the various control modules to store information*
Note: *Where a coded audio unit is fitted, ensure you have the audio unit security code. This code will need to be entered after reconnecting the battery – refer to the owner's handbook supplied with the vehicle.*

Disconnecting

1 Open the bonnet and lower the drivers side window. Remove the key (or keyless fob) from the vehicle.
2 Wait at least 5 minutes and then disconnect the battery at the negative (earth) terminal **(see illustration)**.

3.6c Where fitted remove the protective cover

Removal

3 Disconnect the battery as described above.
4 The battery is located on the left-hand side of the engine compartment.
5 Open the cover, slacken the clamp nut and disconnect the battery positive lead terminal **(see illustration)**.
6 Unscrew the nuts and remove the battery retaining clamp **(see illustrations)**.
7 Remove the battery **(see illustration)**. Take care as the battery is a heavy item.
8 With the battery removed the battery tray can be removed. Remove the the lower plastis tray and then unbolt and remove the main tray **(see illustration)**.

Refitting

9 Position the battery on the battery tray. Where removed refit the cover.
10 Refit the retaining clamp and tighten the retaining nuts securely.

3.2 Disconnect the battery at the main earth (negative) terminal

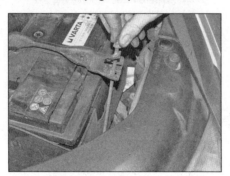

3.6a Undo the battery clamp nuts...

3.7 Remove the battery

Reconnecting

11 Reconnect the battery positive lead and then the negative (earth) lead.
12 Reach through the open drivers window and turn the side lights on for a few minutes. This will allow any accumulated surface charge on the battery to dissipate.
13 Turn the ignition on. Wait for a minute or so before starting the car. The short waiting time will allow all the modules in the vehicle to 'boot ' up and stabilise.
14 After reconnecting the battery, the engine may run erratically until it's been driven for a few minutes to allow the PCM to relearn and adapt itself. If major work has been undertaken on the engine (petrol models only) the idle learning procedure should be performed. To perform the idle lean do the following:
a) Turn the ignition on and wait 5 seconds

3.5 Disconnect the positive cable

3.6b...and then remove the clamp

3.8 The battery tray lower bolts are reached from below

b) *Start the engine and hold the speed at 3,000 rpm*

c) *Hold the engine at 3,000 rpm until the radiator cooling fan cuts in or the temperature gauge reads 90 degrees*

d) *Allow the engine to idle for 5 minutes*

15 If the crankshaft sensor has been replaced perform the crankshaft sensor learn procedure as described Chapter 4A Section 10.

16 Where one touch power windows are fitted the windows should be re-initialised as follows:

a) *Press and hold the window control close button until the window is fully closed.*

b) *Release the button, then press it again for 3 seconds.*

c) *Briefly press the open button to the second detent, then release it. The window should open automatically.*

d) *Briefly press the close button to the second detent, then release it. If the window does not close automatically, repeat the complete procedure.*

e) *Repeat this procedure on each window.*

5.4a Remove the protective caps

5.4c Remove the control wiring plug and...

5.5a Remove the upper bolt...

---

4 Charging system – testing

Note: *Refer to the warnings given in* Safety first! *and in Section 1 of this Chapter before starting work.*

1 If the ignition/no-charge warning light fails to illuminate when the ignition is switched on, first check the alternator wiring connections for security. If all is satisfactory, the alternator maybe at fault and should be renewed or taken to an auto-electrician for testing and repair.

2 If the ignition warning light illuminates when the engine is running, stop the engine and check that the drivebelt is correctly tensioned (see Chapter 1A or 1B) and that the alternator connections are secure. If all is so far satisfactory, have the alternator checked by an auto-electrician for testing and repair.

3 If the alternator output is suspect even

5.4b Where fitted remove the AC compressor wiring loom

5.4d...then the main wiring plug

5.5b...and the lower bolt

---

though the warning light functions correctly, the regulated voltage may be checked as follows.

4 Connect a voltmeter across the battery terminals and start the engine.

5 Increase the engine speed until the voltmeter reading remains steady; the reading should be between 13.5 and 14.8 volts.

6 Switch on as many electrical accessories (eg, the headlights, heated rear window and heater blower) as possible, and check that the alternator maintains the regulated voltage between 13.5 and 14.8 volts.

7 If the regulated voltage is not as stated, the fault may be due to worn brushes, weak brush springs, a faulty voltage regulator, a faulty diode, a severed phase winding, or worn or damaged slip-rings. At the time of writing, it would appear that no parts were available for the alternator. If faulty the complete assembly must be renewed. If in doubt, the alternator should be renewed or taken to an auto-electrician for testing.

5 Alternator – removal and refitting

Removal

1 Disconnect the battery negative lead (see Section 3).

2 Remove the auxiliary drivebelt as described in Chapter 1A or 1B.

Petrol engines

3 On 1.4 litre engines remove the air inlet duct.

4 Remove or prise open the protective caps from the rear of the alternator. Unbolt the main output cable and then unplug the control cable. Disconnect the wiring loom from the support clip **(see illustrations)**.

5 At the rear of the alternator remove the loom support bracket (where fitted). Remove the upper and lower mounting bolts and then lower the alternator from the vehicle **(see illustrations)**.

Diesel engines

6 Remove the front grille as described in Chapter 11.

7 Disconnect the bonnet switch wiring plug and then unbolt the coolant pipe.

5.5c Remove the alternator

5.10 Remove the cooling fan assembly

5.12a Remove the control cable wiring plug

5.12b Prise out the protective cap

8 Unbolt the bonnet slam panel and move it to the side.

9 Disconnect the wiring plug from the AC compressor and the radiator cooling fan. Unclip the loom from the cooling fan shroud.

10 Remove the upper mounting bolts and lift the cooling fan and shroud up and out of the vehicle **(see illustration)**.

11 Release the AC refrigerant pipe from the clamp and move it to the side.

12 Disconnect the wiring plug from the alternator, then prise up the rubber cap, undo the nut and disconnect the battery cable from the alternator **(see illustration)**.

13 Remove the upper bolts and remove the oil protector **(see illustration)**.

14 Remove the lower retaining bolt **(see illustration)** and then remove the alternator.

Refitting

15 Refitting is a reversal of removal. Remembering to tighten the various fasteners to their specified torque where given.

---

6 Starting system – testing

Note: *Refer to the precautions given in Safety first! and in Section 1 of this Chapter before starting work.*

1 If the starter motor fails to operate when the ignition key is turned to the appropriate position, the following possible causes may be to blame:

a) *The battery is faulty.*

b) *The electrical connections between the switch, solenoid, battery and starter motor are somewhere failing to pass the necessary current from the battery through the starter to earth.*

c) *The solenoid is faulty.*

d) *The starter motor is mechanically or electrically defective.*

2 To check the battery, switch on the headlights. If they dim after a few seconds, this indicates that the battery is discharged – recharge (see Section 2) or renew the battery. If the headlights glow brightly, operate the ignition switch and observe the lights. If they dim, then this indicates that current is reaching

5.13 Remove the oil protector

the starter motor, therefore the fault must lie in the starter motor. If the lights continue to glow brightly (and no clicking sound can be heard from the starter motor solenoid), this indicates that there is a fault in the circuit or solenoid – see following paragraphs. If the starter motor turns slowly when operated, but the battery is in good condition, then this indicates that either the starter motor is faulty, or there is considerable resistance somewhere in the circuit.

3 If a fault in the circuit is suspected, disconnect the battery leads (including the earth connection to the body), the starter/solenoid wiring and the engine/transmission earth strap. Thoroughly clean the connections, and reconnect the leads and wiring, then use a voltmeter or test light to check that full battery voltage is available at the battery positive lead connection to the solenoid, and that the earth is sound. Smear petroleum jelly around the battery terminals to prevent corrosion – corroded connections are amongst the most frequent causes of electrical system faults.

4 If the battery and all connections are in good condition, check the circuit by disconnecting the wire from the solenoid blade terminal. Connect a voltmeter or test light between the wire end and a good earth (such as the battery negative terminal), and check that the wire is live when the ignition switch is turned to the start position. If it is, then the circuit is sound – if not, the circuit wiring can be checked as described in Chapter 12.

5 The solenoid contacts can be checked by connecting a voltmeter or test light between the battery positive feed connection on the

5.14 The alternator mounting bolts (show with the engine removed)

starter side of the solenoid, and earth. When the ignition switch is turned to the start position, there should be a reading or lighted bulb, as applicable. If there is no reading or lighted bulb, the solenoid is faulty and should be renewed.

6 If the circuit and solenoid are proved sound, the fault must lie in the starter motor. In this event, it may be possible to have the starter motor overhauled by a specialist, but check on the cost of spares before proceeding, as it may prove more economical to obtain a new or exchange motor.

---

7 Starter motor – removal and refitting

Removal

1 Disconnect the battery negative lead (see Section 3).

2 Jack up and support the front of the vehicle – see 'Jacking and vehicle support' in the Reference chapter. Remove the engine undershield.

1.4 litre petrol engines

3 On the later 1.4 (L13Z) engines, remove the air inlet duct and then unbolt and remove the dipstick. Disconnect the oil pressure warning light switch.

4 Disconnect the wiring plug from the smaller solenoid cable.

5 Prise off the main terminal cover and unbolt the main feed to the starter motor.

6 From the engine bay remove the upper mounting bolt and then working from below

7.6a Remove the upper bolt...

7.6b...and then the lower longer bolt

7.6c Remove the starter motor

7.7 Remove the exhaust front pipe from the support bracket

remove the lower (longer) bolt. Withdraw the starter from below (see illustrations).

1.8 litre petrol engines

Note: *The starter motor is located high up at the rear of the engine. Access is limited.*

7 With reference to Chapter 4A, remove the front section of the exhaust pipe (see illustration).

8 Whilst not strictly necessary, consideration should be given to removing the right-hand driveshaft.

9 Remove the inlet manifold support bracket (see illustration).

10 Unclip the wiring loom from the bracket on the starter motor and from the oil separator on the rear of the engine block.

11 Prise free the cover from the main starter cable and then unclip the solenoid cable. Remove the retaining nut and then remove the main cable from the starter motor.

12 A special bolt is fitted to the upper mounting. Remove the bolt.

13 Undo the starter motor lower mounting bolt. If the driveshaft is still in place, rotate the starter motor to remove it past the driveshaft (see illustrations).

2.2 litre diesel engines

14 Remove the front grille as described in Chapter 11.

15 Disconnect the bonnet switch wiring plug and then unbolt the coolant pipe.

16 Remove the bonnet slam panel.

17 If not already done so remove the engine cover and then remove the dipstick.

18 Remove the oil pressure switch and then unbolt and remove the dipstick guide tube.

19 At the rear of the starter motor remove the wiring loom bracket (one bolt) and then unclip the wiring loom (see illustration).

20 Disconnect the wiring plug from the solenoid and then prise of the insulating cover and unbolt the main starter motor cable (see illustration).

21 Remove the upper and then the lower starter motor mounting bolts (see illustration). Remove the starter motor by lowering it from the engine bay.

Refitting

22 Refitting is a reversal of removal. Tighten all fasteners to their specified torque where given.

7.9 Remove the inlet manifold support bracket

7.13a The starter motor mounting bolts

7.13b Removing the starter motor

7.19 Release the wiring loom

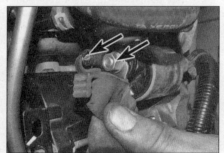

7.20 Peel back the insulating boot to expose the main starter cable. Note the solenoid connection

7.21 The starter motor bolts

Chapter 5 Part B
Ignition

Contents

	Section number			Section number
General information	1	Ignition timing –checking and adjustment		4
Ignition coils –removal and refitting	3	Knock sensor –removal and refitting		5
Ignition system – testing	2			

Degrees of difficulty

Easy, suitable for novice with little experience	**Fairly easy,** suitable for beginner with some experience	**Fairly difficult,** suitable for competent DIY mechanic	**Difficult,** suitable for experienced DIY mechanic	**Very difficult,** suitable for expert DIY or professional

Specifications

General

Firing order	1-3-4-2 (No 1 cylinder at timing chain end)
Ignition timing:	
1.4 (L13A)	8° ± 2° at idle (red pulley mark)
1.4 (L13Z)	0° ± 2° at idle (white pulley mark)
1.8 (R18A)	8° ± 2° at idle (red pulley mark)
Spark plug gap	1.0 -1.1 mm

Torque wrench settings

	Nm	lbf ft
Knock sensor	31	23
Ignition coil	10	7

1 General information

1 The PGM-FI engine management system provides complete control of the ignition timing by determining the optimum timing in response to engine speed, coolant temperature, throttle position, intake air temperature and intake manifold pressure. These parameters are relayed to the engine management system's Electronic Control Unit (ECU) by the crankshaft position and camshaft position (TDC) sensors, throttle position sensor, coolant temperature sensor and the Manifold Absolute Pressure (MAP) sensor. Ignition timing is altered during warm-up, idling and warm running conditions by the ECU.

2 A knock sensor is mounted on the cylinder block to inform the ECU when the engine is 'pinking'. Its sensitivity to a particular frequency of vibration allows it to detect the impulses which are caused by the shock waves set up when the engine starts to pink (pre-ignite). The knock sensor sends an electrical signal to the ECU which retards the ignition timing until the pinking ceases – the ignition timing is then gradually returned to the 'normal' setting. This maintains the ignition timing as close to the knock threshold as possible – the most efficient setting for the engine under normal running conditions.

3 The ignition system itself consists of the ignition switch, battery, and either four or eight (L13A engines) direct-ignition coils, and the spark plugs. The ignition system uses one coil for each cylinder, except on the early 1.4 (L13A) engines which use two coils per cylinder (and two spark plugs). Each coil is mounted directly on the relevant spark plug. The coils are triggered individually in firing order.

Precautions

4 The following precautions must be observed, to prevent damage to the ignition system components and to reduce risk of personal injury:

● Ensure the ignition is switched off before disconnecting any of the ignition wiring.
● Ensure that the ignition is switched off before connecting or disconnecting any ignition test equipment, such as a timing light.
● Do not earth the coil primary or secondary circuits.

 Warning: Voltages produced by an electronic ignition system are considerably higher than those produced by conventional ignition systems. Extreme care must be taken when working on the system with the ignition switched on. Persons with surgically-implanted cardiac pacemaker devices should keep well clear of the ignition circuits, components and test equipment.

2 Ignition system – testing

1 The components of ignition systems are normally very reliable; most faults are far more likely to be due to loose or dirty connections, or to 'tracking' of HT voltage due to dirt, dampness or damaged insulation than to the failure of any of the system's components. Always check all wiring thoroughly before condemning an electrical component and work methodically to eliminate all other possibilities before deciding that a particular component is faulty.

Engine will not start

2 If the engine either will not turn over at all, or only turns very slowly, first check the battery and starter motor as described in Chapter 5A.
3 The anti-theft immobiliser system disables the fuel system when in operation, meaning that the engine will turn over as normal, but will not start. The immobiliser should be deactivated when a properly-coded ignition key is inserted into the ignition switch. If possible, substitute a spare key and recheck.
4 Check the fuses relating to the engine management system in the passenger compartment fuse panel (in the facia) and in the engine compartment fuse/relay box(es) – see Chapter 12.
5 Remove all the ignition coils and spark plugs (see Chapter 1A), then unbolt and withdraw the plastic cover over the intake manifold and disconnect all four injector connectors to disable them and prevent them from spraying fuel into the combustion chamber while work is in progress. Connect the ignition coils to their wiring, fit the spark plug to each coil and place the spark plugs so that each plug body is in firm contact with the metal of the cylinder head. Check for a good spark at each plug as an assistant cranks the engine on the starter motor. If there is no spark at all, the fault lies elsewhere in the system. If the spark is poor, intermittent or missing on one spark plug only, swap components until the source of the fault can be identified. Repairs to the ignition coils are not possible. All that can be done is to substitute a known good component.
6 Ultimately, the vehicle should be referred to a Honda dealer or suitably equipped garage for testing. A diagnostic socket is incorporated in the engine management system wiring harness, into which dedicated electronic test equipment can be plugged – the connector is located under the driver's side of the facia (see Chapter 4A). The tester in the hands of a skilled technician will help to locate the fault quickly and simply, alleviating the need to test all the system components individually, which is a time-consuming operation that carries a high risk of damaging the ECU. If necessary, the system wiring and wiring connectors can be checked as described in Chapter 12, ensuring that the ECU wiring connector is only unplugged with the battery disconnected.

Engine misfires

7 An irregular misfire suggests either a loose connection or intermittent fault in the primary circuit, or an HT fault between the coils and spark plugs.
8 With the ignition switched off, check carefully through the system, ensuring that all connections are clean and securely fastened.
9 Check that the HT coils and their associated wiring connections are clean and dry.
10 Regular misfiring of one spark plug may be due to a faulty spark plug, faulty injector, a faulty coil or loss of compression in the relevant cylinder. Regular misfiring of all the cylinders suggests a fuel supply fault, such as a clogged fuel filter or faulty fuel pump, especially if it occurs in conditions where fuel demand is high.

3 Ignition coils – removal and refitting

Removal

1 Remove the engine cover and disconnect the coil wiring plug **(see illustrations)**.

3.1a Disconnecting the wiring plugs on 1.4 (L13A) engines and...

3.1b...on the later 1.4 (L13Z) engines

3.2a The coil mounting bolts on early 1.4 engines and...

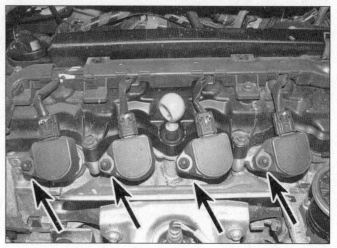

3.2b...on the 1.8 litre engines

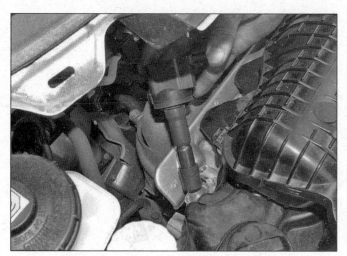

3.3 Remove the coils (1.4 L13Z engine shown)

5.5 Remove the sensor

2 Remove the ignition coil mounting bolts **(see illustrations)**.

3 With the mounting bolts removed lift out the ignition coils **(see illustration)**.

Refitting

4 Refitting is a reversal of removal.

| 4 | **Ignition timing –** |
| | checking and adjustment |

1 It is possible to check the ignition timing with the correct equipment, but even if all this is done/available, the ignition timing cannot be adjusted, and if it is out of specification, a new

Engine Control Unit (ECU) will be needed. If the timing is felt to be incorrect because the engine can be heard pinking, the knock sensor may be faulty (see Section 5).

2 If performance in general is down, carry out the primary operations listed in Chapter 1A, before having the engine management system checked by a Honda dealer or diagnostic specialist.

| 5 | **Knock sensor –** |
| | removal and refitting |

1 The knock sensor is located behind the inlet manifold on all models.

2 Access is only possible with the inlet manifold removed as described in Chapter 4A.

3 Disconnect the battery (Chapter 5A Section 3) and remove the inlet manifold.

4 Unclip the plug to disconnect the sensor wiring.

5 Unscrew the sensor and remove it **(see illustration)**.

6 Clean the sensor and engine block mating faces before fitting.

7 Refitting is a reversal of removal. It is critical for the correct operation of the sensor that it is tightened to the specified torque wrench setting on to a completely clean mating surface.

Chapter 5 Part C
Pre-heating system

Contents

Section number

General information 1
Glow plug control module – removal and refitting 4

Section number

Glow plugs – removal, inspection and refitting 3
Pre-heating system – testing 2

Degrees of difficulty

Easy, suitable for novice with little experience	**Fairly easy,** suitable for beginner with some experience	**Fairly difficult,** suitable for competent DIY mechanic	**Difficult,** suitable for experienced DIY mechanic	**Very difficult,** suitable for expert DIY or professional

Specifications

Torque wrench settings	Nm	lbf ft
Glow plugs	18	13

1 General information

1 To assist cold starting, diesel-engined models are fitted with a preheating system, which comprises glow plugs (one per cylinder), a glow plug control module (relay) and an instrument panel warning lamp, a coolant temperature sensor and the associated electrical wiring.

2 The glow plugs are miniature electric heating elements, encapsulated in a metal case with a probe at one end and electrical connection at the other. Each combustion chamber has one glow plug threaded into it. When the glow plug is energised, it heats up rapidly causing the temperature of the air charge drawn into each of the combustion chambers to rise. The glow plug probe is positioned directly in line with the incoming spray of fuel from the injectors. Hence the fuel passing over the glow plug probe is also heated, allowing its optimum combustion temperature to be achieved more readily. In addition, small particles of the fuel passing over the glow plugs are ignited and this helps to trigger the combustion process.

3 A warning light informs the driver that pre-heating is taking place. The lamp extinguishes when sufficient pre-heating has taken place to allow the engine to be started, but power will still be supplied to the glow plugs for a further period until the engine is started. If no attempt is made to start the engine, the power supply to the glow plugs is switched off to prevent battery drain and glow plug burn-out.

4 The system employs post-glowing (after-heating), which operates as follows: After the engine has been started, the glow plugs continue to operate for a further period of time. This helps to improve fuel combustion whilst the engine is warming-up, resulting in quieter, smoother running and reduced exhaust emissions. The duration of the after-heating period is dependent on the coolant temperature. On models fitted with a Diesel Particulate Filter (DPF) the glow plugs are activated as part of the DPF regeneration process.

3.2 Remove the wiring plugs

3.3 Remove the glow plugs

freezing spray to the glow plug. If a glow plug snaps during removal then consult a diesel specialist who should have the equipment to remove a broken glow plug.

3 Using a deep socket and a torque wrench, unscrew and remove the glow plugs **(see illustration)**.

Inspection

4 Inspect the glow plugs for signs of damage. Burnt or eroded glow plug tips can be caused by a bad injector spray pattern. Have the injectors checked if this sort of damage is found.

5 If the glow plugs are in good condition, check them electrically, as described in Section 2.

6 The glow plugs can be energised by applying 12 volts to them to verify that they heat up evenly and in the required time. Observe the following precautions:

a) *Support the glow plug by clamping it carefully in a vice or self-locking pliers. Remember it will be red hot.*

b) *Make sure that the power supply or test lead incorporates a fuse or overload trip to protect against damage from a short-circuit.*

c) *After testing, allow the glow plug to cool for several minutes before attempting to handle it.*

7 A glow plug in good condition will start to glow red at the tip after drawing current for 5 seconds or so. Any plug which takes much longer to start glowing, or which starts glowing in the middle instead of at the tip, is probably defective.

Refitting

8 Thoroughly clean the glow plugs, and the glow plug seating areas in the cylinder head.

9 Apply a smear of anti-seize compound to the glow plug threads, then refit the glow plug and tighten it to the specified torque.

10 Reconnect the wiring to the glow plug. The connectors are a push-fit.

11 The remainder of refitting is a reversal of removal.

---

2 Pre-heating system – testing

1 Full testing of the system can only be carried out using specialist diagnostic equipment which is connected to the engine management system diagnostic wiring connector. If the pre-heating system is thought to be faulty, some preliminary checks of the glow plug operation may be made as described in the following paragraphs.

2 Connect a voltmeter or 12-volt test lamp between the glow plug supply cable, and a good earth point on the engine.

Caution: Make sure that the live connection is kept well clear of the engine and bodywork

3 Have an assistant activate the pre-heating system by turning the ignition key to the second position, and check that battery voltage is applied to the glow plug electrical connection.

Note: *The supply voltage will be less than battery voltage initially, but will rise and settle as the glow plug heats up. It will then drop to zero when the pre-heating period ends and the safety cut-out operates.*

4 If no supply voltage can be detected at the glow plug, then the glow plug output stage or the supply cable may be faulty.

5 To locate a faulty glow plug, first operate the pre-heating system to allow the glow plugs to reach working temperature, then disconnect the battery negative lead as described in Chapter 5A.

6 Refer to Section 3, and remove the supply cable from No 2 glow plug terminal. Measure the electrical resistance between the glow plug terminal and the engine earth. A reading of anything more than a few Ohms indicates that the glow plug is defective.

7 As a final check, remove the glow plugs and inspect them visually, as described in Section 3.

8 If no problems are found, take the vehicle to a Honda dealer or suitably equipped specialist for testing using the appropriate diagnostic equipment.

---

3 Glow plugs – removal, inspection and refitting

Removal

1 Remove the acoustic engine cover. Before working on any part of the vehicle's electrical systems, it is advisable to disconnect the battery negative (earth) lead (see Chapter 5A Section 3).

2 Grip the lugs at the end of the connectors and pull them from the glow plugs **(see illustration)**.

Caution: Glow plugs can be notoriously difficult to remove. Always use a torque wrench, set to the tightening torque to remove the glow plugs. If the glow plug does not come loose when the tightening torque has been reached then apply penetrating fluid and leave the glow plug to soak. An alternative method is to remove the glow plugs with a hot engine and apply plumbers

---

4 Glow plug control module – removal and refitting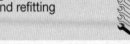

Removal

1 The glow plug control module (relay) is located on the left-hand side of the engine compartment, bolted next to the engine compartment fuse/relay box **(see illustration)**.

2 Unplug the connector to disconnect the control module wiring **(see illustration)**.

3 Remove the mounting nut and remove the controller.

Refitting

4 Refitting is a reversal of removal.

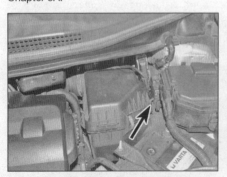

4.1 The glow plug controller

4.2 Disconnect the wiring plug

Chapter 6
Clutch

Contents

Section number

Clutch assembly – removal, inspection and refitting 6
Clutch hydraulic system – bleeding 5
Clutch master cylinder – removal and refitting. 3
Clutch pedal – removal and refitting and adjustment. 2

Section number

Clutch release bearing and fork– removal, inspection and refitting . . 7
Clutch slave cylinder – removal and refitting 4
General Information 1

Degrees of difficulty

Easy, suitable for novice with little experience	Fairly easy, suitable for beginner with some experience	Fairly difficult, suitable for competent DIY mechanic	Difficult, suitable for experienced DIY mechanic	Very difficult, suitable for expert DIY or professional

Specifications

General
Clutch type. . . . . Single dry plate, diaphragm spring, hydraulic actuation

Driven plate
Warp limit . . . . 0.2 mm

Clutch pedal
Height from floor:
    Petrol models . . . . 148.7 mm
    Diesel models . . . . 163.4 mm
Pedal stroke:
    Petrol models . . . . 125-135 mm
    Diesel models . . . . 140-150 mm
Switch adjustment position . . . . 35.5-38.5 mm

Torque wrench settings

	Nm	lbf ft
Clutch pedal:		
Main nuts	13	9
Upper bolt	10	7
Clutch pedal push rod lock nut	17	12
Master cylinder bolts	22	18
Pressure plate retaining bolts	25	19
Slave cylinder mounting bolts	22	16

1 General Information

1 The single dry plate clutch consists of a friction plate, a pressure plate assembly, a release bearing and the release fork lever; all of these components are contained in the large cast-aluminium alloy bellhousing, sandwiched between the engine and the gearbox. The clutch release mechanism is hydraulically-operated and so is self-adjusting and requires no manual adjustment to compensate for wear of the friction material.

2 The friction plate is fitted between the engine flywheel and the clutch pressure plate, and is allowed to slide on the gearbox input shaft splines. Friction lining material is riveted to both sides of the friction plate which, on all petrol-engined models, has a spring-cushioned hub to absorb transmission shocks and help ensure a smooth take-up of the drive. There is no spring-cushioned hub on the diesel-engined models, however, the flywheel being of the dual-mass type, built in two sections with internal torsion springs to take up transmission shocks.

3 The pressure plate assembly is bolted to the engine flywheel. When the engine is running, drive is transmitted from the crankshaft, via the flywheel, to the friction plate (these components being clamped securely together by the diaphragm spring in the pressure plate assembly) and from the friction plate to the gearbox input shaft.

4 The release bearing is located on a guide sleeve at the front of the gearbox, and the bearing is free to slide on the sleeve, under the action of the release fork lever which pivots on a ball-stud inside the bellhousing.

5 To interrupt the drive, the diaphragm spring's pressure must be relaxed. Depressing the clutch pedal pushes on the master cylinder pushrod which thus causes hydraulic pressure to force out the slave cylinder piston which bears on the end of the clutch release fork lever. The release fork acts on its pivot to press the release bearing against the pressure plate diaphragm spring fingers. As the centre of the spring is pushed in, the outside of the spring pivots out, so moving the pressure plate backwards and disengaging its grip on the friction plate.

6 Diesel-engined models are fitted with a Self-Adjusting Clutch (SAC). This is in fact something of a misnomer, as the clutches fitted to petrol-engined models are also self-adjusting, but the SAC device compensates for the effect of friction plate wear on clutch pedal load by altering the attitude of the diaphragm spring fingers by means of a sprung mechanism within the pressure plate cover. This ensures a consistent clutch pedal 'feel' over the life of the clutch, as opposed to the progressively-heavier effort required to depress the pedal of a conventional clutch as its friction plate wears. The pressure plate assembly, like that of a conventional unit, is riveted together and must not be dismantled; any fault with any part of the assembly can be rectified only by the renewal of the friction plate and pressure plate assembly as a set.

Note: *Due to the amount of work necessary to remove and refit clutch components, it is usually considered good practice to renew the clutch friction plate, pressure plate assembly and release bearing as a matched set, even if only one of these is actually worn enough to require renewal.*

2 Clutch pedal – removal and refitting and adjustment

⚠️ *Warning: Hydraulic fluid is poisonous; wash off immediately and thoroughly in the case of skin contact, and seek immediate medical advice if any fluid is swallowed or gets into the eyes. Certain types of hydraulic fluid are inflammable, and may ignite when allowed into contact with hot components; when servicing any hydraulic system, it is safest to assume that the fluid IS inflammable, and to take precautions against the risk of fire as though it is petrol that is being handled. Hydraulic fluid is also an effective paint stripper, and will attack plastics; if any is spilt, it should be washed off immediately, using copious quantities of clean water. Finally, it is hygroscopic (it absorbs moisture from the air) – old fluid may be contaminated and unfit for further use. When topping-up or renewing the fluid, always use the recommended type, and ensure that it comes from a freshly-opened sealed container.*

Removal

1 With reference to Chapter 11, remove the driver's side lower panel (knee panel) as described in Chapter 11.

2 Unbolt the upper support bracket **(see illustration)**.

3 Disconnect the clutch pedal position switch **(see illustration)** – or switches, depending on the model.

4 Prise out the spring locking clip from the master cylinder pushrod clevis pin. Pull out the clevis pin to the left, to disconnect the pushrod from the pedal.

5 Unscrew the two (master cylinder mounting) nuts and the nuts securing the pedal assembly to the bulkhead **(see illustrations)**. Manoeuvre the assembly out from underneath the facia. Do not attempt to dismantle the pedal assembly; if it is worn or damaged the complete assembly must be renewed – no individual components are available.

Refitting

6 Grease the pedal pivot and manoeuvre the pedal assembly into position, ensuring it is correctly engaged with the pushrod clevis. Refit the mounting nuts and bolt and tighten them to the torque wrench settings, where specified.

7 Grease the clevis pin, then press it back

2.2 Remove the upper bolt

2.3 Disconnect the wiring plug

2.5a Remove the master cylinder bolts...

2.5b ...and the pedal nuts

2.11 The clutch position switch (A) and on this model the height adjustment bolt and lock nut (B)

3.6 Remove the clip

into the clutch pedal and master cylinder pushrod, then fit the new clip. Ensure that the clip is securely fastened.

8 Where relevant, reconnect the clutch pedal position switch or switches, then check the pedal adjustments as described below.

9 Check the operation of the clutch pedal then refit the driver's side under cover and lower cover to the facia.

Adjustment

10 The height of the clutch pedal is the distance the pedal sits off the floor (remove any accessory floor mats). This is measured from the centre of the top surface of the pedal to the floor panel at the point where the floor turns up to meet the bulkhead. If the pedal height is not as specified, it must be adjusted.

11 To adjust the clutch pedal, slacken the locknut on the clutch pedal position switch and back the switch out until it no longer touches the pedal, then slacken the locknut on the other switch (where fitted) **(see illustration)**. Slacken the lock nut and turn the push rod to adjust the pedal height. At the same time check the pedal stroke. This is the distance from the fully released position to the fully depressed position. Some free play must exist or the release mechanism will be pressing constantly on the pressure plate spring fingers, resulting in clutch slip and premature clutch wear.

12 When the adjustment is correct, tighten the push rod locknut to the specified torque wrench setting.

13 Turn the clutch position switch (or nut/bolt) clockwise until it just contacts the pedal arm, then turn it in an additional 3/4 to 1 turn. Tighten the locknut to the specified torque wrench setting.

14 Where a second switch is fitted press the pedal to the floor and then releases it to the adjustment position. This is the distance from fully off to partially depressed – not the distance from the floor (see the specifications).

15 Adjust the switch whilst the pedal is held in the adjustment position. Tighten the lock nut.

16 Reconnect the wiring plugs and check the operation of the clutch. Refit the drivers side lower panel. Where a second switch is fitted check the operation of the cruise control (where fitted) and/or the gear shift indicator.

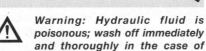

3 Clutch master cylinder – removal and refitting

⚠️ *Warning: Hydraulic fluid is poisonous; wash off immediately and thoroughly in the case of skin contact, and seek immediate medical advice if any fluid is swallowed or gets into the eyes. Certain types of hydraulic fluid are inflammable, and may ignite when allowed into contact with hot components; when servicing any hydraulic system, it is safest to assume that the fluid is inflammable, and to take precautions against the risk of fire as though it is petrol that is being handled. Hydraulic fluid is also an effective paint stripper, and will attack plastics; if any is spilt, it should be washed off immediately, using copious quantities of fresh water. Finally, it is hygroscopic (it absorbs moisture from the air) – old fluid may be contaminated and unfit for further use. When topping-up or renewing the fluid, always use the recommended type, and ensure that it comes from a freshly-opened sealed container.*

Removal

1 With reference to Chapter 11, remove the driver's side lower panel from the facia.

2 Use a syringe and remove as much brake fluid as possible from the clutch master cylinder reservoir.

3 Disconnect the wiring plugs from the clutch position switch (or switches).

4 Prise out the spring locking clip from the master cylinder pushrod clevis pin. Pull out the clevis pin to the left, to disconnect the pushrod from the pedal.

5 Remove the cover from the fluid pipe retaining clip – where fitted.

6 Anticipate some fluid spillage and then pull out the horse shoe pipe retaining clip **(see illustration)**. Remove the clutch fluid pipe. Seal the end of the pipe.

7 Unscrew the two master cylinder mounting nuts **(see illustration 2.5a)**.

8 Lower the master cylinder and remove the clutch fluid supply hose. Seal the pipe.

9 Withdraw the master cylinder from the bulkhead. Recover the O-ring from the hydraulic pipe and dispose of it – a new ones should be used when refitting.

Overhaul

Note: *Check the availability of overhaul kits before dismantling the cylinder.*

10 Press the pushrod into the cylinder body and prise out the circlip.

11 Remove the stopper, then ease out the pushrod, and pull out the piston assembly. If necessary, use compressed air to force the piston from the cylinder body.

12 Carefully examine the bore of the cylinder for rust, scratches, gouges and general wear. If the bore is damaged, the complete cylinder must be renewed. If the bore is in good condition, thoroughly clean the assembly, and renew the seals as described below.

13 Take note of the seal orientation on the piston, and using a small screwdriver, lever the seals from the grooves on the piston.

14 Fit the new seals to the piston, ensuring the seal lips point towards the spring end of the piston. Smear the seals with the assembly grease supplied in the overhaul kit.

15 Insert the piston assembly into the cylinder, spring end first. Ensure the seal lips enter the cylinder bore without catching or folding back.

16 Compress the piston with the pushrod, fit the stopper, then secure with the circlip.

Refitting

17 Refitting is a reversal of removal, noting the following:

a) *Fit a new O-ring to the hydraulic pipe.*

b) *Fit a new hydraulic pipe retaining clip.*

c) *Grease the clevis pin, then press it back into the clutch pedal and master cylinder pushrod and fit a new clip*

d) *Top-up the reservoir, then bleed the system as described in Section 5.*

e) *Check the operation of the clutch pedal then refit the driver's side lower panel to the facia.*

4.2 Release the supply pipe from the transmission

4.3 Remove the roll pins

4 Clutch slave cylinder – removal and refitting

Note: *Refer to the warning at the beginning of Section 2 before proceeding.*

Removal

1 On petrol models remove the air filter housing (Chapter 4A). On diesel models remove the battery and battery tray (Chapter 5A).

2 Unbolt the hydraulic pipe from the top of the gearbox as necessary to work on the slave cylinder **(see illustration)**.

3 Drive out the two roll-pins from the hydraulic pipe union nut **(see illustration)**.

4 Anticipating some fluid spillage, disconnect the hydraulic pipe union from the slave cylinder, then recover and discard the O-ring – a new one must be used when refitting. Either plug or tape over the open connections to prevent fluid loss and the entry of dirt.

5 Unbolt the slave cylinder from the gearbox **(see illustrations)**.

Overhaul

Note: *Check the availability of overhaul kits before dismantling the cylinder.*

6 Unclip the dust boot from the cylinder body, and pull out the pushrod. Extract the piston and spring. If necessary, use compressed air to force the piston from the bore. Recover the piston spring. **Note:** *On diesel-engined models, the one-way valve in the top of the slave cylinder body in line with the hydraulic pipe union is built into the cylinder body and cannot be dismantled. If the valve is faulty, the complete cylinder must be renewed.*

7 Carefully examine the bore of the cylinder for rust, scratches, gouges and general wear. If the bore is damaged, the complete cylinder must be renewed. If the bore is in good condition, thoroughly clean the assembly, and renew the seals as described below.

8 Note their fitted locations, then using a small screwdriver, prise the seals from the piston.

9 Fit the new seals to the piston, ensuring they are fitted as noted on removal. Coat the seals with assembly grease (supplied in the overhaul kit).

10 Insert the spring, large diameter end towards the cylinder bleed nipple, followed by the piston. Ensure the seal's lips enter the cylinder bore without catching or folding back.

11 Squeeze some brake assembly lubricant into the dust boot, then refit the boot and pushrod.

Refitting

12 On refitting, first pull back the slave cylinder's rubber dust boot and apply brake assembly lubricant to the pushrod, the end of the piston and the interior of the boot. Refit the boot and grease the tip of the pushrod; Honda recommend Urea Grease UM264 (Part No. 41211-PY5-305).

13 Engage the pushrod correctly on the clutch release fork lever, refit the slave cylinder mounting bolts and tighten them to the torque wrench setting specified.

14 Fit the new O-ring to the slave cylinder hydraulic pipe connection, then reconnect the hydraulic pipe to the slave cylinder. Ensure the hydraulic pipe is correctly routed and retained by all the necessary clips. Tighten the union nut and fit the roll-pins to secure it. Tighten any bolts disturbed securing the hydraulic pipe to the gearbox.

15 Top-up the reservoir, then bleed the system as described in Section 5. It may be necessary to limit the movement of the release fork lever to get all the air out of the system.

16 Check the operation of the clutch pedal then refit all components removed for access.

4.5a Remove the mounting bolts (petrol model shown)...

4.5b ...and remove the slave cylinder (diesel model)

5 Clutch hydraulic system – bleeding

Note: *Refer to the warning at the beginning of Section 2 before proceeding.*

1 If any part of the hydraulic system is dismantled, or if air has accidentally entered the system, the system will need to be bled. The presence of air is characterised by the pedal having a spongy feel and it results in difficulty in changing gear.

2 During the bleeding procedure, add only clean, unused hydraulic fluid of the recommended type; never re-use fluid that has already been bled from the system. Ensure that sufficient fluid is available before starting work.

3 To reach the slave cylinder bleed nipple, remove the battery tray on diesel engine models and the air filter housing on petrol models

4 Check that the slave cylinder bleed nipple is closed. Remove the dust cap, and clean any dirt from around the bleed nipple **(see illustration).**

5 It is recommended that pressure-bleeding equipment is used to bleed the system. Pressure-bleeding kits are usually operated by the reservoir of pressurised air contained in the spare tyre. However, note that it will probably be necessary to reduce the pressure to a lower level than normal; refer to the instructions supplied with the kit. If a pressure-bleeding kit is not available, use the normal bleeding method described for the brake hydraulic circuit in Chapter 9.

6 By connecting a pressurised, fluid-filled container to the brake fluid reservoir, bleeding can be carried out simply by opening the bleed nipple on the slave cylinder and allowing the fluid to flow out until no more air bubbles can be seen in the expelled fluid.

7 This method has the advantage that the

5.4 Before bleeding the hydraulic system, remove the dust cap and clean any dirt from around the slave cylinder bleed nipple

large reservoir of fluid provides an additional safeguard against air being drawn into the system during bleeding.

8 Collect a clean glass jar, a suitable length of plastic or rubber tubing which is a tight fit over the bleed nipple, and a ring spanner to fit the nipple.

9 Fit the spanner and tube to the slave cylinder bleed nipple, place the other end of the tube in the jar, and pour in sufficient fluid to cover the end of the tube.

10 Connect the pressure-bleeding equipment to the brake fluid reservoir in accordance with the manufacturer's instructions.

11 Slacken the bleed nipple using the spanner, and allow fluid to drain into the jar until no more air bubbles emerge.

12 When bleeding is complete, tighten the bleed nipple, and disconnect the hose and pressure bleeding equipment.

13 Wash off any spilt fluid, check once more that the bleed nipple is tightened securely, and refit the dust cap.

14 Check the hydraulic fluid level in the reservoir, and top-up if necessary (see Weekly checks).

15 Discard any hydraulic fluid that has been bled from the system; it will not be fit for re-use.

16 Check the feel of the clutch pedal. If it feels at all spongy, air must still be present in the system, and further bleeding is required. Failure to bleed satisfactorily after a procedure may be due to worn master or slave cylinder seals.

17 On completion, refit all components removed for access.

6 Clutch assembly – removal, inspection and refitting

⚠️ *Warning: Dust created by clutch wear and deposited on the clutch components may contain asbestos, which is a health hazard. DO NOT blow it out with compressed air or inhale any of it. DO NOT use petrol or petroleum-based solvents to clean off the dust. Brake system cleaner or methylated spirit should be used to flush the dust into a suitable receptacle. After the clutch components are wiped clean with rags, dispose of the contaminated rags and the used cleaner in a sealed, marked container.*

Petrol engine models

Removal

1 Unless the complete engine/transmission unit is to be removed from the vehicle and separated for major overhaul (see Chapter 2D), the clutch can be reached by removing the gearbox as described in Chapter 7A.

2 Before disturbing the clutch, check for paint marks showing the relationship of the pressure plate assembly to the flywheel. If none can be found, make your own using chalk, touch-up paint or a marker pen **(see illustration)**.

3 Working in a diagonal sequence, slacken the pressure plate bolts by half a turn at a time, until spring pressure is released and the bolts can be unscrewed by hand **(see illustration)**.

6.2 Before disturbing the clutch, paint marks showing the relationship of the pressure plate assembly to the flywheel

6.3 Working in a diagonal sequence, slacken the pressure plate bolts half a turn at a time

6.13 Fit the friction plate so that spring hub assembly faces away from the flywheel – note the dowels

6.16 Use a clutch-aligning tool to centralise the friction plate on the crankshaft

4 Prise the pressure plate assembly off its locating dowels, and collect the friction plate, noting which way round the friction plate is fitted.

Inspection

5 With the clutch assembly removed, clean off all traces of clutch dust using a dry cloth. This is best done outside or in a well-ventilated area.

6 Examine the linings of the driven plate for wear and loose rivets, and the rim for distortion, cracks, broken torsion springs and worn splines. The surface of the friction linings may be highly glazed, but, as long as the friction material pattern can be clearly seen, this is satisfactory.

7 If there is any sign of oil contamination, indicated by a continuous or patchy, shiny black discolouration, the plate must be renewed and the source of the contamination traced and rectified. This will be either a leaking crankshaft oil seal or transmission input shaft oil seal – or both.

8 The driven plate must also be renewed if the lining thickness has worn down to, or just above, the level of the rivet heads. Given the amount of dismantling work necessary to gain access to the driven plate, it may be wise to fit a new plate regardless of the old one's condition.

9 Check the machined faces of the flywheel and pressure plate. If either is grooved, or heavily scored, renewal is necessary. Providing the damage is not too serious, the flywheel can be removed as described in Chapter 2A, 2B or 2C and taken to an engineering works, who may be able to clean up the surface by machining.

10 The pressure plate must be renewed if any cracks are apparent, if the diaphragm spring is damaged or its pressure suspect, or if there is excessive warpage of the pressure plate face.

11 With the transmission removed, check the condition of the release bearing, as described in Section 7.

Refitting

12 On reassembly, ensure that the friction surfaces of the flywheel and pressure plate are completely clean, smooth, and free from oil or grease. Use solvent to remove any protective grease from new components.

13 Apply a thin smear of grease to the splines of the friction plate and the gearbox input shaft, and to the crankshaft pilot bush; Honda recommend Urea Grease UM264 (Part No. 41211-PY5-305). Fit the friction plate so that its spring hub assembly faces away from the flywheel (the thickness of the spring hub usually makes it impossible to fit it with the hub against the flywheel); there may also be a marking showing which way round the plate is to be refitted **(see illustration)**.

14 Refit the pressure plate assembly, aligning the marks made on dismantling (if the original pressure plate is re-used), and locating the pressure plate on its locating dowels. Fit the pressure plate bolts, but tighten them only finger-tight, so that the friction plate can still be moved.

15 The friction plate must now be centralised, so that when the gearbox is refitted, its input shaft will pass through the splines at the centre of the friction plate.

16 Centralisation can be achieved by passing a screwdriver or other long bar through the friction plate and into the hole in the crankshaft; the friction plate can then be moved around until it is centred on the crankshaft hole. Alternatively, a clutch-aligning tool can be used to eliminate the guesswork; these can be obtained from most accessory shops **(see illustration)**. A home-made alignment tool can be fabricated from a length of metal rod or wooden dowel which fits closely inside the crankshaft hole, and has insulating tape wound around it to match the diameter of the friction plate's splined centre.

17 When the friction plate is centralised, tighten the pressure plate bolts evenly and in a diagonal sequence to the specified torque setting. Ensure the pressure plate is drawn squarely onto the flywheel, to prevent the pressure plate being distorted.

18 Refit the gearbox as described in Chapter 7A.

Diesel engine models

Caution: Honda state that unless tools are used both on removing and installing the pressure plate assembly, it will be irreversibly damaged. We found, however, that careful, progressive and even slackening of the pressure plate mounting bolts allowed us to dismantle and rebuild the clutch without these special tools, and the setting procedure can also be carried out without them.

Removal

19 Unless the complete engine/transmission unit is to be removed from the vehicle and separated for major overhaul (see Chapter 2D), the clutch can be reached by removing the gearbox as described in Chapter 7A.

20 Before disturbing the clutch, check for paint marks showing the relationship of the pressure plate assembly to the flywheel. If none can be found, make your own using chalk, touch-up paint or a marker pen **(see illustration 6.2)**.

21 If the pressure plate assembly is likely to be re-used and the special tools are available, fit the tool to the engine/gearbox mounting bolt holes (or to the pressure plate itself, as applicable) and tighten down the centre screw to compress the diaphragm spring and lock the mechanism.

22 If the special tools are not being used, be careful to slacken the pressure plate bolts carefully, progressively and evenly. Keep your hands away from the Self-Adjusting Clutch (SAC) mechanism.

Caution: As the diaphragm spring pressure is relaxed, the mechanism's adjusting ring may spring into place. Ensure all fingers are clear of the area.

23 Prise the pressure plate assembly off its locating dowels, and collect the friction plate,

6.27 Fit the friction plate with the TRANSMISSION SIDE marking facing towards the gearbox

6.30 The washer should bear on the centre ring of the self-adjusting mechanism so it can be compressed...

noting which way round the friction plate is fitted.

Inspection

24 With the clutch assembly removed, clean off all traces of clutch dust using a dry cloth. This is best done outside or in a well-ventilated area. Owners should also note that it is considered good practice by many professionals to renew dual-mass flywheels as a matter of course whenever the clutch is renewed.

25 Proceed as described in paragraphs 5 to 12 above. When checking the pressure plate assembly, check also the components of the Self-Adjusting Clutch (SAC) mechanism; if there is any sign of excessive wear or of damage to any part of this, then the complete pressure plate assembly must be renewed.

Refitting

26 Apply a thin smear of grease to the splines of the friction plate and the gearbox input shaft, and to the crankshaft pilot bush; Honda recommend Urea Grease UM264 (Part No. 41211-PY5-305). It is advisable to refit the clutch assembly with clean hands, and to wipe

down the pressure plate and flywheel faces with a clean rag before assembly begins.

27 Fit the friction plate with the greater projecting side of the hub facing away from the flywheel; there may also be a marking showing which way round the plate is to be refitted. On genuine Honda clutches the friction plate should be fitted with the TRANSMISSION SIDE marking facing towards the gearbox **(see illustration)**.

28 The Self-Adjusting Clutch (SAC)'s mechanism must now be reset before refitting the pressure plate. Note that a new pressure plate assembly may be supplied pre-set, in which case this procedure can be ignored; follow the instructions provided by the supplier carefully.

29 A large diameter bolt (M14 at least) long enough to pass through the pressure plate, a matching nut, and several large diameter washers, will be needed for this procedure. Mount the bolt head in the jaws of a sturdy bench vice, with one large washer fitted.

30 Offer the pressure plate over the bolt, friction plate surface facing down, and locate

it centrally over the bolt and washer – the washer should bear on the centre ring or hub **(see illustration)**.

31 Fit several further large washers over the bolt, so that they bear on the ends of the spring fingers, then add the nut and tighten by hand to locate the washers.

32 The purpose of the procedure is to turn the pressure plate's internal adjusting ring so that the three small coil springs visible on the pressure plate's outer surface are fully compressed. Tighten the nut just fitted until the adjusting ring is free to turn. Either push the adjusting ring with a screwdriver or use a pair of thin-nosed, or circlip, pliers in one of the windows in the top surface, opening the jaws of the pliers to turn the adjusting ring anti-clockwise, so that the springs are fully compressed **(see illustration)**.

33 Hold the adjusting ring in this position, then unscrew the centre nut. Once the nut is released, the adjusting ring will be gripped in position, and the screwdriver or pliers can be removed. Take the pressure plate from the vice, and it is ready to fit **(see illustration)**.

6.32...by tightening the nut so that the adjusting ring can be moved anti-clockwise until the small coil springs are fully compressed

6.33 Hold the adjusting ring and unscrew the nut so that the adjusting ring is gripped in position and the pressure plate is ready to fit

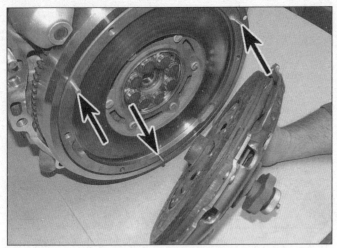

6.35a Refit the pressure plate assembly, aligning the marks made on dismantling

6.35b Use a clutch-aligning tool to centralise the friction plate on the crankshaft

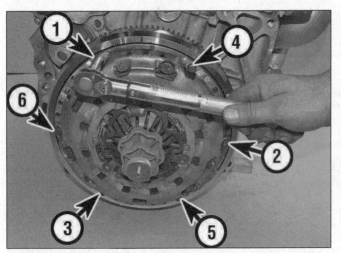

6.35c Tighten the pressure plate bolts evenly in a diagonal pattern. Tighten them in several stages, by half a turn at a time

7.3 Use a screwdriver to slip one leg of the release fork spring clear of the pivot

34 If the Honda special tools are available, fit the pressure plate compressor/flywheel holding tool to the engine/gearbox mounting bolt holes and the clutch alignment arbor and adapter to the pressure plate assembly to centralise the friction plate, then tighten down the compressor's centre screw to compress the diaphragm spring and lock the Self-Adjusting Clutch (SAC) mechanism.

35 When the friction plate is centralised, tighten the pressure plate bolts evenly – in several stages, by half a turn at a time – and in a star pattern to the specified torque setting. Ensure the pressure plate is drawn squarely onto the flywheel, to prevent the pressure plate being distorted and the setting of the Self-Adjusting Clutch (SAC)'s mechanism being lost **(see illustrations)**.

36 Refit the gearbox as described in Chapter 7A.

Note: *The Self-Adjusting Clutch (SAC)'s adjusting ring should be heard moving into place when the diaphragm spring's pressure is relaxed for the first time. As soon as the transmission and clutch components have been refitted and the clutch hydraulic system has been (if necessary) bled, ensure that there is quiet as the clutch pedal is depressed for the first time; a 'buzz' should be heard as the mechanism rotates into place.*

7 Clutch release bearing and fork – removal, inspection and refitting

Removal

1 Access to the clutch release bearing may be gained in one of two ways. Either the engine/transmission assembly can be removed as described in Chapter 2D, and the transmission then separated from the engine, or the engine may be left in the car and the transmission removed independently as described in Chapter 7A.

2 Remove the release fork dust boot, noting how it is fitted.

3 Disengage the release fork spring from the ball-stud pivot. Either use a pair of pliers to compress together the ends of the spring inside the fork so that they can be slipped out of the retaining slots in the fork, or use the tip of a screwdriver to slip one leg of the release fork spring clear of the head of the pivot **(see illustration)**. Withdraw the release fork from the bellhousing, noting which way around the release fork and spring are fitted.

4 Slide the release bearing off the gearbox shaft guide sleeve and withdraw it.

Inspection

5 Check the release mechanism, renewing any component which is worn or damaged. Carefully check all bearing surfaces and points of contact.

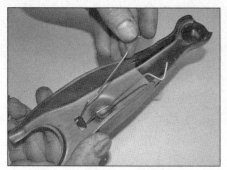

7.8a Fit the spring...

7.8b...and lubricate the pivot

6 When checking the release bearing itself, note that it is packed with grease and so should not be washed in solvent; wipe it clean with a paper towel or rag before examining it. Note also that it is often considered worthwhile to renew the release bearing as a matter of course. Check that the contact surface rotates smoothly and easily, with no sign of noise or roughness, and that the surface itself is smooth and unworn, with no signs of cracks, pitting or scoring. If there is any doubt about its condition, the bearing must be renewed.

Refitting

7 Ensure all components are clean and dry then grease sparingly the contact areas of the release fork (slave cylinder pushrod and ball-stud pivot), the bore of the release bearing and the gearbox shaft guide sleeve, and the splines of the friction plate and the gearbox input shaft; Honda recommend Urea Grease UM264 (Part No. 41211-PY5-305).

8 Fit the spring to the release fork **(see illustrations)**.

9 Engage the tips of the release fork behind the retaining ears of the release bearing's operating arms, then offer up the two together so that the release bearing fits over the gearbox shaft guide sleeve and the release fork passes through the aperture in the bellhousing **(see illustrations)**.

10 Press the release fork on to its ball-stud pivot so that the spring clips over the ball-stud's head **(see illustrations)**.

11 Fit the release fork dust boot, ensuring that it seats correctly in the bellhousing aperture and seals fully around the fork **(see illustration)**.

12 Check the operation of the release mechanism then wipe off any surplus grease.

13 Refit the gearbox as described in Chapter 7A.

7.9a Fit the release arm in to the bell housing...

7.9b...and then locate the release bearing on the arm

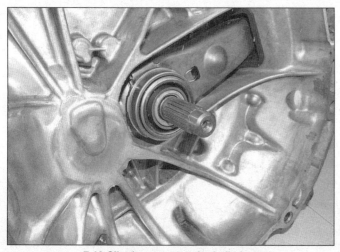

7.10 Clip the arm over the ball pivot

7.11 Fit the sealing boot over the release arm

Notes

Chapter 7 Part A
Manual transmission

Contents

Section number

General information 1
Driveshaft oil seals – renewal 2
Gearchange mechanism and cables – removal and refitting 3
Reverse light switch – removal and refitting 4

Section number

Reverse lockout solenoid – removal, testing and refitting 5
Gearbox – removal and refitting 6
Gearbox overhaul – general information 7

Degrees of difficulty

Easy, suitable for novice with little experience	**Fairly easy,** suitable for beginner with some experience	**Fairly difficult,** suitable for competent DIY mechanic	**Difficult,** suitable for experienced DIY mechanic	**Very difficult,** suitable for expert DIY or professional

Specifications

Torque wrench settings

Bell housing bolts	64	47
Clutch cover bracket	12	9
Gearbox mounting bolts (on transmission)*	59	43
Gear shift cable barcket	27	20
Reverse light switch	29	21
Reverse lock out solenoid	12	9

* Use new nuts/bolts

1 General information

1 The transmission is contained in a cast-aluminium alloy casing bolted to the engine's left-hand end, and consists of the gearbox and final drive differential.
2 Drive is transmitted from the crankshaft via the clutch to the input shaft, which has a splined extension to accept the clutch friction disc, and rotates in tapered roller bearings. From the input shaft, drive is transmitted to the output shaft, which also rotates in tapered roller bearings. From the output shaft, the drive is transmitted to the differential crownwheel, which rotates with the differential case and planetary gears, thus driving the sun gears and driveshafts. The rotation of the

planetary gears on their shaft allows the inner roadwheel to rotate at a slower speed than the outer roadwheel when the car is cornering.
3 The input and output shafts are arranged side-by-side, parallel to the crankshaft and driveshafts, so that their gear pinion teeth are in constant mesh. In the neutral position, the output shaft gear pinions rotate freely, so that drive cannot be transmitted to the crownwheel.
4 Gear selection is via a floor-mounted lever with a cable linkage. The selector linkage causes the appropriate selector fork to move its respective synchro-sleeve along the shaft, to lock the gear pinion to the synchro-hub. Since the synchro-hubs are splined to the output shaft, this locks the pinion to the shaft, so that drive can be transmitted. To ensure that gearchanging can be made quickly and quietly, a synchromesh system is fitted to all forward gears, consisting

of baulk rings and spring-loaded fingers, as well as the gear pinions and synchro-hubs. The synchromesh cones are formed on the mating faces of the baulk rings and gear pinions.

2 Driveshaft oil seals – renewal

1 Oil leaks frequently occur due to wear of the driveshaft oil seals. Renewal of these seals is relatively easy, since the repair can usually be performed without removing the transmission from the car.
2 Driveshaft oil seals are located at the sides of the transmission, where the driveshafts are attached. If leakage at the seal is suspected, raise the car and support it securely on axle stands (see '*Jacking and vehicle support*' in

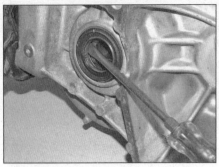

2.4 Prise out the old seal with a lever or scredriver

3.2a Prise open the spring clip and...

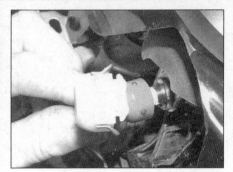

3.2b...release the inner cable

the Reference chapter). If the seal is leaking, lubricant will be found on the sides of the transmission, below the seals.

3 Refer to Chapter 8 and remove the driveshaft(s).

4 Use a screwdriver or lever bar to carefully prise the oil seal out of the transmission casing **(see illustration)**.

5 Using a large section of pipe or a large deep socket (slightly smaller than the outside diameter of the seal) as a drift, fit the new oil seal. Ensure that the spring side of the seal faces into the transmission casing. Drive it into the bore squarely and make sure it's completely seated. Coat the seal lip with transmission fluid.

6 Refit the driveshaft(s). Be careful not to damage the lip of the new seal.

3 Gearchange mechanism and cables – removal and refitting

Removal

1 Remove the the centre console as described in Chapter 11 Section 26.

2 At the base of the gear lever assembly prise open the circlip and release the inner gear shift cable **(see illustrations)**. Repeat the procedure for the other cable.

3 To release the outer cables rotate the locking collar anti-clockwise and slide the outer cable from the slot in the gear lever housing **(see illustrations)**.

4 Open the bonnet and remove the air filter housing as described in Chapter 4A or

Chapter 4B. Additional working space can be made if the battery and battery tray are also removed (Chapter 5A).

5 Working around the wiring loom remove the split pins from the inner cables **(see illustration)**. Recover the washers.

6 Prise up the spring clips from the outer cables **(see illustrations)**. Alternatively remove the cable mounting bracket by undoing the bolts.

7 Jack up and support the front of the vehicle – see 'Jacking and vehicle support' in the Reference chapter.

8 Working underneath the vehicle unbolt the cable support bracket and then remove the nuts from the gasket at the front of the transmission tunnel. Remove the cables from the vehicle.

9 If required the gear lever housing can now be removed.

3.3a Rotate the collar...

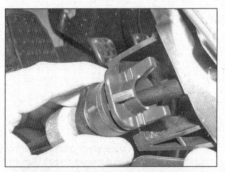

3.3b...and slide out the cable

3.5 Remove the split pins

3.6a Prise up and then...

3.6b...remove the spring clip

3.6c Remove the cable

4.9 Disconnect the wiring plug

5.4 The reverse lock out solenoid (diesel model)

Refitting

10 Refitting is a reversal of removal.
a) *Lightly grease the cable end fittings, at both the gearbox and gearchange lever/ mechanism ends, when refitting; Honda recommend Urea Grease UM264 (Part No. 41211-PY5-305).*
b) *Ensure that the cables are correctly refitted, and routed as before, with no sharp bends.*
c) *On completion, check that all gears can be selected properly before taking the vehicle out on the road.*

4 Reverse light switch – removal and refitting

Testing

1 Put the gear lever in reverse, and turn the ignition switch to the ON (II) position. The reversing lights should go on. Turn off the ignition switch.
2 If the reversing lights don't go on, check the fuses and the the light bulb in the tail light assembly (see Chapter 12).
3 If the fuse and bulbs are both sound, the reversing light switch on the gearbox should be checked. It is located at the front of the gearbox close to the clutch slave cylinder hydraulic pipe. As required, gain access to the switch by removing the air filter assembly as described in Chapter 4A or Chapter 4B.
4 Disconnect the switch wiring plug.
5 A multi-meter set to Ohms will be required. With the gear lever in reverse, there should be continuity between the terminals. With the lever in any other gear, there should be no continuity.
6 If the switch fails this test, renew it (see below).
7 If the switch is good, but there are still no reversing lights, check for power to the switch. If voltage is not available, trace the circuit between the switch and the fuse panel. If power is present, trace the circuit between the switch and the reversing lights for an open-circuit condition.

Renewal

8 If not already done, gain access to the switch as described. Before working on any part of the vehicle's electrical systems, it is advisable to disconnect the battery negative (earth) lead (see *Disconnecting the battery* 5A).
9 A large deep socket or spanner will be needed to unscrew the switch. Disconnect the wiring plug **(see illustration)** and remove the switch.
10 Refitting is a reversal of removal, but replace the sealing washer and tighten the switch to the specified torque. Test the operation of the lights on completion.

5 Reverse lockout solenoid – removal, testing and refitting

1 A reverse lockout solenoid is fitted to all manual transmission models covered by this manual. At speeds of 12 mph or more the solenoid is activated and reverse gear can not be selected. At speeds of less than 12 mph or with the ignition turned off, reverse gear can be selected.

Removal

2 The solenoid is mounted on top of the gearbox. On petrol gearboxes remove the air filter housing (Chapter 4A). On diesel models remove the battery and battery tray as described in Chapter 5A.

6.2a Remove the battery tray (diesel model shown)

3 If working on the diesel model, jack up and support the front of the vehicle (see *'Jacking and vehicle support'* in the Reference chapter) and then remove the engine undershield. Support the transmission and then remove the gearbox mounting as described in Chapter 2C.
4 Disconnect the wiring plug and remove the mounting bolts **(see illustration)**. Withdraw the solenoid from the gearbox. On diesel models recover the actuator pin and spring.

Refitting

5 Refitting is a reversal of removal, but clean the mating surface and apply a bead of sealant. Use Honda 08C70-K0334M, or a commercially available equivalent. If using Honda's own sealant the solenoid must be fitted within 5 minutes of applying. Tighten the bolts to the specified torque.

6 Gearbox – removal and refitting

Removal

1 Open the bonnet and remove the windscreen cowl panels as described in Chapter 12.
2 Remove the air filter housing as described in Chapter 4A or Chapter 4B **(see illustrations)** and then remove the battery and battery tray as described in Chapter 5A.
3 Disconnect the wiring plugs from the reverse light, the lockout solenoid and the vehicle speed sensor. On early 1.4 litre engines disconnect the oxygen sensor wiring plug. Unclip and unbolt the wiring loom from the gearbox.
4 Trace the clutch slave cylinder fluid pipe back from the cylinder to the fluid hose union, and unbolt the pipe/union support bracket. Unclip the pipe from the top of the transmission. Remove the two slave cylinder mounting bolts, and move the cylinder clear of the transmission, if possible without bending the pipe. Secure the slave cylinder and hose to the side.
Caution: Be careful not to bend or kink the clutch hydraulic pipe, and don't depress

6.2b The air filter inlet duct must be removed

6.5 Remove the cable support bracket

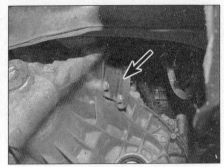

6.6 Unbolt the support bracket

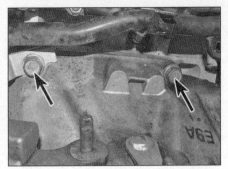

6.8 Remove the upper mounting bolts

the clutch pedal while the slave cylinder is removed.

5 Remove the split pin and washers securing the cable ends to the transmission levers, and disconnect the cables. Unscrew the bolts securing the gearchange cable bracket to the top of the transmission, then move the whole assembly to one side, taking care not to bend the cables **(see illustration)**.

6 Remove the air filter housing support bracket **(see illustration)**.

7 As no lifting eye is provided, then a suitable one must be fabricated. Remove the engine breather hose from the end of the cylinder head and fit a suitable bracket to the air filter mounting. An M8 bolt will be required.

8 Loosen the transmission to engine bolts which are accessible from above **(see illustration)**.

9 Loosen the front wheel nuts, and if possible, also loosen both driveshaft nuts while the car is still on the ground. Jack up the front of the car, and support it on axle stands (see '*Jacking and vehicle support*' in the Reference chapter). Note that the car must be raised sufficiently high for the transmission to be lowered out and withdrawn from underneath. Remove the front wheels and the engine undertray.

10 Drain the transmission fluid as described in Chapter 1A or Chapter 1B.

11 Remove the driveshafts as described in Chapter 8.

12 On diesel models only, remove the subframe as described in Chapter 10.

13 At the base of the bell housing, remove the bolts and take off the small cover plate from below the flywheel **(see illustration)**.

14 Unbolt and remove the engine rear mounting (torque rod). The engine will still be supported by the main left and right-hand engine mountings.

15 The engine must now be supported from above. Honda specify the use of an 'H' shape support bar. This has a leg at each side that rests on the strut tower and bonnet slam panel. A third beam rests on theses legs and over the engine. The engine is then supported from this beam. As this tool (or commercial equivalent) is unlikely to be available to the home mechanic and alternative method of supporting the engine will be required.

16 The safest way for the home mechanic to support the engine whilst the transmission is removed is to use an engine crane. Note however that the legs of the crane must be positioned so that the gearbox can be supported from below whilst it is removed from the engine.

17 Install the engine crane and take the weight of the engine and gearbox assembly.

18 Remove the left-hand gearbox mounting **(see illustrations)** as described in Chapter 2A, Chapter 2B or Chapter 2C.

19 Support the transmission from below, using a jack and a flat piece of wood. Have an assistant ready to support the transmission as the jack is lowered. Slowly lower the engine crane and jack so that the transmission clears the bodywork.

20 Unscrew the remaining transmission to engine bolts, then carefully pull the transmission away from the engine until the transmission shaft is clear of the clutch pressure plate. If necessary, carefully prise the transmission away at first, to release the alignment dowels **(see illustration)**. Do not allow the weight of the transmission to hang on the input shaft (support the unit until it is completely clear of the engine).

21 Check round the transmission that everything has been disconnected from it, and that there is nothing in the way which might hinder its removal.

22 With the help of an assistant to guide the unit out, lower the transmission on the jack until it can be removed from under the car **(see illustration)**. Recover the two dowel pins, noting their fitted locations, and store them for safekeeping.

6.13 Remove the flywheel cover plate

6.18a Remove the left-hand mounting and...

6.18b...then remove the mounting base from the gearbox

6.20 Pull the gearbox away from the engine

Refitting

23 If removed, fit the clutch components (see Chapter 6). It is recommended that the clutch components are at least inspected, if not renewed, while the transmission is removed.

24 If the clutch components were not removed, clean the transmission input shaft splines. Lubricate the splines with oil or the recommended lubricant. Do NOT use a multi-purpose grease.

25 Make sure the two locating dowels are installed in the transmission mating face.

26 Raise the transmission on the jack, then use the alignment marks made on dismantling to align it with the engine.

27 Make sure the transmission is at the right height, then slide it onto the engine so that the transmission shaft enters the clutch. It may be necessary to 'wiggle' the transmission slightly, to align the shaft splines with those of the clutch – if great difficulty is experienced when new clutch components have been fitted, it may mean that the clutch disc has not been centred (see Chapter 6). With the splines aligned, the transmission should slide onto the two dowels, and fully up to the engine.

28 While your assistant holds the transmission in place, insert two or three transmission-to-engine bolts initially, and tighten them fully by hand to hold the unit fully onto the dowels.

29 Further refitting is a reversal of removal, noting the following points:

a) *As far as possible, fit all engine/ transmission mounting bolts hand-tight only at first. Delay fully tightening the engine/transmission mounting bolts until the weight of the engine is resting on its mountings.*

b) *Tighten all nuts/bolts to the specified torque.*

c) *On diesel models, refer to Chapter 10 when refitting the subframe – new subframe bolts must be used. Also, ensure that the appropriate new nuts and locking/ split pins are used when reconnecting the steering/suspension components.*

d) *Lightly grease the gearchange cable end fittings and slave cylinder pushrod end when refitting.*

e) *Refill the transmission with fluid as described in Chapter 1A or 1B.*

f) *Check the operation of the clutch, and bleed the system if necessary as described in Chapter 6.*

g) *Where the subframe was removed, have the front wheel alignment checked at the earliest opportunity.*

7 Gearbox overhaul – general information

1 Overhauling a manual transmission is a difficult and involved job for the home mechanic. In addition to dismantling and reassembling many small parts, clearances must be precisely measured and, if necessary, changed by selecting shims and spacers. Internal transmission components are also often difficult to obtain, and in many instances, extremely expensive. Because of this, if the transmission develops a fault or becomes noisy, the best course of action is to have the unit overhauled by a specialist repairer, or to obtain an exchange reconditioned unit.

2 Nevertheless, it is not impossible for the

6.22 Lower the transmission

more experienced mechanic to overhaul the transmission, provided the special tools are available, and the job is done in a deliberate step-by-step manner, so that nothing is overlooked.

3 The tools necessary for an overhaul include internal and external circlip pliers, bearing pullers, a slide hammer, a set of pin punches, a dial test indicator, and possibly a hydraulic press. In addition, a large, sturdy workbench and a vice will be required.

4 During dismantling of the transmission, make careful notes of how each component is fitted, to make reassembly easier and more accurate.

5 Before dismantling the transmission, it will help if you have some idea what area is malfunctioning. Certain problems can be closely related to specific areas in the transmission, which can make component examination and renewal easier. Refer to the Fault finding Section of this manual for more information.

Chapter 7 Part B
Automatic transmission

Contents

Section number

Fault finding – general 2
General information 1
Interlock system – component renewal 6
Selector cable – renewal and adjustment 4

Section number

Selector lever – removal and refitting. 3
Transmission – removal and refitting 7
Transmission range switch – renewal and adjustment. 5

Degrees of difficulty

Easy, suitable for novice with little experience	Fairly easy, suitable for beginner with some experience	Fairly difficult, suitable for competent DIY mechanic	Difficult, suitable for experienced DIY mechanic	Very difficult, suitable for expert DIY or professional

Specifications

Lubrication

Transmission fluid. . . . . Honda ATF-Z1
Capacity:
    At fluid change . . . . 2.4 litres
    At overhaul . . . . 5.75 litres

Torque wrench settings

Bell housing bolts.	64	47
Drain plug.	49	36
Fluid cooler bolts	26	20
Gear selector cable:		
At transmission.	14	10
At gear lever	22	16
Transmission mounting bracket*	59	43
Torque converter bolts	12	9

Use new nut/bolts

1 General information

1 The automatic transmission fitted to the Honda Civic is a five speed, electronically controlled transmission of Honda's own design. All gear selection is controlled by the engine management Power Control Module (PCM) in response to the information gathered by the various engine sensors. Manual selection of the correct gear is also possible via the gear selection lever.

2 Internally the transmission has more in common with a traditional manual transmission, rather then a conventional automatic transmission. The gears are mounted on shafts (a mainshaft, a countershaft and a secondary shaft) and gear changes are made by hydraulically controlled wet clutches. Seven PCM controlled solenoids control the operation of the clutches, hydraulic pressure and the torque converter lock-up.

3 The lock-up mechanism operates on all forward gears. When commanded by the PCM pressurised fluid is drained from the torque converter and the internal clutch effectively locks the crankshaft, torque converter and mainshaft together in a single unit. Locking the transmission eliminates pump loses and improves efficiency.

4 A safety interlock is fitted that prevents

the vehicle starting in any gear other than N (Neutral) or P (Park). In the event of a fault with the system the locking solenoid can be disengaged with the uses of the vehicle key (as described in Section 6)

5 The gear shift lever has seven available positions:

P (Park)	The front wheels are locked mechanically via the park pawl gear
R (Reverse)	The 5th clutch and the reverse selector are engaged
N (Neutral)	All clutches released
D (Drive)	Normal driving position. The transmission shift up (and down) as conditions dictate
D3 (Drive)	Used for fast acceleration. 1st, 2nd and 3rd gears only. The lock-up only operates in 3rd gear.
2 (Second)	Stays in second, Used for improved traction on loose surfaces.
1 (First)	Stays in first. Used for engine braking.

6 Because of the need for special test equipment, the complexity of many parts, and the need for scrupulous cleanliness when servicing the transmission, the amount which the owner can do is limited. Repairs to the final drive differential are also not recommended. Most major repairs and overhaul operations should be left to a Honda dealer or specialist, who will have the necessary equipment for fault diagnosis and repair. The information in this Chapter is therefore limited to removal and refitting of the transmission as a complete unit

7 In the event of a transmission problem occurring, consult a Honda dealer or transmission specialist before removing the transmission from the car, since the majority of fault diagnosis is carried out with the transmission in situ.

2 Fault finding – general

Note: *Automatic transmission malfunctions may be caused by five general conditions: poor engine performance, improper adjustments, hydraulic malfunctions, mechanical malfunctions or malfunctions in the computer or its signal network. Diagnosis of these problems should always begin with a check of the easily-repaired items: fluid level and condition (see Chapter 1A), and selector cable adjustment (Section 3). Next, perform a road test to determine if the problem has been corrected or if more diagnosis is necessary. If the problem persists after the preliminary*

tests and corrections are completed, additional diagnosis should be done by a dealer service department or transmission specialist.

Preliminary checks

1 Drive the vehicle to warm the transmission to normal operating temperature.
2 Check the fluid level as described in Chapter 1A:
a) *If the fluid level is unusually low, add enough fluid to bring the level within the designated area of the dipstick, then check for external leaks (see below).*
b) *If the fluid level is abnormally high, drain off the excess, then check the drained fluid for contamination by coolant. The presence of engine coolant in the automatic transmission fluid indicates that a failure has occurred in the internal radiator walls that separate the coolant from the transmission fluid.*
c) *If the fluid is foaming, drain it and refill the transmission, then check for coolant in the fluid, or a high fluid level.*
3 Check the engine idle speed. If the engine is malfunctioning, do not proceed with the preliminary checks until it has been repaired and runs normally.
4 Inspect the selector cable linkage (see Section 4). Make sure that it's properly adjusted and that the linkage operates smoothly.

Fluid leak diagnosis

5 Most fluid leaks are easy to locate visually. Repair usually consists of renewing a seal or gasket. If a leak is difficult to find, the following procedure may help.
6 Identify the fluid. Make sure it's transmission fluid and not engine oil or brake fluid (automatic transmission fluid is typically a deep red colour).
7 Try to pinpoint the source of the leak. Drive the vehicle several miles, then park it over a large sheet of cardboard. After a minute or two, you should be able to locate the leak by determining the source of the fluid dripping onto the cardboard.
8 Make a careful visual inspection of the suspected component and the area immediately around it. Pay particular attention to gasket mating surfaces. A mirror is often helpful for finding leaks in areas that are hard to see.
9 If the leak still cannot be found, clean the suspected area thoroughly with a degreaser, then dry it.
10 Drive the vehicle for several miles at normal operating temperature and varying speeds. After driving the vehicle, visually inspect the suspected component again.
11 Once the leak has been located, the cause must be determined before it can be properly repaired. If a gasket is renewed but

the sealing flange is bent, the new gasket will not stop the leak. The bent flange must be straightened.
12 Before attempting to repair a leak, check to make sure that the following conditions are corrected or they may cause another leak. **Note:** *Some of the following conditions cannot be fixed without highly specialised tools and expertise. Such problems must be referred to a transmission specialist or a dealer service department.*

Fault diagnosis

13 Should a fault be recognised by the engine management system's Electronic Control Unit (ECU), a fault code will be generated and stored in the unit's memory, and the 'D' indicator on the instrument panel's transmission display will flash.
14 First ensure that all the system wiring connectors are securely connected and free of corrosion.
15 If these checks fail to reveal the cause of the problem, the vehicle should be taken to a Honda dealer or suitably equipped garage for testing. A diagnostic socket is incorporated in the wiring harness, into which dedicated electronic test equipment can be plugged – the connector is located under the driver's side of the facia.
16 Fault codes can only be extracted from the ECU using a dedicated fault code reader. A Honda dealer will have such a reader, but they are also available from other suppliers. Note however that only Honda's HDS (Honda Diagnostic System) factory scan tool will have the complete ability to interrogate the ECU, identify faults and if necessary update the system software. After market diagnostic equipment will have some of the functionality of the official factory tool, but will not (especially where the automatic transmission is concerned) have the full capability of the official Honda tool.
17 Using this equipment in the hands of a skilled technician, faults can be pinpointed quickly. Testing all the system components individually in an attempt to locate the fault by elimination is a time consuming operation that is unlikely to be fruitful (particularly if the fault occurs dynamically), and carries a high risk of damage to the ECU's internal components.

Clearing fault codes

18 Once the fault has been identified and the problem corrected (usually by fitting a new component), the fault code must be cleared. In some cases, this will happen automatically once the ignition has been switched on and off enough times – if the fault does not recur, it may clear itself.
19 If the fault has been repaired and the fault code remains (the 'D' is still flashing) then before connecting diagnostic equipment

then it is always worth disconnecting the battery and leaving it disconnected for at least an hour. If this fails to clear the fault codes, then diagnostic equipment will need to be connected to both clear and check for additional fault codes.

3 Selector lever – removal and refitting

1 Disconnect the battery as described in Chapter 5A.
2 Remove the rear section of the centre console as described in Chapter 11 and then prise free the locking ring from the gear indicator panel.
3 Lift off the gear position indicator panel and then remove the front section of the centre console.
4 Working in the passenger foot well prise out the clip and remove the air distribution duct.
5 Remove the lock nut from the end of the shift cable and then open the locking catch on the main cable (outer) housing. Rotate the collar anti-clockwise until it stops and then retain it in this position by engaging the locking catch **(see illustration)**.
6 Push the collar forward and then slide it from the slot in the selector lever housing. Do not remove the the cable by pulling (or pushing) on the inner cable guide.
7 Disconnect the wiring plugs from the inter lock solenoid and the panel illumination.
8 Release the wiring loom and then remove the selector lever mounting bolts. Remove the selector lever.
9 Refitting is a reversal of removal, but ensure the inner cable is fitted to the base of the gear shift correctly – the cable retaining bolt has a square section and that must engage correctly with the square section of the inner cable. Check and if necessary adjust the cable as described in Section 4.

4 Selector cable – renewal and adjustment

Renewal

1 Disconnect the battery and then remove the selector cable at the gear shift lever as described in Section 3.
2 Jack up and support the front of the vehicle – see '*Jacking and vehicle support*' in the Reference chapter. Remove the engine undershield.
3 Remove the cable protective cover at the transmission and then unbolt the outer cable retaining bracket. Prise up the lock washer tab and then remove the bolt. Remove the cable from the control lever.
4 Remove the heat shield and then unbolt the cable support bracket. Note that it is held in place by a single nut – the cut-out that fits over the stud does not have a nut fitted by design.
5 Remove the three nuts that retain the cable grommet and then pull out the cable.

6 Refitting is reversal of removal, but use a new lock washer and check and adjust the cable as described below.

Adjustment

7 Turn the ignition on and select 'R' on the display. With the lever in the reverse position a 6.0 mm drill bit should pass easily through the guide hole in the side of the selector lever assembly and into the base of the lever. Remove the drill bit and cycle through the gears – the selector lever display should correspond to the instrument panel display.
8 If adjustment is required, slacken the inner cable retaining nut and adjust the position of the selector lever so that 'R' is diaplayed at the lever and the drill bit fits easily. Check that the outer cable is positioned correctly and then slide the inner cable back until 'R' is displayed on the instrument panel.
9 Turn the ignition off and tighten the inner cable lock nut. Not that the bolt has a square section under the bolt head and this must engage correctly with the slot in the inner cable end. Remove the drill bit, turn the ignition on and check that the indicators on the lever gear selection panel correspond to the gear position high lighted on the instrument panel.
10 Refit the remaining components in reverse order to removal.

5 Transmission range switch – renewal and adjustment

Renewal

1 Remove the air cleaner as described in Chapter 4A.
2 Remove the battery and its tray as described in Chapter 5A.
3 Move the selector lever to the N position.
4 The transmission range switch is located on the end of the transmission. Jack up and support the front of the vehicle (see '*Jacking and vehicle support*' in the Reference chapter and then remove the engine undershield.
5 Remove the protective cover and then disconnect the wiring plug.
6 If the same switch is to be refitted, mark its fitted position relative to the transmission – this will make refitting and adjustment easier.
7 Unscrew the two switch mounting bolts, and lift it off its shaft.
8 Before refitting the switch, ensure that the shaft on the transmission is in the N position – this should be the case if the selector lever inside the car is also in the N position.
9 The switch has to be 'aligned with itself' before fitting – the centre part (which turns) has to align with the switch body. Using a 2.0 mm thick feeler blade across the face of the switch, align the two slots in the centre of

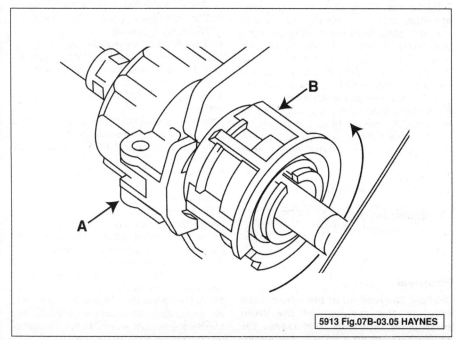

3.5 Release the cable by first releasing the catch (A). Rotate the collar (B) and re-engage the catch (A) to lock it into position

5913 Fig.07B-03.05 HAYNES

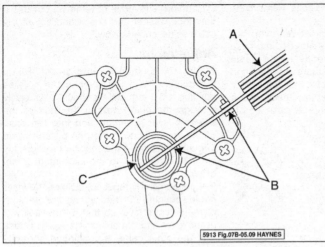

5.9 Align the range switch

A: 2 mm feeler gauge
B: Cut outs in the switch

C: Cut outs in the rotary
section of the switch

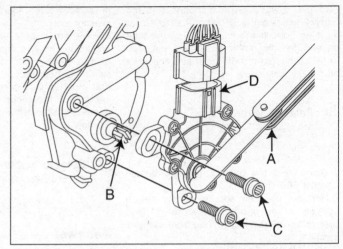

5.10 Hold the feeler gauge firmly in position whilst installing the switch

A: Feeler gauge
B: Control shaft

C: Adjustment screws
D: Switch

the switch with the slots on the edge of the switch body, just above one of the slotted mounting holes (see illustration).

10 Keeping the switch aligned in this position and offer it carefully onto the transmission shaft (see illustration).

11 With the feeler blade still holding the switch aligned, tighten the two switch mounting bolts securely.

12 Reconnect the wiring plug, then clip on the switch cover.

13 Refit the components removed for access.

14 Turn the ignition on, then move the selector lever through all positions, and check that the instrument panel display follows the selected gear.

15 Check that the engine can only be started in positions P or N, and that the reversing lights come on when R is selected.

Adjustment

16 To adjust the switch, follow the renewal procedure, with the exception that the switch does not have to be removed – for adjustment only, the switch mounting bolts need only be loosened.

6 Interlock system – component renewal

1 If the system is faulty first check the fuses in the under dashboard fuse box. The relevant fuses to check are fuses No 10 and No 35. Both are 7.5 amp fuses.

2 If the shift lever can not be moved out of the 'P' (Park) position it is possible to override the interlock. Remove the cover from the access point next to the gear selector lever. Insert the ignition key and press down on it and then, press in the gear selector lever and move the lever to the 'N' (Neutral) position.

3 To access the inter lock components, remove the selector lever assembly as described in Section 3.

4 There are two components to the interlock assembly at the gear selector assembly:
The park switch.
The shift lock solenoid.

5 The park lock switch whilst separate, is part of the gear position indicator panel and is replaced with the gear indicator panel.

6 With the lever assembly on the bench remove the two screws and lift off the shift lever knob. Discard the screws as Honda recommend that they are replaced.

7 Unclip the wiring loom from the lever assembly and then release the position indicator panel from the main body of the lever. Move the indicator panel up the gear lever and then unclip and remove the shift lock extension (RHD models only). Unscrew the micro switch and lift the assembly up and over the gear lever (see illustration).

8 The shift lock solenoid is removed by releasing the locking tabs. Lift the switch up, disconnect the wiring plug and recover the solenoid, plunger and spring (see illustration 6.7).

9 Refitting is a reversal of removal. Refit the gear shift lever assembly to the vehicle.

7 Transmission – removal and refitting

Removal

Caution: The removal of the transmission requires the removal of the front suspension subframe. This leaves the engine hanging on a hoist in the engine compartment and located only by the engine right-hand mounting. Great care will be required to minimise the risk of personal injury and of expensive component damage.

1 Remove the windscreen wiper arms and then remove the upper and lower windscreen cowl panels as described in Chapter 12.

2 Remove the air cleaner assembly and intake air duct as described in Chapter 4A.

3 From the top of the transmission, unplug their connectors and free the wiring harnesses from the retaining brackets as necessary to disconnect the following:
a) The clutch pressure solenoid
b) The remaining solenoid valves
c) The earth terminal
d) The loom retaining bracket form the air filter housing bracket
e) The transmission range switch
f) The speed sensor (from the countershaft)
g) The speed sensor (from the mainshaft)
h) The clutch pressure sensor

4 Remove the air filter housing mounting bracket.

5 Jack up and support the front of the vehicle (see 'Jacking and vehicle support' in the Reference chapter) and the remove both front road wheels

6 Remove the engine undershield.

7 Drain the transmission fluid as described in Chapter 1A.

8 Have a suitable container ready and then release the hose clips and disconnect the fluid hoses from the oil cooler metal fluid pipes. Plug or tape over the open connections.

9 Unbolt the oil cooler – there is no need to disconnect the coolant hoses. Secure the cooler out of harms way.

10 At the front of the transmission disconnect the wiring plugs from the shift solenoid and the clutch pressure switch. Unbolt (or unclip) and then remove the wiring loom.

11 The wiring loom must now be removed from the engine. Remove the engine cover

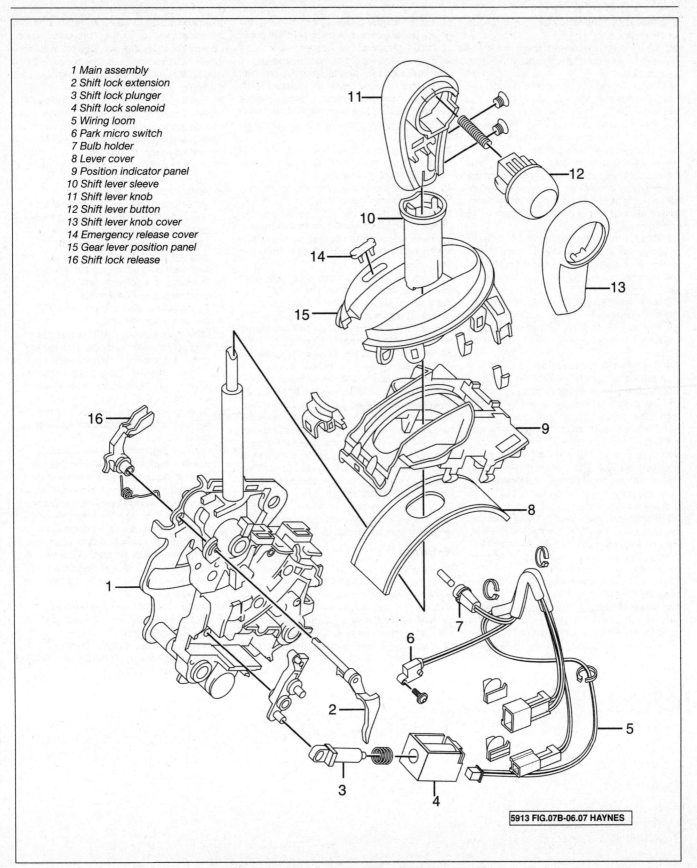

1 Main assembly
2 Shift lock extension
3 Shift lock plunger
4 Shift lock solenoid
5 Wiring loom
6 Park micro switch
7 Bulb holder
8 Lever cover
9 Position indicator panel
10 Shift lever sleeve
11 Shift lever knob
12 Shift lever button
13 Shift lever knob cover
14 Emergency release cover
15 Gear lever position panel
16 Shift lock release

5913 FIG.07B-06.07 HAYNES

6.7 The component parts of the gear shift lever assembly

and then unbolt the wiring loom from the top of the engine.

12 Disconnect the wiring plugs from the alternator and then disconnect the wiring plugs from the EGR valve and coolant temperature sensor etc. Disconnect the vacuum hose at the left-hand end of the engine.

13 Free the loom from the mounting bracket at the left-hand end of the cylinder head and then remove the mounting bracket.

14 A suitable bracket (lifting eye) must now be fabricated to support the engine whilst the transmission is removed. The bracket is fitted to the loom support bracket mounting point. Use a M8 bolt with a maximum length of 16 mm to mount the bracket.

15 Remove the front section of the exhaust system. Discard the gaskets as new ones must be used when refitting the exhaust pipe.

16 With reference to Chapter 2B, remove the rear engine torque rod.

17 With reference to Chapter 8, remove both front driveshafts.

18 Remove the steering rack mounting bolts and the steering rack stiffener plate (see Chapter 10).

19 Support the front subframe on a trolley jack (with a suitable block of wood to spread the load) and then remove the six subframe mounting bolts. Lower the subframe slightly and then secure the steering rack to the vehicle body. Fully lower the subframe and remove it from the vehicle.

20 Support the engine from the previously installed bracket. This should be done from above with an engine crane or support bar – supporting from below is possible, but will be awkward.

21 Disconnect the selector cable from the transmission as described in Section 4. Secure the cable clear of the transmission, taking care not to bend it any more than necessary..

22 Unbolt the torque converter cover plate from the base of the bell housing.

23 Before disturbing the torque converter, check for paint marks showing the relationship of the torque converter to the driveplate. If none can be found, make your own using chalk, touch-up paint or a marker pen. Unscrew and remove the eight torque

converter-to-driveplate bolts, turning the engine using a socket on the crankshaft pulley bolt to bring each of the bolts into view.

24 Support the weight of the transmission on a transmission jack or a large trolley jack and a flat piece of wood. Have an assistant ready to support the transmission as the jack is lowered. This is a heavy assembly, and it must be adequately supported while the mountings are removed.

25 Ensuring that the engine is securely supported, unscrew the engine/transmission left-hand mounting bracket.

26 Unscrew the two uppermost engine bell housing-to-transmission bolts.

27 Remove the lower bell housing bolts. Check round the transmission that everything has been disconnected from it, and that there is nothing in the way which might hinder its removal.

28 Carefully pull the transmission away from the engine until the transmission is clear of the locating dowels. If necessary, push the torque converter back into the transmission – take care that it does not fall out as the transmission is lowered.

29 With the help of the assistant to guide the unit out, lower the transmission on the jack and engine crane, until it can be removed from under the vehicle. Recover the two locating dowels, noting their fitted locations, and store them for safekeeping. Either remove the torque converter (in which case be prepared for significant fluid spillage when the torque converter is removed) or devise a method of keeping it inside the housing (such as bolting a metal strip across its face, secured through the bellhousing bolt holes).

30 If the transmission is being exchanged or renewed, unbolt any ancillary components remaining from the transmission.

Refitting

31 If the torque converter was removed, refit it using a new O-ring seal. Have an assistant ready to keep the converter pressed into the housing as the transmission is refitted.

32 Make sure the two locating dowels are installed in the transmission mating face.

33 Raise the transmission on the jack, then slide it onto the engine so that the torque converter seats against the driveplate; align

the marks made or noted on removal. It may be necessary to 'wiggle' the transmission slightly to align the two dowels with their locations in the engine bellhousing – with the dowels aligned, the transmission should slide fully up to the engine.

34 While your assistant holds the transmission in place, insert two or three engine bellhousing-to-transmission bolts initially, and tighten them fully by hand to hold the unit fully onto the dowels.

35 Further refitting is a reversal of removal, noting the following points:

a) As far as possible, fit all engine/ transmission mounting bolts hand-tight only at first. Delay fully tightening these bolts until the weight of the engine/ transmission unit is resting on its mountings and note that a particular sequence is to be followed to ensure that the unit is correctly settled on its mountings (see Chapter 2B).

b) Tighten all nuts/bolts to the specified torque wrench settings.

c) When reconnecting the fluid hose to the fluid cooler metal fluid pipe, position the clip 2 to 4 mm from the hose end.

d) Before tightening the torque converter-to-driveplate bolts, align the marks made on dismantling.

e) Refer to Section 4 when reconnecting the selector cable, and adjust the cable as described.

f) Refill the transmission with fluid as described in Chapter 1A. Note that the transmission may require more fluid than in a normal fluid change, since the torque converter may be empty (the converter is not drained during a fluid change).

g) On completion, start the engine. Allow the engine to reach its proper operating temperature with the transmission in P or N, then switch it off and check the fluid level. Road test the vehicle and check for fluid leaks.

h) As the front subframe was removed, have the front wheel alignment checked at the earliest opportunity.

i) On models fitted with HID (Xenon) headlights have the headlight aim checked and adjusted if necessary.

Chapter 8
Driveshafts

Contents

Section number

Driveshaft damper – removal and refitting 8
Driveshaft overhaul – general information 2
Driveshafts – removal and refitting 3
General Information 1

Section number

Inner constant velocity joint gaiter – renewal 6
Intermediate driveshaft – removal and refitting 4
Intermediate driveshaft support bearing – removal and refitting 7
Outer constant velocity joint gaiter – renewal 5

Degrees of difficulty

Easy, suitable for novice with little experience	Fairly easy, suitable for beginner with some experience	Fairly difficult, suitable for competent DIY mechanic	Difficult, suitable for experienced DIY mechanic	Very difficult, suitable for expert DIY or professional

Specifications

General

Driveshaft type . . . .   Equal-length solid-steel shafts, splined to inner and outer constant velocity joint. 1.8 litre petrol and diesel models have an intermediate shaft fitted to the right-hand side of the transmission
Outer constant velocity joint type . . . .   Ball-and-cage
Inner constant velocity joint type . . . .   Tripod

Lubrication

Lubricant type . . . .   Special grease supplied in repair kit, or suitable molybdenum disulphide grease.
CV joint grease capacity (approximate):
    Outboard joint 110-130g
    Inboard joint 155-175g

Torque wrench settings

	Nm	lbf
Anti-roll bar drop link nut	30	22
Driveshaft hub nut*	181	134
Intermediate driveshaft support bracket bolts	39	29
Roadwheel nuts	108	80
Track control arm ball joint nut**	73.5	54
Transmission drain plug	39	29
Transmission filler plug	44	33

*Use new nuts/bolts
** Use a new nut. Tighten to the specified torque and then tighten further
to align the castellated nut with the hole in the ball joint sank. Always fit a new spilt pin.

3.3 Release the locking tab

3.4 An alternative method of slackening the hub nut is to fabricate a simple tool that locates on the hub. Hold it in place with the wheel nuts

1 General Information

1 Drive is transmitted from the differential to the front wheels by means of two solid-steel driveshafts equipped with constant velocity (CV) joints at their inner and outer ends. All models have a dynamic damper fitted to the central section of the driveshaft. Diesel models and 1.8 petrol models have an intermediate shaft fitted to the right-hand side of the transmission. The shaft is supported by a bracket and bearing bolted to the rear of the engine block.

2 A ball-and-cage type CV joint is fitted to the outer end of each driveshaft. The joint has an outer member, which is splined at its outer end to accept the wheel hub, and is threaded so that it can be fastened to the hub by a large nut. The joint contains six balls within a cage, which engage with the inner member. The complete assembly is protected by a flexible gaiter secured to the driveshaft and joint outer member.

3 At the inner end, the driveshaft is splined

to engage a tripod type CV joint, containing needle roller bearings and cups. On the left-hand side, the driveshaft inner CV joint engages directly with the differential sun wheel. On diesel and 1.8 petrol models the right-hand side driveshaft connects to the intermediate shaft and the inner end of the intermediate driveshaft engages with the differential sun wheel. As on the outer joints, a flexible gaiter secured to the driveshaft and CV joint inner member protects the complete assembly.

2 Driveshaft overhaul – general information

1 Road test the car, and listen for a metallic clicking from the front as the car is driven slowly in a circle with the steering on full-lock. Repeat the check on full-left and full-right lock. This noise may also be apparent when pulling away from a standstill with lock applied. If a clicking noise is heard, this indicates wear in the outer constant velocity joints.

2 If vibration, consistent with road speed, is

felt through the car when accelerating, there is a possibility of wear in the inner constant velocity joints.

3 Driveshafts – removal and refitting

Removal

1 Firmly apply the handbrake and chock the rear wheels. Remove the wheel trim or centre cap. Note that on some models the wheel trim is held in place by the wheel nuts and can only be removed with the wheel. Loosen the front wheel nuts, then jack up the front of the car and support it on axle stands (see 'Jacking and vehicle support' in the Reference chapter). Remove the appropriate front roadwheel.

2 With reference to Chapters 1A or 1B, drain the transmission fluid. Refit the drain plug with a new washer and tighten to the specified torque.

3 Using a suitable punch or chisel free the locking tab from the driveshaft hub nut **(see illustration)**.

4 Refit the front wheel and then lower the vehicle to the ground. With the vehicle on the ground slacken (but do not remove) the driveshaft hub nut. Jack up the front of the car and support it on axle stands (see 'Jacking and vehicle support' in the Reference chapter). Remove the roadwheel **(see illustration)**.

Note: *Slackening the driveshaft hub nut with an assistant applying the foot brake is not recommended.*

5 Remove the previously-slackened driveshaft retaining nut **(see illustration)**. Discard the nut – a new one must be fitted.

6 Using a soft faced hammer, or a block of wood to protect the driveshaft, drive the end of the driveshaft approximately 15 to 20 mm into the wheel hub **(see illustration)**.

3.5 Remove the nut

3.6 Free the driveshaft by tapping it out of the swivel hub

3.7 Remove the anti-roll bar drop link

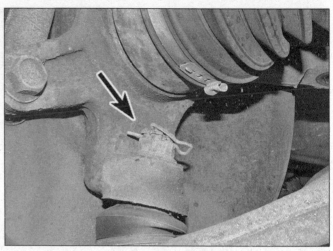

3.8a Remove the split pin

7 Use a hex key to counter hold the ball joint shank and then remove the anti-roll bar drop link lower mounting **(see illustration)**.

8 Remove the split pin from the castellated nut on the track control arm ball joint. Slacken the control arm balljoint nut until the end of the balljoint shank is level with the top of the nut **(see illustrations)**.

9 Detach the lower control arm balljoint from the swivel hub using a balljoint separator tool **(see illustration)**.

10 Push down on the control arm arm using a stout bar to release the balljoint shank from the swivel hub **(see illustration)**. Take care not to damage the balljoint dust cover during and after disconnection.

11 Swivel the suspension strut and hub assembly outwards and withdraw the driveshaft CV joint from the hub flange.

12 Carefully lever the inner end of the driveshaft from the transmission, using a large screwdriver or lever bar positioned between the transmission and the CV joint housing. The inner end of the shaft is secured with a circlip, which must be released – do not pull on the shaft, as the inner joint may separate. Support the CV joints and carefully remove the driveshaft from the car. To prevent damage to the driveshaft oil seal, hold the inner CV joint

3.8b Slacken the nut

3.9 Use a balljoint separator tool to detach the balljoint from the hub carrier

horizontal until the driveshaft is clear of the transmission **(see illustrations)**.

13 On models fitted with an intermediate driveshaft a drift should be used to release the main driveshaft from the intermediate driveshaft.

Refitting

14 Refitting is a reversal of removal, but observe the following points.

a) *Prior to refitting, remove all traces, rust, oil and dirt from the splines of the outer CV*

joint, and lubricate the splines of the inner joint with wheel bearing grease.

b) *Fit new circlips to the inboard end of the driveshaft.*

c) *Lubricate the splines of the driveshaft with a suitable grease.*

d) *Tighten all nuts and bolts to the specified torque.*

e) *Fit an new castle nut to the lower arm ball joint and tighten it to the specified torque. Increase the torque if necessary to align the castle nut with the split pin hole in the*

3.10 Lower the track control arm

3.12a Release the driveshaft...

3.12b...and remove it

3.14a Fit a new 'castle' nut

3.14b Fit a new split pin

5 Remove the bolts securing the bearing bracket to the engine block. Note the positions of the bolts as they are different. The dowel bolts fit above and below the main section of the bearing bracket.

6 Holding the shaft level at all times pull it from the differential housing.

Refitting

7 Refitting is a reversal of removal.

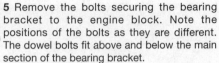

5 Outer constant velocity joint gaiter – renewal

3.14c Tighten the new hub nut to the specified torque – Note the hub holding tool

3.14d Secure the new driveshaft hub nut by staking it in place

Dismantling

1 Remove the appropriate driveshaft from the vehicle as described in Section 3.

2 Cut the gaiter clamps from the outer CV joint and then slide the gaiter back down the shaft.

3 Mark the relationship between the shaft and the joint before removing the joint.

4 The outer joint is secured on the shaft by a small circlip at the outer end. Mount the shaft in a vice, then, using a soft-headed mallet (or a hammer and block of wood), tap the outer joint off the shaft. Remove the circlip and discard it – a new one must be used. Slide the old gaiter from the shaft.

Inspection

5 Thoroughly wash the outer CV joints in degreaser and blow them dry with compressed air, if available.

Note: *Because the outer joint can't be dismantled, it is difficult to wash away all the old grease and to rid the bearing of degreaser once it's clean. But it is imperative that the job be done thoroughly.*

 Warning: Wear eye protection when using compressed air.

6 Bend the outer CV joint housing at an angle to the driveshaft to expose the bearings, inner race and cage. Inspect the bearing surfaces for signs of wear **(see illustration)**.

ball joint shank. Fit a new split pin and bend open the end of the pin **(see illustrations)**.

f) Fit a new driveshaft hub nut and tighten it to the specified torque. Using a blunt chisel or drift stake it in place **(see illustrations)**.

g) If not already done so, fit a new sealing washer to the transmission drain plug and refit the plug, tightening it to the specified torque.

h) Refill the transmission with the correct amount of fluid as described in Chapter 7A or 7B as appropriate. Fit a new washer to the filler plug and tighten it to the specified torque.

4 Intermediate driveshaft – removal and refitting

Removal

1 Drain the transmission fluid as described in Chapter 1A or 1B.

2 Remove the right-hand driveshaft as described in Section 3.

3 Where fitted remove the protection bracket and heat shield.

4 Remove the rear engine torque rod and then remove the mounting bracket **(see illustration)**.

4.4 Remove the torque rod mounting to access the bearing support

5.6 Rotate the joint and inspect it for wear

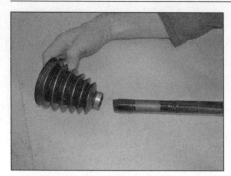

5.7a Slide the inner clip and the new boot onto the shaft...

5.7b...and then remove the protective tape

5.8a Fit a new circlip into the groove...

If the bearings are damaged or worn, a new driveshaft will probably be needed – check the availability of spare parts, or try to source a good secondhand item.

Reassembly

7 Slide the inner clip, then the new outer gaiter, onto the driveshaft **(see illustrations)**. It's a good idea to wrap tape around the splines of the shaft to prevent damage to the gaiter.

8 Fit a new circlip into the groove at the end of the shaft and then fit the larger gaiter clip to the boot **(see illustrations)**.

9 Slide the joint on to the end of the driveshaft and locate it onto the circlip **(see illustrations)**. Place the driveshaft in a vice and (with a block of wood protecting the end of the joint) drive the joint onto the shaft using a suitable hammer. When the joint is secure on the shaft, fit the gaiter onto the joint, and sit it into the grooves.

10 Add the grease from the repair kit to the outer joint – try to 'squirt' the grease into the centre, as this will distribute it around the ball-bearings. Work the grease around the joint's insides. Put most of the grease into the joint, and any left over into the gaiter **(see illustrations)**.

11 Tighten the gaiter clips. The method of tighten will vary, depending on the type of clip supplied with the replacement gaiter kit **(see illustrations)**.

12 Refit the driveshaft as described in Section 3.

5.8b...and then fit the larger clip to the gaiter

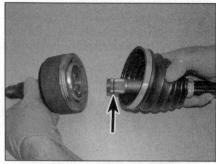

5.9a Slide the joint onto the shaft

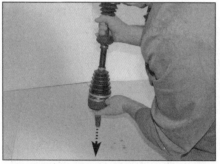

5.9b An alternative method to fit the shaft is to drop it smartly onto a hard (wood) surface

5.10a Squirt the grease into the centre of the outer joint...

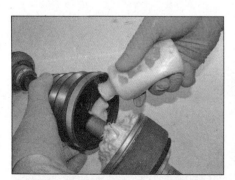

5.10b...and put any left over into the gaiter

5.11a Ear type clips should be tightened with a special tool, but carpenters pincers will also work

5.11b The special pliers wil close and flatten the clip in one movement. The maximum height should be no more than 6 mm

6 Inner constant velocity joint gaiter – renewal

1 Remove the driveshaft(s) as described in Section 3.

Dismantling

2 If you have any doubts about the condition of the outer gaiter, this would be a good time to renew it as well.

3 Cut off both gaiter clamps, and slide the gaiter towards the centre of the driveshaft (see illustrations).

4 Scribe or paint alignment marks on the outer race and the tripod bearing assembly (see illustration) so they can be returned to their original position, then slide the outer race off the tripod bearing assembly.

6.3a Cut off or release the gaiter clamps and discard them

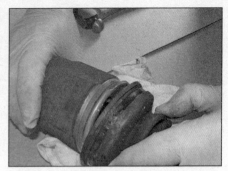

6.3b Slide the gaiter towards the centre of the driveshaft

5 Secure the roller bearings in position with tape or remove them.

6 Remove the circlip, and carefully drive the tripod from the end of the shaft (see illustrations). Discard the circlip, a new one

(supplied in the repair kit) must be fitted. Remove the gaiter.

Inspection

7 Clean the old grease from the outer race and the tripod bearing assembly. Carefully dismantle each section of the tripod assembly, one at a time so as not to mix up the parts, and clean the needle bearings with degreaser.

8 Inspect the rollers, tripod, bearings and outer race for scoring, pitting or other signs of abnormal wear, which will warrant the renewal of the inner CV joint.

Reassembly

9 Wrap the splines of the shaft with electrical tape and then slide the new gaiter onto the shaft along with the smaller clip (see illustrations).

10 Refit the tripod to the driveshaft. Drive it fully into place, until the new circlip can be installed (see illustrations). If the roller

6.4 Paint alignment marks on the shaft and the joint

6.6a Remove the circlip from the end of the shaft...

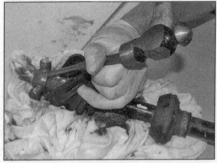

6.6b... then carefully drive the tripod from the shaft

6.9a Slide the new gaiter and smaller diameter clip onto the shaft

6.9b Remove the protective tape

6.10a Fit the tripod...

6.10b...and drive it onto the shaft if necessary

6.10c Fit the new circlip

6.12a Fill the outer race with half of the grease...

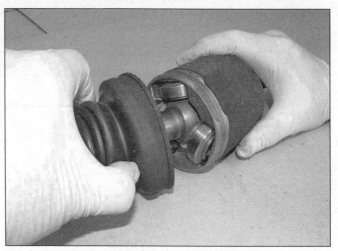

6.12b...and then fit the shaft into the race

6.13a This type of clip is threaded together...

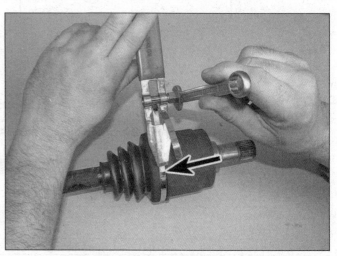

6.13b...then pulled tight using a special tool

bearings are disturbed they should be refitted with the higher shoulder to the outside.

11 Lubricate the tripod rollers with some of the grease supplied in the gaiter kit, then fill the housing and gaiter with the remainder.

12 Pack the housing with the specified amount of grease from the overhaul kit. Align the housing with the previously made marks

and then slide it onto the tripod. Keep the shaft up right at all times **(see illustrations)**.

13 Fit the new retaining clips **(see illustrations)**. A variety of gaiter clips may be supplied with the repair kit. Tightening them is similar for all types.

14 Fit a new circlip to the end of the shaft.

15 Refit the driveshaft assembly (see Section 3).

6.13c Fold the end over...

6.13d..and then flatten it down to secure it. Cut off the excess

7 Intermediate driveshaft support bearing – removal and refitting

Removal

1 If the bearing is suspect it can be replaced. Note however that a driveshaft with a faulty bearing will normally have covered a high mileage. It may be more cost effective to replace the complete driveshaft with an exchange, reconditioned assembly as the constant velocity joints are likely to be worn anyway.

2 Remove the right-hand driveshaft as described in Section 3 and then remove the intermediate shaft as described in Section 4.

3 The bearing must be pressed from the shaft using a hydraulic press. If access to a hydraulic press in not available, most engineering workshops (automotive or otherwise) would be prepared to carry out this task for a modest fee.

4 Mount the intermediate shaft in a vice and then remove the outer circlip, the oil seal and then the inner circlip.

5 The assembly must now be mounted in a hydraulic press and the driveshaft pushed out from the housing.

6 With the driveshaft removed the bearing retaining circlip can be removed. Remove the circlip and then using the hydraulic press, press the bearing out of the housing

Refitting

7 Refitting is a reversal of removal, but a new bearing, circlips and oil seal must be used.

8 Driveshaft damper – removal and refitting

1 All models have a damper assembly fitted to the driveshafts. The damper maybe of one of two types depending on the model. They vary in length only. The positioning of the damper on the driveshaft is critical, so before starting work measure the distance between the damper and the outer face of the outer constant velocity joint.

Removal

2 Remove the driveshaft as described in Section 3 and then remove the inner CV joint as described in Section 6.

3 Cut off the retaining clip and the remove the damper from the driveshaft.

Refitting

4 Refitting is a reversal of removal. If the original fitting position has been lost then the table shows the correct positioning of the damper **(see illustration)**.

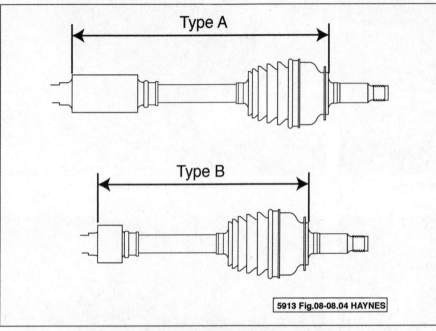

8.4 The specified distance is measured at point X

Engine	Driveshaft position	Damper type	Specified distance (X)
1.4 Manual transmission	Left	B	272.5 – 277.5 mm
	Right	A	275.0 – 280.0 mm
1.8 Manual transmission	Left	B	279.5 – 284.5 mm
	Right	B	287.5 – 284.5 mm
1.8 Automatic transmission	Left and right	B	287.5 – 292.5 mm
2.2 Manual transmission	Left and right	B	265.0 – 269.0 mm

Chapter 9
Braking system

Contents

	Section number		Section number
ABS hydraulic unit – removal and refitting	14	Handbrake lever – removal and refitting	18
ABS wheel sensor – testing, removal and refitting	15	Hydraulic system – bleeding	5
Brake light switch – removal and refitting	17	Master cylinder –removal, overhaul and refitting	7
Brake pedal – removal, refitting and adjustment	2	Rear brake caliper – removal, overhaul and refitting	12
Brake pipes and hoses – renewal	6	Rear brake disc – inspection, removal and refitting	13
Front brake caliper – removal, overhaul and refitting	9	Rear brake pads – renewal	11
Front brake disc – inspection, removal and refitting	10	Vacuum pump – testing, removal and refitting	20
Front brake pads – renewal	8	Vacuum servo unit – testing, removal and refitting	3
General information	1	Vacuum servo unit check valve – removal, testing and refitting	4
Handbrake cables – removal, refitting and adjustment	19	VSA (Vehicle Stability Assist) – general information	16

Degrees of difficulty

Easy, suitable for novice with little experience	**Fairly easy,** suitable for beginner with some experience	**Fairly difficult,** suitable for competent DIY mechanic	**Difficult,** suitable for experienced DIY mechanic	**Very difficult,** suitable for expert DIY or professional

Specifications

Front brakes

Type	Ventilated disc, with single sliding piston caliper
Disc thickness:	
New	23.0 mm
Minimum	21.0 mm
Maximum disc/hub run-out (installed)	0.10 mm
Brake pad friction material minimum thickness	1.5 mm

Rear disc brakes

Type	Solid disc, with single-piston floating caliper
Disc thickness:	
New	9.0 mm
Minimum	8.0 mm
Maximum disc/hub runout (installed)	0.10 mm
Brake pad friction material minimum thickness	1.5 mm

Brake pedal

Pedal height	152 mm
Pedal free play	1 – 1.5 mm
Position switch clearance	0.7 mm

Torque wrench settings

	Nm	lbf ft
ABS wheel sensor securing bolts	10	7
Brake pedal assembly:		
Bolt	22	16
Nuts	13	9
Brake pipe to master cylinder:		
ABS equipped models	15	11
VSA equipped models	22	16
Brake pipe to hydraulic control unit	15	11
Brake pipe unions	15	11
Brake hose banjo bolt	34	25
Front caliper guide bolts*	35	26
Front caliper mounting bracket bolts	108	80
Handbrake lever mountings	22	16
Master cylinder to servo mountings	15	11
Rear caliper bracket	55	41
Rear caliper guide bolts*	35	26
Roadwheel nuts	108	80
Vacuum pump bolts	22	16

Use new nut/bolts

---

1 General information

1 The braking system is of the servo-assisted, dual circuit hydraulic type, with ventilated front disc brakes. All models having solid rear discs. An anti-lock braking system (ABS) is fitted to all models. Many models featuring VSA (Vehicle Otability Assist)– refer to Section 16 for further information on the ABS/VSA operation.

2 The front and rear disc brakes are actuated by single-piston sliding type calipers, which ensure that equal pressure is applied to each disc pad.

3 The rear disc brake calipers incorporate mechanical handbrake mechanisms, providing an independent mechanical means of rear brake application.

4 On petrol models, the vacuum servo unit uses inlet manifold depression (generated only when the engine is running) to boost the effort applied by the driver at the brake pedal and transmits this increased effort to the master cylinder pistons. On diesel models vacuum is supplied by an engine driven vacuum pump.

Precautions

5 The car's braking system is one of its most important safety features. When working on the brakes, there are a number of points to be aware of, to ensure that your health (or even your life) is not being put at risk.

● *Brake fluid is poisonous. Take care to keep it off bare skin, and in particular not to get splashes in your eyes. The fluid also attacks paintwork and plastics – wash off spillages immediately with cold water. Finally, brake fluid is highly flammable, and should be handled with the same care as petrol.*

● *Make sure the ignition is off (take out the key) before disconnecting any braking system hydraulic union, and do not switch it on until after the hydraulic system has been bled. Failure to do this could lead to air entering the ABS hydraulic unit. If air enters the hydraulic unit pump, it will prove very difficult (in some cases impossible) to bleed the unit (see Section 5).*

● *When servicing any part of the system, work carefully and methodically – do not take short-cuts; also observe scrupulous cleanliness when overhauling any part of the hydraulic system.*

● *Always renew components in axle sets, where applicable – this means renewing brake pads, shoes, etc, on BOTH sides, even if only one set of pads is worn, or one wheel cylinder is leaking (for example). In the instance of uneven brake wear, the cause should be investigated and fixed (on disc brakes, sticking caliper pistons is a likely problem).*

● *Use only genuine Honda parts, or at least those of known good quality*

● *Although genuine Honda brake pads and shoes are asbestos-free, the dust created by wear of non-genuine parts may contain asbestos, which is a health hazard. Never blow it out with compressed air, and don't inhale any of it.*

● *DO NOT use petroleum-based solvents to clean brake parts; use brake cleaner or methylated spirit only.*

● *DO NOT allow any brake fluid, oil or grease to contact the brake pads or disc.*

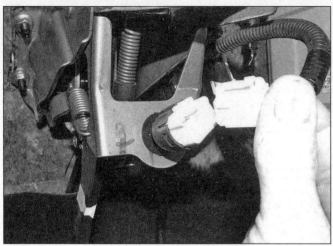

2.1 Disconnect the wiring plug

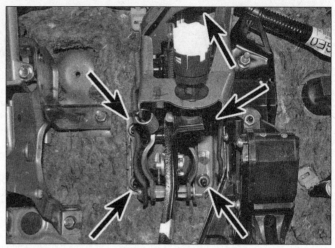

2.4 Remove the nuts and bolt

2 Brake pedal – removal, refitting and adjustment

Removal

1 Disconnect the pedal position switch wiring plug **(see illustration)**.
2 Pull out the spring clip, then withdraw the clevis pin from the brake servo push rod.
3 Unhook the return spring from the top of the pedal, and remove it.
4 Remove the pedal bracket (complete with the pedal) by unscrewing the two mounting nuts on either side and the single upper bolt **(see illustration)**. Note that these are also the mounting nuts for the brake servo – take care when removing the bracket so that the servo is not disturbed.
5 Check the condition of the clevis pin and its spring clip – these are vital components connecting the brake pedal to the master cylinder, and if their condition is at all suspect, new parts should be fitted.

Refitting

6 Refitting is a reversal of removal, noting the following points:
a) If removed, tighten the pedal mounting bracket nuts securely.
b) Always fit a new split pin to the pivot pin.
c) Check the operation of the brakes before taking the car out on the road.

Adjustment

Pedal height

7 The height of the brake pedal is the distance the pedal sits off the floor, measured from the top surface of the pedal. If the pedal height is not as specified, it must be adjusted.
8 Fold back the carpet to expose the cut out in the insulation.Open the cut out in the insulation. The height is checked at 90 degrees from the pedal to the floor panel.

9 To adjust the brake pedal, twist the pedal position switch anti-clockwise and back the switch out until it no longer touches the pedal, then loosen the locknut on the brake pushrod. Turn the servo push rod to adjust the pedal height. When the adjustment is correct, tighten the locknut against the push rod to lock it.
10 Adjust the pedal position switch as described below.

Pedal position switch

11 Push in the switch until the plunger section of the switch is fully compressed.
12 Turn the swich 45 degrees to lock it in position. This will set the clearance between the pedal and the switch automatically
13 Check the pedal free play and the rubber pad against the specification. Readjust the switch position if required.
14 Reconnect the wiring plug and check the operation of the brake lights.

3 Vacuum servo unit – testing, removal and refitting

Testing

1 To test the operation of the servo unit, depress the footbrake several times to exhaust the vacuum, then start the engine whilst keeping the pedal firmly depressed.
2 As the engine starts, there should be a noticeable 'give' in the brake pedal as the vacuum builds-up. Allow the engine to run for at least two minutes, then switch it off. If the brake pedal is now depressed it should feel normal, but further applications should result in the pedal feeling firmer, with the pedal stroke decreasing with each application.
3 If the servo does not operate as described, inspect the servo unit check valve as described in Section 4.
4 If the servo unit still fails to operate satisfactorily, the fault lies within the unit itself.

Apart from external components, no spares are available, so a defective servo must be renewed.

Removal

5 Servo units should not be dismantled. They require special tools not normally found in most repair workshops. They are fairly complex and because of their critical relationship to brake performance it is best to renew a defective servo unit or fit a rebuilt one.
6 Remove the windscreen upper and lower cowl panels – as described in Chapter 12.
7 To remove the servo, first remove the brake master cylinder as described in Section 7.
8 Disconnect the vacuum hose from the servo.
9 Unbolt and unclip the wiring loom from in front of the servo.
10 At the inner wing unbolt the AC refrigerant support bracket.
11 Remove the driver's side facia lower trim panel as described in Chapter 11.
12 Locate the pushrod clevis pin connecting the servo to the brake pedal. Remove the spring clip with pliers and pull out the clevis pin.
13 Remove the four nuts in front of the brake pedal holding the brake servo to the bulkhead **(see illustration 2.4)**.
14 Slide the servo straight out from the bulkhead until the studs clear the holes and then rotate the servo to extract it from the engine bay.

Refitting

15 Refitting is a reversal of removal, noting the following points:
a) Tighten the servo mounting nuts to the specified torque.
b) Use a new split pin when reconnecting the servo pushrod to the brake pedal.
c) After the final refitting of the master cylinder and brake hoses and pipes, bleed the brakes as described in Section 5.
d) Check and if necessary adjust the brake pedal height as described in Section 2.

4 Vacuum servo unit check valve – removal, testing and refitting

Removal

1 Trace the servo vacuum hose from the centre on the inlet manifold, at the rear, back to the servo itself, and disconnect it. Be careful not to damage the hose when removing it from the servo fitting.

2 The check valve is an integral part of the hose. Disconnect the other end from the inlet manifold. Remove the hose from the engine compartment, freeing it from any securing clips, and noting how it is routed.

Testing

3 Examine the hose for signs of damage, such as splits at the ends, and renew if necessary. The valve may be tested by blowing through it in both directions. Air should flow through the valve in one direction only – when blown through from the servo unit end of the valve. Renew the valve if this is not the case.

Refitting

4 Refitting is a reversal of removal. Ensure that the hose clips are secure, to prevent leaks. Check the operation of the brakes before taking the car onto the road.

5 Hydraulic system – bleeding

General

1 The correct operation of any hydraulic system is only possible after removing all air from the components and circuit; this is achieved by bleeding the system.

2 During the bleeding procedure, add only clean, unused hydraulic fluid of the recommended type; never re-use fluid that has already been bled from the system. Ensure that sufficient fluid is available before starting work.

3 If there is any possibility of incorrect fluid being already in the system, the system must be flushed completely with uncontaminated, correct fluid, and new seals should be fitted to the various components.

4 If air has entered the hydraulic system because of a leak, ensure that the fault is cured before proceeding further.

5 Park the car on level ground, switch off the engine, remove the key, and select first or reverse gear (or P on automatic transmission models). Chock the wheels and release the handbrake.

6 Check that all pipes and hoses are secure, unions tight and bleed screws closed. Clean any dirt from around the bleed screws – if they have not been opened for some time, use a small wire brush to clean the threads, then apply a maintenance spray such as WD-40, and allow time for it to soak in. If a bleed screw has seized, do not apply heat to it, as brake fluid is highly flammable.

7 Unscrew the master cylinder reservoir cap and top the master cylinder reservoir up to the MAX level line; refit the cap loosely. Remember to maintain the fluid level at least above the MIN level line throughout the procedure, or there is a risk of further air entering the system.

8 There are several one-man, do-it-yourself brake bleeding kits currently available from motor accessory shops. It is recommended that one of these kits is used whenever possible, as they greatly simplify the bleeding operation, and also reduce the risk of expelled air and fluid being drawn back into the system. If such a kit is not available, the basic (two-man) method must be used, which is described in detail below.

9 If a kit is to be used, prepare the car as described previously, and follow the kit manufacturer's instructions. The procedure may vary slightly according to the type of kit being used; general procedures are as outlined below in the relevant sub-section.

10 Whichever method is used, the same sequence must be followed (paragraphs 11 and 12) to ensure the removal of all air from the system.

Bleeding sequence

11 If the system has been only partially disconnected, and the correct precautions were taken to minimise fluid loss, it should be necessary only to bleed that part of the system (ie, the primary or secondary circuit).

12 If the complete system is to be bled, then it should be done working in the following sequence:

a) Right-hand front brake.
b) Left-hand front brake.
c) Right-hand rear brake.
d) Left-hand rear brake.

Bleeding

Basic (two-man) method

13 Collect a clean glass jar, a length of plastic or rubber tubing which is a tight fit over the bleed screw, and a ring spanner to fit the screw. The help of an assistant will also be required.

14 Remove the dust cap from the first screw in the sequence. Fit the spanner and tube to the screw, place the other end of the tube in the jar, and pour in sufficient fluid to cover the end of the tube.

15 Ensure that the master cylinder reservoir fluid level is maintained at least above the MIN level line throughout the procedure.

16 Have the assistant fully depress the brake pedal several times to build-up pressure, then maintain it on the final stroke.

17 While pedal pressure is maintained, unscrew the bleed screw (approximately one turn) and allow the compressed fluid and

5.22 Bleeding the brakes with a one way valve bleeding kit

air to flow into the jar. The assistant should maintain pedal pressure, following it down to the floor if necessary, and should not release it until instructed to do so. When the flow stops, tighten the bleed screw again. Have the assistant release the pedal slowly.

18 Repeat the steps given in paragraphs 16 and 17 until the fluid emerging from the bleed screw is free from air bubbles. Remember to recheck the fluid level in the master cylinder reservoir every five strokes or so. If the master cylinder has been drained and refilled, and air is being bled from the first screw in the sequence, allow approximately five seconds between strokes for the master cylinder passages to refill.

19 When no more air bubbles appear, tighten the bleed screw securely, remove the tube and spanner, and refit the dust cap. Do not overtighten the bleed screw.

20 Repeat the procedure on the remaining screws in the sequence until all air is removed from the system and the brake pedal feels firm.

Using a one-way valve kit

21 As their name implies, these kits consist of a length of tubing with a one-way valve fitted to prevent expelled air and fluid being drawn back into the system; some kits include a translucent container, which can be positioned so that the air bubbles can be more easily seen flowing from the end of the tube.

22 The kit is connected to the bleed screw, which is then opened **(see illustration)**. The user returns to the driver's seat and depresses the brake pedal with a smooth, steady stroke and slowly releases it; this is repeated until the expelled fluid is clear of air bubbles.

23 Note that these kits simplify work so much that it is easy to forget the master cylinder reservoir fluid level; ensure that this is maintained at least above the MIN level line at all times.

Using a pressure-bleeding kit

24 These kits are usually operated by the reservoir of pressurised air contained in the spare tyre, although it may be necessary to reduce the pressure in the tyre to lower than normal; refer to the instructions supplied with the kit.

25 By connecting a pressurised, fluid-filled container to the master cylinder reservoir, bleeding can be carried out simply by opening each screw in turn (in the specified sequence) and allowing the fluid to flow out until no more air bubbles can be seen in the expelled fluid.

26 This method has the advantage that the large reservoir of fluid provides an additional safeguard against air being drawn into the system during bleeding.

27 Pressure-bleeding is particularly effective when bleeding 'difficult' systems, or when bleeding the complete system at the time of routine fluid renewal.

All methods

28 When bleeding is complete and firm pedal feel is restored, wash off any spilt fluid, tighten the bleed screws securely and refit their dust caps.

29 Check the hydraulic fluid level, and top-up if necessary (see Weekly checks).

30 Discard any hydraulic fluid that has been bled from the system; it will not be fit for re-use.

31 Check the feel of the brake pedal. If it feels at all spongy, air must still be present in the system, and further bleeding is required. Failure to bleed satisfactorily after several repetitions of the bleeding procedure may be due to worn master cylinder seals.

---

6 Brake pipes and hoses – renewal

1 If any pipe or hose is to be renewed, minimise fluid loss by removing the master cylinder reservoir cap and then tightening it down onto a piece of polythene (taking care not to damage the sender unit) to obtain an airtight seal. Alternatively, flexible hoses can be sealed, if required, using a proprietary brake hose clamp; metal brake pipe unions can be plugged (if care is taken not to allow dirt into the system) or capped immediately they are disconnected. Place a wad of rag under any union that is to be disconnected, to catch any spilt fluid.

2 If a flexible hose is to be disconnected, unscrew the brake pipe union nut before removing the horseshoe clip which secures the hose to its mounting bracket.

3 To unscrew the union nuts, it is preferable to obtain a brake pipe spanner of the correct size (split ring); these are available from motor accessory shops. Failing this, a close-fitting open-ended spanner will be required, though if the nuts are tight or corroded, their flats may be rounded off if the spanner slips. In such a case, a self-locking wrench is often the only way to unscrew a stubborn union, but it follows that the pipe and the damaged nuts must be renewed on reassembly. Always clean a union and surrounding area before disconnecting it. If disconnecting a component with more than one union, make

a careful note of the connections before disturbing any of them.

4 If a brake pipe is to be renewed, it can be obtained, cut to length and with the union nuts and end flares in place, from Honda dealers. All that is then necessary is to bend it to shape, following the line of the original, before fitting it to the car. Alternatively, most motor accessory shops can make up brake pipes from kits, but this requires very careful measurement of the original to ensure that the new pipe is of the correct length. The safest answer is usually to take the original to the shop as a pattern.

5 On refitting, do not overtighten the union nuts – it is not necessary to exercise brute force to obtain a sound joint.

6 Ensure that the pipes and hoses are correctly routed with no kinks, and that they are secured in the clips or brackets provided. In the case of flexible hoses, make sure that they cannot contact other components during movement of the steering and/or suspension assemblies.

7 After fitting, remove the polythene from the reservoir (or remove the plugs or clamps, as applicable), and bleed the hydraulic system as described in Section 5. Wash off any spilt fluid, and check carefully for fluid leaks.

---

7 Master cylinder – removal, overhaul and refitting

Removal

1 The master cylinder is located on the driver's side of the engine compartment, mounted on the servo unit.

2 Remove the windscreen upper and lower cowl panels – as described in Chapter 12.

3 Remove the clutch fluid reservoir mounting bracket **(see illustration)**. Move the reservoir to one side, without disconnecting the fluid hose.

4 Remove as much fluid as you can from the brake fluid reservoir before starting, using a syringe. If a syringe is not available, the fluid can be soaked out with clean paper towel. Take care not to drip hydraulic fluid onto paintwork or hot engine components.

5 Remove the bolt and then remove the master cylinder reservoir.

6 Disconnect the brake fluid level sensor wiring plug at the driver's side of the reservoir.

7 Loosen the two brake pipe union nuts on the side of the master cylinder. To prevent rounding off the corners on these nuts, the use of a brake pipe nut spanner, which wraps around the nut, is preferred. Place some absorbent rag or towel underneath, pull the brake pipes away slightly from the master cylinder. Either plug or tape over the open connections to prevent contamination.

8 Unscrew and remove the two nuts attaching the master cylinder to the servo. Pull the master cylinder off the studs and out

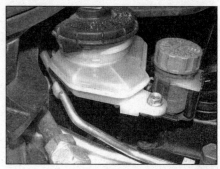

7.3 Remove the bolt

of the engine compartment. Again, be careful not to spill the fluid as this is done. Recover the master cylinder pushrod seal – a new one should be obtained for refitting.

Overhaul

Note: *Honda supply service kits for the master cylinder. However if the master cylinder is leaking it is recommended that the complete assembly is replaced.*

9 Unscrew the reservoir front mounting bolt. Wrap some clean rag or paper towel around the reservoir, then release the hose clips, disconnect the two hoses, and remove the reservoir from the cylinder.

10 Push the rear piston into the cylinder body, and extract the circlip.

11 Remove the screw which secures the reservoir to the top of the cylinder, and withdraw it. Recover the two grommets – new ones must be used on reassembly.

12 Push the rear piston inwards, then extract the stop pin through the cylinder front port.

13 Remove the stopper, then ease out the piston assemblies. If necessary, use compressed air to force the piston from the cylinder body.

14 Carefully examine the bore of the cylinder for rust, scratches, gouges and general wear. If the bore is damaged, the complete cylinder must be renewed. If the bore is in good condition, thoroughly clean the assembly, and renew the seals as described below.

15 Take note of the seal orientation on the piston, and using a small screwdriver, lever the seals from the grooves on the piston.

16 Smear the new seals with clean brake fluid, then fit them to the piston as noted on removal.

17 Apply a little of the assembly grease (which should be supplied in the overhaul kit) to the piston bodies and O-rings.

18 Insert the primary piston assembly into the cylinder, spring end first. Ensure the seal lips enter the cylinder bore without catching or folding back. Align the piston slot with the stop pin hole at the top of the cylinder.

19 Fit the secondary piston, and use it to push the primary piston in far enough to refit the stop pin, though the cylinder front port.

20 Push the rear piston inwards, fit the stopper, then secure with the circlip.

21 Using two new grommets, refit the reservoir, and secure with the screw.

Refitting

22 Apply some of the overhaul kit's assembly grease to a new pushrod seal, and fit it to the rear of the cylinder, with the grooved side against the master cylinder.
23 Fit the master cylinder over the studs on the servo, and tighten the attaching nuts only finger-tight at this stage.
24 Thread the brake pipe fittings into the master cylinder. Since the master cylinder is still loose, it can be moved slightly in order for the fittings to thread in easily. Do not strip the threads as the fittings are tightened.

25 Fully tighten the mounting nuts and pipe unions to the specified torque.
26 Fill the master cylinder reservoir with fluid, then bleed the master cylinder and the brake system as described in Section 5. Check the operation of the brakes before taking the car out on the road.

8 Front brake pads – renewal

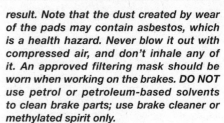

⚠ **Warning: Renew both sets of front brake pads at the same time – never renew the pads on only one wheel, as uneven braking may** result. Note that the dust created by wear of the pads may contain asbestos, which is a health hazard. Never blow it out with compressed air, and don't inhale any of it. An approved filtering mask should be worn when working on the brakes. DO NOT use petrol or petroleum-based solvents to clean brake parts; use brake cleaner or methylated spirit only.

1 Apply the handbrake, then slacken the front roadwheel nuts. Jack up the front of the vehicle and support it on axle stands. Remove both front roadwheels.
2 Follow the accompanying photos (illustrations 8.2a to 8.2t) for the actual pad renewal procedure. Be sure to stay in order and read the caption under each illustration, and note the following points:
a) New pads may have an adhesive foil on the backplates. Remove this foil prior to installation.
b) Thoroughly clean the caliper guide surfaces, and apply a little brake assembly (polycarbamide) grease.
c) Always open the caliper bleed nipple to allow the piston to be pushed back into the caliper. Pushing the fluid back into the master cylinder carries the risk of damaging the master cylinder seals.

Caution: Pushing back the piston causes a reverse-flow of brake fluid, which has been known to 'flip' the master cylinder rubber

8.2a Remove the brake flexible hose mounting bolt

8.2b Remove the lower bolt while holding the sliding pivot bolt with another spanner...

8.2c... and then pivot the caliper up to expose the brake pads

8.2d Secure the caliper with wire or stout cord

8.2e Remove the inner brake pad from the disc. Note the 'screech' pin

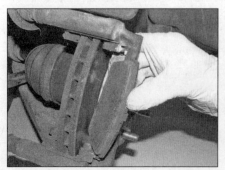

8.2f Lift the outer pad from the caliper bracket

8.2g Recover the shim from the piston and...

8.2h...the anti-rattle shims from the bottom of the mounting bracket...

8.2i...and the top

8.2j Attach a bleeding kit and open the bleed nipple

8.2k Use a piston spreading tool to push the piston back into the caliper...

8.2l...until it is flush with the caliper body

8.2m Clean all the surfaces with a wire brush...

8.2n...and check that the sliding pivots move freely

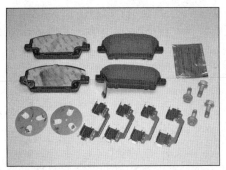

8.2o Honda replacement brake pad kits are supplied with all the parts to complete the job correctly

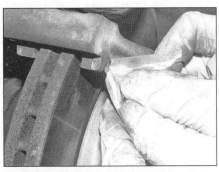

8.2p Lubricate the contact surfaces with the supplied grease (Molykote M77 or similar)

8.2q Fit the new anti-rattle/pad retaining shims and the new piston shim

8.2r Install the new brake pads

8.2s Peel off the backing to expose the adhesive

8.2t Lower the caliper into position and fit a new lower pivot bolt. Tighten the bolt to the specified torque

seals, resulting in a total loss of braking. To avoid this, clamp the caliper flexible hose and open the bleed screw – as the piston is pushed back, the fluid can be directed into a suitable container using a hose attached to the bleed screw. Close the screw just before the piston is pushed fully back, to ensure no air enters the system.

3 Replace the flexible hose mounting bracket bolt.

4 Depress the brake pedal repeatedly, until the pads are pressed into firm contact with the brake disc, and normal (non-assisted) pedal pressure is restored.

5 Repeat the above procedure on the remaining front brake caliper.

6 Refit the roadwheels, then lower the vehicle to the ground and tighten the roadwheel nuts to the specified torque.

7 Check the hydraulic fluid level as described in *Weekly checks*.

Caution: New pads will not give full braking efficiency until they have bedded-in. Be prepared for this, and avoid hard braking as far as possible for the first hundred miles or so after pad renewal.

9 Front brake caliper – removal, overhaul and refitting

Note: *Refer to the warning at the beginning of the previous Section before proceeding.*

Removal

1 Apply the handbrake. Loosen the front wheel nuts, then jack up the front of the vehicle and support it on axle stands. Remove the appropriate front wheel.

2 Fit a brake hose clamp to the flexible hose leading to the caliper. This will minimise brake fluid loss during subsequent operations.

3 Loosen the banjo bolt on the caliper end of the flexible brake hose. Once loosened, do not try to unscrew the hose at this stage.

4 Remove the upper and lower caliper pivot bolts as described for brake pad replacement in Section 8.

5 Remove the banjo bolt and recover the washers. Dispose of the washers – they must be replaced.

6 If required, the caliper bracket can be now be unbolted from the hub.

Overhaul

Note: *Before starting work, check on the availability of parts (caliper overhaul kit/seals).*

7 With the caliper on the bench, brush away all traces of dust and dirt, but take care not to inhale any dust, as it may be harmful to your health.

8 Pull the dust cover rubber seal from the end of the piston.

9 Apply low air pressure to the fluid inlet union, to eject the piston. Only low air pressure is required for this, such as is produced by a foot-operated tyre pump.

Caution: The piston may be ejected with some force. Position a thin piece of wood between the piston and the caliper body to prevent damage to the end face of the piston in the event of it being ejected suddenly.

10 Using a suitable blunt instrument, prise the piston seal from the groove in the cylinder bore **(see illustration)**. Take care not to scratch the surface of the bore.

11 Clean the piston and caliper body with brake cleaner or methylated spirit, and allow to dry. Examine the surfaces of the piston and cylinder bore for wear, damage and corrosion. If the piston alone is unserviceable, a new piston must be obtained, along with seals. If the cylinder bore is unserviceable, the complete caliper must be renewed. The seals must be renewed, regardless of the condition of the other components.

12 Coat the piston and seals with clean brake fluid, then manipulate the piston seal into the groove in the cylinder bore.

13 Push the piston squarely into its bore, taking care not to damage the seal.

14 Fit the dust cover rubber seal onto the piston and caliper, then depress the piston fully.

Refitting

15 If removed, refit the caliper bracket and tighten the bolts to the specified torque.

16 Refit the brake pads as described in Section 8,

17 Refit and tighten the flexible hose banjo bolt using new washers. Ensure the hose is not kinked or twisted.

18 Bleed the brake circuit according to the procedure given in Section 5, remembering to remove the brake hose clamp from the flexible hose. Make sure there are no leaks from the hose connections. Test the brakes carefully before returning the vehicle to normal service.

10 Front brake disc – inspection, removal and refitting

Note: *To prevent uneven braking, BOTH front brake discs must be renewed or reground at the same time.*

Inspection

1 Apply the handbrake. Loosen the relevant wheel nuts, jack up the front of the vehicle and support it on axle stands. Remove the appropriate front wheel.

2 Remove the front brake caliper from the disc with reference to Section 9, and undo the two caliper bracket securing bolts. Do not disconnect the flexible hose. Support the caliper on an axle stand, or suspend it out of the way with a piece of wire, taking care to avoid straining the flexible hose.

3 Temporarily refit two of the wheel nuts to diagonally-opposite studs, with the flat sides of the nuts against the disc. Tighten the nuts progressively, to hold the disc firmly.

4 Scrape any corrosion from the disc. Rotate the disc, and examine it for deep scoring, grooving or cracks. Using a micrometer, measure the thickness of the disc in several places and compare the with the specifications. Light wear and scoring is normal, but if excessive, the disc should be removed, and either reground by a specialist, or renewed. If regrinding is undertaken, the minimum thickness must be maintained. Obviously, if the disc is cracked, it must be renewed.

5 Using a dial gauge or a flat metal block and feeler gauges, check that the disc run-out 10 mm from the outer edge does not exceed the limit given in the Specifications. To do this, fix the measuring equipment, and rotate the disc, noting the variation in measurement as the disc is rotated. The difference between

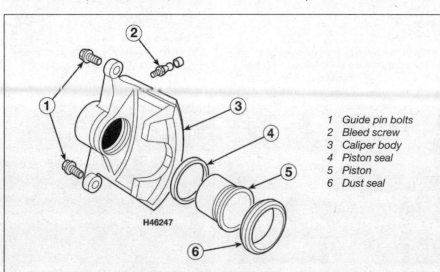

1 Guide pin bolts
2 Bleed screw
3 Caliper body
4 Piston seal
5 Piston
6 Dust seal

9.10 Front brake caliper exploded view

10.10a Remove the screws...

10.10b...and lift off the disc

10.11 A stuck disc can be removed by screwing M8 bolts into the holes provided. Tighten the bolts evenly to remove the disc

10.12 Apply copper grease to the hub before fitting the disc

the minimum and maximum measurements recorded is the disc run-out.

6 If the run-out is greater than the specified amount, check for variations of the disc thickness as follows. Mark the disc at eight positions 45° apart then, using a micrometer, measure the disc thickness at the eight positions, 15 mm in from the outer edge. If the variation between the minimum and maximum readings is greater than the specified amount, the disc should be renewed.

7 The hub face run-out can also be checked in a similar way. First remove the disc as described later in this Section, fix the measuring equipment, then slowly rotate the hub, and check that the run-out does not exceed the amount given in the Specifications. If the hub face run-out is excessive, this should be corrected (by renewing the hub bearings – see Chapter 10) before rechecking the disc run-out.

Removal

8 With the wheel, caliper and bracket removed, remove the wheel nuts which were temporarily refitted in paragraph 3.

9 Mark the disc in relation to the hub, if it is to be refitted.

10 Remove the disc retaining screws **(see illustrations)**. These are often corroded in place and an impact driver may be needed to remove them.

11 If the disc is being removed to renew and it it is corroded in place it can be hammered off from the rear (wear eye protection). If the disc is to be refitted, screw holes are provided on the factory discs (they may not be present if the discs have been replaced by a previous owner) that allow the disc to be forced off the hub **(see illustration)**.

Refitting

12 Make sure that the disc and hub mating surfaces are clean, then locate the disc on the wheel studs **(see illustration)**. Align the previously-made marks if the original disc is being refitted.

13 Refit the retaining screws (replacement discs are usually supplied with new screws).

14 Refit the brake caliper and bracket with reference to Section 9.

15 Refit the wheel, and lower the vehicle to the ground. Tighten the wheel nuts to their specified torque.

16 Test the brakes carefully before returning the vehicle to normal service.

11 Rear brake pads – renewal

Warning: Renew both sets of rear brake pads at the same time – never renew the pads on only one wheel, as uneven braking may result. Note that the dust created by wear of the pads may contain asbestos, which is a health hazard. Never blow it out with compressed air, and don't inhale any of it. An approved filtering mask should be worn when working on the brakes. DO NOT use petrol or petroleum-based solvents to clean brake parts; use brake cleaner or methylated spirit only.

1 Chock the front wheels, slacken the rear road wheel nuts, then jack up the rear of the vehicle and support it on axle stands (see *'Jacking and vehicle support'* in the Reference chapter). Remove the rear wheels.

2 With the handbrake lever fully released, follow the accompanying photos **(see illustrations 11.2a to 11.2o)** for the actual pad renewal procedure. Be sure to stay in order and read the caption under each illustration, and note the following points:

a) If re-installing the original pads, ensure they are fitted to their original position.

b) Thoroughly clean the caliper guide surfaces and guide bolts.

c) If new pads are to be fitted, use a piston retraction tool to push the piston back and twist it clockwise at the same time.

d) Open the brake nipple (fit a brake bleeding bottle) when pushing the piston into the caliper. Avoid pushing the fluid back up to the master cylinder

Caution: Pushing back the piston causes a reverse-flow of brake fluid, which has been known to 'flip' the master cylinder rubber seals, resulting in a total loss of braking. To avoid this, clamp the caliper flexible hose and open the bleed screw – as the piston is pushed back, the fluid can be directed into a suitable container using a hose attached to the bleed screw. Close the screw just before the piston is pushed fully back, to ensure no air enters the system.

3 Depress the brake pedal repeatedly, until the pads are pressed into firm contact with the brake disc, and normal (non-assisted) pedal pressure is restored.

4 Repeat the above procedure on the remaining brake caliper.

5 If necessary, adjust the handbrake as described in Section 19.

6 Refit the roadwheels, then lower the vehicle to the ground and tighten the roadwheel nuts to the specified torque.

7 Check the hydraulic fluid level as described in *Weekly checks*.

Caution: New pads will not give full braking efficiency until they have bedded-in. Be prepared for this, and avoid hard braking as far as possible for the first hundred miles or so after pad renewal.

11.2a Remove the upper and lower retaining bolts and then...

11.2b...lift of the caliper

11.2c Suspend the caliper so that there is no strain on the brake hose

11.2d Remove the brake pads

11.2e Remove the anti-rattle/pad retaining springs from the bottom...

11.2f...and from the top of the caliper/ brake pad mounting bracket

11.2g Use a piston wind back tool and rotate the piston back into the caliper

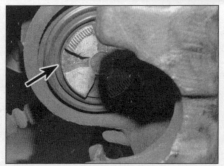

11.2h The cut-outs in the piston must be mate with the locating tab on the rear of the inner brake pad

11.2i Check that the sliding pivots move freely and clean the caliper bracket mounting surfaces

11.2j Fit the new anti-rattle/pad retaining shims

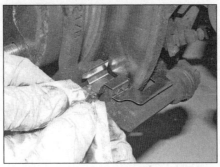

11.2k Lubricate the contact points with the grease supplied in the brake pad kit

11.2l Fit the new pads and remove the protective cover from the back of the pads

11.2m Refit the caliper. Check that the cut-outs in the piston align with the tab on the brake pad

11.2n Fit the new bolts...

11.2o...and tighten them to the specified torque

12 Rear brake caliper – removal, overhaul and refitting

Removal

1 Chock the front wheels, and engage 1st gear. Loosen the rear wheel nuts, jack up the rear of the vehicle and support it on axle stands. Remove the appropriate rear wheel.

2 Fit a brake hose clamp to the flexible hose leading to the caliper. This will minimise brake fluid loss during subsequent operations.

3 Remove the banjo bolt on the caliper end of the flexible hose. Recover the washers and dispose of them – they must be replaced.

4 Unclip the handbrake inner cable fitting from the lever on the caliper, then remove the rear retaining clip and detach the outer cable from the bracket **(see illustrations)**.

5 Remove the caliper mounting bolts as described in Section 11.

Overhaul

6 Some of the parts required to overhaul the rear caliper are available from Honda. No parts of the handbrake mechanism are available. If there is any fault with the caliper other than a damaged dust seal or main seal, then the fitting of a exchange replacement caliper will be the most effective solution.

7 The seals are replaced in a similar manner to the front brake caliper (see Section 9) but

12.4a Lever the operating arm on the caliper forward...

12.4b...unhook and...

12.4c...remove the handbrake cable

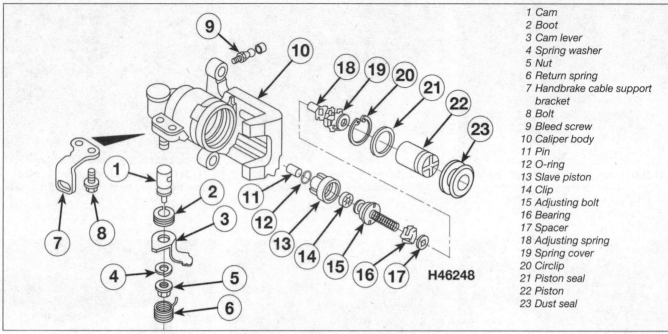

1 Cam
2 Boot
3 Cam lever
4 Spring washer
5 Nut
6 Return spring
7 Handbrake cable support
  bracket
8 Bolt
9 Bleed screw
10 Caliper body
11 Pin
12 O-ring
13 Slave piston
14 Clip
15 Adjusting bolt
16 Bearing
17 Spacer
18 Adjusting spring
19 Spring cover
20 Circlip
21 Piston seal
22 Piston
23 Dust seal

H46248

12.7 Typical rear brake caliper exploded view

the piston must be unwound as well as being pushed out **(see illustration)**.

Refitting

8 Refit the caliper, and where applicable the bracket, by reversing the removal operations. Refit the brake flexible hose banjo bolt with new washers. Refer to the points made in Section 19 when reconnecting the handbrake cable. Tighten the mounting bolts and wheel nuts to the specified torque, and do not forget to remove the brake hose clamp from the flexible brake hose.

9 Bleed the brake circuit according to the procedure given in Section 5. Make sure there are no leaks from the hose connections. Test the brakes carefully before returning the vehicle to normal service.

14.4 Remove the protective cover

14.5a Release the locking catch...

14.5b...and remove the wiring plug

14.6 Remove the brake lines

13 Rear brake disc – inspection, removal and refitting

1 The removal of the rear brake disc is very similar to the removal of the front brake disc. Inspect and remove the disc as outlined in Section 10.

14 ABS hydraulic unit – removal and refitting

Removal

1 The Anti-lock brake modulator (ABS) is located below the the right-hand headlight.
2 Disconnect the battery – see '*disconnecting the battery* in Chapter 5A '.
3 Jack up and support the front of the vehicle (see '*Jacking and vehicle support*' in the Reference chapter). Remove the front bumper and the front wing liner as described in Chapter 11.
4 Unbolt and remove the protective cover **(see illustration)**.
5 Release the locking catch from the wiring plug and then disconnect the wiring plug **(see illustrations)**. Place the wiring plug in a clean plastic bag to avoid any possibility of it becoming contaminated with brake fluid.
6 To minimise fluid loss drain the master cylinder with a syringe. Anticipate some fluid spillage and then (after noting their positions) remove the brake lines from the modulator **(see illustration)**.

14.7a Remove the bolts from the side...

14.7b...and the front

15.5 The front ABS sensor mounting bolt

7 Unbolt the mounting bracket and remove the bracket complete with the modulator **(see illustrations)**.

8 Unbolt the modulator from the mounting bracket.

Refitting

9 Refitting is a reversal of removal, noting the following:

a) *Tighten the brake lines to the specified torque.*

b) *Bleed the brakes as described in Section 5.*

c) *Check that the ABS warning light comes on (and then goes off when the engine starts).*

d) *Test drive the vehicle. If the brake pedal is soft or feels spongy bleed the brakes again.*

15 ABS wheel sensor – testing, removal and refitting

Testing

1 Checking of the sensors is done either by substitution for a known good unit, or by interrogating the ABS ECU for stored fault codes, using dedicated test equipment found at a Honda dealer or suitably-equipped garage.

Removal

2 All the sensors are removed in a similar manner.

3 Apply the handbrake and loosen the relevant wheel nuts. Jack up the wheel of the vehicle and support it on axle stands. Remove the wheel.

4 Trace the sensor wiring and then disconnect the wiring plug. Release the wiring from the retaining clips as required.

5 Unscrew the sensor mounting bolt from the hub carrier and withdraw the sensor **(see illustration)**. Note that the sensors maybe corroded into the housing. Apply ample penetrating fluid and only remove the sensor if absolutely necessary as they are often damaged when removed.

Refitting

6 Refitting is a reversal of the removal procedure.

16 VSA (Vehicle Stability Assist) – general information

1 The VSA system is an expanded version of the ABS system. It is integrated with the ABS and uses the same wheel sensors. Models fitted with VSA have an additional sensors fitted. These are a yaw sensor **(see illustration)** mounted on the transmission tunnel and a steering angle sensor mounted on the steering column.

2 The VSA system controls braking in a more sophisticated manner than the standard ABS system. By monitoring the the speed of the individual wheels, the steering direction

and the yaw of the vehicle VSA can respond rapidly to most braking situations. The system features the following:

TCS (Traction Control System). Where wheel slippage is detected (via the wheel speed sensor) the VSA modulator can apply brake pressure to slow the slipping wheel and restore traction.

EBD (Electronic Brake Distribution). The braking force is distributed from the front to the rear brakes as required depending on the loading of the rear wheels.

BA (Brake Assist). The VSA modulator/control unit monitors normal braking and when an emergency braking system is detected the modulator increases the braking force without the driver having to increase the brake pedal pressure.

3 An over ride switch is provided on all VSA equipped models. Switching the system off allows the vehicle to be driven off when stuck in mud or fresh snow for example. Turn the system back on as soon as traction is restored.

17 Brake light switch – removal and refitting

1 Removal, refitting and adjustment of the switch is covered in Section 2

18 Handbrake lever – removal and refitting

Removal

1 Remove the centre console as described in Chapter 11.

2 Disconnect the warning light wiring plug and then (after noting the position of the nut) remove the cable adjustment nut.

3 Remove the mounting bolts **(see illustration)** from the lever and then remove the lever.

Refitting

4 Refitting is a reversal of removal. If necessary adjust the handbrake cable as described in Section 19.

16.1 The yaw sensor

18.3 Remove the mounting bolts

19.6 Remove the clips and bolts and remove the protective cover

19.7a Unbolt the metal mounting brackets...

19.7b...and unclip the plastic mounting brackets

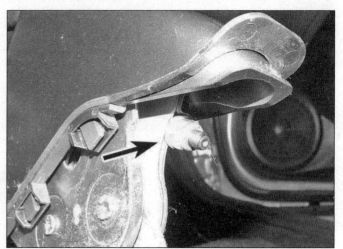

19.12 The handbrake adjusting nut

19 Handbrake cables – removal, refitting and adjustment

Removal

1 Jack up and support the rear of the vehicle as described in Chapter 14. Chock the front wheels and then remove both rear wheels.
2 Release the handbrake and then unhook the cables from the brake caliper (see illustrations 12.4a, 12.4b and 12.4c).
3 Remove the centre console as described in Chapter 11.
4 Slacken the handbrake adjustment nut to the end of the threads.
5 Unhook the cables from the equaliser bracket.
6 Remove the protective cover from beneath the vehicle (see illustration).
7 Work along the cables on both sides and release each cable form the mounting various mounting clips (see illustrations).

8 Working from above (and below) remove the guide bracket and then remove the cables from the vehicle. Note that the cables are handed – mark them 'L' or 'R' if necessary.

Refitting

9 Refitting is a reversal of the removal procedure, but carry out the adjustment procedure (as described below)

Adjustment

10 The handbrake should be fully locked out after 6 to 7 clicks on the ratchet mechanism.
11 If adjustment is required, jack up and support the rear of the vehicle (see 'Jacking and vehicle support' in the Reference chapter). Chock the front wheels and then remove both rear wheels.
12 Remove the blanking plug and fully slacken off the adjusting nut (see illustration). Ensure the operating lever (at both calipers) is back on the stop.
13 Pull the handbrake lever on 1 click only and then refit the rear wheels (where

removed). Turn the adjusting nut on the lever until a slight drag is felt at the rear wheels.
14 Release the handbrake and check that the rear brakes do not drag.
15 Fully engage the handbrake and check that the brakes are fully locked out. Wear gloves and physically attempt to rotate the rear wheels. Whilst this is not a definitive test of the handbrake performance, it will provide a good indication that the handbrake is functioning.
16 Refit the blanking plug and lower the vehicle to the ground.

20 Vacuum pump – testing, removal and refitting

Testing

1 Removing the vacuum pump is a long and complicated procedure. The output of the pump should be checked before condemning the pump.

20.7 The vacuum pump mounting bolts must be unscrewed from inside timing chain case

20.8a Remove and discard the O-ring from the pump mounting boss...

20.8b...and from pump flange

20.10 Refitting vacuum pump

2 Attach a vacuum gauge to the the pump outlet and check that the vacuum produced is at least 700 mm Hg (27.6 in.Hg) after one minute. Any pump that can not achieve these figures must be replaced.

Removal

Note: *Liquid gasket (Honda Part No. 08C70-K0334M or equivalent) must be available on reassembly, in addition to a new auxiliary drivebelt, new cylinder head cover gaskets, vacuum pump O-rings and engine mounting fasteners and any other items (gaskets, seals, etc) found to be in need of renewal during the procedure.*

3 The braking system vacuum pump is bolted to the left-hand face of the timing chain case, at the rear right-hand end of the cylinder block. It is driven by the timing chain from the crankshaft. Unfortunately its mounting bolts

are unscrewed from inside the timing chain case, thus necessitating a lot of preliminary dismantling before the pump can be removed.
4 Remove the timing chain as described in Chapter 2C.
5 Referring as necessary to the relevant Sections of Chapters 4B and 4C, remove the exhaust pipe front (flexible) section and the warm-up catalytic converter, the exhaust manifold cover and the cover over the turbocharger outlet elbow.
6 Disconnect the vacuum hose from the pump.
7 Unscrew the vacuum pump mounting bolts **(see illustration)**.
8 Remove the pump. Withdraw and discard the two sealing O-rings from the pump mounting boss and flange; these must be renewed whenever the pump is disturbed **(see illustrations)**.

Refitting

9 Thoroughly clean the mating surfaces of the vacuum pump, the timing chain case, the cylinder head, the cylinder block and the sump. Clean any oil or old gasket material and sealant from the mating surfaces and from the bolt holes and threads. Be very careful not to allow dirt and debris to fall into the sump. Degrease the surfaces completely before applying sealant.
10 With the new O-rings fitted to the grooves in the pump boss and flange, and lubricated with a smear of grease, refit the pump and tighten its mounting bolts to the specified torque wrench setting **(see illustration)**.
11 The remainder of reassembly is the reverse of the removal procedure, referring to the relevant text for details where required.

Notes

Chapter 10
Suspension and steering

Contents

	Section number
General Information	1
Front swivel hub – removal and refitting	2
Front wheel bearings – renewal	3
Front suspension strut – removal, overhaul and refitting	4
Front suspension control arm – removal and refitting	5
Front anti-roll bar components – removal and refitting	6
Front subframe – removal and refitting	7
Rear hub – inspection, removal and refitting	8
Rear coil spring – removal and refitting	9

	Section number
Rear shock absorber – removal and refitting	10
Rear axle – removal and refitting	11
Steering wheel – removal and refitting	12
Steering column – removal and refitting	13
Steering rack – removal and refitting	14
Steering rack gaiters – renewal	15
Track rod end – removal and refitting	16
Wheel alignment and steering angles – general information	17

Degrees of difficulty

Easy, suitable for novice with little experience	**Fairly easy,** suitable for beginner with some experience	**Fairly difficult,** suitable for competent DIY mechanic	**Difficult,** suitable for experienced DIY mechanic	**Very difficult,** suitable for expert DIY or professional

Specifications

Front suspension
Type . . . . Independent, with MacPherson struts incorporating coil springs and telescopic shock absorbers. Anti-roll bar fitted to all models

Rear suspension
Type . . . . Torsion bar with separate coil springs and hydraulic telescopic shock absorbers.

Steering
Type . . . . Electric power-assisted rack-and-pinion.

Wheel alignment and steering angles
Front wheel:
    Camber angle . . . . $0.00° \pm 30'$
    Castor angle . . . . $4°14' \pm 30'$
    Toe setting . . . . 0 ± 2 mm
Rear wheel:
    Camber . . . . $-1°\,00 \pm 30'$
    Total toe . . . . 4 ± 2 mm (toe in)

Tyres
Tyre pressures . . . . See *Weekly checks*

Torque wrench settings

	Nm	lbf ft
Front suspension		
ABS sensor	10	7
Anti-roll bar clamp plate bolts*	60	44
Anti-roll bar drop link nuts*	29	22
Control arm ball joint castle nut*		
Without flanged nut*	59	43
With flanged castle nut*	74	54
Control arm to subframe:		
Damper bolt*	20	14
Front bolt*	63	46
Rear bush bolt (outer)*	106	78
Rear bush bolt (inner)*	88	65
Driveshaft bolt	181	134
Subframe bolts:		
Central stiffener*	60	44
M14 bolts*	106	78
M10 bolts*	60	44
Suspension strut piston nut*	54	40
Suspension strut to hub carrier*	106	78
Suspension strut upper mounting*	54	40
Rear suspension		
Axle pivot bolts*	101	75
Rear hub bearing nut*	181	134
Rear hub stub axle bolts	93	69
Shock absorber lower mounting bolt	54	40
Shock absorber upper mounting nut	20	15
Steering		
Steering electric motor (to steering rack)	20	14
Steering column mounting bolts	22	16
Steering column mounting nuts	13	9
Steering rack mounting bolts:		
Stiffener bracket bolts*	60	44
Main (long) M10 rack bolt*	60	44
M10 bolts*	43	32
Steering wheel bolt	39	29
Steering shaft universal joint pinch-bolt	28	21
Track rod end balljoint nuts	59	43
Roadwheel nuts	108	80

1 General Information

1 The independent front suspension is of the MacPherson strut type, incorporating coil springs and integral telescopic shock absorbers. The struts are located by transverse control arms, which are attached to the front subframe via rubber bushes at their inner ends, and incorporate a balljoint at their outer ends. The hub carriers, which carry the hub bearings, brake calipers and the hub/disc assemblies, are bolted to the MacPherson struts, and connected to the control arms through the balljoints. A front anti-roll bar is fitted to all models, and is attached to the subframe and to the MacPherson struts via link arms.

2 The rear suspension is a torsion beam axle, with compact springs fitted between the axle and the rear floor. Separate shock absorbers are bolted to the 'trailing arm' ends of the axle, and to the body shell. The rear hubs are also mounted directly to the ends of the axle. The axle pivots on two bushed mountings attached to the rear floor.

3 All models have electric power assisted rack-and-pinion steering. An electric motor at the base of the steering column is fitted to provide the turning assistance. The advantage of the EPS (Electric Power Steering) system is that it only operates when the wheels are turned – a torque sensor signals the motor – whereas on a hydraulic steering system, the pump runs at all times, taking power from the engine. The system has an electronic control unit mounted behind the facia. The vehicle speed sensor signals the steering system to provide extra assistance at low speeds.

2 Front swivel hub – removal and refitting

Removal

1 Jack up and support the front of the vehicle – see 'Jacking and vehicle support' in the Reference chapter. Remove the appropriate front wheel.

2 Remove the mounting bolt from the front brake flexible hose and then remove the brake caliper either complete with the mounting bracket, or by removing the the caliper and then the mounting bracket. Secure the caliper from the suspension strut so that the brake flexible hose is not under any strain.

3 With reference to Chapter 9, remove the brake disc.

4 Relieve the staking in the front hub nut and then undo and remove the nut as described in Chapter 8 Section 3. With the nut removed check that the driveshaft is free and can be moved back into the hub. If necessary, refit the nut and drive the shaft back into the hub using a soft faced hammer. Note the driveshaft will only move a short distance, the important point is that it is free in the swivel hub. Apply penetrating fluid as required and work the driveshaft back and forth in the hub.

5 Remove the spit pin and nut from the track rod end and then using a ball joint splitting tool, break the taper on the ball joint

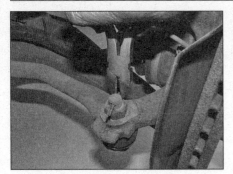

2.5a Remove the split pin

2.5b Break the taper. Note that the track rod end nut has been refitted to avoid damaging the threads

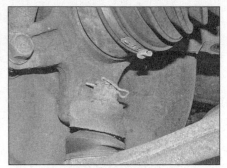

2.6a Remove the split pin...

2.6b...slacken the nut...

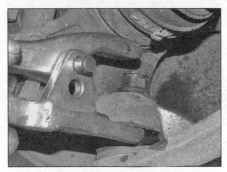

2.6c...and install a ball joint splitting tool

2.8 Remove the strut to hub bolts

and remove the track rod from the steering knuckle (see illustrations).

6 Swivel the hub and to gain access to the lower ball joint and remove the split pin and ball joint nut (see illustration).

7 Using the ball joint splitting tool to break the taper on the control arm ball joint. Dispose of the split pin and nut as new ones must be used. Leave the hub on the control arm for the time being.

8 Remove the nuts and bolts from the suspension strut and pivot the hub assembly away from the strut (see illustration).

9 Lift the hub off the bottom ball joint and (with an assistant holding the driveshaft) pull the swivel hub assembly off the driveshaft and remove it from the vehicle.

Refitting

10 Refitting is a reversal of removal, noting the following:

a) Always fit a new split pin and nut to the control arm ball joint.

b) Always fit new nuts and bolt to the suspension strut.

c) Always fit a new driveshaft/hub nut and stake it in place after fully tightening.

d) When installing the ball joint castle nut, tighten it to the specified torque and then, where necessary, further tighten the nut until the split pin can be fitted.

e) Raise the suspension with a suitable jack under the control arm before fully tightening all nuts/bolts (see illustration).

3 Front wheel bearings – renewal

Note: *A press, a suitable puller, or a selection of large bolts, washers and other improvised tools will be required for this operation. Obtain a bearing kit before proceeding.*

1 Remove the the swivel hub as described in Section 2.

2 Securely support the hub carrier, on two metal bars for instance, with the inner face uppermost then, using a metal bar or tube of suitable diameter, press or drive out the hub flange – we used a large bolt and nut (the same diameter as the end of the hub's splined end) and a hammer (see illustrations).

2.10 Raise the suspension so that it is loaded before finally tightening all nuts and bolts

3.2a We fitted a large bolt, packed out with a nut, then used a hammer...

3.2b...to drive out the hub flange

3.3a Mount the flange in a vice, then use a chisel...

3.3b...to start moving the inner race...

3.3c...until it can be removed

3.3d A knife-edge puller can be used if available

3.4a Remove the three screws...

3.4b...and take off the disc shield

3.5a The bearing circlip has two holes...

3.5b...into which circlip pliers are inserted and compressed...

3.5c...to remove the circlip from its groove

Alternatively, use the puller to separate the hub from the bearing. Note that the bearing inner race will remain on the hub. Take care not to damage the brake disc splash shield.

3 The bearing inner race left on the hub flange must now be removed. To do this, grip the edge of the flange in a vice, and drive the race off with a chisel, then a punch. Tap the race at the top and both sides (even turn the flange over in the vice) to stop it jamming as it comes off. Take care not to mark the hub flange bearing surface. Alternatively, if available, use a knife-edge puller **(see illustrations)**.

4 Take off the disc shield, which is secured by three screws **(see illustrations)**.

5 Preferably using circlip pliers (two small screwdrivers could be used as a substitute), extract the bearing circlip **(see illustrations)**.

6 Now the bearing itself must be removed. Apply a generous amount of spray lubricant to start with. We mounted the hub in a vice, then used a threaded bar, an old bearing and some washers, with a nut fitted on either end of the bar. With this arrangement, we were able to drive out the old bearing **(see illustration)**.

7 Using emery paper, clean off any burrs or raised edges from the hub flange and hub carrier which might stop the components going back together **(see illustration)**.

3.6 Driving out the old bearing

3.7 Clean up the bearing surface in the hub carrier

3.8 Lubricate the hub carrier and the new bearing

3.9 Fit the new bearing the right way round, and tap it in squarely to start

3.11a Fit a threaded bar, collar, nuts and washers...

3.11b...then tighten the nut and tap the bearing home

3.12 Fit the bearing circlip into its groove

3.13 Refit the disc splash shield

3.14a Mount the flange in a vice, then lubricate it...

3.14b...fit the hub assembly over a threaded rod...

3.14c...then tighten the nuts on the rod to pull in the flange

8 Apply a light coat of lubricant to the inside of the hub carrier, and to the outside of the new bearing **(see illustration)**.

9 Note that the new bearing should be marked in some way to indicate its direction of fitting – genuine Honda bearings should have a brown side, which is fitted into the hub first **(see illustration)**.

Caution: The magnetic surface (coloured brown) is the pick for the ABS sensor. Do not damage it, drop it or let it contact a strong magnetic source.

10 Start fitting the bearing by offering it squarely into the carrier, then give it a few light taps with the hammer all round to locate it – keep the bearing square as this is done, or it will jam.

11 Fitting the bearing by tapping it in all the way with a hammer will likely damage it. We used a length of threaded bar (available from

motor factors, DIY stores, etc), with a nut, some large washers and a drilled plate on the inside of the hub carrier. With a drilled collar, another washer, and a nut on the outside, the whole assembly was mounted in a vice, and the nut tightened to press the new bearing in place. The actual method was to tighten the nut slightly, give the old bearing a few taps round its edge, tighten the nut some more, and so on until the bearing was fully home **(see illustrations)**.

12 Fit the new bearing circlip, ensuring that it locates fully into its groove all round **(see illustration)**.

13 Refit the brake disc shield, tightening its three screws securely **(see illustration)**.

14 The hub flange can be pressed into the new bearing using a very similar method to the one just used for the bearing **(see illustrations)**.

15 On completion, refit the swivel hub as described in Section 2.

4 Front suspension strut – removal, overhaul and refitting

Removal

1 Loosen the appropriate front wheel nuts, then jack up the front of the car and support it on axle stands (see *'Jacking and vehicle support'* in the Reference chapter). Remove the appropriate front roadwheel.

2 Undo the nut securing the anti-roll bar drop link balljoint to the suspension strut. Use an Allen key to counterhold the balljoint

4.2 Use an Allen key to counterhold the anti-roll bar link balljoint nut

4.3a Unclip the wiring loom...

4.3b...and unbolt the brake flexible hose

shank **(see illustration)**. A new nut will be required.

3 Unbolt the brake hose from the bracket on the suspension strut and release the ABS speed sensor loom from the base of the strut **(see illustrations)**.

4 Remove the bolts securing the swivel hub to the shock absorber. If necessary lever the hub away from the base of the shock absorber, but take care not to pull the driveshaft out of the transmission **(see illustration)**. Note which way the bolts are inserted – from the front. Dispose of the nuts and bolts.

5 Open the bonnet and remove the access panel from the windscreen cowl **(see illustration)**.

6 Remove the cover from the centre of the strut tower and then slacken off the mounting bolts. Mark the position of the strut **(see illustrations)** fully remove the the nuts and (ideally with the aid of an assistant) manoeuvre the strut out from underneath the wheel arch.

7 Note the direction marks on the strut top plate **(see illustration)**.

Overhaul

Note: *A spring compressor tool will be required for this operation.*

8 With the suspension strut resting on a bench, or clamped in a vice, fit a spring compressor tool, and compress the coil spring to relieve the pressure on the spring seats. Ensure that the compressor tool is securely located on the spring, in accordance with the tool manufacturer's instructions **(see illustration)**.

9 Counterhold the strut piston rod with an Allen key or hexagon bit, and unscrew the piston rod nut **(see illustration)**. Dispose of the nut – new one must be used.

10 Check for paint marks showing the relationship of the components to each other. If none can be found, make your own using chalk, touch-up paint or a marker pen.

4.4 Release the hub from the strut

4.5 Remove the access panel

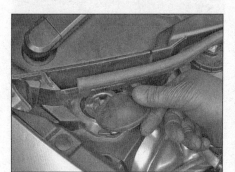

4.6a Remove the centre cover

4.6b DO NOT remove the centre nut

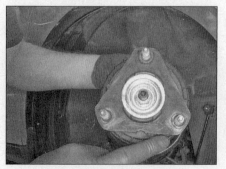

4.7 Note the direction arrows.

4.8 Fit a coil spring compressor and try to 'catch' as many coils as possible

4.9 Unscrew the strut piston rod nut

4.15 Slide the bump stop into position

4.17 Refit the upper spring seat and top mounting

a) *The arrow marks on the strut top mounting plate should point to the outside of the vehicle.*
b) *Refit the strut top mounting nuts, but do not tighten them fully at this stage.*
c) *Refit the swivel hub to the strut and fit the new pinch-bolts and nuts. Push the bolts through as noted on removal. Do not tighten the nuts fully at this stage.*
d) *Carefully load the suspension with the vehicles weight by using a jack applied to the lower arm.*
e) *Tighten all nuts and bolts to the specified torque, using new nuts/bolts where necessary,.*

Remove the top mounting, strut bearing, spring upper seat and mounting cushion, the spring (with compressor tool still fitted), and finally the rubber bump stop.

11 With the strut assembly now completely dismantled, examine all the components for wear, damage or deformation, and check the strut bearing for smoothness of operation. Renew any of the components as necessary.

12 Examine the strut for signs of fluid leakage. Check the strut piston for signs of pitting along its entire length, and check the strut body for signs of damage. While holding it in an upright position, test the operation of the strut by moving the piston through a full stroke, and then through short strokes of 50 to 100 mm. In both cases, the resistance felt should be smooth and continuous. If the resistance is jerky or uneven or if there is any visible sign of wear or damage to the strut, renewal is necessary.

13 If any doubt exists as to the condition of the coil spring, carefully remove the spring compressors and check the spring for distortion and signs of cracking. Renew the spring if it is damaged or distorted, or if there is any doubt as to its condition.

14 Inspect all other components for damage or deterioration, and renew any that are suspect.

15 Begin reassembly by sliding the rubber bump stop onto the strut **(see illustration)** and then fit the dust seal.

16 If the spring compressor tool has been removed from the spring or if new springs are being fitted, refit the compressor and compress the spring sufficiently to enable it to be refitted to the strut.

17 Refit the top mounting plate and strut bearing **(see illustration)**.

18 Slide the spring over the strut, and position it so that the lower end of the spring is resting against the stop on the lower seat **(see illustrations)**.

19 Fit a new piston rod self-locking nut, and tighten it to the specified torque wrench setting; the easiest way of doing this is to use a reversible torque wrench (that can tighten left-hand threads) and a hexagon bit to tighten the piston rod while counterholding the nut with a spanner. Provided this final step is not forgotten, it may be easier to carry out when the strut is back in the vehicle **(see illustration)**.

20 Slowly slacken the spring compressor tool to relieve the tension in the spring. Check that the ends of the spring locate correctly against the stops on the spring seats. If necessary, turn the spring and the upper seat so that the components locate correctly before the compressor tool is removed. Remove the compressor tool when the spring is fully seated.

Refitting

21 Refitting is a reversal of removal, but note the following;

5 Front suspension control arm – removal and refitting

Note: *At the time of writing Honda do not supply the balljoint separately from the control arm. However replacements maybe available from after market suppliers.*

Removal

1 Loosen the appropriate front wheel nuts. Chock the rear wheels and apply the handbrake. Jack up the front of the vehicle and support it on axle stands (see *'Jacking and vehicle support'* in the Reference chapter). Remove the appropriate front roadwheel.

2 Undo the bolt securing the headlight levelling sensor bracket to the control arm (where fitted).

3 Remove the split pin from the front swivel hub ball joint. Slacken the nut until it is level with the end of the balljoint shank, then using a balljoint separator tool, detach the suspension control arm balljoint from the hub carrier **(see illustrations 2.6a, 2.6b and 2.6c)**. Discard the nut – a new one must be fitted.

4 Use a stout bar to lever the control arm downwards and over the end of the balljoint shank. Take care not to damage the balljoint dust cover during and after disconnection.

5 If working on the left-hand control arm

4.18a Install the spring assembly...

4.18b...and ensure the spring locates correctly against the stop in the lower spring seat

4.19 Fit a new piston lock nut

5.5 A flexible damper is fitted to the left-hand arm

5.6a Remove the front bolt...

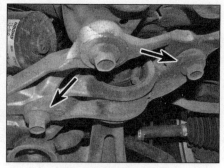

5.6b...and the rear bolts

remove the damper **(see illustration)** – dispose of the nut as a new one must be fitted.

6 Remove the front pivot bolt and then remove the rear bush mounting bolts **(see illustrations)**. Dispose of the bolts. New ones must be used when the arm is refitted.

7 Lower the control arm from the vehicle.

Refitting

8 Refitting is a reversal of removal, noting the following:

a) *Refit the arm with all new nuts and bolts.*

b) *Raise the control arm with a suitable jack so that the suspension is compressed before fully tightening the nuts and bolt.*

6 Front anti-roll bar components – removal and refitting

Removal

1 Loosen the appropriate front wheel nuts. Chock the rear wheels and apply the handbrake. Jack up the front of the vehicle and support it on axle stands (see *'Jacking and vehicle support'* in the Reference chapter). Remove the appropriate front roadwheel, then release the fasteners and remove the engine undershield.

2 Undo the nut securing the anti-roll bar drop link balljoint to the anti-roll bar. If the drop link requires replacement undo the upper ball

joint from the suspension strut as well. Use an Allen key to counterhold the balljoint shank **(see illustrations)**. A new nut (or nuts) will be required.

3 Remove the control arms from both sides as described in Section 5.

4 Unbolt and then remove the subframe central reinforcing plate. Dispose of the bolts – new ones must be used when refitting.

5 At both sides remove the anti-roll bar clamp plates **(see illustration)**. Dispose of the bolts – new ones must be used for refitting.

6 Lower the ant-roll bar from the vehicle.

Refitting

7 Refitting is a reversal of removal, noting the following:

a) *Observe the directional markings on the anti-roll bar bushes.*

b) *Align the bushes with the paint marks on the bar before refitting.*

c) *Replace the mounting bolts and tighten them to the specified torque.*

7 Front subframe – removal and refitting

Note: *The most likely reason to remove the front subframe is to work on the steering rack. All the other components mounted on the subframe can be removed and refitted without*

recourse to to removing the subframe. The simplest method is to remove the subframe complete with as many sub assemblies as possible. Note however it is possible to remove the subframe side members on their own.

Removal

1 Disconnect the battery – see *'disconnecting the battery'*. At the base of the steering column unbolt the column to steering rack pinch bolt. Mark the relationship between the column and the steering rack pinion to aid refitting laterand then slide the column joint of the pinion.

2 Loosen the appropriate front wheel nuts. Chock the rear wheels and apply the handbrake. Jack up the front of the vehicle and support it on axle stands (see *"Jacking and vehicle support'* in the Reference chapter). Remove the front roadwheels.

3 Remove the engine undershield.

4 At both side remove the anti-roll bar drop links from the anti-roll bar – see Section 6. On models fitted with HID (Zenon) headlights disconnect the control arm.

5 With reference to Section 2 and Section 16 release the control arm and the track rod end from the swivel hub.

6 Disconnect the wiring plugs from the power steering motor **(see illustration)**. Protect the wiring plugs from contamination by placing them in plastic bags or covering them in insulation tape.

6.2a Remove the drop link mounting nut and...

6.2b...release the drop link

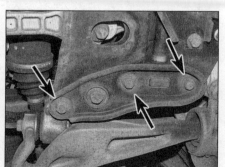

6.5 Remove the bolts

7.6 Disconnect the wiring plugs

7.7 Remove the torque rod

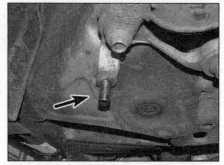

7.10 A bolt drill, or socket (in this case) makes a perfect subframe aligning tool

7 At the front of the subframe remove the engine torque rod (dog bone) from the subframe and then remove it from the rear of the engine **(see illustration)**.

8 The subframe must now be supported with a suitable jack from below. Use a block of wood to spread the load and support the subframe.

9 Before removing the subframe make alignment marks between the subframe and vehicle body. Remove the subframe mounting bolts and with the aid of an assistant lower the subframe form the body.

Refitting

10 With the aid of an assistant raise the subframe into position.The subframe must be aligned as it is refitted. Use the previously made marks to initially align the subframe. As the subframe approaches the fitted position fit a suitable tool into the subframe alignment hole. Honda list a specific tool for this purpose, but a large bolt or drill bit is a perfect substitute **(see illustration)**.

11 The remainder of refitting is a reversal of removal, noting the following points:

a) Replace all the subframe mounting bolts and tighten them to the specified torque.
b) Follow the procedure in the appropriate sections when refitting the swivel hub, anti-roll bar drop links and track rod ends.
c) Have the front wheel alignment checked and adjusted at the earliest opportunity.
d) Using diagnostic equipment check and memorize the torque sensor neutral position.
e) On models fitted with HID (Zenon) headlights the aim should be checked with suitable diagnostic equipment.

8 Rear hub – inspection, removal and refitting

Note: *The rear hub bearings are not adjustable. They cannot be renewed separately, and are supplied with the rear hub as a complete assembly. Note however that after market suppliers may list the bearings as a separate part.*

Inspection

1 To check the bearings for excessive wear,

chock the front wheels, then jack up the rear of the car and support it on axle stands. Fully release the handbrake.

2 Grip the rear wheel at the top and bottom, and attempt to rock it. A small amount of play is acceptable, but if excessive movement is noted, or if there is any rumbling noise heard when the wheel is spun, it is indicative that the wheel bearings are worn. Worn wheel bearings can usually be heard from inside the car at certain speeds.

Removal

Note: *The rear hub nut first has to be loosened. The nut is tightened to an extremely high torque, and for this reason loosen the nut with the wheel on the ground. Either remove the wheel trim or prise out the alloy wheel centre cap (where possible) for access to the nut.*

8.4a Remove the dust cap

8.4b Raise the staked section of the hub nut

3 Jack up and support the rear of the vehicle – see 'Jacking and vehicle support' in the Reference chapter. Remove the appropriate rear wheel.

4 Remove the dust cap **(see illustrations)** and relieve the staking on the hub nut.

5 Refit the wheel and lower the vehicle to the ground.Significant force will be required to loosen the nut, so be sure to use only good-quality, close-fitting tools. A long-handled 'breaker bar' will be needed, to provide the necessary leverage.

6 Slacken the nut and discard it (a new one will be required for refitting) **(see illustration)**. Jack up and remove the rear wheel.

7 Remove the brake caliper and disc as described in Chapter 9.

8 Pull off the rear hub from the stub axle **(see illustration)**.

8.6 Remove and discard the hub nut

8.8 Remove the hub

9 If required the stub axle can now be removed from the rear axle assembly.

Refitting

10 Clean the stub axle, then slide the hub flange into position and secure with a new hub nut, lightly oiled, and tightened by hand only at this stage. It is preferable to tighten the hub nut with the wheel refitted and the car lowered to the ground.

11 Refit the brake disc and brake caliper.

12 Refit the wheel, then lower the car to the ground and tighten the wheel nuts to the specified torque.

13 Stake the nut collar into the stub axle groove, then refit the dust cap, tapping it squarely into place **(see illustration)**.

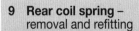

9 Rear coil spring – removal and refitting

Removal

1 Slacken the rear wheel nuts. Chock the front wheels, select 1st gear, then jack up the rear of the car, and support securely on axle stands (see *Jacking and vehicle support* in the Reference chapter). Remove both rear wheels.

2 On models fitted with HID (Xenon) headlights unbolt the headlight levelling sensor.

3 Unclip the ABS wheel sensor from the

8.13 Stake the new hub nut in place

mounting bracket and move it to the side **(see illustration)**.

4 A plastic cover is fitted over the axle trailing arm. Honda recommend removing this, but with care (and a suitable jack) it is possible to remove the coil spring without disturbing the cover.

5 Position a jack under the 'trailing arm' end of the rear axle, and raise it slightly to take the pressure off the lower end of the shock absorber **(see illustration)**.

6 Unscrew the shock absorber lower mounting bolt **(see illustration)**. If necessary, use a pin punch to tap the bolt out to the inside. Separate the shock absorber from the rear axle mounting bracket.

7 Repeat the procedure and disconnect the other shock absorber from the rear axle.

8 Lower the rear axle completely on the jack,

9.3 Unclip the ABS sensor wiring loom

but do not allow it to hang down, as this may strain the brake pipes/hoses.

9 Lift each spring out of its lower seat in the axle, and recover the upper mounting rubber **(see illustrations)**.

10 Check the condition of the upper mounting rubbers, and if necessary, obtain new ones for reassembly.

Refitting

11 Fit the upper mounting rubber onto each spring, aligning the stepped part with the end of the spring **(see illustration)**.

12 Offer each spring onto its lower seat in the rear axle, and align the spring end with the stop on the seat.

13 Raise each end of the axle in turn, and refit the shock absorber lower mounting bolt. Raise the axle further to compress the suspension, then tighten the bolt to the specified torque. Repeat this procedure on the other rear shock absorber.

14 Refit the HID headlight level sensor (where removed) and clip the ABS wheel sensor wiring loom back into place.

15 Refit the rear wheels, then lower the car to the ground and tighten the wheel nuts to the specified torque.

16 On models fitted with HID (Xenon) headlights, suitable diagnostic equipment will be required to calibrate the headlight levelling system.

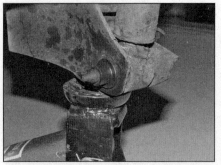

9.5 Support the axle trailing arm

9.6 Remove the shock absorber lower bolt

9.9a Manoeuvre the spring around the wiring loom and...

9.9b...and remove it towards the rear

9.11 Note the locating pegs on the lower spring seat

10.2 Support the axle rear trailing arm

10.3a Remove the mounting bolt and...

10.3b...lever the shock absorber from the axle

10 Rear shock absorber – removal and refitting

Removal

1 Slacken the relevant rear wheel nuts. Chock the front wheels, select 1st gear (or P), then jack up the rear of the car, and support securely on axle stands (see *'Jacking and vehicle support'* in the Reference chapter). Remove the rear wheel.

2 Position a jack under the 'trailing arm' end of the rear axle, and raise it slightly to take the pressure off the lower end of the shock absorber **(see illustration)**.

3 Unscrew the shock absorber lower mounting bolt. If necessary, use a pin punch to tap the bolt out to the inside. Separate the shock absorber from the rear axle mounting bracket **(see illustrations)**.

4 Inside the boot, remove the parcel shelf. Remove the access cover in the side trim panel for access to the strut upper mounting nut **(see illustration)**.

5 Hold the shock absorber piston rod with a hex key to stop it turning, then unscrew the upper mounting nut **(see illustration)**. Discard the nut – a new one should be used when refitting.

6 Take off the upper mounting washer and mounting rubber, then withdraw the shock absorber into the rear wheel arch.

7 Recover the lower mounting rubber, which may still be stuck to the top of the rear wheel arch.

8 Check the condition of the shock absorber. It should move freely up and down with a consistent resistance. There should be no oil leaks and the mounting rubbers must be in good condition **(see illustration)**.

Refitting

9 Fit the lower mounting rubber to the top of the shock absorber, then offer it up into the rear wheel arch.

10 Fit the lower end of the shock absorber into the rear axle bracket. If the rear axle is still being supported on a jack, it may be necessary to adjust the height of the jack to line up the shock absorber. Refit the lower mounting bolt – tap it in if necessary, then tighten it by hand at this stage.

11 Inside the boot, refit the upper mounting rubber and the top washer, then screw on the (new) upper mounting nut by hand.

12 Raise the jack under the rear axle, so that the suspension is compressed, approximately the same as if the car were resting on its wheels. Tighten the shock absorber lower mounting bolt to the specified torque.

13 With the axle still raised on the jack, tighten the upper mounting nut fully. Since the piston rod must again be held with a 5 mm Allen key, a crows foot socket will be required to torque the nut correctly. Refit the access cover to the side trim panel.

14 Lower the jack from under the rear axle.

15 Refit the rear wheel, then lower the car to the ground and tighten the wheel nuts to the specified torque.

11 Rear axle – removal and refitting

Removal

Note: *The rear axle can be removed with the rear brake calipers and hubs still attached. Alternatively remove the calipers discs and hubs. Whichever method is chosen the brake lines must be disconnected.*

1 Jack up and support the rear of the vehicle – see *'Jacking and vehicle support'* in the Reference chapter. Remove the rear wheels.

2 Fit brake hose clamps to the flexible brake hoses in front of the axle and disconnect the brake hoses. If no brake hose clamps are available, open the bleed nipples and allow the brake fluid to drain from the calipers and brake lines. Which ever method is used anticipate the loss of brake fluid as the hoses are disconnected.

3 Unbolt the rear brake calipers complete with the caliper bracket. Remove the brake discs, splash guide and hubs (see Chapter 9 and Section 8).

4 Unbolt and remove the rear wheel sensors from the axle. Trace the wiring back from the

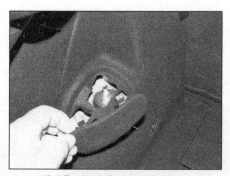

10.4 Remove the access panel

10.5 Remove the upper mounting

10.8 Check the condition of the lower bush.

sensors, and unclip it from the axle. Tie the sensors and wiring up, clear of the axle – there is no need to disconnect them.

5 On models fitted with HID (Xenon) headlights disconnect the levelling sensor.

6 Remove the shock absorber mountings (Section 10) and remove the rear coil springs (Section 9).

7 Support the rear axle with a suitable jack and then remove the rear mounting bolts – discard the bolts as they must be replaced. With the aid of an assistant lower the axle from the vehicle.

Refitting

8 Refitting is a reversal of removal, noting the following points:

a) Use new axle pivot bolts, tightened by hand initially. Raise the axle to its approximate 'working' position, then tighten the bolts to the specified torque.

b) Refit the springs as described in Section 9, and the rear hubs as described in Section 8.

c) Ensure that the ABS wiring is correctly routed, and secured with the clips.

d) On completion, top-up the brake fluid level, then bleed the brakes as described in Chapter 9.

e) On models fitted with HID lights, the levelling system must be calibrated with suitable diagnostic equipment.

12 Steering wheel – removal and refitting

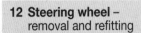
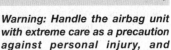

Warning: Handle the airbag unit with extreme care as a precaution against personal injury, and always hold it with the cover facing away from the body.

Removal

1 Drive the car forwards, and park it with the front wheels in the straight-ahead position.

2 Remove the driver's airbag as described in Chapter 12.

12.3 Disconnect the wiring plug

3 Disconnect the wring plug (see illustration).

4 Slacken, but do not fully undo the steering wheel centre retaining bolt (see illustration).

5 A suitable puller tool will be required to remove the steering wheel. Do not be tempted to remove it by any other method.

6 Fit a suitable pulley to the bolt holes provide in the steering wheel (see illustration). Do not insert the bolts more than 5 mm into the steering wheel or the airbag clockspring will be damaged. Fit stop nuts to the bolts to prevent this from happening. Operate the puller until the steering wheel is free from the splines. Remove the puller.

7 Fully remove the steering wheel bolt. Make alignment marks between the steering wheel centre and the column shaft (see illustration) and then remove the steering wheel, feeding the wiring loom through the wheel as the wheel is removed.

Refitting

8 Ensure that the front wheels are still in the straight-ahead position.

9 Check the airbag rotary contact unit is still aligned. Refer to Chapter 12 if necessary. Remove the securing tape if fitted.

10 Fit the steering wheel aligning the clockspring and the pins for the self cancelling function of the indicators as the wheel is lowered into position.

12.4 Slacken the steering wheel retaining nut

11 Refit the steering wheel retaining bolt, and tighten it to the specified torque.

12 Refit the airbag unit to the steering wheel as described in Chapter 12.

13 Steering column – removal and refitting

Removal

Note: If an assistant is available it is possible to remove the column complete with the steering wheel, airbag and switches.

1 Disconnect the battery negative lead – see Chapter 5A.

2 Remove the lower facia panel and then fully extend and lower the steering column.

3 Remove the drivers airbag as described in Chapter 12 and then remove the steering wheel as described in Section 12.

4 Remove the column shrouds as described in Chapter 11.

5 Adjust the column to the fully up position.

6 Remove the cover from the lower universal joint (see illustration).

7 Release the column adjuster and push the column fully inwards. Secure the two telescopic sections of the column together with cable ties and then extend the column to fully tension the cable ties. Note that there are alignment marks between the two sections of the telescopic shaft.

12.6 Install a suitable puller

12.7 Mark the position of the steering wheel in relation to the column

13.6 Remove the cover

13.9 Free the loom from the column

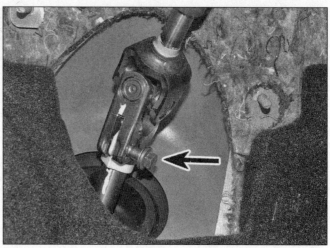

13.11 Remove the pinch bolt

13.12a Remove the nuts and bolts (1 nut and 1 bolt hidden by the loom)

13.12b Remove the column

8 Mark the position of the lower joint in relation to the steering rack pinion shaft.
9 Disconnect the wiring plugs from the column **(see illustration)**.
10 Secure the clockspring in position and then remove the screws and pull off the clockspring and column switches as a complete assembly.

11 Undo the steering column lower pinch-bolt **(see illustration)** and pull the joint upwards from the pinion.
12 Undo the 2 retaining bolts and the 2 retaining nuts. Manoeuvre the column from the vehicle **(see illustrations)**.
13 If required, drill out the security bolts, and

remove the steering lock from the column **(see illustrations)**. No further dismantling of the assembly is recommended.

Refitting

14 Refitting is a reversal of removal.

13.13a Remove the key reader coil...

13.13b ...and the ignition switch

13.13c Drill out the shear bolts and remove the key cylinder

14 Steering rack – removal and refitting

Removal

1 Remove the steering column lower cover and remove the pinch bolt (see illustrations 13.6 and 13.11). Mark the relationship between the column and the steering rack pinion.

2 The steering rack can only be removed with the front subframe. Follow the procedure for subframe removal in Section 7.

3 With the subframe on the ground and clear of the vehicle remove the protective boot from the steering rack pinion.

4 Unbolt and remove the stiffener plate and then remove the steering rack mounting bracket.

5 Lift the steering rack from the subframe.

6 With the steering rack on the bench disconnect the wiring plug from the steering angle sensor (the plug closest to the steering pinion) and then unclip the motor wiring plugs from the mounting bracket.

7 Remove the three motor mounting bolts and then lift out the motor. Recover the large O-ring and discard it.

Refitting

8 If the motor has been removed from the steering rack obtain a new O-ring. Lubricate the O-ring and the driveshaft on the motor with a silicon based grease and then refit

the motor to the steering rack. Torque the mounting bolts to the specified torque.

9 Check the condition of the steering rack mounting rubbers, lubricate them with water and then refit the steering rack to the subframe. Ensure the locating tabs on the flexible mounting align with the marks on the steering rack.

10 Install the upper cover and stiffener bracket. Fit the new bolts loosely and then tighten the stiffener bracket bolts, followed by the main (long) steering rack mounting bolt. Tighten the single front bolt (at the opposite end of the steering rack) followed by the two rear mounting bolts (see illustration).

11 Refit the protective cover to the to the steering rack pinion and then refit the subframe as described in Section 7.

12 Refit the remaining components in reverse order to removal and then:

a) Have the tracking checked and adjusted if necessary.

b) Using suitable diagnostic equipment have the torque sensor neutral position checked and adjusted.

c) On models with HID (Zenon) headlights calibrate the headlight levelling system. This must be done with suitable diagnostic equipment.

15 Steering rack gaiters – renewal

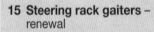

1 Remove the track rod end on the side

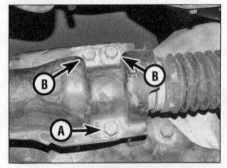

14.10 Tighten the front bolt (A), before rear bolts (B)

16.4 Disconnect the track rod end

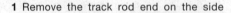

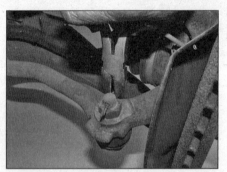

16.3 Remove the spilt pin and discard it

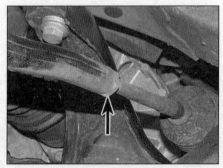

16.5 Slacken the track rod end lock nut

concerned as described in Section 16. Unscrew the locknut from the track rod.

2 Release the two clips and slide off the gaiter.

3 Clean the 'gaiter section' of the track rod and rack, then apply a little grease around the housing on the end of the rack, where the track rod fits. Also apply a little grease to the wider groove at the inner end of the track rod – do not grease the narrower groove where the gaiter outer clip will locate.

4 Clean the gaiter inner clip groove on the rack.

5 Slide the new gaiter into position, and secure with the inner and outer clips.

6 Refit the track rod end locknut, screwing it onto the track rod to the position noted when the nut was removed.

7 Refit the track rod end as described in Section 16.

16 Track rod end – removal and refitting

1 If the track rod end rubber boot is damaged, a new one can be obtained from Honda dealers. Once the track rod end has been disconnected (as described later in this Section), the old boot can be unclipped. Wipe the balljoint clean (do not use excessive amounts of solvent), then pack it with fresh grease and fit the new boot. However, bear in mind that if the boot has been damaged for some time, it is likely that dirt will have got into the balljoint, and a new track rod end may soon be needed.

Removal

2 Slacken the relevant front wheel nuts. Apply the handbrake, then jack up the front of the car, and support securely on axle stands (see 'Jacking and vehicle support' in the Reference chapter). Remove the wheel.

3 Extract the split pin from the track rod balljoint nut (a new split pin will be needed when refitting). Unscrew the nut, but leave it attached by a couple of threads for now (see illustration).

4 Disconnect the track rod end from the strut, either using a balljoint separator tool, or by tapping the end of the balljoint stud (use a block of wood and the still-fitted nut to protect the threads). When the balljoint separates, unscrew the nut completely, and move the track rod clear (see illustration).

5 Just slacken the track rod end locknut (move it as little as possible) (see illustration). Once the locknut is slackened, gently turn it back up against the track rod end. If the locknut is left in this position, it can be used as a guide to the correct fitted position of the track rod end.

6 Without disturbing the locknut, unscrew the track rod end from the track rod, counting the number of turns necessary to remove it.

Refitting

7 Screw the track rod end onto the track rod the number of turns noted during removal (or up to the locknut), then tighten the locknut while holding the track rod in position (the track rod has flats to accept a spanner).

8 Clean the balljoint and its seat in the steering arm before fitting – it must be fitted dry. Offer the balljoint into position, taking care not to damage the boot.

9 Tighten the balljoint nut to the specified torque. From this point, tighten the nut slightly as required to align the split pin holes (do not loosen to align), then fit a new pin to secure.

10 Refit the roadwheel, then lower the car to the ground, and tighten the wheel nuts to the specified torque.

11 Have the front wheel alignment checked (see Section 17) at the earliest opportunity.

17 Wheel alignment and steering angles – general information

1 A car's steering and suspension geometry is defined in four basic settings – all angles are expressed in degrees (toe settings are also expressed as a measurement); the relevant settings are camber, castor, steering axis inclination, and toe setting **(see illustration)**. On the models covered by this manual, only the front wheel toe settings are adjustable.

2 Camber is the angle at which the front wheels are set from the vertical when viewed from the front or rear of the car. Negative camber is the amount (in degrees) that the wheels are tilted inward at the top from the vertical.

3 The front camber angle is adjusted by slackening the steering knuckle-to-suspension strut mounting bolts and repositioning the hub carrier assemblies as necessary.

4 Castor is the angle between the steering axis and a vertical line when viewed from each side of the car. Positive castor is when the steering axis is inclined rearward at the top.

5 Steering axis inclination is the angle (when viewed from the front of the vehicle) between the vertical and an imaginary line drawn through the front suspension strut upper mounting and the control arm balljoint.

6 Toe setting is the amount by which the distance between the front inside edges of the roadwheels (measured at hub height) differs from the diametrically opposite distance measured between the rear inside edges of the roadwheels. Toe-in is when the roadwheels point inwards, towards each other at the front, while toe-out is when they splay outwards from each other at the front.

7 The front wheel toe setting is adjusted by altering the length of the steering track rods on both sides. This adjustment is normally referred to as the tracking.

8 The rear wheel toe setting is adjusted by rotating the lateral link front mounting bolt in the chassis. The bolt incorporates an eccentric washer, and the pivot point for the link varies as the bolt is rotated.

9 All other suspension and steering angles are set during manufacture, and no adjustment is possible. It can be assumed, therefore, that unless the vehicle has suffered accident damage, all the preset angles will be correct.

10 Special optical measuring equipment is necessary to accurately check and adjust the front and rear toe settings and front camber angles, and this work should be carried out by a Honda dealer or similar expert. Most tyre-fitting centres have the expertise and equipment to carry out at least a front wheel toe setting (tracking) check for a nominal charge.

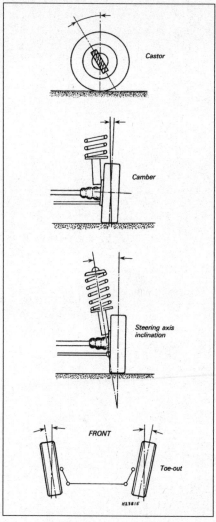

17.1 Front wheel geometry

Chapter 11
Bodywork and fittings

Contents

Section number

Body side-trim mouldings and adhesive emblems –
 removal and refitting.................................... 21
Bonnet – removal and refitting............................. 8
Bonnet lock and cable – removal, refitting and adjustment........ 9
Bumper covers – removal and refitting 6
Centre console – removal and refitting...................... 26
Door – removal and refitting.............................. 14
Door handle and lock components – removal and refitting 13
Door inner trim panel – removal and refitting................. 10
Door window glass – removal and refitting 11
Door window regulator – removal and refitting 12
Exterior mirror and glass – removal and refitting 15
Facia and crossmember – removal and refitting 28
General Information 1
Glovebox – removal and refitting.......................... 27

Section number

Grille – removal and refitting 7
Interior mirror – removal and refitting...................... 16
Interior trim panels – removal and refitting.................. 25
Maintenance – bodywork and underframe.................... 2
Maintenance – upholstery and carpets 3
Major body damage – repair 5
Minor body damage – repair 4
Seat belts – removal and refitting......................... 24
Seats – removal and refitting 23
Sunroof – general information and adjustment 22
Support struts – removal and refitting 18
Tailgate – removal and refitting........................... 17
Tailgate lock components – removal and refitting 19
Wheel arch liner – removal and refitting.................... 29
Windscreen and fixed windows – removal and refitting.......... 20

Degrees of difficulty

Easy, suitable for novice with little experience 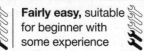	Fairly easy, suitable for beginner with some experience	Fairly difficult, suitable for competent DIY mechanic	Difficult, suitable for experienced DIY mechanic	Very difficult, suitable for expert DIY or professional

Specifications

Torque wrench settings	Nm	lbf ft
Bonnet hinge bolts..	18	13
Bumper reinforcement bolts.................................	22	16
Crossmember bolts	22	16
Door glass bolts..	10	7
Door hinge bolts..	29	22
Front seat mounting bolts	34	25
Gear lever support bracket bolts	22	16
Passenger's airbag nuts/bolts	10	7
Rear seat nut/bolts..	34	25
Seatbelts		
Front inertia reel bolt upper bolt.........................	10	7
Front inertia reel lower bolt.............................	32	24
Front lower anchorage	32	24
Front seat belt buckle	32	24
Front seat bolts shoulder height adjuster.....................	22	16
Front upper anchorage.................................	32	24
Rear belt buckle stalks.................................	32	24
Rear centre inertia reel	32	24
Rear centre lower anchorage	32	24
Rear outer inertia reel upper bolt	10	7
Rear outer inertia reel lower bolt	32	24
Rear outer lower anchorage.............................	32	24
Rear upper anchorage	32	24
Tailgate hinge bolts..	22	16
Windscreen wiper linkage to body bolts	10	7
Windscreen wiper motor link arm nut	31	23
Windscreen wiper motor to linkage bolts......................	10	7

1 General Information

1 The bodyshell and underframe on all models are of unitary construction and feature variable thickness steel. Many of the structural panels are fabricated from high strength steel and the majority are also zinc coated.

2 An additional safety crossmember is incorporated between the A-pillars in the upper area of the bulkhead, and the facia and steering column are secured to it. The bulkhead area is further reinforced by additional stiffener plates bolted to the A-pillars.

3 All doors are reinforced and incorporate side impact protection, which is secured in the door structure. There are additional impact absorbers to the front and rear of the vehicle, behind the bumper assemblies.

4 Automatic seat belts are fitted to all models, and the front seat safety belts are equipped with a pyrotechnic pretension seat lap belt and inertia reel. In the event of a serious front impact, the system is triggered and pulls the lower anchor buckle downwards to tension the seat belt. It is not possible to reset the tensioner once fired, and it must therefore be renewed. The tensioners are fired by an explosive charge similar to that used in the airbag, and are triggered via the airbag control module. The safety belt retractor, which is fitted in the base of the B-pillar, has a device to control the seat belt, if the deceleration force is enough to activate the airbags.

5 Central locking and an immobiliser system are standard on all models. Higher specification models also feature ultrasonic sensors and a self-powered alarm siren.

6 Many of the procedures in this Chapter require the battery to be disconnected; refer to Chapter 5A.

2 Maintenance – bodywork and underframe

1 The general condition of a vehicle's bodywork is the one thing that significantly affects its value. Maintenance is easy, but needs to be regular. Neglect, particularly after minor damage, can lead quickly to further deterioration and costly repair bills. It is important also to keep watch on those parts of the vehicle not immediately visible, for instance the underside, inside all the wheel arches, and the lower part of the engine compartment.

2 The basic maintenance routine for the bodywork is washing – preferably with a lot of water, from a hose. This will remove all the loose solids which may have stuck to the vehicle. It is important to flush these off in such a way as to prevent grit from scratching the finish. The wheel arches and underframe need washing in the same way, to remove any accumulated mud, which will retain moisture and tend to encourage rust. Paradoxically enough, the best time to clean the underframe and wheel arches is in wet weather, when the mud is thoroughly wet and soft. In very wet weather, the underframe is usually cleaned of large accumulations automatically, and this is a good time for inspection.

3 Periodically, except on vehicles with a wax-based underbody protective coating, it is a good idea to have the whole of the underframe of the vehicle steam-cleaned, engine compartment included, so that a thorough inspection can be carried out to see what minor repairs and renovations are necessary. Steam-cleaning is available at many garages, and is necessary for the removal of the accumulation of oily grime, which sometimes is allowed to become thick in certain areas. If steam-cleaning facilities are not available, there are some excellent grease solvents available which can be brush-applied; the dirt can then be simply hosed off. Note that these methods should not be used on vehicles with wax-based underbody protective coating, or the coating will be removed. Such vehicles should be inspected annually, preferably just prior to Winter, when the underbody should be washed down, and any damage to the wax coating repaired. Ideally, a completely fresh coat should be applied. It would also be worth considering the use of such wax-based protection for injection into door panels, sills, box sections, etc, as an additional safeguard against rust damage, where such protection is not provided by the vehicle manufacturer.

4 After washing paintwork, wipe off with a chamois leather to give an unspotted clear finish. A coat of clear protective wax polish will give added protection against chemical pollutants in the air. If the paintwork sheen has dulled or oxidised, use a cleaner/polisher combination to restore the brilliance of the shine. This requires a little effort, but such dulling is usually caused because regular washing has been neglected. Care needs to be taken with metallic paintwork, as special non-abrasive cleaner/polisher is required to avoid damage to the finish. Always check that the door and ventilator opening drain holes and pipes are completely clear, so that water can be drained out. Brightwork should be treated in the same way as paintwork. Windscreens and windows can be kept clear of the smeary film which often appears, by the use of proprietary glass cleaner. Never use any form of wax or other body or chromium polish on glass.

3 Maintenance – upholstery and carpets

1 Mats and carpets should be brushed or vacuum-cleaned regularly, to keep them free of grit. If they are badly stained, remove them from the vehicle for scrubbing or sponging, and make quite sure they are dry before refitting. Seats and interior trim panels can be kept clean by wiping with a damp cloth. If they do become stained (which can be more apparent on light-coloured upholstery), use a little liquid detergent and a soft nail brush to scour the grime out of the grain of the material. Do not forget to keep the headlining clean in the same way as the upholstery. When using liquid cleaners inside the vehicle, do not over-wet the surfaces being cleaned. Excessive damp could get into the seams and padded interior, causing stains, offensive odours or even rot.

Caution: If the inside of the vehicle gets wet accidentally, it is worthwhile taking some trouble to dry it out properly, particularly where carpets are involved. Do not leave oil or electric heaters inside the vehicle for this purpose.

4 Minor body damage – repair

Minor scratches in bodywork

1 If the scratch is very superficial, and does not penetrate to the metal of the bodywork, repair is very simple. Lightly rub the area of the scratch with a paintwork renovator, or a very fine cutting paste, to remove loose paint from the scratch, and to clear the surrounding bodywork of wax polish. Rinse the area with clean water.

2 Apply touch-up paint to the scratch using a fine paint brush; continue to apply fine layers of paint until the surface of the paint in the scratch is level with the surrounding paintwork. Allow the new paint at least two weeks to harden, then blend it into the surrounding paintwork by rubbing the scratch area with a paintwork renovator or a very fine cutting paste. Finally, apply wax polish.

3 Where the scratch has penetrated right through to the metal of the bodywork, causing the metal to rust, a different repair technique is required. Remove any loose rust from the bottom of the scratch with a penknife, then apply rust-inhibiting paint to prevent the formation of rust in the future. Using a rubber or nylon applicator, fill the scratch with bodystopper paste. If required, this paste can be mixed with cellulose thinners to provide a very thin paste which is ideal for filling narrow scratches. Before the stopper-paste in the scratch hardens, wrap a piece of smooth cotton rag around the top of a finger. Dip the finger in cellulose thinners, and quickly sweep it across the surface of the stopper-paste in the scratch; this will ensure that the surface of the stopper-paste is slightly hollowed. The scratch can now be painted over as described earlier in this Section.

Dents in bodywork

4 When deep denting of the vehicle's bodywork has taken place, the first task is to

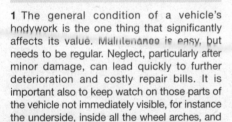

pull the dent out, until the affected bodywork almost attains its original shape. There is little point in trying to restore the original shape completely, as the metal in the damaged area will have stretched on impact, and cannot be reshaped fully to its original contour. It is better to bring the level of the dent up to a point which is about 3 mm below the level of the surrounding bodywork. In cases where the dent is very shallow anyway, it is not worth trying to pull it out at all. If the underside of the dent is accessible, it can be hammered out gently from behind, using a mallet with a wooden or plastic head. Whilst doing this, hold a suitable block of wood firmly against the outside of the panel, to absorb the impact from the hammer blows and thus prevent a large area of the bodywork from being 'belled-out'.

5 Should the dent be in a section of the bodywork which has a double skin, or some other factor making it inaccessible from behind, a different technique is called for. Drill several small holes through the metal inside the area – particularly in the deeper section. Then screw long self-tapping screws into the holes, just sufficiently for them to gain a good purchase in the metal. Now the dent can be pulled out by pulling on the protruding heads of the screws with a pair of pliers.

6 The next stage of the repair is the removal of the paint from the damaged area, and from an inch or so of the surrounding 'sound' bodywork. This is accomplished most easily by using a wire brush or abrasive pad on a power drill, although it can be done just as effectively by hand, using sheets of abrasive paper. To complete the preparation for filling, score the surface of the bare metal with a screwdriver or the tang of a file, or alternatively, drill small holes in the affected area. This will provide a really good 'key' for the filler paste.

7 To complete the repair, see the Section on filling and respraying.

Rust holes or gashes in bodywork

8 Remove all paint from the affected area, and from an inch or so of the surrounding 'sound' bodywork, using an abrasive pad or a wire brush on a power drill. If these are not available, a few sheets of abrasive paper will do the job most effectively. With the paint removed, you will be able to judge the severity of the corrosion, and therefore decide whether to renew the whole panel (if this is possible) or to repair the affected area. New body panels are not as expensive as most people think, and it is often quicker and more satisfactory to fit a new panel than to attempt to repair large areas of corrosion.

9 Remove all fittings from the affected area, except those which will act as a guide to the original shape of the damaged bodywork (e.g. headlight shells etc). Then, using tin snips or a hacksaw blade, remove all loose metal and any other metal badly affected by corrosion.

Hammer the edges of the hole inwards, in order to create a slight depression for the filler paste.

10 Wire-brush the affected area to remove the powdery rust from the surface of the remaining metal. Paint the affected area with rust-inhibiting paint, if the back of the rusted area is accessible, treat this also.

11 Before filling can take place, it will be necessary to block the hole in some way. This can be achieved by the use of aluminium or plastic mesh, or aluminium tape.

12 Aluminium or plastic mesh, or glass-fibre matting, is probably the best material to use for a large hole. Cut a piece to the approximate size and shape of the hole to be filled, then position it in the hole so that its edges are below the level of the surrounding bodywork. It can be retained in position by several blobs of filler paste around its periphery.

13 Aluminium tape should be used for small or very narrow holes. Pull a piece off the roll, trim it to the approximate size and shape required, then pull off the backing paper (if used) and stick the tape over the hole; it can be overlapped if the thickness of one piece is insufficient. Burnish down the edges of the tape with the handle of a screwdriver or similar, to ensure that the tape is securely attached to the metal underneath.

Filling and respraying

14 Before using this Section, see the Sections on dent, deep scratch, rust holes and gash repairs.

15 Many types of bodyfiller are available, but generally speaking, those proprietary kits which contain a tin of filler paste and a tube of resin hardener are best for this type of repair. A wide, flexible plastic or nylon applicator will be found invaluable for imparting a smooth and well-contoured finish to the surface of the filler.

16 Mix up a little filler on a clean piece of card or board – measure the hardener carefully (follow the maker's instructions on the pack), otherwise the filler will set too rapidly or too slowly. Using the applicator, apply the filler paste to the prepared area; draw the applicator across the surface of the filler to achieve the correct contour and to level the surface. As soon as a contour that approximates to the correct one is achieved, stop working the paste – if you carry on too long, the paste will become sticky and begin to 'pick-up' on the applicator. Continue to add thin layers of filler paste at 20-minute intervals, until the level of the filler is just proud of the surrounding bodywork.

17 Once the filler has hardened, the excess can be removed using a metal plane or file. From then on, progressively-finer grades of abrasive paper should be used, starting with a 40-grade production paper, and finishing with a 400-grade wet-and-dry paper. Always wrap the abrasive paper around a flat rubber, cork, or wooden block – otherwise the surface of the filler will not be completely flat.

During the smoothing of the filler surface, the wet-and-dry paper should be periodically rinsed in water. This will ensure that a very smooth finish is imparted to the filler at the final stage.

18 At this stage, the 'dent' should be surrounded by a ring of bare metal, which in turn should be encircled by the finely 'feathered' edge of the good paintwork. Rinse the repair area with clean water, until all of the dust produced by the rubbing-down operation has gone.

19 Spray the whole area with a light coat of primer – this will show up any imperfections in the surface of the filler. Repair these imperfections with fresh filler paste or bodystopper, and once more smooth the surface with abrasive paper. Repeat this spray-and-repair procedure until you are satisfied that the surface of the filler, and the feathered edge of the paintwork, are perfect. Clean the repair area with clean water, and allow to dry fully.

20 The repair area is now ready for final spraying. Paint spraying must be carried out in a warm, dry, windless and dust-free atmosphere. This condition can be created artificially if you have access to a large indoor working area, but if you are forced to work in the open, you will have to pick your day very carefully. If you are working indoors, dousing the floor in the work area with water will help to settle the dust which would otherwise be in the atmosphere. If the repair area is confined to one body panel, mask off the surrounding panels; this will help to minimise the effects of a slight mis-match in paint colours. Bodywork fittings (e.g. chrome strips, door handles etc) will also need to be masked off. Use genuine masking tape, and several thicknesses of newspaper, for the masking operations.

21 Before commencing to spray, agitate the aerosol can thoroughly, then spray a test area (an old tin, or similar) until the technique is mastered. Cover the repair area with a thick coat of primer; the thickness should be built up using several thin layers of paint, rather than one thick one. Using 400-grade wet-and-dry paper, rub down the surface of the primer until it is really smooth. While doing this, the work area should be thoroughly doused with water, and the wet-and-dry paper periodically rinsed in water. Allow to dry before spraying on more paint.

22 Spray on the top coat, again building up the thickness by using several thin layers of paint. Start spraying at one edge of the repair area, and then, using a side-to-side motion, work until the whole repair area and about 2 inches of the surrounding original paintwork is covered. Remove all masking material 10 to 15 minutes after spraying on the final coat of paint.

23 Allow the new paint at least two weeks to harden, then, using a paintwork renovator, or a very fine cutting paste, blend the edges of the paint into the existing paintwork. Finally, apply wax polish.

Plastic components

24 With the use of more and more plastic body components by the vehicle manufacturers (e.g. bumpers. spoilers, and in some cases major body panels), rectification of more serious damage to such items has become a matter of either entrusting repair work to a specialist in this field, or renewing complete components. Repair of such damage by the DIY owner is not really feasible, owing to the cost of the equipment and materials required for effecting such repairs. The basic technique involves making a groove along the line of the crack in the plastic, using a rotary burr in a power drill. The damaged part is then welded back together, using a hot-air gun to heat up and fuse a plastic filler rod into the groove. Any excess plastic is then removed, and the area rubbed down to a smooth finish. It is important that a filler rod of the correct plastic is used, as body components can be made of a variety of different types (e.g. polycarbonate, ABS, polypropylene).

25 Damage of a less serious nature (abrasions, minor cracks etc) can be repaired by the DIY owner using a two-part epoxy filler repair material. Once mixed in equal proportions, this is used in similar fashion to the bodywork filler used on metal panels. The filler is usually cured in twenty to thirty minutes, ready for sanding and painting.

26 If the owner is renewing a complete component himself, or if he has repaired it with epoxy filler, he will be left with the problem of finding a suitable paint for finishing which is compatible with the type of plastic used. At one time, the use of a universal paint was not possible, owing to the complex range of plastics encountered in body component applications. Standard paints, generally speaking, will not bond to plastic or rubber satisfactorily. However, it is now possible to obtain a plastic body parts finishing kit which consists of a pre-primer treatment, a primer and coloured top coat. Full instructions are normally supplied with a kit, but basically, the method of use is to first apply the pre-primer to the component concerned, and allow it to dry for up to 30 minutes. Then the primer is applied, and left to dry for about an hour before finally applying the special-coloured top coat. The result is a correctly-coloured component, where the paint will flex with the plastic or rubber, a property that standard paint does not normally posses.

5 Major body damage – repair

1 Where serious damage has occurred, or large areas need renewal due to neglect, it means that complete new panels will need welding-in; this is best left to professionals. If the damage is due to impact, it will also be necessary to check completely the alignment of the bodyshell; this can only be carried out accurately by a Honda dealer or suitably equipped body shop, using special jigs. If the body is left misaligned, it is primarily dangerous, as the car will not handle properly, and secondly, uneven stresses will be imposed on the steering, suspension and possibly transmission, causing abnormal wear or complete failure, particularly to items such as the tyres.

6 Bumper covers – removal and refitting

Front bumper cover

1 Jack up and support the front of the vehicle – see 'Jacking and vehicle support' in the Reference chapter. Remove both front wheels.
2 At the base of the bumper remove the screws and clips **(see illustrations)**.
3 At both sides, prise free the wheel arch trim panel – there is no need to remove it completely. With the wheel arch trim held away from the bumper remove the screws from both sides **(see illustration)**.
4 With the aid of and assistant release the bumper from the clips below the headlight **(see illustration)** and then remove the bumper.
5 Where fitted disconnect the headlight washer hose and fog light wiring plug as the bumper is removed.

Refitting

6 Refitting is a reversal of the removal procedure.

Rear bumper cover

7 Jack up and support the rear of the vehicle – see 'Jacking and vehicle support' in the Reference chapter. Remove both rear wheels.
8 Where fitted remove the mudflaps on both sides and release the small quarter panel **(see illustrations)**.
9 Remove the clips and free the wheel arch

6.2a Remove the screws and...

6.2b prise out the trim clips

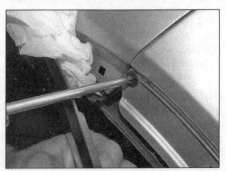
6.3 Remove the screws

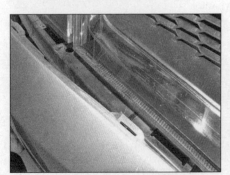
6.4 Release the bumper cover

6.8a Remove the mudflaps and...

6.8b...and quarter panel

6.9a Release the wheel arch trim...

6.9b...and place a clean rag behind it to keep it clear of the bumper cover

6.10a Remove the screws and...

6.10b...and retaining clips

6.11a Remove the blanking cap and then...

6.11b...remove the bolt

trim from the wheel arch. There is no need to remove it completely **(see illustrations)**.

10 Remove the screw from the wheel arch and then at the base of the bumper remove the screws and retaining clips **(see illustrations)**.

11 Open the tailgate and remove the four blanking caps from the bumper. Remove a bolt from each side and then slacken the remaining two bolts **(see illustrations)**.

12 With the aid of an assistant free the bumper cover from the rear wing and from beneath the rear lamps **(see illustration)**. Remove the slackened bolts and then remove the bumper from the vehicle. On models fiited with rear parking sensors, disconnect the wiring plug as the cover is removed.

13 With the cover removed, the bumper reinforcement can now be unbolted and removed, if required.

Refitting

14 Refitting is a reversal of the removal procedure. Check the operation of the parking sensors (where fitted).

7   Grille – removal and refitting

Removal

1 Open the bonnet, release the trim clips and remove the bonnet slam panel/grille cover **(see illustrations)**.

6.12 Free the bumper cover from the rear wing

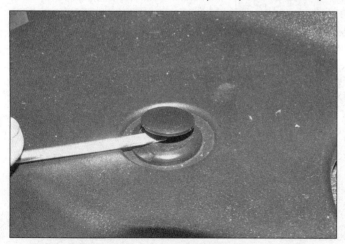

7.1a Prise out the centre peg to release the trim clip

7.1b Remove the grille/slam panel cover

7.2a Remove the mounting bolts at each side and centre

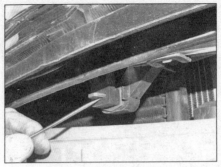

7.2b Release the tabs (shown with bumper cover removed)...

7.2c...and remove the grille

2 Remove the mounting bolts from the radiator support and bumper support brackets. Free the grille from the mounting tabs **(see illustrations)**.

Refitting

3 Refitting is a reversal of removal.

8 Bonnet – removal and refitting

Note: *The aid of an assistant is essential if removing the bonnet.*

1 Mark the position of the hinges in relation to the body, as a guide to refitting. To avoid any damage to the paintwork, protect the area at the base of the windscreen – clean old blankets are ideal for this purpose.

2 Support the bonnet at both sides and then

remove the bonnet hinge bolts. Remove the bonnet.

3 Refitting is a reversal of removal, using the previously made alignment marks. Check and adjust the bonnet catch if necessary.

9 Bonnet lock and cable – removal, refitting and adjustment

Removal

1 Open the bonnet, remove the trim clips and lift off the grille/slam panel cover as described in Section 8.

2 Disconnect the wiring plug from the bonnet open warning switch and release the loom form the retaining clip.

3 Mark the position of the lock assembly as an aid to refitting **(see illustration)**.

4 Remove the bolts and turn over the lock to

access the release cable. Unhook the small spring and release the inner cable. Prise free the outer cable and remove the lock **(see illustrations)**.

5 If required the release cable can now be replaced. Unclip the cable from the cable clips on the slam panel and inner wing.

6 Working in the cabin, remove the drivers side kick panel by prising it free and then and then unbolt the bonnet release handle **(see illustrations)**.

7 Tie a length of stout cord to the end of the cable and pull the cable into the engine bay. Ensure the end of the cord remains in the cabin, as theis will be used to pull the new cable into position.

Refitting and adjustment

8 If the release cable is being replaced, tie the new cable to the length of cord and pull it into the cabin. Refit the cable into the release handle and replace the trim panel.

9 Fit the cable to the lock. Connect the bonnet open warning switch wiring connector and bolt the lock into position using the previously made marks to align it correctly.

10 If the front of the bonnet is not level with the front wings, the lock may be moved up or down within the mounting holes. Precise alignment is easier if the grille is removed. After making an adjustment, raise or lower the rubber buffers to support the bonnet correctly.

11 Check that the bonnet opens and closes correctly and that the safety catch functions and then refit the grille (where removed) and the slam panel/grille cover trim.

9.3 Mark the position of the lock

9.4a Remove the small spring...

9.4b...and release the cable

9.6a Unbolt the handle...

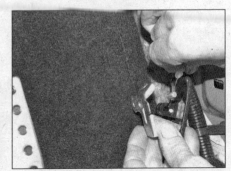

9.6b...and release the cable

10.2a Prise off the cover and...

10.2b...disconnect the tweeter wiring plug (where fitted)

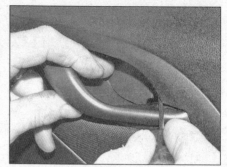

10.3a Remove the cover and...

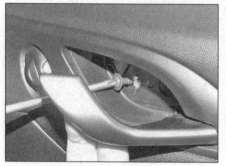

10.3b...then the screw

10.4a Remove the cover and then...

10.4b...remove the screw

10 Door inner trim panel – removal and refitting

1 Lower the appropriate window and disconnect the battery negative (earth) lead (Chapter 5A).

Front door

2 With the door glass fully lowered prise off the mirror cover panel **(see illustrations)**.
3 Prise off the cover from the inner release handle and remove screw **(see illustrations)**.
4 Remove the cover from the door pull handle and then remove screw **(see illustrations)**.
5 Starting at the bottom of the panel release the trim clips with a trim tool. Suitable wedges can be fabricated to hold the panel clear of the door frame – this will allow you to see the locating clips and place the trim tool as close as possible to the clips to release them. Work around door frame and remove the panel. Some of the panel clips will inevitable stay in the door frame **(see illustration)** and these should be recovered once the panel is removed.

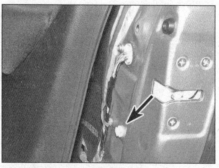

10.5 Remove the panel. Note the clip left in the door frame.

6 Support the panel and disconnect the release cable, the lock cable, the power window wiring plug and the mirror switch wiring plug. Release the wiring loom from the door trim panel and remove the panel **(see illustrations)**.

10.6a Release the outer cable...

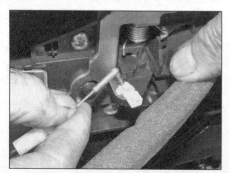

10.6b...and unhook the inner

10.6c Release the lock cable...

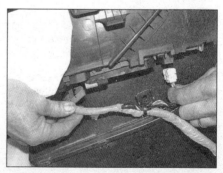

10.6d...and disconnect the wiring plugs

10.7 Pincers are an ideal tool for removing the trim clips

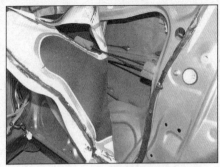

10.8 Remove the membrane

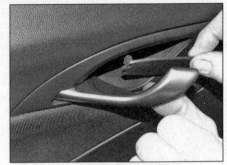

10.10a Remove the cover...

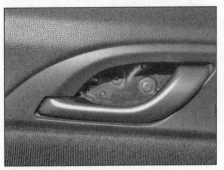

10.10b...and then the screw

10.12 Remove the quarter panel

10.13 Use a suitable plastic trim tool to release the door panel

7 With the panel removed, recover any trim clips left in the door frame (see illustration). Replace the damaged ones and fit them to the door trim panel before refitting the panel

8 To access the the lock mechanism, glass and window regulator the door membrane must be removed. Unhook the latch and lock cables from the support strut and disconnect the latch wiring plug. Release the wiring loom and then unscrew the support strut. With care peel back the membrane (see illustration) and feed the cables and wiring loom through the membrane as it is removed. The sealant is extremely sticky, so protect it from contamination and if necessary cover it with plastic – kitchen cling film is ideal for this purpose.

9 Refitting is a reversal of removal. Obtain and replace any damaged trim clips.

Rear door

10 With the glass fully lowered, prise off the cover from the door release handle and remove the screw (see illustrations).

11 Remove the cover from pull handle and then remove screw.

12 Starting at the rear edge carefully release the small quarter panel (see illustration).

13 Starting at the bottom of the panel release the trim clips with a trim tool (see illustration). Suitable wedges can be fabricated to hold the panel clear of the door frame – this will allow you to see the locating clips and place the trim tool as close as possible to the clips to release them. Work around door frame and remove panel. Some of the panel clips will inevitably

stay in the door frame and these should be recovered once the panel is removed.

14 Support the trim panel and disconnect the door release cable, the door lock cable and the power window electrical connector. Remove the panel.

15 To access the the lock mechanism, glass and window regulator the door membrane must be removed. Unhook the latch and lock cables from the support strut and disconnect the latch wiring plug. Release the wiring loom and then unscrew the support strut. With care peel back the membrane and feed the cables and wiring loom through the membrane as it is removed. The sealant is extremely sticky, so protect it from contamination and if necessary cover it with plastic – kitchen cling film is ideal.

16 Refitting is a reversal of the removal procedure. Obtain and replace any damaged trim clips

11.2a Remove the bolts...

11 Door window glass – removal and refitting

Front door

1 Remove the door inner trim panel as described in Section 10 and then remove the door membrane.

2 Remove the power window switch panel from the door and reconnect the battery. Alternatively have and assistant hold up the door trim panel with the switch connected and then reconnect the battery. Turn on the ignition and adjust the position of the glass, so that the retaining bolts are accessible (see illustrations). Turn off the ignition and disconnect the battery.

3 Refitting is a reversal of removal. Check

11.2b...and lift out the glass

11.5 Slacken, but do not remove the bolts at this stage

11.8 Removing the rear door glass

12.2 Disconnect the wiring plug

that the glass moves up and down freely. If necessary slight adjustment is possible. Adjust the glass by slackening the mounting bolts and pushing it forward into the front guide channel. Tighten the bolts and check that the glass moves freely up and down.

Rear door

4 Remove the door inner trim panel and membrane, as described in Section 10.

5 Remove the power window switch panel from the door and reconnect the battery. Alternatively have an assistant hold up the door trim panel with the switch connected and then reconnect the battery. Turn on the ignition and adjust the position of the glass, so that the retaining bolts are accessible **(see illustration)**. Turn off the ignition and disconnect the battery.

6 Remove the rear guide channel lower mounting bolt and then slacken the upper bolt. Pivot the channel away from the glass.

7 Fully remove the glass retaining bolts and then lower the glass. Release the glass from the rear guide channel – it may be necessary to pull the rubber seal from the channel in order to release the glass.

8 Lift the glass up, rotate it in the door frame and then remove it **(see illustration)**.

9 Refitting is a reversal of removal. Check

that the glass moves up and down freely. If necessary slight adjustment is possible. Adjust the glass by slackening the mounting bolts and pushing it forward into the front guide channel. Tighten the bolts and check that the glass moves freely up and down.

12 Door window regulator – removal and refitting

Front door

1 Follow the procedure for glass removal in Section 11, but do not fully remove the glass, simply tape it in the up position using strong adhesive tape (Gaffer tape).

2 Disconnect the wiring plug from the regulator **(see illustration)**.

3 Slacken the silver headed bolt and remove all the other bolts. Release the silver headed bolt from the keyhole slot and then manoeuvre the regulator from the door frame **(see illustration)**.

4 Refitting is a reversal of removal. Check and adjust the position of the door glass as in Section 11.

Rear door

5 Follow the procedure for glass removal in

12.3 Remove the regulator from the door frame

Section 11, but do not fully remove the glass. Tape the glass in the fully closed position using strong adhesive tape (Gaffer tape).

6 Slacken the silver mounting bolt and remove all the other bolts. Slide the silver bolt from the key hole slot and manoeuvre the regulator through the hole in the door frame. Disconnect the wiring plug and then fully remove the regulator from the door frame **(see illustrations)**.

7 Refitting is a reversal of removal. Check and adjust the position of the door glass as described Section 11

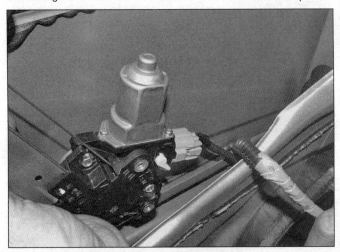

12.6a Disconnect the wiring plug and...

12.6b...remove the regulator

13.3a Remove the bolt...

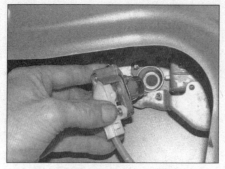

13.3b...and release the key cylinder and cable from the handle

13.4 Remove the plate

13 Door handle and lock components – removal and refitting

Exterior handle – front

1 Ensure the door glass is fully raised before starting work.

2 Remove the door trim panel, support bracket and membrane as described in Section 10.

3 If working on the drivers door, fit a 5 mm hex key to the bolt and loosen it whilst pressing on it **(see illustrations)**. Remove the lock cylinder assembly by releasing the retaining hook. Release the cable from the cable clip and lower the lock cylinder away from the outer handle. If working on the passenger door just remove the bolt. Honda recommend that the hex head bolt is replaced.

4 Remove the two blanking plugs and then remove the bolts holding the cover plate in position. Unhook the cover plate and remove it **(see illustration)**.

5 Release the outer a handle from the door skin and unhook the link rod **(see illustration)**. Honda recommend that the small plastic grommet is replaced every time the link rod is removed from the outer handle. Remove the handle form the vehicle.

6 Refitting is a reversal of removal, but a new link rod connector and special screw should be fitted.

Exterior handle – rear

7 Prise up and remove the rear quarter trim panel and remove the now exposed bolts **(see illustration)**.

8 Partially pull out the handle and then disconnect the link rod. Protect the paint work if necessary **(see illustration)**.

9 Refitting is a reversal of removal, but fit a new link rod connector to the handle before refitting the handle.

Interior handle

10 Remove the door inner trim panel as described in Section 10.

11 Remove the screws and release the handle from the door trim.

12 Refitting is a reversal of removal.

Latch – front

13 Remove the inner trim panel and membrane as described in Section 10.

14 If working on the drivers door, remove the hex head screw and then unhook the key cylinder. Unhook the lock handle link rod from the latch assembly at the latch. Note that it is easier to remove the handle and then disconnect the link rod at the handle rather than at the latch.

15 Remove the screws from the outer edge of the door frame and the single screw from the inside **(see illustration)**.

16 Manoeuvre the latch from the door complete with the lock cable, release cable, the key/cylinder cable (if working on the drivers door) and the link rod **(see illustration)**.

17 The cables can be replaced once the

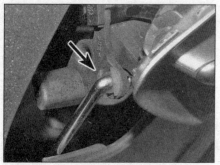

13.5 Unhook the link rod

13.7 Remove the bolts

13.8 Disconnect the link rod

13.15 Remove the screws

13.16 Remove the latch assembly (drivers side shown)

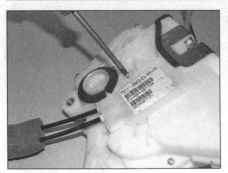

13.17a Remove the cover to...

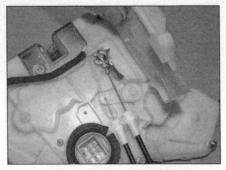

13.17b...to access the cables

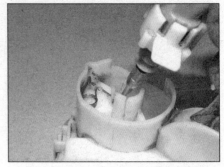

13.18 Remove the cylinder lock cable

screw and the latch cover plate are removed on the bench **(see illustrations)**.

18 If working on the drivers door the cylinder lock cable can be removed. Note the location of the small return spring and then depress the 'wings' of the collar. Remove the cable with the collar **(see illustration)**.

19 Refitting is a reversal of removal.

Latch – rear

20 Remove the inner trim panel and membrane as described in Section 10.

21 Remove the lower bolt from the rear glass guide channel.

22 Remove the outer handle as described in this Section and then disconnect the link rod. Remove the outer door frame screws and the single screw from the inner door frame. Manoeuvre the latch assembly past the glass guide channel and out of the door frame **(see illustrations)**.

23 The cables can be replaced once the screw and the cable cover plate are removed on the bench.

24 Refitting is a reversal of removal.

Lock cylinder

25 Remove the inner trim panel and membrane as described in Section 10.

26 Remove the hex head bolt and release the cable retainer from the door reinforcement strut **(see illustration)**. Work the cylinder assembly free from the lock handle.

27 Remove the screws and release the cable from the cylinder assembly.

28 The key cylinder is held in place by two

anti-tamper screws. Make a cut with a hacksaw in the heads of the screws and use a screwdriver to release them. Alternatively the screws can be removed with a pair of pliers **(see illustration)**.

29 Remove the cover plate and cylinder cover. At the rear remove the operating arm and then the circlip **(see illustration)**.Note the location of the return spring.

30 Refitting is a reversal of removal, but new anti-tamper screws should be fitted.

14 Door – removal and refitting

Removal

1 Disconnect the battery negative (earth) lead (Chapter 5A).

2 Mark or measure the position of the door in relation to the bodywork. Mark the position of the hinges on the door frame.

3 Remove the trim panel from the base of the A-pillar or the B- pillar trim panel if working on the rear door – see Section 25. Disconnect the wiring plug and feed the loom out of the pillar. It is also possible to remove the wiring loom from from the door and feed it out of the door hinge panel.

4 Unbolt the door check strap.

5 Position a trolley jack under the door. The head of the jack should be covered with a suitable material to avoid damage to the door.

6 Have an assistant support the door, then undo the retaining bolts in the top and bottom hinges.

7 Carefully lift the door from the hinges, and with the aid of the trolley jack (and an assistant) remove the door from the vehicle.

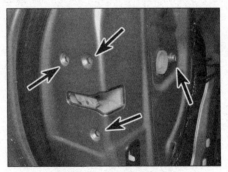

13.22a Remove the screws

13.22b Remove the latch assembly

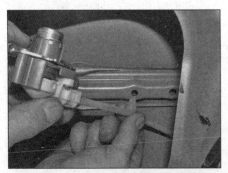

13.26 Release the cable and cylinder

13.28 With luck the screws can be released with pliers

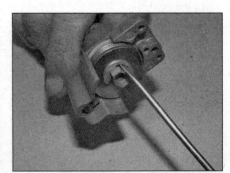

13.29 Remove the circlip

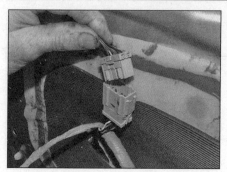

15.3a Disconnect the wiring plug

15.3b Release the loom

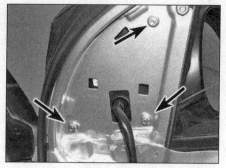

15.4 Remove the nuts

15.7 Release the mirror

15.8 Disconnect the wiring plugs

Refitting

8 Refitting is a reversal of the removal procedure, but check that the door lock passes over the striker centrally. If necessary, reposition the striker.

15 Exterior mirror and glass – removal and refitting

Removal and refitting

Mirror

1 Prise free the cover trim. On models fitted with a speaker disconnect the wiring plug. Remove the cover trim.
2 Remove the door trim panel as described in Section 10.
3 Disconnect the wiring plug and then release the loom from the retaining clip **(see illustrations)**.

4 Support the mirror and remove the mounting nuts **(see illustration)**. Feed the loom through the door and remove the mirror.
5 Refitting is a reversal of removal.

Mirror glass

6 Protect the mirror paintwork with masking tape and then adjust the mirror fully outwards and upwards.
7 Using a long flat bladed screwdriver (again covered in masking tape) release the mirror glass by inserting the screwdriver through the slot provided in the base of the mirror and then twisting the screwdriver to release the mirror **(see illustration)**. Do not attempt to pry the mirror glass free from mirror.
8 Where fitted disconnect the heated mirror electrical connectors **(see illustration)**.
9 Before refitting the mirror, check that the actuator controls and covers are correctly located. Reconnect the wiring plugs and then (preferably wearing gloves) push the mirror back into position.

16 Interior mirror – removal and refitting

1 Unclip the mirror cover. On models fitted with an auto dimming mirror disconnect the wiring plug.
2 Pull down the hook and release the mounting from the base. On models fitted with an auto dimming mirror remove the single screw. Slide the mirror to the rear and remove it.
3 Refitting is a reversal of removal.

17 Tailgate – removal and refitting

Removal

1 Disconnect the battery negative (earth) lead (Chapter 5A).
2 Remove the tailgate inner trim panels as described in Section 25.
3 Disconnect the wiring loom from the rear windscreen, the aerial, the tailgate release switch and the tailgate mounted lamps.
4 Free the wiring loom from the retaining clips and the release the flexible grommet from the tailgate **(see illustration)**.
5 Feed the wiring loom out of the tailgate and then have an assistant support the tailgate.
6 Pry free the spring clips and remove the support struts. Mark the position of the hinges and then unbolt and remove the tailgate **(see illustrations)**. Store the tailgate safely.

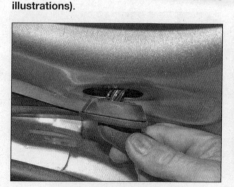

17.4 Release the grommet

17.6a Remove the support struts

17.6b Remove the hinge bolts

Refitting

7 Refitting is a reversal of the removal procedure, but check that the tailgate is located centrally in the body aperture, and that the striker enters the lock centrally. If necessary, loosen the mounting nuts and reposition the tailgate as required.

18 Support struts – removal and refitting

Removal

1 Have an assistant support the tailgate or bonnet in its open position.
2 Prise off the upper spring clip securing the strut to the tailgate, boot or bonnet. Pull the socket from the ball-stud.
3 Similarly prise off the bottom clip, and pull the socket from the ball-stud. Withdraw the strut.

Refitting

4 Refitting is a reversal of the removal procedure, making sure that the strut is fitted the same way up as when it was removed.

19 Tailgate lock components – removal and refitting

Removal

1 Remove the tailgate interior trim panel as described in Section 25.
2 Disconnect the electrical connector from the tailgate latch assembly.
3 Remove the mounting bolts partially remove the latch and then disconnect the wiring plug. Remove the latch.
4 Refitting is a reversal of the removal procedure.

20 Windscreen and fixed windows – removal and refitting

1 The windscreen and rear window on all models are bonded in place with special mastic, as are the rear side windows. Special tools are required to cut free the old units and fit new ones; special cleaning solutions and primer are also required. It is therefore recommended that this work is entrusted to a Honda dealer or windscreen replacement specialist.

21 Body side-trim mouldings and adhesive emblems – removal and refitting

Removal

1 Body side trims and mouldings are attached either by retaining clips or adhesive bonding. On bonded mouldings, insert a length of strong cord (fishing line is ideal) behind the moulding or emblem concerned. With a sawing action, break the adhesive bond between the moulding or emblem and the panel.
2 Thoroughly clean all traces of adhesive from the panel using methylated spirit, and allow the location to dry.
3 On mouldings with retaining clips, unclip the mouldings from the panel, taking care not to damage the paintwork.

Refitting

4 Peel back the protective paper from the rear face of the new moulding or emblem. Carefully fit it into position on the panel concerned, but take care not to touch the adhesive. When in position, apply hand pressure to the moulding/emblem for a short period, to ensure maximum adhesion to the panel.
5 Renew any broken retaining clips before refitting trims or mouldings.

22 Sunroof – general information and adjustment

Sunroof mechanism and motor

2 Removal of the sunroof, mechanism and/or motor involves removal of the headlining. This is a complex task, which requires patience and dexterity, and is considered to be beyond the scope of a DIYer. Consequently, we recommend this task be entrusted to a Honda dealer or upholstery specialist.

Drain tubes

3 There are four drain tubes, one located in each corner of the sunroof aperture.
4 To remove any obstruction insert a length of suitable nylon wire down through the tubes. If the obstruction cannot be cleared, access the drain tubes as follows:
5 The front drain tubes go down the front A-pillars; remove the lower trim panel to gain access to the drain tube.
6 The rear drain tubes go down the C-pillars (Hatchback) or D-pillars (Estate); remove the rear side trims to gain access.

23 Seats – removal and refitting

1 Disconnect the battery negative lead, and position the lead away from the battery (see Chapter 5A).

⚠️ *Warning: Before proceeding, wait a minimum of 10 minutes, as a precaution against accidental firing of the airbag unit or seat belt pretensioner. This period ensures that any residual electrical energy is dissipated.*

Front seats

2 Slide the seat fully forward and remove the covers. Remove the rear mounting bolts **(see illustration)**.
3 Slide the seat fully rearward and remove the bolt covers. Remove the front bolts **(see illustration)**.
4 Raise the seat slightly and disconnect the wiring plug(s) **(see illustration)**.
5 With the aid of an assistant remove the seat, taking care to avoid damaging the paintwork.
6 Refitting is a reversal of removal, but apply thread locking compound to the fixing bolts and tighten them to the specified torque.

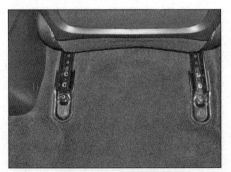
23.2 Remove the bolts

23.3 Remove the covers to access the bolts

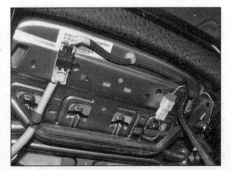
23.4 Disconnect the wiring plugs

Rear seats

7 Remove the rear seat headrests by fully extending them and press the release slide.

8 Pull up the cover and feed the seatbelt buckles through the seat back.

9 Unbolt and remove the right-hand centre seat belt lower mounting.

10 Fold down both seats.

11 Release the clips and pull up the front edge of the rear floor mat.

12 Working on the left-hand seat remove the seat buckle tension spring bolt. and then release the wiring loom.

13 Remove the mounting bolts from both seats and (with the aid of an assistant) remove the seats from the vehicle.

14 Refitting is a reversal of the removal procedure, tighten the mounting bolts to the specified torque.

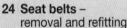

24 Seat belts –
removal and refitting

⚠ *Warning: Be careful when handling the seat belt tensioning device, it contains a small explosive charge (pyrotechnic device) similar to the one used to deploy the airbag(s). Clearly, injury could be caused if these are released in an uncontrolled fashion. Once fired, the tensioner cannot be reset, and must be renewed. Note also that seat belts and associated components which have been subject to impact loads must be renewed.*

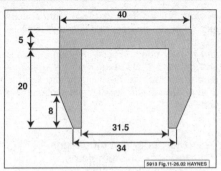

24.2 Construct a jig to the dimensions shown

Front seat belt

1 Disconnect the battery negative lead, and position the lead away from the battery (see Chapter 5A).

⚠ *Warning: Before proceeding, wait a minimum of 10 minutes, as a precaution against accidental firing of the seat belt tensioner. This period ensures that any residual electrical energy is dissipated.*

⚠ *Warning: There is a potential risk of the seat belt tensioning device firing during removal, so it should be handled carefully. Once removed, treat it with care – do not allow use chemicals on or near it, and do not expose it to high temperatures, or it may detonate.*

2 Fabricate a suitable jig from stiff cardboard (2 – 2.5 mm thick) to the dimensions shown **(see illustration)**.

24.3 A length of 2 mm welding rod can be used instead of the cardboard jig

3 Insert the jig into the latch assembly and then using a small screwdriver inserted through the hole unlock the belt from the connector **(see illustration)**.

4 Apply tension to the belt and remove the screwdriver to release the belt.

5 Remove the front seat as described in Section 23.

6 With reference to Section 25, remove the B-pillar lower and upper trim panels.

7 Remove the upper anchor bolt **(see illustration)**.

8 At the base of the B-pillar disconnect the wiring plug from the pre-tensioner and the inertia reel. Unbolt the pre-tensioner and then unbolt and remove the inertia reel **(see illustrations)**.

9 Remove the inertia reel from the B-pillar

10 Refitting is a reversal of removal, but apply thread locking compound to the anchor bolts before refitting.

24.7 The upper mounting bolt

24.8a Unbolt the pre-tensioner...

24.8b...to access the inertia reel

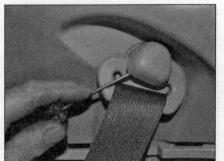

24.11a Remove the cover...

24.11b...and then the bolt

24.17 Unzip the cover

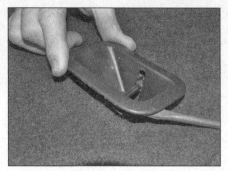
24.18 Remove the latch trim

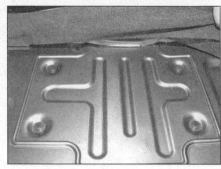
24.19 The inertia reel cover

24.20 Unbolt the inertia reel

Rear side seat belt

11 Remove the upper anchor bolt cover and then unbolt the upper anchor (see illustrations).
12 Remove the rear side panel and the C-pillar upper trim panel as described in Section 25.
13 Remove the lower anchor mounting bolt. Note the order of the washers on the bolt as it is removed.
14 At the base of the pillar remove the inertia reel upper mounting bolt and then the lower mounting bolt.
15 Refitting is a reversal of removal, but apply thread locking compound to the anchor bolts before refitting.

Rear centre seat belt

16 Remove the rear seats as described in Section 23.
17 Unzip the centre seat back cover (see illustration).
18 Prise free the seat latch trim. This is a very tight fit in the housing and it is very easy to damage the metal seat frame (see illustration).
19 Carefully peel back the upholstery to reveal the inertia reel cover (see illustration).
20 Remove the cover and unbolt the inertia reel (see illustration). Remove the upper guide panel, feed the webbing through the seat and remove the inertia reel
21 Refitting is a reversal of removal, but apply thread locking compound to the anchor bolts before refitting.

Seat belt stalks

22 The front stalks are accessed by removing the seats as described in Section 23.

25 Interior trim panels – removal and refitting

Note: *This section covers the removal and installation of the interior trim panels. It may be necessary to remove an overlapping trim before you can remove the one required. For more information on trim removal, look at the relevant Chapters and Sections, where the trims may need to be removed to carry out any other procedures (eg, to remove the steering column you will need to remove the shrouds).*
Note: *A selection of plastic trim removal tools will be required. Where these are not available then protect the panels with tape and wrap*

insulating tape or masking tape around the tool used to minimise any damage to the trim. Refitting is a reversal of removal unless otherwise indicated, note however that any damaged trim clips should be always be replaced.

Sunvisor removal

1 Remove the cover to expose the mounting screws (see illustrations). Remove the screws and then remove the visor.
2 The catch end of the sunvisor is a bayonet type fitting in the headlining/roof panel. Turn the catch anti-clockwise to remove it (see illustration).
3 Refitting is a reversal of removal.

Passenger grab handle removal

4 Using a suitable tool, prise out the locking peg. Repeat the procedure at the other end of the handle (see illustration).
5 Using a small screwdriver depress the locking inner locking tabs (see illustration) and remove the grab handle.
6 Refitting is a reversal of removal.

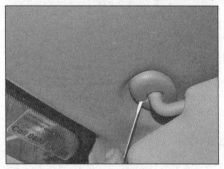
25.1a Remove the cover and then...

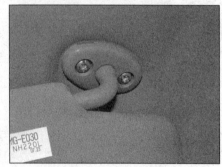
25.1b ...remove the screws

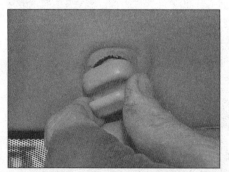
25.2 Remove the sunvisor catch

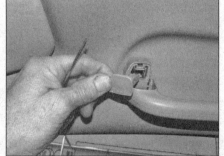
25.4 Prise out the locking peg

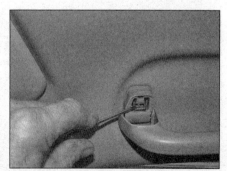
25.5 Release the locking tabs

25.9 Removing the A-pillar trim panels.

25.12a Prise free the lower panel and...

25.12b...note the location of the retaining clips

25.14a Unhook the panel from the roof...

25.14b...and remove it

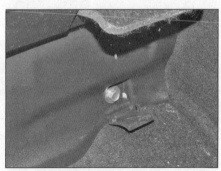

25.18 Remove the shelf support panel

A-pillar trim removal

7 Disconnect the battery (Chapter 5A) and wait a minimum of 10 minutes before removing the A-pillar trims.

8 The A-pillar trims cover the front edge of the side curtain air bags. Avoid using any sharp tool when removing them.

9 Using a plastic trim tool prise free the trim panels **(see illustration)**. They are retained by a special type of trim clip, that is hard to release.

10 Refitting is a reversal of removal, but the retaining clips must be replaced..

B-pillar trim removal

11 Partially release the weather seal and then remove the front and rear door sill trim panels. Slide the seat fully forwards.

12 Pull the lower panel free from the base of the pillar **(see illustrations)**.

13 Follow the procedure shown in Section 24 and release the seatbelt anchor.

14 Pull up the base of the upper C-pillar trim and then unhook it at the top. Pass the seatbelt through the guide as it is removed **(see illustrations)**.

15 Refitting is a reversal of removal.

C-pillar trim removal

16 Remove the rear seats (Section 23) and then remove the parcel shelf.

17 As the C-pillar trims are part of the load area side panels and because they are installed first the load area trim panels must be removed before the C-pillar trims can be removed.

18 Lift out the spare wheel well cover and then unbolt the support bracket from the front edge of the wheel well **(see illustration)**.

19 Prise free the weather seal from the tailgate and then remove the tailgate slam panel **(see illustration)**.

20 At the base of the C-pillar remove the small filler panel and then remove the load area tie down strap brackets. Remove the storage compartment cover and then prise the panel free from the rear first **(see illustration)**. The storage compartment can be removed

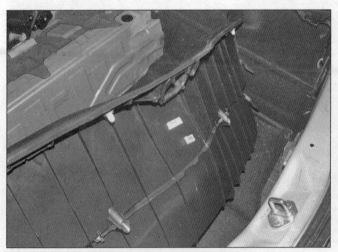

25.19 Remove the rear slam panel

25.20 Remove the panel

25.24 Remove the panel

25.25 Removing the kick panel

25.29 Remove the upper cowl (shown with the steering wheel removed for clarity)

first to allow the panel to come away from the rear edge of the inner wing/wheel arch if necessary.

21 As the panel is removed disconnect the wiring plug from the boot lamp (right-hand side) or the 12 volt power outlet (left-hand side).

22 Remove the cover from the rear seatbelt upper anchor and remove the bolt. Prise free the upper section of the C-pillar trim.

23 Refitting is a reversal of removal. Replace any damaged trim clips.

Front sill trim

24 Partially release the weather seal and then prise up the panel. Unhook the ends from the side kick panel and the B-pillar trim panel. Remove the panel **(see illustration)**.

Kick panels

25 Partially release the weather seal and then prise out the panel **(see illustration)**. If removing the right-hand panel, manoeuvre it over the bonnet and fuel filler flap release handles.

Steering column shrouds removal

26 Remove the lower (knee) trim panel from below the column.

27 Fully extend and lower the column.

28 At the base of the lower shroud locate the small hole in the left-hand side of the shroud. Using a suitable screwdriver passed through the guide hole, twist the screwdriver to release the left-hand side of the upper cover.

25.30a Remove the screws and...

25.30b...remove the lower cowl

29 Unhook the left-hand end of the upper cover and (turning the steering wheel as necessary) release the right-hand end of the upper cover **(see illustration)**.

30 Remove the screws from the lower shroud and remove the shroud **(see illustrations)**.

31 Refitting is a reversal of removal.

Luggage area side panel removal

32 The panel is combined with the C-pillar trim panel and is removed with the C-pillar trim as described in this Section.

Tailgate trim panel

33 The trim panel is composed of four sections. An upper section that covers the high level brake light, two side sections and

the main lower section. The upper sections must be removed before the main lower panel can be removed.

34 Prise free the upper brake light cover.

35 Prise free the side panels.

36 Remove the screws from the grab handles and then prise free the main panel.

26 Centre console – removal and refitting

1 Disconnect the battery as described in Chapter 5A. Wait a minimum of 10 minutes before starting work.

2 The centre console is in two sections – front and rear. The rear must be removed before the front section can be removed

Rear section

3 Slide both front seats fully forward. If the centre console is to be removed to access the facia and heater, then consider removing both front seats to improve access.

4 At the base of the console remove the blanking plugs and then remove the bolts **(see illustrations)**.

5 Slide both seats to the rear and then remove the front blanking plugs and bolts.

6 Work the rear section free from the front section.

7 Pivot the rear of the console upwards and then disconnect the wiring plugs – the number

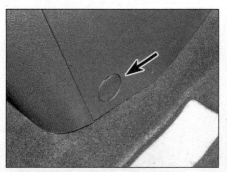

26.4a Remove the blanking plug and...

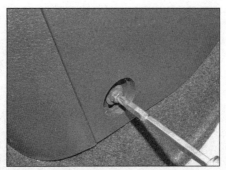

26.4b...and then the bolt

26.7a Pivot the rear section upwards...

26.7b...and disconnect the wiring plug(s)

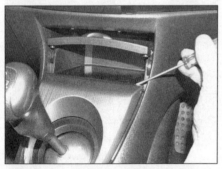

26.11 Remove the gear lever trim panel

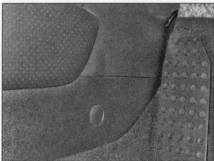

26.13a Remove the blanking plug...

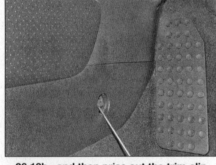

26.13b...and then prise out the trim clip

26.14 Remove the panel

26.15 Remove the front section of the centre console

27.3 Remove the facia end panel

27.5 Depress the centre peg to release the clip

will vary depending on the trim level (see illustrations).

8 Lift the console up and out of the vehicle.

9 Refitting is a reversal of the removal procedure. Replace any damaged trim clips.

Front section

10 Remove the rear section and then remove the drivers footrest by either removing the clips (models with a metal footrest) or by simply prising it free.

11 Open the storage compartment and then (starting at the front edge) prise free the gear lever trim (see illustration).

12 On models fitted with automatic transmission remove the bezel from the shift lever and then prise free the gear indicator panel.

13 At the front of the console remove the blanking plugs and then prise free the now exposed trim clips (see illustrations).

14 Remove the drivers side facia end panel, remove the single screw and then remove the lower steering column knee panel (see illustration).

15 Disengage the front section of the console from the facia by pulling it towards the rear of the vehicle. Lift up the front section and manoeuvre it over the gear lever and out of the vehicle (see illustration).

16 Refitting is a reversal of the removal procedure. Replace any damaged trim clips.

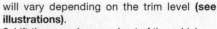

27 Glovebox –
removal and refitting

1 Disconnect the battery as described in Chapter 5A. Wait a minimum of 10 minutes before starting work.

2 Remove both sections of the centre console as described in Section 26.

3 Prise free the side panel from the lower section of the passenger A-pillar (see illustration).

4 Where fitted, pull down the trim panel from beneath the glovebox and then open the glovebox.

5 Remove the screws and trim clips from the upper edge of the glovebox (see illustration).

27.6 The bolt at the rear of the glovebox. The support bracket fits into the slot

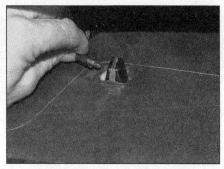

27.7a Disconnect the wiring plug

Note the outer screws also hold the bump stops for the glovebox lid.

6 At the rear of the glovebox slacken the single bolt – there is no need to remove it as it slots into the support bracket **(see illustration)**.

7 At the front lower edge remove the remaining screws and pull the glovebox forward, disconnect the wiring plug and remove the glovebox **(see illustrations)**.

8 Refitting is a reversal of the removal procedure. Replace any damaged trim clips.

28 Facia and crossmember – removal and refitting

1 Disconnect the battery as described in Chapter. 5A Wait a minimum of 10 minutes before starting work.

Facia

2 Remove the instrument panel lower cover

and then remove the instrument panel as described in Chapter 12.

3 Remove the centre console as described in Section 26.

4 Protect the facia and then prise up and remove the facia centre upper cover **(see illustration)**.

5 Remove the glovebox (Section 27).

6 Remove the audio unit and the centre air distribution vent as described in Chapter 12.

7 Remove both A-pillar trims – see Section 25.

8 Remove the passenger airbag as described in Chapter 12.

9 Where fitted remove the navigation unit (SatNav) or alternatively remove the audio display unit – see Chapter 12.

10 Prise free and then disconnect the wiring plug from sunlight sensor **(see illustration)**.

11 Remove the steering column assembly as described in Chapter 10.

12 On models fitted with SatNav from under the facia unclip the GPS antenna cable.

13 Remove the support stay from the rear of the glovebox **(see illustration)**.

14 The screws securing the facia to the crossmember must now be removed. There are 12 in total – 5 on the drivers side and 7 on

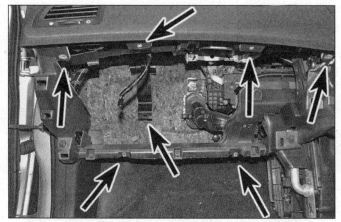

27.7b The glovebox removed, showing the screw and clip locations and the support bracket

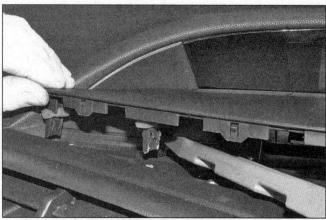

28.4 Remove the centre shelf

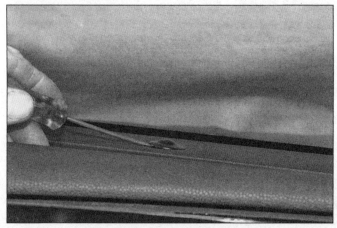

28.10 Remove the sunlight sensor

28.13 The glovebox support stay

28.14 Remove the facia

28.18 Remove the wiring plugs from the fusebox

the passenger side. Note that both facia end screws are captive in the facia panel. Lift up the facia and free it from the guide pins. With the aid of an assistant remove the facia from the vehicle **(see illustration)**. Place the facia on a soft surface, resting on it's back or front.

15 Refitting is a reversal of the removal procedure. On completion, check the operation of all electrical components.

Crossmember

Note: *It is possible to remove the crossmember with the facia still attached, but as most components have to be removed to release the facia and there is a great risk of*

cosmetic damage to the facia this method is not recommended.

16 Remove the facia as described above.

17 At the base of the right-hand A-pillar disconnect the wiring plugs from the door connector and roof wiring loom.

18 From above the pedal assembly disconnect the wiring plugs from the brake, clutch and accelerator pedal switches and then remove the large multi-plugs from the fusebox **(see illustration)**.

19 Disconnect the wiring plug from the gear lever and then remove the gear lever housing to the side (as described in Chapter 7A or Chapter 7B). This will allow access to the SRS

control unit and earth connection.

20 Unbolt and then remove the gear lever support plate **(see illustration)**. Detach the wiring loom as the plate is removed.

21 Disconnect the wiring plug and unbolt the earth connection from the airbag (SRS) control unit **(see illustrations)**.

22 At the base of the A-pillar on the left-hand side disconnect the wiring plugs from door connector and the audio aerial **(see illustration)**.

23 Remove the crossmember bolt from above the pedal box and the bolt holding the crossmember to the bulkhead – next to the heater housing **(see illustrations)**.

28.20 Remove the bolts

28.21a Remove the wiring plugs from the SRS control module...

28.21b...and then remove the earth connection

28.22 Disconnect the wiring plugs

28.23a Remove the pedal support bracket bolt

28.23b Remove bracket bolt

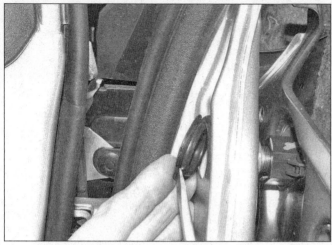

28.25a Remove the blanking plugs

28.25b Remove the bolts

24 As a guide to refitting, make alinement marks between the crossmember and the body shell.

25 On the outside of the left-hand A-pillar remove the blanking plugs. Unscrew the special bolts. Note that if the inner captive section rotates then a 21 mm spanner must be used on the inside of the A-pillar to allow the main bolt to be removed **(see illustrations)**. If the use of a spanner is required the bolt must be replaced.

26 On the outside of the right-hand A-pillar remove the exterior trim panel **(see illustrations)** and then the lower blanking plugs. Remove the bolts. Note the bolts are all different, so note their locations as they are removed.

27 Have an assistant support the crossmember and then (if not already done so) remove the centre support bracket bolts. Remove the bracket and manoeuvre the crossmenber from the vehicle.

28 Before refitting the crossmember screw the adjuster nut sleeves back into the crossmember **(see illustration)**.

29 Install the crossmember and lightly tighten the right-hand bolts and the special left-hand bolts.

30 Fully tighten the right-hand bolts to the specified torque and then tighten the left-hand bolts. As the left-hand bolts are tightened the inner sleeve nut will contact the inside of the A-pillar. If the sleeve nut does not contact the A-pillar, the bolt and sleeve nut must be replaced. Check that the crossmember is aligned with the marks made on removal and then fully tighten the left-hand bolts to the specified torque.

31 The remainder of refitting is a reversal of the removal procedure.

29 Wheel arch liner –
removal and refitting

1 A full length liner is only fitted to the front wings. The rear inner wings have a small quarter liner fitted, that is removed after the mud flap has been removed..

Removal

2 Jack up and support the front of the vehicle – see 'Jacking and vehicle support' in the Reference chapter. Remove the appropriate front road wheel.

3 Prise free the wheel arch trim.

4 Remove the screws from the front lower edge of the bumper.

5 Work around the liner and remove the multiple trim clips.

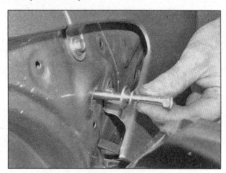

28.26b...and remove the bolt

28.26a Remove the trim panel...

6 Manoeuvre the liner from the wheel arch.

Refitting

7 Refitting is a reversal of the removal procedure. Tighten the wheel nuts to the specified torque.

28.28 Wind in the tolerance adjuster sleeve nuts

Chapter 12
Body electrical systems

Contents

Section number

Aerial – removal and refitting 18
Airbag system – general information and precautions............ 20
Airbag system components – removal and refitting.............. 21
Anti-theft alarm system – general information 22
Audio system – removal and refitting........................ 17
Central locking system – general information 15
Electrical connectors 4
Electrical fault finding – general information 2
Electronic control modules – removal and refitting 23
Exterior light bulbs – renewal............................. 7
Exterior light units – removal, refitting and beam adjustment 9
Fuses and relays – general information 3

Section number

General information and precautions......................... 1
Horns – removal and refitting............................. 14
Ignition switch – removal and refitting 5
Instrument panel – removal and refitting 11
Interior light bulbs – renewal 8
Parking aid components – general, removal and refitting 16
Speakers – removal and refitting 19
Switches – removal and refitting 6
Windscreen washer system components – removal and refitting ... 13
Windscreen wiper components – removal and refitting.......... 12
Xenon gas discharge headlight system – removal, refitting and
  adjustment 10

Degrees of difficulty

Easy, suitable for novice with little experience 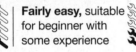	**Fairly easy,** suitable for beginner with some experience	**Fairly difficult,** suitable for competent DIY mechanic	**Difficult,** suitable for experienced DIY mechanic	**Very difficult,** suitable for expert DIY or professional

Specifications

System type	12 volt, negative earth	
Bulbs	**Power rating (watts)**	**Type**
Direction indicators	21	PY21W
Direction indicator side repeaters**	5	WY5W
Foglamp:		
Front	55	H11
Rear	21	P21W
Headlight:		
Halogen:		
Dipped	55*	H7
Main	55	H1
Gas discharge (Xenon):		
Dipped	35	D3S
Main	55	H7
Glovebox light	5	W5W
High-level brake light	LED	
Interior light	5	W5W
Number plate light	5	W5W
Luggage compartment light	5	W5W
Reading light	5	W5W
Reversing light	16	W16W
Sidelights	5	W5W
Stop/tail light	21/5	P21/5W
Tail light	5	W5W
Vanity mirror	5	W5W

1 * Check the wattage of the existing bulb and replace like for like.

2 ** LEDs are fitted

Torque wrench settings

	Nm	lbf ft
Airbag control unit nuts	10	7
Crash sensor bolts	10	7
Drivers airbag bolts*	10	7
Passenger airbag nuts/bolts	10	7
Windscreen wiper arm spindle nut	29	21
Windscreen wiper link arm	31	23
Windscreen wiper motor bolts	10	7
Windscreen wiper linkage to body bolts	10	7

* New nuts/bolts must be used.

1 General information and precautions

⚠️ **Warning: Before carrying out any work on the electrical system, read through the precautions given in 'Safety first!' at the beginning of this manual, and in Chapter 5A.**

1 The electrical system is of 12 volt negative earth type. Power for the lights and all electrical accessories is supplied by a lead-acid type battery which is charged by the alternator.

2 This Chapter covers repair and service procedures for the various electrical components not associated with the engine. Information on the battery, alternator and starter motor can be found in Chapter 5A.

3 It should be noted that prior to working on any component in the electrical system, the battery negative terminal should first be disconnected to prevent the possibility of electrical short-circuits and/or fires. **Note:** *If the vehicle has a security-coded radio, check that you have a copy of the code number before disconnecting the battery. Refer to your Honda dealer if in doubt.*

2 Electrical fault finding – general information

Note: *Refer to the precautions given in 'Safety first!' and in Chapter 5A before starting work. The following tests relate to testing of the main electrical circuits, and should not be used to test delicate electronic circuits (such as anti-lock braking systems), particularly where an electronic control unit is used.*

General

1 Typically, electrical circuit consists of an electrical component, any switches, relays, motors, fuses, fusible links or circuit breakers related to that component, and the wiring and connectors which link the component to both the battery and the chassis. To help to pinpoint a problem in an electrical circuit, wiring diagrams are included at the end of this Chapter.

2 Have a good look at the appropriate wiring diagram before attempting to diagnose an electrical fault, to obtain a complete understanding of the components included in the particular circuit concerned. The possible sources of a fault can be narrowed down by noting if other components related to the circuit are operating properly. If several components or circuits fail at one time, the problem is likely to be related to a shared fuse or earth connection.

3 An electrical problem will usually stem from simple cause, such as loose or corroded connections, a faulty earth connection, a blown fuse, a melted fusible link, or a faulty relay (refer to Section 3 for details of testing relays). Visually inspect the condition of all fuses, wires and connections in a problem circuit before testing the components. Use the wiring diagrams to determine which terminal connections will need to be checked in order to pinpoint the trouble-spot.

4 The basic tools required for electrical fault finding include a circuit tester or voltmeter (a 12 volt bulb with a set of test leads can also be used for certain tests); a self-powered test light (sometimes known as a continuity tester); an ohmmeter (to measure resistance); a battery and set of test leads; and a jumper wire, preferably with a circuit breaker or fuse incorporated, which can be used to bypass suspect wires or electrical components. Before attempting to locate a problem with test instruments, use the wiring diagram to determine where to make the connections.

5 Sometimes, an intermittent wiring fault (usually caused to a poor or dirty connection, or damaged wiring insulation) can be pinpointed by performing a wiggle test on the wiring. This involves wiggling the wiring by hand to see if the fault occurs as the wiring is moved. It should be possible to narrow down the source of the fault to a particular section of wiring. This method of testing can be used in conjunction with any of the tests described in the following sub-Sections.

6 Apart from problems due to poor connections, two basic types of fault can occur in an electrical circuit: open-circuit, or short-circuit.

7 Largely, open-circuit faults are caused by a break somewhere in the circuit, which prevents current from flowing. An open-circuit fault will prevent a component from working, but will not cause the relevant circuit fuse to blow.

8 Low resistance or short-circuit faults are caused by a 'short'; a failure point which allows the current flowing in the circuit to 'escape' along an alternative route, somewhere in the circuit. This typically occurs when a positive supply wire touches either an earth wire, or an earthed component such as the bodyshell. Such faults are normally caused by a breakdown in wiring insulation, A short circuit fault will normally cause the relevant circuit fuse to blow.

9 Fuses are designed to protect a circuit from being overloaded. A blown fuse indicates that there may be problem in that particular circuit and it is important to identify and rectify the problem before renewing the fuse. Always renew a blown fuse with one of the correct current rating; fitting a fuse of a different rating may cause an overloaded circuit to overheat and even catch fire.

Finding an open-circuit

10 One of the most straightforward ways of finding an open-circuit fault is by using a circuit test meter or voltmeter. Connect one lead of the meter to either the negative battery terminal or a known good earth. Connect the other lead to a connector in the circuit being tested, preferably nearest to the battery or fuse. Switch on the circuit, bearing in mind that some circuits are live only when the ignition switch is moved to a particular position. If voltage is present (indicated either by the tester bulb lighting or a voltmeter reading, as applicable), this means that the section of the circuit between the relevant connector and the battery is problem-free. Continue to check the remainder of the circuit in the same fashion. When a point is reached at which no voltage is present, the problem must lie between that point and the previous test point with voltage. Most problems can be traced to a broken, corroded or loose connection.

⚠️ **Warning: Under no circumstances may live measuring instruments such as ohmmeters, voltmeters or a bulb and test lead be used to test any of the airbag circuitry. Any testing of these components must be left to a Honda dealer or specialist, as there is a danger of activating the system if the correct procedures are not followed.**

Finding a short-circuit

11 Loading the circuit during testing will produce false results and may damage your test equipment, so all electrical loads must be disconnected from the circuit before it can be checked for short circuits. Loads are the components which draw current from a circuit, such as bulbs, motors, heating elements, etc.

12 Keep both the ignition and the circuit under test switched off, then remove the relevant fuse from the circuit, and connect a circuit test meter or voltmeter to the fuse connections.

13 Switch on the circuit, bearing in mind that some circuits are live only when the ignition switch is moved to a particular position. If voltage is present (indicated either by the tester bulb lighting or a voltmeter reading, as applicable), this means that there is a short-circuit. If no voltage is present, but the fuse still blows with the load(s) connected, this indicates an internal fault in the load(s).

Finding an earth fault

14 The battery negative terminal is connected to 'earth': the metal of the engine/ transmission and the car body – and most systems are wired so that they only receive a positive feed, the current returning through the metal of the car body. This means that the component mounting and the body form part of that circuit. Loose or corroded mountings can therefore cause a range of electrical faults, ranging from total failure of a circuit, to a puzzling partial fault. In particular, lights may shine dimly (especially when another circuit sharing the same earth point is in operation), motors (eg, wiper motors or the radiator auxiliary cooling fan motor) may run slowly, and the operation of one circuit may have an apparently unrelated effect on another. Note that on many vehicles, earth straps are used between certain components, such as the engine/transmission and the body, usually where there is no metal-to-metal contact between components due to flexible rubber mountings, etc **(see illustrations)**.

15 To check whether a component is properly earthed, disconnect the battery and connect one lead of an ohmmeter to a known good earth point. Connect the other lead to the wire or earth connection being tested. The resistance reading should be zero; if not, check the connection as follows.

16 If an earth connection is thought to be faulty, dismantle the connection and clean back to bare metal both the bodyshell and the wire terminal or the component earth connection mating surface. Be careful to remove all traces of dirt and corrosion, then use a knife to trim away any paint, so that a clean metal-to-metal joint is made. On reassembly, tighten the joint fasteners securely; if a wire terminal is being refitted, use serrated washers between the terminal and the bodyshell to ensure a clean and secure connection. When the connection is remade, prevent the onset of corrosion in the future by applying a coat of petroleum jelly or silicone-based grease or by spraying on (at regular intervals) a proprietary ignition sealer or a water dispersant lubricant.

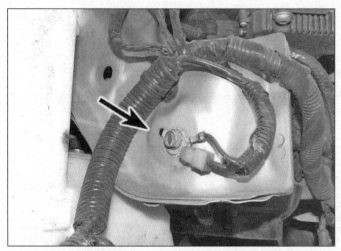

2.14a Earth connections are on the left-hand side of the front panel (bumper removal required)...

2.14b ...on the left-hand inner wing...

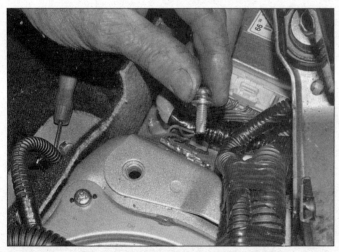

2.14c ...on the front of the transmission tunnel...

2.14d...and on the right-hand engine mount...

3 Fuses and relays – general information

Main fuses

1 Two fuseboxes are fitted to all models. One is located in the cabin and the other under the bonnet.

2 The cabin fuse box. is located on the right-hand (drivers side) of the facia above and to the left of the bonnet and fuel filler release handles **(see illustration)**.

3 The under bonnet fusebox is located in the left-hand side of the engine bay close to the battery **(see illustrations)**.

4 Each fuse is numbered. The fuse ratings and circuits they protect are listed in the owners handbook and in the wiring diagrams at the end of this Chapter.

5 To remove a fuse, first switch off the circuit concerned (or the ignition), then pull the fuse out of its terminals – a pair of tweezers provided specifically for this purpose are fitted on the underside of the engine compartment fusebox cover **(see illustration)**. The wire within the fuse should be visible; if the fuse is blown the wire will have a break in it, which will be visible through the plastic casing.

6 Always renew a fuse with one of an identical rating; never use a fuse with a different rating from the original or substitute anything else. Never renew a fuse more than once without tracing the source of the trouble. The fuse rating is stamped on top of the fuse; note

that the fuses are also colour-coded for easy recognition.

7 If a new fuse blows immediately, find the cause before renewing it again; a short to earth as a result of faulty insulation is most likely. Where a fuse protects more than one circuit, try to isolate the defect by switching on each circuit in turn (if possible) until the fuse blows again. Always carry a supply of spare fuses of each relevant rating on the vehicle.

8 Note that some circuits are protected by 'maxi' fuses fitted in the engine compartment fusebox. These fuses are physically much bigger than the normal fuses, and have correspondingly higher ratings.

Relays

9 Relays are located in the interior fuse box and the engine compartment fusebox. The interior fuse box holds the fuel injection relay, the power window relay and the starter relay. The engine compartment fuse box holds the AC compressor clutch relay and the cooling fan control relay.

10 The relays are of sealed construction, and cannot be repaired if faulty. The relays are of the plug-in type, and may be removed by pulling directly from their terminals. In some cases, it will be necessary to prise the two plastic clips outwards before removing the relay.

11 If a circuit or system controlled by a relay develops a fault and the relay is suspect, operate the system; if the relay is functioning, it should be possible to hear it click as it is

energised. If this is the case, the fault lies with the components or wiring of the system. If the relay is not being energised, then either the relay is not receiving a main supply or a switching voltage, or the relay itself is faulty. Testing is by the substitution of a known good unit, but be careful; while some relays are identical in appearance and in operation, others look similar but perform different functions.

12 To renew a relay, first ensure that the ignition switch is off. The relay can then simply be pulled out from the socket and the new relay pressed in.

4 Electrical connectors

1 Most electrical connections on these vehicles are made with multiwire plastic connectors. The mating halves of many connectors are secured with locking clips molded into the plastic connector shells. The mating halves of some large connectors, such as some of those under the instrument panel, are held together by a bolt through the center of the connector.

2 To separate a connector with locking clips, use a small screwdriver to pry the clips apart carefully, then separate the connector halves. Pull only on the shell, never pull on the wiring harness, as you may damage the individual wires and terminals inside the connectors. Look at the connector closely before trying to separate the halves. Often the locking clips are engaged in a way that is not immediately clear. Additionally, many connectors have more than one set of clips.

3 Each pair of connector terminals has a male half and a female half. When you look at the end view of a connector in a diagram, be sure to understand whether the view shows the harness side or the component side of the connector. Connector halves are mirror images of each other, and a terminal shown on the right side end-view of one half will be on the left side end-view of the other half.

4 It is often necessary to take circuit voltage measurements with a connector connected. Whenever possible, carefully insert a small straight pin (not your meter probe) into the rear of the connector shell to contact the terminal inside, then clip your meter lead to the pin. This kind of connection is called "backprobing." When inserting a test probe into a terminal, be careful not to distort the terminal opening. Doing so can lead to a poor connection and corrosion at that terminal later. Using the small straight pin instead of a meter probe results in less chance of deforming the terminal connector. "T" pins are a good choice as temporary meter connections. They allow for a larger surface area to attach the meter leads too.

5 Typical electrical connectors:

3.2 The cabin fusebox

3.3a The under bonnet fusebox

3.3b **Remove the cover to access the fuses. Note the position of the fuse puller tool**

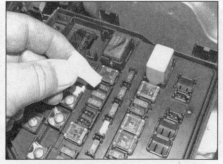

3.5 **Pulling a fuse with the provided tool**

4.5a Most electrical connectors have a single release tab that you depress to release the connector

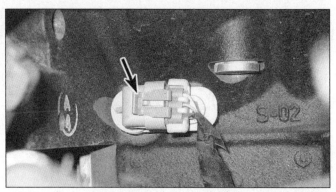

4.5b Some electrical connectors have a retaining tab which must be pried up to free the connector

4.5c Some connectors have two release tabs that you must squeeze to release the connector

4.5d Some connectors use wire retainers that you squeeze to release the connector

4.5e Critical connectors often employ a sliding lock (1) that you must pull out before you can depress the release tab (2)

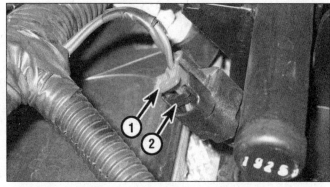

4.5f Here's another sliding-lock style connector, with the lock (1) and the release tab (2) on the side of the connector

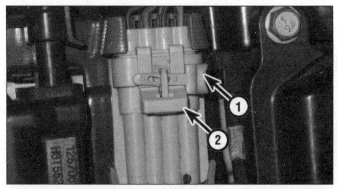

4.5g On some connectors the lock (1) must be pulled out to the side and removed before you can lift the release tab (2)

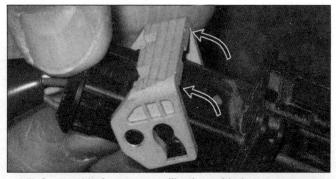

4.5h Some critical connectors, like the multi-pin connectors at the Electronic Control Module employ pivoting locks that must be flipped open

5.2a Remove the key reader coil...

5.2b...and the main switch

5.2c Drill out the shear bolts

6.3a Remove the screws

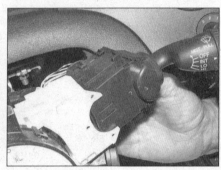

6.3b Slide out the switch and...

6.3c...disconnect the wiring plug

5 Ignition switch – removal and refitting

Removal

1 Remove the steering column as described in Chapter 10.
2 Remove the key reader coil and the electrical part of the switch and then drill out the heads of the shear bolts using a suitable drill bit **(see illustrations)**.

Refitting

3 Fit the lock with the new shear bolts, but do not fully tighten them at this stage.
4 Insert the key and check that the key turns freely and the steering lock disengages.
5 Fully tighten the shear bolts until the heads of the bolts shear off.

6 Refit the remaining components in the reverse order of removal.

6 Switches – removal and refitting

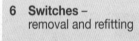

Steering column switches

1 Release the locking lever and fully extend and lower the steering column.
2 Remove the upper and lower columns shrouds as described in Chapter 11.
3 Both switches are removed in a similar manner. Remove the the screws, slide out the switch and disconnect the wiring plug **(see illustrations)**.
4 Refitting is a reversal of removal.

Glovebox light switch

5 Remove the glovebox as described in Chapter 11.

6 Refitting is a reversal of removal.

Door mirror adjuster

7 Remove the door trim panel as described in Chapter 11 Section 10.
8 Place the panel on a protective surface and remove the screws. Alternatively remove the complete switch panel from the door trim and then remove the screws. Remove the switch **(see illustration)**.

Facia panel switches

9 All of the facia switches, apart from the hazard warning light switch are mounted on the instrument panel surround.

Hazard warning light switch

10 Remove the audio unit as described in Section 17.
11 Place the audio unit face down on a soft surface and remove the switch **(see illustration)**.
12 Refitting is a reversal of removal.

6.8 Remove the screws

6.11a Remove the screw...

6.11b...and then remove the switch

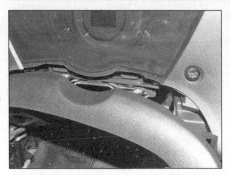

6.14a Remove the lower panel – disconnect the wiring plug as the panel is removed

6.14b Remove the main panel – disconnect the wiring plugs as the panel is removed

6.18a Remove the screws...

Instrument panel switches

13 The instrument panel mounted switches are:
● Window demister switch
● Engine start switch
● Heater control switch
● Headlight height adjuster
● VSA (Vehicle Stability Assist) switch – where fitted

14 Access to all the switches is gained by first removing the instrument panel lower trim and then the main switch panel **(see illustrations)**.

15 Turn the panel over and place it on a soft surface. Remove the screws from the appropriate switch and remove it.

16 Refitting is a reversal of removal.

Window switches

17 Remove the door trim panel as described in Chapter 11 Section 10.

18 Remove the support panel from the door interior trim panel, remove the switch panel screws and then remove the panel **(see illustrations)**.

19 Refitting is a reversal of removal.

Courtesy light switches

20 The switches are fitted at the base of the B and C-pillars. Open the blanking cover and unscrew the switch **(see illustrations)**.

21 Remove the switch and disconnect the wiring plug **(see illustration)**. To stop the wiring plug from disappearing into the door pillar either tape it to the pillar or tie a section of cord around it so it can be recovered from the interior of the pillar if necessary.

22 Refitting is a reversal of removal.

Handbrake warning switch

23 Remove the centre console as described in Chapter 11.

24 Detach the wiring connector from the switch.

25 Release the locking tab and detach the switch.

26 Refit in the reverse order of removal.

Brake light switch

27 Refer to Chapter 9.

Steering wheel switches

28 Remove the driver's airbag as described in Section 21.

29 Disconnect the wiring plug **(see illustration)**.

6.18b...and release the panel from the door trim

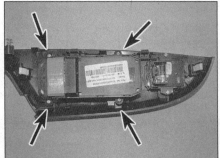

6.18c Remove the screws

6.20a Open the cover...

6.20b...and remove the screw

6.21 Pull the switch free from the panel

6.29 Disconnect the wiring plug

6.30 Remove the loom cage screws

6.31a Remove the screws from the rear...

6.31b...and lift the switch assembly from the steering wheel

6.32a Remove the screws and...

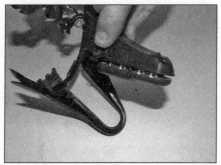

6.32b...lift out the switches

30 Undo the screws and release the wiring loom cage **(see illustration)**.
31 At the rear of the steering wheel, remove the switch mounting screws and then remove the complete switch and loom assembly **(see illustrations)**.
32 With the switch assembly on the bench, separate the switches from the surround **(see illustrations)**.
33 Refitting is a reversal of removal.

Seat heating switches

34 Where fitted the seat heating switches are mounted in the centre console. Remove the centre console as described in Chapter 11.

35 Remove the screws and release the switch.
36 Refitting is a reversal of removal.

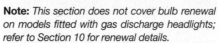

7 Exterior light bulbs – renewal

Note: *This section does not cover bulb renewal on models fitted with gas discharge headlights; refer to Section 10 for renewal details.*
1 Whenever a bulb is renewed, note the following points:
a) *Remember that if the light has just been in use, the bulb may be extremely hot.*

b) *Do not touch the bulb glass with the fingers, as the small deposits can cause the bulb to cloud over. If the bulb is accidentally touched with bare hands clean it with methylated spirits before fitting.*
c) *Always check the bulb contacts and holder, ensuring that there is clean metal-to-metal contact. Clean off any corrosion or dirt before fitting a new bulb.*
d) *Wherever bayonet-type bulbs are fitted, ensure that the live contacts bear firmly against the bulb contact.*
e) *Always ensure that the new bulb is of the correct rating and that it is completely clean before fitting it.*

Halogen main beam

2 Access to all of the headlight mounted bulbs is limited. Removal of the battery improves access to the left-hand bulbs and on 1.8 petrol models removal of the air intake duct further improves access. On diesel models accces to the left-hand headlight bulbs requires the removal of the windscreen washer reservoir and the coolant expansion tank.
3 If working on the left-hand headlight remove the battery as described in Chapter 5A.
4 Remove the cover and disconnect the wiring plug **(see illustrations)**.

7.4a Remove the cover...

7.4b...and disconnect the wiring plug

7.5a Release the bulb retaining spring clip...

7.5b..and remove the bulb

7.7a Remove the cover...

5 Release the spring clip and remove the bulb **(see illustrations)**. Note the orientation of the bulb as it is removed.

6 Fit the new bulb using a reversal of the removal procedure.

Halogen dipped beam

7 Remove the cover and disconnect the wiring plug **(see illustrations)**.

8 Release the bulb retaining spring clip and (noting the bulb orientation) remove it **(see illustrations)**.

9 Fit the new bulb using a reversal of the removal procedure.

Front direction indicator

10 Jack up and support the front of the vehicle (see '*Jacking and vehicle support*' in the Reference chapter). Remove the road wheel.

11 Access requires partial removal of the wing liner. Remove the trim clips and carefully bend the front upper section of the wing liner down. It may be easier to remove the complete wing liner in cold weather.

12 Reach up and remove the bulb holder complete with the bulb **(see illustration)**.

13 Remove the bulb from the bulb holder **(see illustration)**.

Front sidelight

14 Remove the bulb cover and pull the bulb complete with the holder from the headlight **(see illustration)**.

15 Pull the capless bulb from the bulb holder **(see illustration)**.

7.7b...and disconnect the wiring plug

7.8a Release the spring clip...

7.8b...and remove the bulb

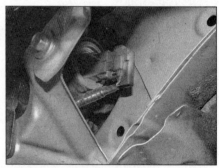

7.12 Remove the bulb complete with the bulb holder and wiring plug

7.13 Remove the bulb from the bulb holder

7.14 Remove the bulb holder

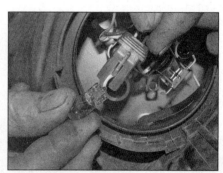

7.15 Remove the bulb from the holder

7.29 Remove the cover panel

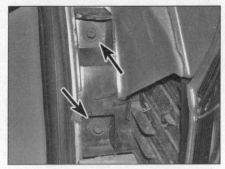

7.30a Remove the bolts...

7.30b...pull the lamp free...

7.30c...and remove the bulb holder

7.31 Remove the bulb

16 Fit the new bulb using a reversal of the removal procedure.

Front foglamp

17 Remove the mounting bolt and pull the foglight from the bumper.
18 Rotate the bulbholder anti-clockwise and pull it from the foglamp. Note that the bulb is integral with the bulbholder.
19 Disconnect the wiring plug from the bulb holder.
20 Fit the new bulb using a reversal of the removal procedure.

Direction indicator side repeater

21 The side repeater is located in the door mirror. On all models the bulb is a LED type and can not be replaced. The complete lamp must be replaced if the bulb is faulty, as described in Section 9.

8.2 Remove the cover

Rear combination lights

Tailgate mounted lamps

22 Remove the trim panel from the tailgate.
23 Identify which bulb requires replacement. The tailgate mounted bulbs are removed by twisting the bulb holder from the lamp and then removing the bulb from the holder by pulling the capless type bulb free.
24 Refitting is a reversal of removal.
25 Remove the rear light unit as described in Section 9.
26 Undo the bolts, and remove the bulbholder.
27 Press and twist the relevant bulb anti-clockwise, and withdraw it from the bulbholder.
28 Fit the new bulb using a reversal of removal procedure.

8.3 Remove the bulb

Wing mounted lamps

29 Open the tailgate and remove the trim panel that covers the mounting bolts **(see illustration)**.
30 Remove the mounting bolts and pull the lamp free. Rotate the bulb holder anti-clockwise and remove the bulb holder from the lamp **(see illustrations)**. Repeat the procedure for the other bulb and then store the lamp safely.
31 Pull the large capless bulb from the bulb holder to remove it **(see illustration)**.
32 Refitting is a reversal of removal.

High-level brake light

33 The high level brake light uses LED type bulbs. If a fault develops with the lamp the entire assembly must be replaced. Removal of the lamp is described in Section 9.

---

8   Interior light bulbs – renewal

---

1 Whenever a bulb is renewed, note the following points:
a) *Remember that if the light has just been in use, the bulb may be extremely hot.*
b) *Always check the bulb contacts and holder, ensuring that there is clean metal-to-metal contact between the bulb and its live and earth. Clean off any corrosion or dirt before fitting a new bulb.*
c) *Wherever bayonet-type bulbs are fitted, ensure that the live contact(s) bear firmly against the bulb contact.*
d) *Always ensure that the new bulb is of the correct rating and that it is completely clean before fitting it.*
e) *Some vehicles feature LED type bulbs. If these fail the entire lamp will require replacement.*

Interior lights

Front courtesy light

2 Use a small screwdriver or trim tool and prise the cover free **(see illustration)**.
3 Pull the capless (wedge) type bulb free from the bulb holder **(see illustration)**.
4 Fit a new bulb using a reversal of the removal procedure.

8.5 Remove the cover

8.6 Remove the bulb

8.10a Remove the lens...

Rear courtesy light

5 Use a small screwdriver or trim tool and prise the cover free **(see illustration)**.
6 Prise free the festoon type bulb **(see illustration)**.
7 Fit a new bulb using a reversal of the removal procedure.

Glovebox

8 Open the glovebox and prise free the lamp. Tune the bulb holder anti-clockwise to release the bulb holder. Pull out the bulb from the bulb holder.
9 Fit a new bulb using a reversal of the removal procedure.

Vanity mirror lights

10 Using a small screwdriver, release the lamp cover **(see illustrations)**.

11 Fit a new bulb using a reversal of the removal procedure.

Luggage area light

12 Remove the complete lamp using a small screwdriver or trim tool **(see illustration)**.
13 Disconnect the wiring plug, remove the cover and pull the capless bulb free from the bulb holder **(see illustrations)**.
14 Fit the new bulb using a reversal of the removal procedure.

Instrument panel bulbs

15 On all models covered by this Manual, it is not possible to renew the instrument panel bulbs individually as they are of LED design and soldered to a printed circuit board. It is

not possible to renew a single LED. Where an LED is not functioning, the complete instrument panel must be renewed.

Switch illumination

16 All the switches are illuminated by LEDs except the hazard warning switch and (where fitted) the VSA switch. Refer to Section 6 and remove the hazard switch or the VSA switch and then remove the bulb.

Heater/air conditioning control panel illumination

17 The control panel contains several replaceable bulbs. Remove the instrument panel cover as described in Section 6.
18 Use a small screwdriver to remove the bulbs **(see illustrations)**.

8.10b...and remove the bulb

8.12 Remove the lamp

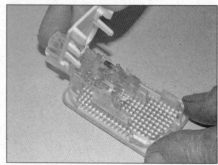

8.13a Remove the cover...

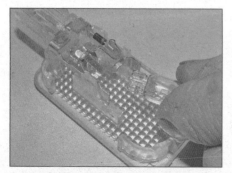

8.13b...and pull out the bulb

8.18a Remove the bulb

8.18b Note the locking guide on the rear of the panel

9.2a Remove the upper bolt...

9.2b...the lower bolt...

9.2c...and the outer bolt

9 Exterior light units – removal, refitting and beam adjustment

Headlight unit

Removal

Caution: On models equipped with gas discharge headlights, disconnect the battery negative lead, as described in Chapter 5A, prior to working on the headlights.

1 Remove the grille and front bumper as described in Chapter 11.

2 Remove the mounting bolts, pull the headlight forwards slightly and disconnect the wiring plug **(see illustrations)**.

Refitting

3 Refitting is a reversal of the removal procedure. On completion check for satisfactory operation, and have the headlight beam adjustment checked as soon as possible (see below). Where HID headlights are fitted the beam aim and direction must be adjusted with suitable diagnostic equipment.

Front foglamp

Removal

4 Jack up and support the front of the vehicle (see *Jacking and vehicle support* in the Reference chapter).

5 Remove the appropriate road wheel and then remove the wing liner as described in Chapter 11.

6 Undo the 2 mounting bolts, withdraw the foglamp from the front bumper, and disconnect the wiring.

Refitting

7 Refitting is a reversal of removal, but have the foglamp beam setting checked at the earliest opportunity. An approximate adjustment can be made by positioning the car 10 metres in front of a wall marked with the centre point of the foglamp lens. Turn the

9.2d Disconnect the wiring plug...

adjustment screw as required. Note that only height adjustment is possible – there is no lateral adjustment.

Direction indicator side repeater

Removal

8 Remove the door mirror glass as described in Chapter 11.

9 Using a suitable trim tool, remove the mirror outer cover, disconnect the wiring plug and remove the mounting screws **(see illustrations)**. Remove the lamp.

Refitting

10 Refitting is a reversal of removal.

9.9a Disconnect the wiring plug

9.2e...and disconnect the loom from the cable clip

Rear lights

Tailgate mounted lights

11 The tailgate mounted lamp contains the foglight, the brake light, reversing light and number plate light. The lamp is in three sections, with the outer sections containing the rear side and brake lights. The high level brake light is also mounted in the tailgate.

12 Open the tailgate and remove the tailgate trim panels as described in Chapter 11.

13 Remove the wiring plugs from the bulb holders, or remove the bulb holders complete with the bulbs. Disconnect the remaining wiring plug.

14 Remove the nuts and remove the

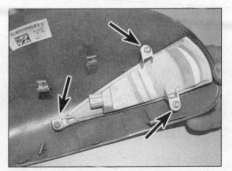

9.9b Remove the screws

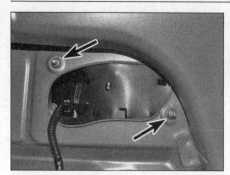

9.14a Remove the nuts (outer lamp shown)

9.14b Remove the outer lamp...

9.14c...or remove the inner lamp

appropriate lamp from the tailgate **(see illustrations)**.

15 Refitting is a reversal of removal.

High-level brake light

16 The high level brake light is lit by a series of LED type bulbs.

17 Remove the tailgate upper trim panel.

18 Remove the mounting screws and disconnect the wiring plug **(see illustration)**. Remove the lamp.

19 Refitting is a reversal of removal.

Beam adjustment

Halogen headlights

20 Accurate adjustment of the headlight beam is only possible using optical beam setting equipment, and this work should therefore be carried out by a Honda dealer or suitably-equipped workshop. All MOT testing stations have this equipment.

21 For reference, the headlights can be adjusted using the adjuster screws, accessible via the top of each light unit.

22 All models are equipped with an electrically-operated headlight beam adjustment system which is controlled through the switch in the facia. Ensure that the switch is set to the basic O position before adjusting the headlight aim.

HID (Xenon) headlights

23 Adjustment of the beam is automatic on HID equipped vehicles. However if any work is performed on the headlights or suspension, then the position of the beam should be checked and if necessary adjusted using a suitable diagnostic tool. Checking is possible with standard equipment.

24 Models fitted with HID headlights must have a headlight washer system fitted and working.

---

10 Xenon gas discharge headlight system – removal, refitting and adjustment

---

General information

1 Xenon gas discharge headlights (alternatively called HID – High Intensity Discharge lamps) are fitted to certain higher specification models. The headlights dipped beam bulbs produce light by means of an electric arc, rather than by heating a metal filament as in conventional halogen bulbs. A conventional halogen bulb is also fitted to augment the main beam light output. The arc is generated by a control circuit which operates at voltages of above 28 000 volts. The intensity of the emitted light means that the headlight beam has to be controlled dynamically to avoid dazzling other road users. An electronic control unit monitors the vehicle's pitch and overall ride height by sensors mounted on the front and rear suspension and adjusts the beam range accordingly, using the range control motors built into the headlight units.

2 All bulbs apart from the Xenon dipped beam bulbs are removed in the same manner as the bulbs fitted to the conventional halogen headlights.

⚠️ **Warning: The discharge bulb starter circuitry operates at extremely high voltages. To avoid the risk of electric shock, ensure that the battery negative cable is disconnected before working on the headlight units (see Chapter 5A), then additionally switch the dipped beam on and off to discharge any residual voltage.**

Headlight dipped beam

Caution: The dipped beam bulb is under gas pressure of at least 10 bar, therefore it is recommended that protective glasses and suitable gloves are worn during this procedure.

3 Remove the rear cover and disconnect the wiring plug by turning it 45 degrees anti-clockwise.

4 Rotate the locking collar and remove the bulb. Store the bulb in a safe place if it is not to be immediately refitted.

5 Refitting is a reversal of removal.

Front ride height sensor

Removal

6 The sensor is mounted on the lower control arm of the left-hand wheel. Apply

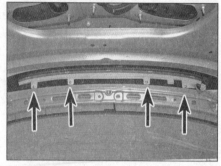

9.18 Remove the mounting screws

the handbrake, then jack up the front of the vehicle and support it on axle stands (see *'Jacking and vehicle support'* in the Reference chapter). Remove the wheel.

7 Disconnect the wiring plug.

8 Undo the bolts from the sensor and remove the sensor from the vehicle.

Refitting

9 Refitting is a reversal of removal. Note that if a new sensor has been fitted, then a calibration procedure must be carrier out. This requires access to Honda diagnostic equipment – entrust this task to a Honda dealer or suitably-equipped specialist.

Rear ride height sensor

Removal

10 The sensor is secured to the left-hand lower control arm and the rear subframe. Chock the front wheels, then jack up the rear of the vehicle and support it on axle stands (see *'Jacking and vehicle support'* in the Reference chapter).

11 Disconnect the sensor wiring plug, then undo the bolts and remove the sensor, bracket and lever arm assembly.

Refitting

12 Refitting is a reversal of removal. Note that if a new sensor has been fitted, then a calibration procedure must be carried out. This requires access to Honda diagnostic equipment – entrust this task to a Honda dealer or suitably-equipped specialist.

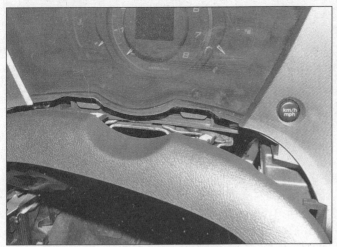

11.4a Prise up the panel...

11.4b...and disconnect the wiring plug

Beam adjustment

13 After any repair is made to the suspension, or if the ride height sensors are removed then they must be calibrated using dedicated Honda test equipment. Therefore this task should be entrusted to a Honda dealer or suitably-equipped specialist.

---

11 Instrument panel –
removal and refitting

Note: *If the instrument panel is to be replaced because it is faulty, suitable diagnostic equipment will be required to retrieve the data from the instrument panel. This must be saved and then uploaded to the new instrument panel.*

Removal

1 The instrument panel is in two sections – the upper speedometer display and the lower tachometer display.
2 Disconnect the battery negative lead as described in Chapter 5A.

3 Fully extend the steering column, and move it to its lowest position.
4 Prise up and remove the lower instrument panel cover. Disconnect the temperature sensor wiring plug as the panel is removed **(see illustrations)**.
5 Remove the screws and then carefully prise free the screen cover and switch assemblies **(see illustration)**. Disconnect the wiring plugs as the panel is removed.
6 Remove the screws and release the tachometer. Disconnect the wiring

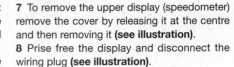

plug and remove the panel **(see illustrations)**.
7 To remove the upper display (speedometer) remove the cover by releasing it at the centre and then removing it **(see illustration)**.
8 Prise free the display and disconnect the wiring plug **(see illustration)**.

Refitting

9 Refitting is a reversal of removal, but see the note at the beginning of this section.

11.5 Prise free the switch panel

11.6a Remove the display...

11.6b...and disconnect the wiring plug

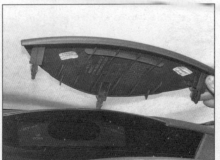

11.7 Remove the upper cover

11.8 Remove the display

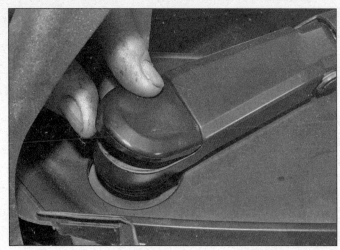

12.3a Pull off the cap…

12.3b …and undo the nut

12 Windscreen wiper components – removal and refitting

Wiper blades

1 Refer to *Weekly checks*.

Wiper arms

Removal

2 If the wipers are not in their parked position, switch on the ignition, and allow the motor to automatically park.

3 Before removing an arm, mark its parked position on the glass with a strip of adhesive tape. Prise off the cover and unscrew the spindle nut **(see illustrations)**. Ease the arm from the spindle by rocking it slowly from side-to-side. If any difficulty is encountered a small two legged puller can be used to free the arm. Note also that specialist wiper arm puller tools are also available.

Refitting

4 Refitting is a reversal of removal, but before

12.8 Remove the centre cowl panel

tightening the spindle nuts, position the wiper blades as marked before removal.

Wiper motor

Removal

5 Remove the wiper arms as described in above.

6 The motor is removed as a complete assembly along with the linkage assembly.

12.9 Remove both quarter panels

7 Disconnect the battery (see *Disconnecting the battery* in Chapter 5A).

8 Prise free the trim clips and remove the windscreen cowl centre panel **(see illustration)**.

9 Remove the clips and release the quarter panels. Lift them over the wiper spindle arms and remove them **(see illustration)**.

10 Remove the bolts and slide out the metal lower panel (lower scuttle panel) **(see illustrations)**.

12.10a Remove the screws…

12.10b …and remove the panel

12.11a Remove the left-hand bolts...

12.11b...the right-hand bolts...

12.11c...and the centre bolts (one shown, but two fitted)

12.11d Disconnect the wiring plug...

12.11e...and pivot the linkage slightly to remove it

11 Remove the bolts from the spindle mountings at both sides and then remove the centre bolts. Lift out the linkage and motor sufficiently to gain access to the wiring plug and disconnect it **(see illustrations)**. Remove the wiper motor and linkage from the vehicle.
12 If required the wiper motor can be separated from the linkage. Index marks are present on the wiper motor crank arm, the motor mounting plate and on the link arms. If these are obscure make marks to aid refitting.
13 Lever off the link arms and unbolt the crank arm from the motor. Remove the three bolts and remove the motor.

Refitting

14 Refitting is a reversal of removal. Lubricate all the pivot points with multipurpose grease.

13 Windscreen washer system components – removal and refitting

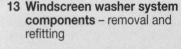

1 All models covered by this manual are fitted with a windscreen washer system. Models fitted Zenon (HID) headlights also have mandatory headlight washers fitted.
2 The fluid reservoir for the windscreen/headlight washer is located behind the right-hand end of the bumper cover. The windscreen washer fluid pump is attached to the side of the reservoir body.
3 The reservoir fluid level must be regularly topped-up with windscreen washer fluid containing an antifreeze agent, but not cooling system antifreeze – see *Weekly checks*.
4 To remove the pump, jack up and support the front of the vehicle (see *Jacking and vehicle support* in the Reference chapter). Remove the right-hand road wheel and the wing liner. On models fitted with Zenon headlights the front bumper must be removed to access the headlight washer pump.
5 Disconnect the wiring plug, place a clean container beneath the pump and prise off the outlet pipe **(see illustrations)**.
6 Work the pump free from the retaining grommet **(see illustration)**.
7 Remove the grommet and check that the filter is clear **(see illustration)**.

13.5a Disconnect the wiring plug...

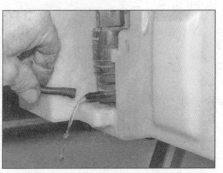

13.5b...and remove the outlet hose

13.6 Pull the pump from the grommet in the reservoir

13.7 Pull the grommet from the reservoir

13.8a Remove the front...

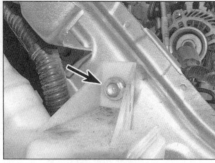

13.8b...the upper and...

13.8c...the rear mounting bolts

13.8d Remove the filler neck

13.10a Remove the screws and...

13.10b...and disconnect the washer hose

8 To remove the reservoir, remove the front bumper cover and then remove the reservoir filler neck. Disconnect the wiring plug(s). Release the washer hose(s) and then remove the mounting bolts. Unbolt the reservoir and remove it from the vehicle **(see illustrations)**.

9 To remove the washer jets, first remove the windscreen cowl panel by removing the clips and lifting the panel free.

10 Turn over the panel and remove the fixing screws. Remove the jet and disconnect the washer hose **(see illustrations)**.

11 The windscreen washer jets can be adjusted by inserting a pin into the jet and altering the aim as required.

12 To remove the headlight washer jets on models fitted with Zenon headlights, remove the bumper cover as described in Chapter 11.

14.3 The right-hand horn

Remove the two upper mounting screws and the single lower mounting screw. Remove the jet.

14 Horns – removal and refitting

Removal

1 The horns are located behind the front bumper cover on both sides. Raise the front of the vehicle and support it securely on axle stands (see *'Jacking and vehicle support'* in the Reference chapter).

2 Remove the front bumper cover as described in Chapter 11.

3 Disconnect the horn wiring plug, undo the mounting bolt and remove the horn from the vehicle **(see illustration)**.

Refitting

4 Refit in the reverse order of removal. Check for satisfactory operation on completion.

15 Central locking system – general information

1 All models featured in this manual feature central locking. The vehicle can either be locked or unlocked with the key, or where supplied with the remote key fob.

2 Most models have a 'dead lock' feature (called 'super locking' by Honda). Dead locking disconnects the inner door release handle form the locking system. If a window is broken to gain entry the door can not be opened from the inside.

3 Dead locking is activated by pressing the lock button on the key fob twice (within 5 seconds) or by turning the key in the door to the lock position, releasing the key and turning it to the lock position again (within 5 seconds).

4 If the central locking fails to operate check the following:
a) *Remote key fob battery*
b) *Under bonnet fuse number 22 (10 amp)*
c) *Under bonnet fuse number 21 (15 amp)*
d) *Under bonnet fuse number 16 (15 amp)*
e) *Under cabin fuse number 25 (20 amp)*

5 If all the fuses are intact, then further investigation is best carried out using suitable diagnostic equipment – consult your Honda dealer or suitably equipped garage.

16 Parking aid components – general, removal and refitting

General information

1 Four ultrasound sensors located in the rear bumper measure the distance to the closest object behind the car, and inform the driver using acoustic signals from the from the instrument panel control module.

2 The system includes a control module and self-diagnosis program, and therefore, in the event of a fault, the vehicle should be taken to a Honda dealer or suitably-equipped specialist who will be able to interrogate the system.

Control Module

Removal

3 The control unit is located behind the right-hand luggage compartment side trim panel. Remove the luggage compartment side panel trim as described in Chapter 11, and remove the foam padding behind the panel.

Refitting

4 Refitting is a reversal of removal.

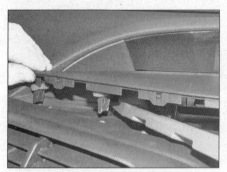
17.4 Remove the cover

17.5b...and the lower mounting screws

17.5d...disconnect the wiring plugs

Range/distance sensor

Removal

5 Remove the rear bumper as described in Chapter 11.

6 Disconnect the sensor wiring plug, then remove the locking ring. Pull the sensor from position.

Refitting

7 Refitting is a reversal of removal.

---

17 Audio system – removal and refitting

Note: *This Section applies only to factory fitted audio equipment.*
Note: *Where required, note down the audio*

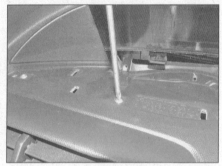
17.5a Remove the upper mounting screws...

17.5c Pull the audio unit forward and...

17.8 Remove the screws

---

unit key code before disconnecting the battery.

1 A wide variety of audio systems are fitted to the Honda Civic. The type of audio unit fitted is based on the trim level, with high end models having an integrated audio and navigation (SatNav) system fitted. The audio unit comprises of an upper separate display panel and a lower main control unit. All audio units form part of the anti-theft/immobiliser system.

Removal

Main control unit

2 Disconnect the battery negative lead as described in Chapter 5A.

3 Remove the centre console as described in Chapter 11.

4 Prise free the facia centre cover **(see illustration)**.

5 Remove the upper and lower mounting screws and pull the audio unit forward. Disconnect the wiring plugs and remove the audio unit **(see illustrations)**.

6 With the audio unit on the bench remove the frame mounting screws and seperate the main body from the trim panel/air vents.

Display unit

7 Prise free the centre facia panel as described above.

8 Remove the mounting screws **(see illustration)** and pull the display forward to release it. Disconnect the wiring plug as the unit is removed.

9 The upper display is a very tight fit in the aperture. We removed the upper instrument panel (Section 11) to provide a better access point to insert a trim tool. Even then releasing the display was problematic.

Refitting

10 Refitting is a reversal of removal. Reconnect the battery and where required enter the audio unit anti-theft key code.

---

18 Aerial – removal and refitting

1 The aerial for the audio unit is incorporated into the tailgate glass. Removal and refitting of the aerial requires replacement of the tailgate glass. Repair of minor breaks in the aerial wire (in the glass) can be fixed with the use of a conductive paint – this is widely available.

2 Replacement of the aerial cable requires the headlining to be removed. This is an involved task, requiring patience and dexterity. Consequently, we recommend you entrust this task to a Honda dealer or upholstery specialist.

3 The aerial also includes a control module located in the tailgate. Remove the tailgate trim as described in Chapter 11. Disconnect the wiring plug, remove the screws and remove the module. Refit in the reverse order.

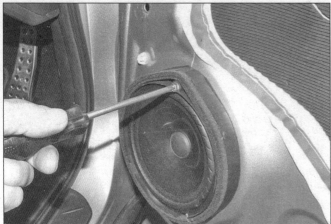

19.2 Remove the screws

19.3 Disconnect the wiring plug

19 Speakers – removal and refitting

Door speakers

1 To remove a door mounted speaker, remove the appropriate door trim panel as described in Chapter 11.

2 Remove the screws securing the speaker to the door **(see illustration)**.

3 Disconnect the wiring plugs as the speaker is withdrawn **(see illustration)**.

4 Refit in the reverse order of removal.

Front tweeter speakers

5 Prise the the trim panel from the door **(see illustration)**.

6 Disconnect the wiring plug **(see illustration)**.

7 Release the retaining clips and remove the speaker from the panel **(see illustration)**.

8 Refitting is a reversal of removal.

20 Airbag system – general information and precautions

Warning: Before carrying out any operations on the airbag system, disconnect the battery negative terminal (see Chapter 5A). When operations are complete, make sure no one is inside the vehicle when the battery is reconnected.

• Note that the airbag(s) must not be subjected to temperatures in excess of 90°C. When the airbag is removed, ensure that it is stored the correct way up (pad upwards) to prevent possible inflation.

• Do not allow any solvents or cleaning agents to contact the airbag assemblies. They must be cleaned using only a damp cloth.

• The airbags and control unit are both sensitive to impact. If either is dropped or damaged they should be renewed.

• Disconnect the airbag control unit wiring plug prior to using arc-welding equipment on the vehicle.

1 A driver's and passenger's airbag, side airbags (seat mounted) and overhead curtain airbags are fitted as standard equipment to all models in the range. The driver's airbag is fitted to the centre of the steering wheel. The passenger's airbag is fitted to the upper surface of the facia, above the glovebox. The airbag system comprises the airbag unit(s) (complete with gas generators), impact sensors, the control unit and a warning light in the instrument panel.

2 The airbag system is triggered in the event of a direct or offset frontal impact above a predetermined force. The airbag is inflated within milliseconds, and forms a safety cushion between the driver and the steering wheel or (where applicable) the passenger and the facia. This prevents contact between the upper body and the steering wheel, column and facia, and therefore greatly reduces the risk of injury. The airbag then deflates almost immediately through vents in the side of the airbag. The side airbags and overhead curtain airbags are triggered by side impacts, registered by the sensors fitted to the base of the B-pillars on each side.

3 Every time the ignition is switched on, the airbag control unit performs a self-test. The self-test takes approximately 7 seconds, and during this time the airbag warning light on the facia is illuminated. After the self-test has been completed, the warning light should go out. If the warning light fails to come on, remains illuminated after the initial 7 second period, or comes on at any time when the vehicle is being driven, there is a fault in the airbag system. The vehicle should then be taken to a Honda dealer or specialist for examination at the earliest possible opportunity.

19.5 Remove the speaker panel

19.6 Disconnect the wiring plug

19.7 Unclip the tweeter from the panel

21.3a Open the access panel

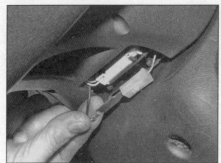

21.3b Disconnect the earth (ground) connector and then...

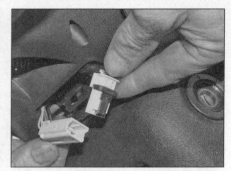

21.3c...and then the main airbag wiring plug

21 Airbag system components
– removal and refitting

Note: *Refer to the warnings in Section 20 before carrying out the following operations.*
1 Disconnect the battery negative terminal (see Chapter 5A). Wait at least 10 minutes for any residual electrical energy to dissipate before commencing work.

Driver's airbag

2 Set the steering wheel and front wheels in the 'straight-ahead' position.
3 Remove the small access panel from the base of the steering wheel and disconnect the wiring plugs **(see illustrations)**.
4 Insert the ignition key and rotate the steering wheel to access the airbag mounting bolts. From the rear remove the T30 torx bolts

21.4 Remove the mounting bolts

21.9 Lowering the passenger airbag

(see illustration) and discard them – new ones must be fitted.
5 Remove the airbag and store it safely.
6 Refitting is a reversal of removal, but note the following:
a) *New bolts must be used – tightened to the specified torque.*
b) *After reconnecting the battery turn the ignition on without entering the vehicle.*
c) *Check that the SRS warning light comes on and then goes off after 6 seconds.*
d) *Check that the horn works.*

Passenger airbag

7 Remove the glovebox as described in Chapter 11.
8 Disconnect the wiring plug **(see illustration)** from the airbag and then release the connector from the bracket.
9 Remove the mounting bolts from the front bracket and then remove the nuts from the

21.8 Disconnect the wiring plug

21.14 Disconnect the clockspring wiring plug

rear and sides. Note that access is limited and awkward. Lower the airbag and manoeuvre it from the facia, rotating it slightly to clear the crossmember **(see illustration)**.
10 Refitting is a reversal of removal, but after completing the work confirm the correct operation of the SRS system by reconnecting the battery and turning the ignition on. The SRS light will come on and go off after 6 seconds if the system is functioning correctly.

Airbag wiring contact unit (clockspring)

Note: *The clockspring can be removed complete with the column switch assembly or removed separately. Removing it with the switch assembly is the simplest solution.*
11 Set the steering in the straight ahead position.
12 Remove the airbag as described above and then remove the steering wheel as described in Chapter 10.
13 With reference to Chapter 11 remove the upper and lower steering column shrouds.
14 Disconnect the wiring plugs from the clockspring/switch assembly **(see illustration)**.
15 Unhook the upper locking tab with a suitable bent pick tool and the unhook the lower tab. Remove the clockspring.
16 If the contact unit is to be refitted, apply tape to lock the unit in position **(see illustration)**. Do not attempt to rotate the unit.
17 Refitting is a reversal of removal, but if there is any doubt as to the correct position

21.16 Secure the clockspring in the straight ahead position with suitable tape

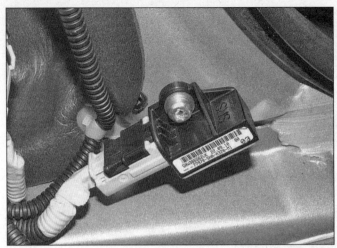

21.27 The B-pillar impact sensor

21.34 The front right-hand impact sensor

of the clock spring it must be centralised as follows:
a) *Rotate the clockspring clockwise until a resistance is felt.*
b) *Rotate the clockspring anti-clockwise 3 turns – the arrow mark will be vertical.*
c) *Tape the clockspring in position.*

Side airbags

18 The side airbags are incorporated into the side of the front and rear seats. Removal of the units requires the seat upholstery to be removed. This is a specialist task, which we recommend should be entrusted to a Honda dealer or specialist.

Head/overhead curtain airbags

19 Renewal of the head airbags/inflatable curtain requires removal of the headlining. This is a specialist task, and should be entrusted to a Honda dealer or specialist.

SRS control unit.

20 Remove the centre console as described in Chapter 11.
21 Disconnect the wiring plugs.
22 Remove the torx screws and remove the control unit.
23 Refitting is a reversal of removal, but after completing the work confirm the correct operation of the SRS system by turning the ignition on. The SRS light will come on and go off after 6 seconds if the system is functioning correctly.

Impact sensors

Side sensors

24 Impact sensors are fitted at the base of both B-pillars and the C-pillars.
25 If working on the B-pillar sensors, remove the front seat on the appropriate side.
26 With reference to Chapter, remove the B-pillar trim panel.
27 Disconnect the sensor wiring pug, then undo the bolt and remove the sensor **(see**

illustration). Take great care not to damage the sensor wiring harness. Note that the sensor must be handled carefully. Do not refit a sensor that has been dropped or knocked.
28 If working on the C-pillar sensors remove the appropriate seat and seat cushion.
29 Disconnect the wiring plug and unbolt the sensor.
30 Refitting is a reversal of removal, but after completing the work confirm the correct operation of the SRS system by turning the ignition on. The SRS light will come on and go off after 6 seconds if the system is functioning correctly.

Front sensors

31 Front sensors are located behind both the left and right-hand wing liners.
32 Jack up and support the front of the vehicle – see '*Jacking and vehicle support*' in the Reference chapter.
33 Remove the appropriate front wheel and then remove the wing liner.
34 Disconnect the wiring plug and remove the sensor **(see illustration)**.
35 Refitting is a reversal of removal, but after completing the work confirm the correct operation of the SRS system by turning the ignition on. The SRS light will come on and go off after 6 seconds if the system is functioning correctly.

22 Anti-theft alarm system – general information

1 An anti-theft alarm and immobiliser system is fitted as standard equipment. Should the system become faulty, the vehicle should be taken to a Honda dealer or specialist for examination. They will have access to a special diagnostic tester which will quickly trace any fault present in the system.

23 Electronic control modules – removal and refitting

Note: *Both modules are included in the vehicle's sophisticated self-diagnosis system. Should a fault occur, have the system interrogated using suitable diagnostic equipment, via the diagnostic plug located under the driver's side of the facia* **(see illustration).**

Removal

1 Disconnect the battery negative lead as described in Chapter 5A Section 3.

ECM (Electronic Control Module) Petrol models

2 Suitable diagnostic equipment will be required if the main ECM requires replacement. It is not possible to simply swap one control unit for another without the ability to upload and download the correct operating software.
3 Remove the battery as described in Chapter 5A.

23.0 The diagnostic plug is located under the driver's side of the facia

23.4a Remove the cover and then...

23.4b...remove the single inner bolt...

23.4c...and the two outer bolts

23.5a Disconnect the wiring plugs...

23.5b...and protect them from contamination

4 Remove the ECM cover and then remove the three mounting bolts **(see illustrations)**.

5 Disconnect the wiring plugs. It is always best practise to protect the ECM wiring plugs from damage or contamination by sealing them in plastic bags **(see illustrations)**.

ECM (Electronic Control Module) – Diesel models

6 The diesel model ECM is located behind the glovebox. Remove the glovebox as described in Chapter 11.

7 Remove the door step panel and the kick (scuff) panel.

8 Disconnect the wiring plugs and then remove the protective bracket. Remove the bolts and then remove the control unit from the vehicle.

MICU (Multiplex Integrated Control Unit)

9 The MICU is Honda's name for the electronic control unit that controls many of the non critical body functions. It is part of

the interior fusebox. Amongst the functions controlled by the MICU are:
a) *Interior lights*
b) *Exterior lights*
c) *Horn*
d) *Keyless entry*
e) *Door locks*
f) *Alarm system*
g) *Signal lamps and hazard warnings*
h) *Wash/wipe system*
i) *Interlock (automatic transmission models only)*

10 Remove the door step trim panel and the right-hand kick (scuff) panel as described in Chapter 11.

11 Raise the locking latches and disconnect the wiring plugs from the fuse side of the control unit **(see illustration)**.

12 Remove the three mounting bolts and lower the fusebox/MICU to reach the wiring plugs and relays at the rear **(see illustrations)**. Disconnect the wiring plugs and remove the MICU form the vehicle.

Refitting

13 Refitting is a reversal of removal. Reconnect the battery and follow the starting procedure outlined in Chapter 5A.

23.11 Disconnect the fuse side wiring plugs

23.12a Remove the nuts and lower the MICU to...

23.12b...to access the rear mounted wiring plugs

Fuse and relay box in passenger compartment

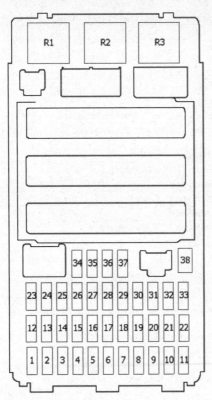

FUSE	VALUE	DESCRIPTION
1	7.5A	Automatic light unit, Climate control, Headlight levelling control unit, Headlight levelling actuator(s), Headlight levelling switch, Illumination electric mirror switches, Electric mirror switch Or Automatic light unit, Climate control unit, Headlight levelling control unit, Headlight levelling actuator(s), Headlight levelling switch, Illumination electric mirror switches, Electric mirror switch, Rear-view mirror dimming control
2	15A	Engine control unit, Immobiliser control unit, Inertia switch, Multiplex control unit Or Engine control unit, Immobiliser control unit, Multiplex control unit
3	10A	Alternator Engine control unit, Oxygen sensor behind the catalytic converter, Reverse lock solenoid, Automatic transmission control unit, Brake pedal switch, Canister purge solenoid, Mass airflow meter with air temperature sensor, Battery sensor (ELD) module Or Alternator Engine control unit, Oxygen sensor behind the catalytic converter, Reverse lock solenoid, Brake pedal switch, Mass airflow meter with air temperature sensor, Canister purge solenoid Hall/MRE sensor on the inlet camshaft, Battery sensor (ELD) module
4	7.5A	Electronic power steering ABS or ESP Yaw rate sensor
5	15A	Seat heater (20A also used)
6	20A	Front fog light(s), Front fog light relay Or Front fog light(s), Front fog light relay, Daylight running system
7	10A	Daylight running system Or Daylight running system, Daylight running system relay
8	7.5A	Ignition switch Start inhibitor relay
9	7.5A	SRS control unit

10	7.5A	Reversing light switch, Instrument panel, Parking assistance, Multiplex control unit Or Reversing light switch, Instrument panel, Multiplex control unit
11	10A	SRS control unit
12	10A	Right main beam Or Multiplex control unit
13	10A	Left main beam
14	7.5A	Interior light(s)
15	7.5A	Daylight running system, Number plate light, Tail light(s)
16	15A	Headlight washer control unit, Right dipped beam (10A also used) Or Right dipped beam
17	15A	Left dipped beam (10A also used)
18	20A	Multiplex control unit
19	15A	Multiplex control unit
20	7.5A	Multiplex control unit
21	30A	Multiplex control unit (20A also used)
22	7.5A	Gear-shift control unit Or Not used
23	7.5A	Engine control unit
24	20A	Sunroof motor
25	20A	Superlocking actuators, Superlocking relay, Multiplex control unit Or Superlocking actuators, Superlocking relay
26	20A	Power windows main switch
27		Not used
28	20A	Rear accessory socket, Rear accessory socket relay Or Accessory socket
29	20A	Cigarette lighter, Cigarette lighter relay
30	20A	Passenger's power window switch
31	30A	Front accessory socket, Front accessory socket relay Or Headlight washer control unit, Headlight washer motor (20A also used)
32	20A	Rear right power window Or Not used
33	20A	Rear left power window Or Not used
34		Not used
35	7.5A	Accessory socket, Audio unit, Cigarette lighter, Handsfree control unit, Navigation display, Navigation control unit, Multiplex control unit Or Air-conditioning cut-off relay, Multiplex control unit, Ignition switch
36	10A	Air conditioning compressor clutch relay, Blower motor Climate control unit, Electric mirror, Heated electric mirrors, Seat heater, Radiator fan relay, Heated rear windscreen relay Or Air-conditioning compressor clutch relay, Blower motor relay, Climate control unit, Heater control unit, Electric mirror, Heated electric mirrors, Seat heater, Radiator fan relay, Heated rear windscreen relay, Electric mirror switch, Heated mirror(s) switch, Heated mirror relay, Heated seat switches
37	7.5A	Multiplex control unit
38	30A	Multiplex control unit
R1		Power window relay Or Not used
R2		Fuel pump relay
R3		Starter relay

Fuse and relay box in engine compartment

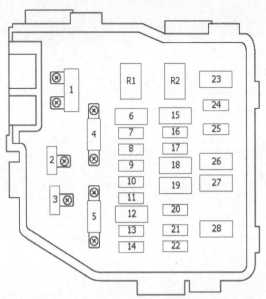

FUSE	VALUE	DESCRIPTION
1	100A	Battery Power distribution, ESP control unit (70A also used) (80A also used)
2	50A	Ignition switch, Fuse and relay box in passenger compartment, Fuses 18 - 21 (60A also used)
3	40A	ESP control unit (20A also used)
4	80A	Fuse and relay box in passenger compartment, fuses 5 - 7, 27 - 29, 31
5	40A	Transmission control unit, (70A – Glow plug control unit for N22A)
6	40A	Fuse and relay box in passenger compartment, fuses 24 - 26, 30 Power window relay Or Fuse and relay box in passenger compartment, Fuses 24 - 26, 30
7	7.5A	Air-conditioning compressor clutch
8	15A	Engine control unit
9	15A	Engine control unit, Hall/MRE sensor on the crankshaft, Hall/MRE sensor on The outlet camshaft, Electronic throttle control, Fuel injector(s), Fuel pump relay, Main relay, (20A for N22A)
10	15A	Ignition coil(s) Or Not used
11	15A	Ignition coil(s) Or Not used
12	30A	Heated rear windscreen Noise-cancelling capacitor
13	15A	Oxygen sensor in front of the catalytic converter, Relay oxygen sensor in front of the catalytic converter, Fuse and relay box in engine Compartment fuse 20, (30A – Headlight washer control unit for N22A)
14	15A	Ignition coil(s), Ignition coil relay Or Ignition coil(s), Ignition coil relay, Fuse and relay box in passenger compartment, fuses 10, 11 (30A also used) Or Not used for N22A
15	20A	Air-conditioning fan (30A for N22A)
16	15A	Multiplex control unit Immobiliser control unit, Instrument panel, Handsfree telephone control unit, Audio unit, Climate control, Navigation, Data link connector, Ultrasonic sensor, Alarm unit

17	7.5A	Automatic light unit, Cargo light(s), Interior ligh t(s)
18	20A	Radiator fan motor (30A for N22A)
19	40A	Blower motor
20	7.5A	Air-conditioning condenser fan relay, Engine oil le vel sensor Or Not used
21	15A	Brake pedal switch, Horns, Horn relay, Multiplex co ntrol unit
22	10A	Multiplex control unit
23	30A	Fuel heater, Fuse and relay box in engine compartme nt(for N22A) Or Not used
24	15A	Inlet manifold shut-off valve(for N22A) Or Not used
25	15A	Engine control unit (for N22A) Or Not used
26	30A	Headlight washer Or 40A – PTC heater (for N22A) Or Not used
27	40A	PTC heater (for N22A) Or Not used
28	40A	PTC heater (for N22A) Or Not used
R1		Air-conditioning compressor clutch relay
R2		Fan control relay

WIRE COLOR CODE INDEX

BK – BLACK
BN – BROWN
BU – BLUE
GN – GREEN
GY – GREY
LB – LIGHT BLUE
LG – LIGHT GREEN
RD – RED
OG – ORANGE
PK – PINK
YE – YELLOW
WH – WHITE

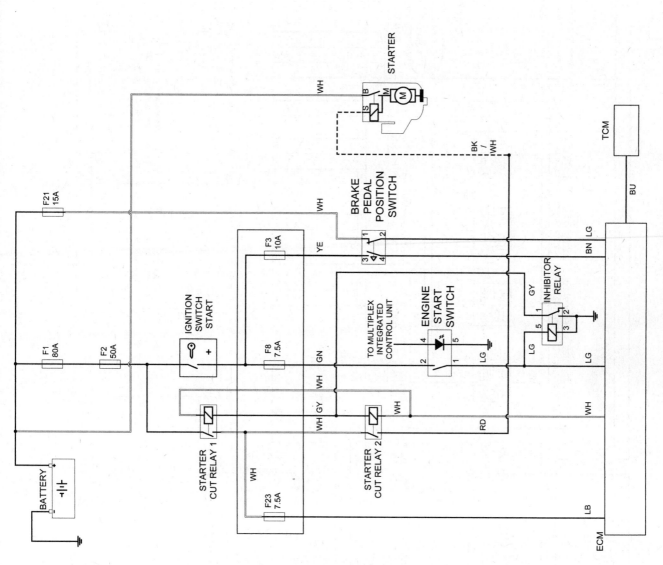

Starting systems –1.4, 1.8 and 2.2 litre model

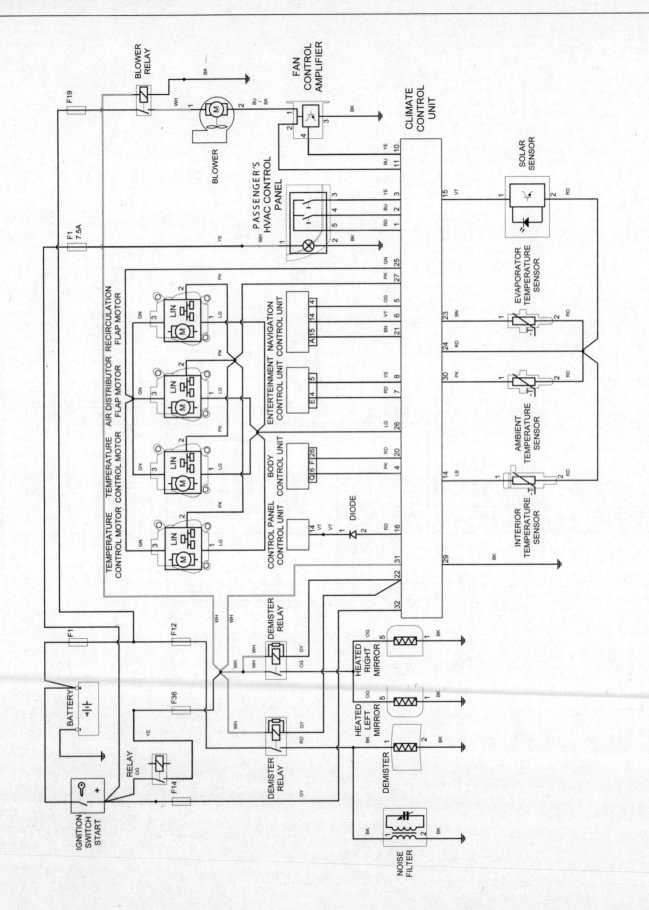

Climate Control

Power windows

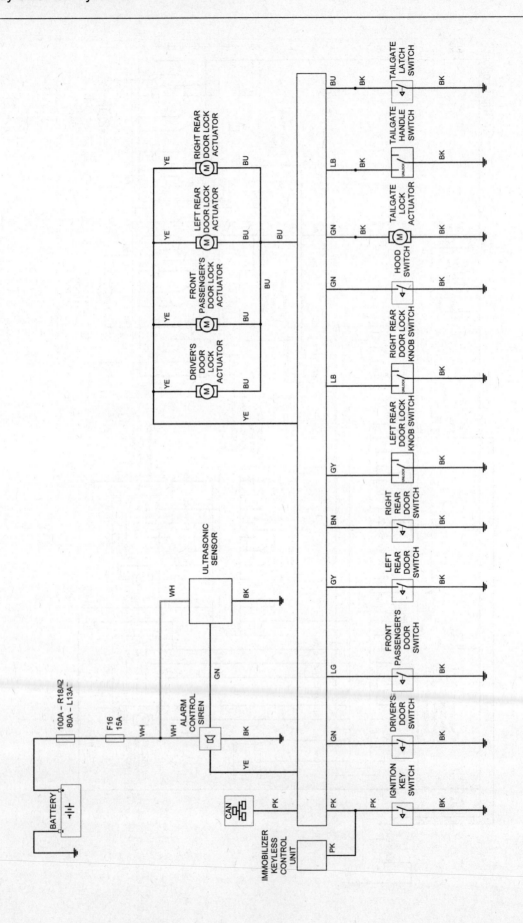

Power doors with alarm

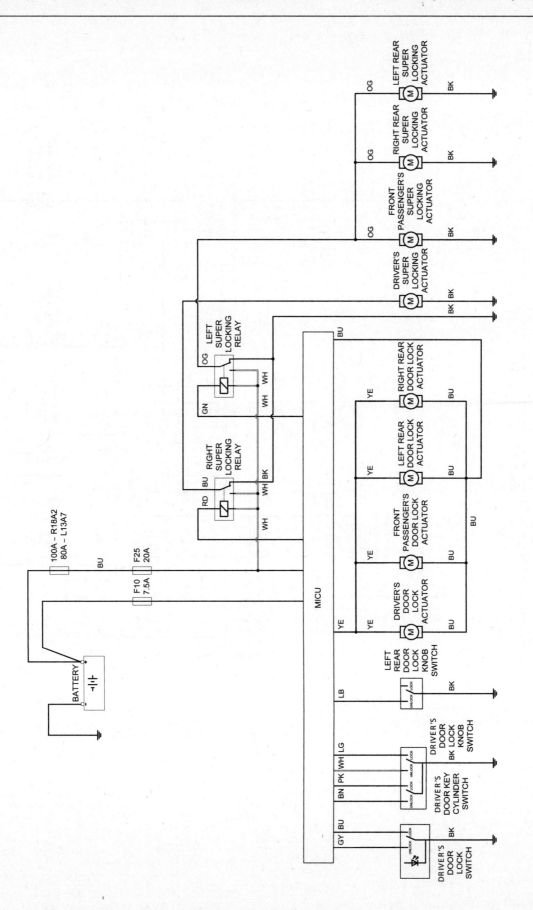

Power doors without alarm with deadlock

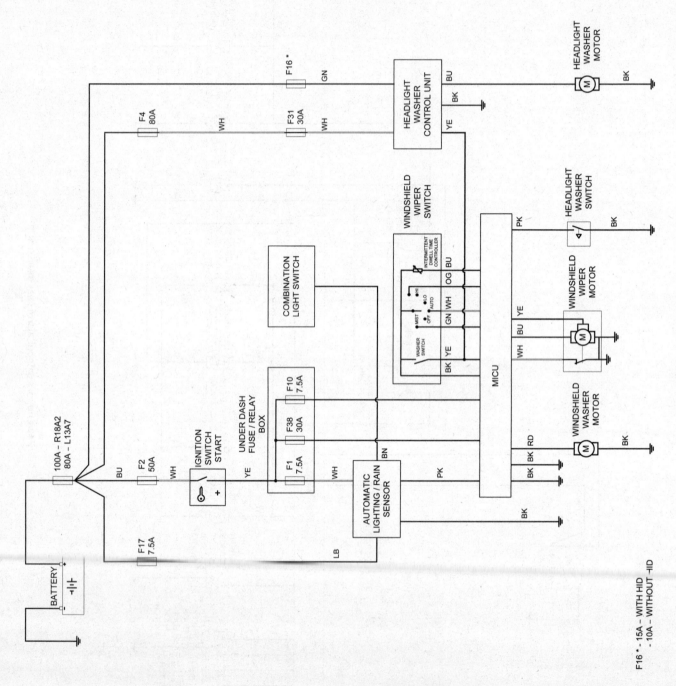

Windscreen wiper and washer

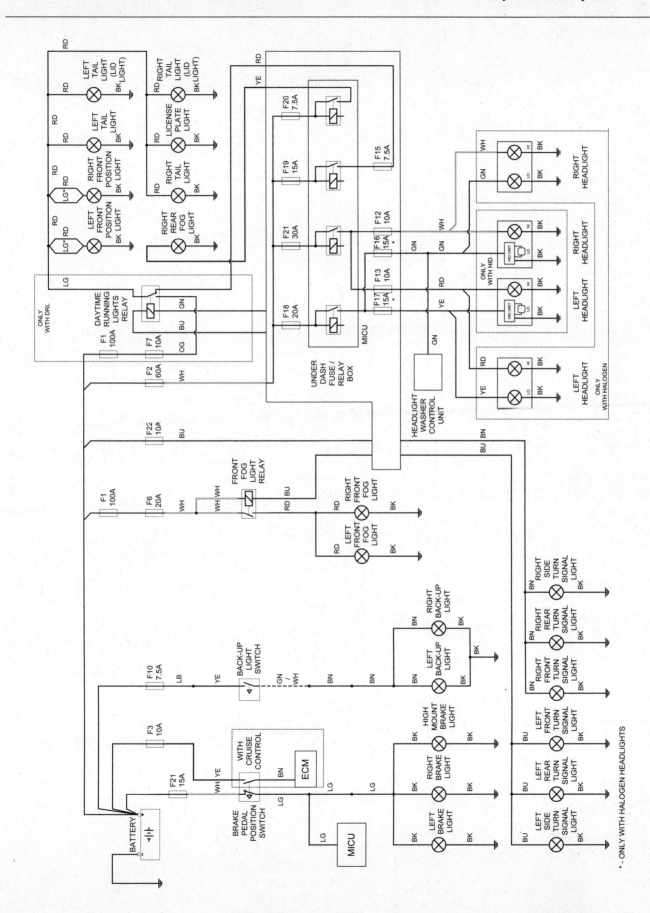

Exterior lighting

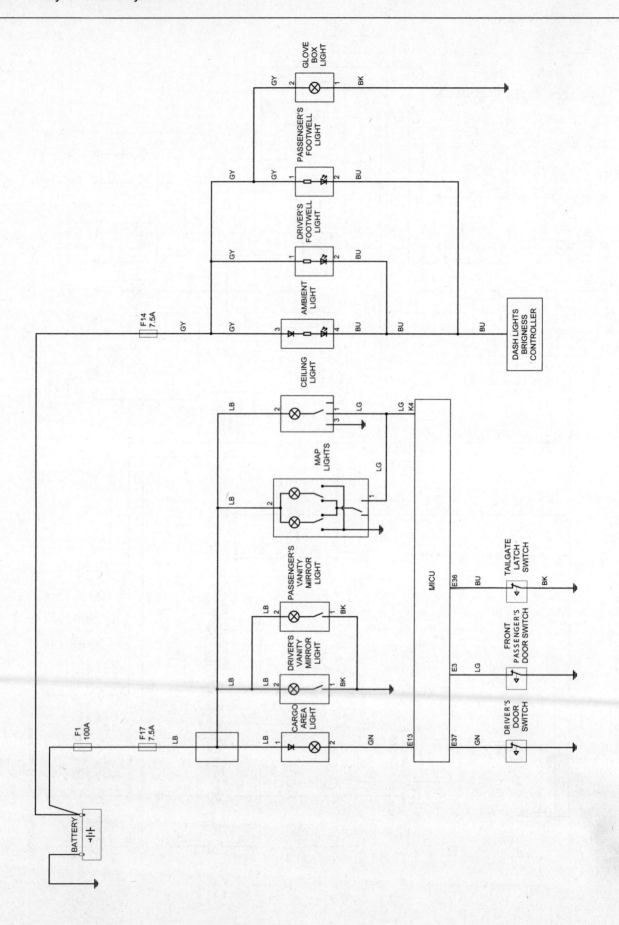

Interior lighting

Sound system

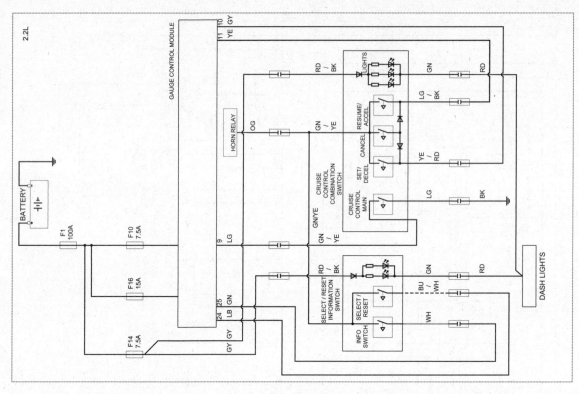

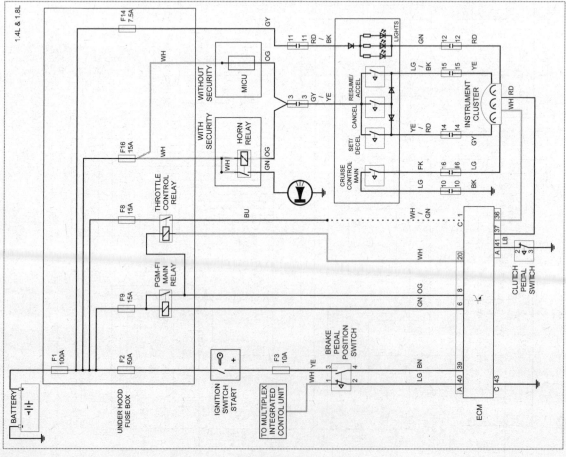

Cruise Control – 1.4 1.8 and 2.2 litre models

Reference REF•1

Dimensions and weights .... **REF•1**
Fuel economy........................... **REF•2**
Conversion factors..................... **REF•6**
Buying spare parts .... **REF•7**
Vehicle identification numbers .... **REF•7**
General repair procedures .... **REF•8**

Jacking and vehicle support .... **REF•9**
Tools and working facilities .... **REF•10**
MOT test checks .... **REF•12**
Fault finding .... **REF•16**
Glossary of technical terms .... **REF•26**
Index .... **REF•32**

Dimensions and weights

Note: *All figures are approximate, and may vary according to model. Refer to manufacturer's data for exact figures.*

Dimensions
Overall length .... 4248 mm
Overall width.. 1765 mm
Wheelbase .... 2635 mm
Height .... 1460 mm

Weights
Gross vehicle weight .... See Vehicle identification plate
Maximum towing weight .... See Vehicle identification plate

Fuel economy

Although depreciation is still the biggest part of the cost of motoring for most car owners, the cost of fuel is more immediately noticeable. These pages give some tips on how to get the best fuel economy.

Working it out

Manufacturer's figures

Car manufacturers are required by law to provide fuel consumption information on all new vehicles sold. These 'official' figures are obtained by simulating various driving conditions on a rolling road or a test track. Real life conditions are different, so the fuel consumption actually achieved may not bear much resemblance to the quoted figures.

How to calculate it

Many cars now have trip computers which will

display fuel consumption, both instantaneous and average. Refer to the owner's handbook for details of how to use these.

To calculate consumption yourself (and maybe to check that the trip computer is accurate), proceed as follows.

1. Fill up with fuel and note the mileage, or zero the trip recorder.
2. Drive as usual until you need to fill up again.
3. Note the amount of fuel required to refill the tank, and the mileage covered since the previous fill-up.
4. Divide the mileage by the amount of fuel used to obtain the consumption figure.

For example:

Mileage at first fill-up (a) = 27,903
Mileage at second fill-up (b) = 28,346
Mileage covered (b - a) = 443
Fuel required at second fill-up = 48.6 litres

The half-completed changeover to metric units in the UK means that we buy our fuel in litres, measure distances in miles and talk

about fuel consumption in miles per gallon. There are two ways round this: the first is to convert the litres to gallons before doing the calculation (by dividing by 4.546, or see Table 1). So in the example:

48.6 litres ÷ 4.546 = 10.69 gallons
443 miles ÷ 10.69 gallons = 41.4 mpg

The second way is to calculate the consumption in miles per litre, then multiply that figure by 4.546 (or see Table 2).

So in the example, fuel consumption is:

443 miles ÷ 48.6 litres = 9.1 mpl
9.1 mpl x 4.546 = 41.4 mpg

The rest of Europe expresses fuel consumption in litres of fuel required to travel 100 km (l/100 km). For interest, the conversions are given in Table 3. In practice it doesn't matter what units you use, provided you know what your normal consumption is and can spot if it's getting better or worse.

Table 1: conversion of litres to Imperial gallons

litres	1	2	3	4	5	10	20	30	40	50	60	70
gallons	0.22	0.44	0.66	0.88	1.10	2.24	4.49	6.73	8.98	11.22	10.47	15.71

Table 2: conversion of miles per litre to miles per gallon

miles per litre	5	6	7	8	9	10	11	12	13	14
miles per gallon	23	27	32	36	41	46	50	55	59	64

Table 3: conversion of litres per 100 km to miles per gallon

litres per 100 km	4	4.5	5	5.5	6	6.5	7	8	9	10
miles per gallon	71	63	56	51	47	43	40	35	31	28

Maintenance

A well-maintained car uses less fuel and creates less pollution. In particular:

Filters

Change air and fuel filters at the specified intervals.

Oil

Use a good quality oil of the lowest viscosity specified by the vehicle manufacturer (see *Lubricants and fluids*). Check the level often and be careful not to overfill.

Spark plugs

When applicable, renew at the specified intervals.

Tyres

Check tyre pressures regularly. Under-inflated tyres have an increased rolling resistance. It is generally safe to use the higher pressures specified for full load conditions even when not fully laden, but keep an eye on the centre band of tread for signs of wear due to over-inflation.

When buying new tyres, consider the 'fuel saving' models which most manufacturers include in their ranges.

Driving style

Acceleration

Acceleration uses more fuel than driving at a steady speed. The best technique with modern cars is to accelerate reasonably briskly to the desired speed, changing up through the gears as soon as possible without making the engine labour.

Air conditioning

Air conditioning absorbs quite a bit of energy from the engine – typically 3 kW (4 hp) or so. The effect on fuel consumption is at its worst in slow traffic. Switch it off when not required.

Anticipation

Drive smoothly and try to read the traffic flow so as to avoid unnecessary acceleration and braking.

Automatic transmission

When accelerating in an automatic, avoid depressing the throttle so far as to make the transmission hold onto lower gears at higher speeds. Don't use the 'Sport' setting, if applicable.

When stationary with the engine running, select 'N' or 'P'. When moving, keep your left foot away from the brake.

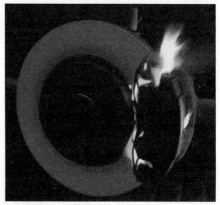

Braking

Braking converts the car's energy of motion into heat – essentially, it is wasted. Obviously some braking is always going to be necessary, but with good anticipation it is surprising how much can be avoided, especially on routes that you know well.

Carshare

Consider sharing lifts to work or to the shops. Even once a week will make a difference.

Electrical loads

Electricity is 'fuel' too; the alternator which charges the battery does so by converting some of the engine's energy of motion into electrical energy. The more electrical accessories are in use, the greater the load on the alternator. Switch off big consumers like the heated rear window when not required.

Freewheeling

Freewheeling (coasting) in neutral with the engine switched off is dangerous. The effort required to operate power-assisted brakes and steering increases when the engine is not running, with a potential lack of control in emergency situations.

In any case, modern fuel injection systems automatically cut off the engine's fuel supply on the overrun (moving and in gear, but with the accelerator pedal released).

Gadgets

Bolt-on devices claiming to save fuel have been around for nearly as long as the motor car itself. Those which worked were rapidly adopted as standard equipment by the vehicle manufacturers. Others worked only in certain situations, or saved fuel only at the expense of unacceptable effects on performance, driveability or the life of engine components.

The most effective fuel saving gadget is the driver's right foot.

Journey planning

Combine (eg) a trip to the supermarket with a visit to the recycling centre and the DIY store, rather than making separate journeys.

When possible choose a travelling time outside rush hours.

Load

The more heavily a car is laden, the greater the energy required to accelerate it to a given speed. Remove heavy items which you don't need to carry.

One load which is often overlooked is the contents of the fuel tank. A tankful of fuel (55 litres / 12 gallons) weighs 45 kg (100 lb) or so. Just half filling it may be worthwhile.

Lost?

At the risk of stating the obvious, if you're going somewhere new, have details of the route to hand. There's not much point in achieving record mpg if you also go miles out of your way.

Parking

If possible, carry out any reversing or turning manoeuvres when you arrive at a parking space so that you can drive straight out when you leave. Manoeuvering when the engine is cold uses a lot more fuel.

Driving around looking for free on-street parking may cost more in fuel than buying a car park ticket.

Premium fuel

Most major oil companies (and some supermarkets) have premium grades of fuel which are several pence a litre dearer than the standard grades. Reports vary, but the consensus seems to be that if these fuels improve economy at all, they do not do so by enough to justify their extra cost.

Roof rack

When loading a roof rack, try to produce a wedge shape with the narrow end at the front. Any cover should be securely fastened – if it flaps it's creating turbulence and absorbing energy.

Remove roof racks and boxes when not in use – they increase air resistance and can create a surprising amount of noise.

Short journeys

The engine is at its least efficient, and wear is highest, during the first few miles after a cold start. Consider walking, cycling or using public transport.

Speed

The engine is at its most efficient when running at a steady speed and load at the rpm where it develops maximum torque. (You can find this figure in the car's handbook.) For most cars this corresponds to between 55 and 65 mph in top gear.

Above the optimum cruising speed, fuel consumption starts to rise quite sharply. A car travelling at 80 mph will typically be using 30% more fuel than at 60 mph.

Supermarket fuel

It may be cheap but is it any good? In the UK all supermarket fuel must meet the relevant British Standard. The major oil companies will say that their branded fuels have better additive packages which may stop carbon and other deposits building up. A reasonable compromise might be to use one tank of branded fuel to three or four from the supermarket.

Switch off when stationary

Switch off the engine if you look like being stationary for more than 30 seconds or so. This is good for the environment as well as for your pocket. Be aware though that frequent restarts are hard on the battery and the starter motor.

Windows

Driving with the windows open increases air turbulence around the vehicle. Closing the windows promotes smooth airflow and

reduced resistance. The faster you go, the more significant this is.

And finally...

Driving techniques associated with good fuel economy tend to involve moderate acceleration and low top speeds. Be considerate to the needs of other road users who may need to make brisker progress; even if you do not agree with them this is not an excuse to be obstructive.

Safety must always take precedence over economy, whether it is a question of accelerating hard to complete an overtaking manoeuvre, killing your speed when confronted with a potential hazard or switching the lights on when it starts to get dark.

Conversion factors

Length (distance)

Inches (in)	x 25.4	= Millimetres (mm)	x 0.0394	= Inches (in)	
Feet (ft)	x 0.305	= Metres (m)	x 3.281	= Feet (ft)	
Miles	x 1.609	= Kilometres (km)	x 0.621	= Miles	

Volume (capacity)

Cubic inches (cu in; in^3)	x 16.387	= Cubic centimetres (cc; cm^3)	x 0.061	= Cubic inches (cu in; in^3)	
Imperial pints (Imp pt)	x 0.568	= Litres (l)	x 1.76	= Imperial pints (Imp pt)	
Imperial quarts (Imp qt)	x 1.137	= Litres (l)	x 0.88	= Imperial quarts (Imp qt)	
Imperial quarts (Imp qt)	x 1.201	= US quarts (US qt)	x 0.833	= Imperial quarts (Imp qt)	
US quarts (US qt)	x 0.946	= Litres (l)	x 1.057	= US quarts (US qt)	
Imperial gallons (Imp gal)	x 4.546	= Litres (l)	x 0.22	= Imperial gallons (Imp gal)	
Imperial gallons (Imp gal)	x 1.201	= US gallons (US gal)	x 0.833	= Imperial gallons (Imp gal)	
US gallons (US gal)	x 3.785	= Litres (l)	x 0.264	= US gallons (US gal)	

Mass (weight)

Ounces (oz)	x 28.35	= Grams (g)	x 0.035	= Ounces (oz)	
Pounds (lb)	x 0.454	= Kilograms (kg)	x 2.205	= Pounds (lb)	

Force

Ounces-force (ozf; oz)	x 0.278	= Newtons (N)	x 3.6	= Ounces-force (ozf; oz)	
Pounds-force (lbf; lb)	x 4.448	= Newtons (N)	x 0.225	= Pounds-force (lbf; lb)	
Newtons (N)	x 0.1	= Kilograms-force (kgf; kg)	x 9.81	= Newtons (N)	

Pressure

Pounds-force per square inch (psi; lbf/in^2; lb/in^2)	x 0.070	= Kilograms-force per square centimetre (kgf/cm^2; kg/cm^2)	x 14.223	= Pounds-force per square inch (psi; lbf/in^2; lb/in^2)	
Pounds-force per square inch (psi; lbf/in^2; lb/in^2)	x 0.068	= Atmospheres (atm)	x 14.696	= Pounds-force per square inch (psi; lbf/in^2; lb/in^2)	
Pounds-force per square inch (psi; lbf/in^2; lb/in^2)	x 0.069	= Bars	x 14.5	= Pounds-force per square inch (psi; lbf/in^2; lb/in^2)	
Pounds-force per square inch (psi; lbf/in^2; lb/in^2)	x 6.895	= Kilopascals (kPa)	x 0.145	= Pounds-force per square inch (psi; lbf/in^2; lb/in^2)	
Kilopascals (kPa)	x 0.01	= Kilograms-force per square centimetre (kgf/cm^2; kg/cm^2)	x 98.1	= Kilopascals (kPa)	
Millibar (mbar)	x 100	= Pascals (Pa)	x 0.01	= Millibar (mbar)	
Millibar (mbar)	x 0.0145	= Pounds-force per square inch (psi; lbf/in^2; lb/in^2)	x 68.947	= Millibar (mbar)	
Millibar (mbar)	x 0.75	= Millimetres of mercury (mmHg)	x 1.333	= Millibar (mbar)	
Millibar (mbar)	x 0.401	= Inches of water (inH$_2$O)	x 2.491	= Millibar (mbar)	
Millimetres of mercury (mmHg)	x 0.535	= Inches of water (inH$_2$O)	x 1.868	= Millimetres of mercury (mmHg)	
Inches of water (inH$_2$O)	x 0.036	= Pounds-force per square inch (psi; lbf/in^2; lb/in^2)	x 27.68	= Inches of water (inH$_2$O)	

Torque (moment of force)

Pounds-force inches (lbf in; lb in)	x 1.152	= Kilograms-force centimetre (kgf cm; kg cm)	x 0.868	= Pounds-force inches (lbf in; lb in)	
Pounds-force inches (lbf in; lb in)	x 0.113	= Newton metres (Nm)	x 8.85	= Pounds-force inches (lbf in; lb in)	
Pounds-force inches (lbf in; lb in)	x 0.083	= Pounds-force feet (lbf ft; lb ft)	x 12	= Pounds-force inches (lbf in; lb in)	
Pounds-force feet (lbf ft; lb ft)	x 0.138	= Kilograms-force metres (kgf m; kg m)	x 7.233	= Pounds-force feet (lbf ft; lb ft)	
Pounds-force feet (lbf ft; lb ft)	x 1.356	= Newton metres (Nm)	x 0.738	= Pounds-force feet (lbf ft; lb ft)	
Newton metres (Nm)	x 0.102	= Kilograms-force metres (kgf m; kg m)	x 9.804	= Newton metres (Nm)	

Power

Horsepower (hp)	x 745.7	= Watts (W)	x 0.0013	= Horsepower (hp)	

Velocity (speed)

Miles per hour (miles/hr; mph)	x 1.609	= Kilometres per hour (km/hr; kph)	x 0.621	= Miles per hour (miles/hr; mph)	

Fuel consumption*

Miles per gallon, Imperial (mpg)	x 0.354	= Kilometres per litre (km/l)	x 2.825	= Miles per gallon, Imperial (mpg)	
Miles per gallon, US (mpg)	x 0.425	= Kilometres per litre (km/l)	x 2.352	= Miles per gallon, US (mpg)	

Temperature

Degrees Fahrenheit = (°C x 1.8) + 32   Degrees Celsius (Degrees Centigrade; °C) = (°F - 32) x 0.56

It is common practice to convert from miles per gallon (mpg) to litres/100 kilometres (l/100km), where mpg x l/100 km = 282

Spare parts are available from many sources, including maker's appointed garages, accessory shops, and motor factors. To be sure of obtaining the correct parts, it will sometimes be necessary to quote the vehicle identification number. If possible, it can also be useful to take the old parts along for positive identification. Items such as starter motors and alternators may be available under a service exchange scheme – any parts returned should be clean.

Our advice regarding spare parts is as follows.

Officially appointed garages

This is the best source of parts which are peculiar to your car, and which are not otherwise generally available (eg, badges, interior trim, certain body panels, etc). It is also the only place at which you should buy parts if the vehicle is still under warranty.

Accessory shops

These are very good places to buy materials and components needed for the maintenance of your car (oil, air and fuel filters, light bulbs, drivebelts, greases, brake pads, touch-up paint, etc). Components of this nature sold by a reputable shop are usually of the same standard as those used by the car manufacturer.

Besides components, these shops also sell tools and general accessories, usually have convenient opening hours, charge lower prices, and can often be found close to home. Some accessory shops have parts counters where components needed for almost any repair job can be purchased or ordered.

Motor factors

Good factors will stock all the more important components which wear out comparatively quickly, and can sometimes supply individual components needed for the overhaul of a larger assembly (eg, brake seals and hydraulic parts, bearing shells, pistons, valves). They may also handle work such as cylinder block reboring, crankshaft regrinding, etc.

Tyre and exhaust specialists

These outlets may be independent, or members of a local or national chain. They frequently offer competitive prices when compared with a main dealer or local garage, but it will pay to obtain several quotes before making a decision. When researching prices, also ask what extras may be added – for instance fitting a new valve and balancing the wheel are both commonly charged on top of the price of a new tyre.

Other sources

Beware of parts or materials obtained from market stalls, car boot sales or similar outlets. Such items are not invariably sub-standard, but there is little chance of compensation if they do prove unsatisfactory. in the case of safety-critical components such as brake pads, there is the risk not only of financial loss, but also of an accident causing injury or death.

Second-hand components or assemblies obtained from a car breaker can be a good buy in some circumstances, but this sort of purchase is best made by the experienced DIY mechanic.

Vehicle identification numbers

Modifications are a continuing and unpublicised process in vehicle manufacture, quite apart from major model changes. Spare parts manuals and lists are compiled upon a numerical basis, the individual vehicle identification numbers being essential to correct identification of the component concerned.

When ordering spare parts, always give as much information as possible. Quote the car model, year of manufacture, body and engine numbers as appropriate.

The vehicle identification plate is situated on the driver's side B-pillar (see illustration). The vehicle identification number is also repeated in the form of plate visible through the windscreen on the passenger's side (see illustration).

The engine number is located on the left-hand front side of the engine cylinder block. Other identification numbers or codes are stamped on major items such as the gearbox, etc.

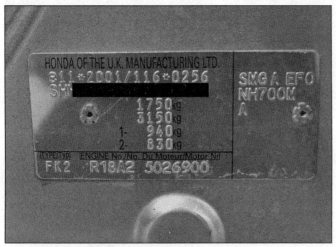

The VIN plate is mounted at the base of the left-hand side B-pillar…

…and stamped into the body work beneath the windscreen cowl panels

Whenever servicing, repair or overhaul work is carried out on the car or its components, observe the following procedures and instructions. This will assist in carrying out the operation efficiently and to a professional standard of workmanship.

Joint mating faces and gaskets

When separating components at their mating faces, never insert screwdrivers or similar implements into the joint between the faces in order to prise them apart. This can cause severe damage which results in oil leaks, coolant leaks, etc upon reassembly. Separation is usually achieved by tapping along the joint with a soft-faced hammer in order to break the seal. However, note that this method may not be suitable where dowels are used for component location.

Where a gasket is used between the mating faces of two components, a new one must be fitted on reassembly; fit it dry unless otherwise stated in the repair procedure. Make sure that the mating faces are clean and dry, with all traces of old gasket removed. When cleaning a joint face, use a tool which is unlikely to score or damage the face, and remove any burrs or nicks with an oilstone or fine file.

Make sure that tapped holes are cleaned with a pipe cleaner, and keep them free of jointing compound, if this is being used, unless specifically instructed otherwise.

Ensure that all orifices, channels or pipes are clear, and blow through them, preferably using compressed air.

Oil seals

Oil seals can be removed by levering them out with a wide flat-bladed screwdriver or similar implement. Alternatively, a number of self-tapping screws may be screwed into the seal, and these used as a purchase for pliers or some similar device in order to pull the seal free.

Whenever an oil seal is removed from its working location, either individually or as part of an assembly, it should be renewed.

The very fine sealing lip of the seal is easily damaged, and will not seal if the surface it contacts is not completely clean and free from scratches, nicks or grooves. If the original sealing surface of the component cannot be restored, and the manufacturer has not made provision for slight relocation of the seal relative to the sealing surface, the component should be renewed.

Protect the lips of the seal from any surface which may damage them in the course of fitting. Use tape or a conical sleeve where possible. Where indicated, lubricate the seal lips with oil before fitting and, on dual-lipped seals, fill the space between the lips with grease.

Unless otherwise stated, oil seals must be fitted with their sealing lips toward the lubricant to be sealed.

Use a tubular drift or block of wood of the appropriate size to install the seal and, if the seal housing is shouldered, drive the seal down to the shoulder. If the seal housing is unshouldered, the seal should be fitted with its face flush with the housing top face (unless otherwise instructed).

Screw threads and fastenings

Seized nuts, bolts and screws are quite a common occurrence where corrosion has set in, and the use of penetrating oil or releasing fluid will often overcome this problem if the offending item is soaked for a while before attempting to release it. The use of an impact driver may also provide a means of releasing such stubborn fastening devices, when used in conjunction with the appropriate screwdriver bit or socket. If none of these methods works, it may be necessary to resort to the careful application of heat, or the use of a hacksaw or nut splitter device. Before resorting to extreme methods, check that you are not dealing with a left-hand thread!

Studs are usually removed by locking two nuts together on the threaded part, and then using a spanner on the lower nut to unscrew the stud. Studs or bolts which have broken off below the surface of the component in which they are mounted can sometimes be removed using a stud extractor.

Always ensure that a blind tapped hole is completely free from oil, grease, water or other fluid before installing the bolt or stud. Failure to do this could cause the housing to crack due to the hydraulic action of the bolt or stud as it is screwed in.

For some screw fastenings, notably cylinder head bolts or nuts, torque wrench settings are no longer specified for the latter stages of tightening, "angle-tightening" being called up instead. Typically, a fairly low torque wrench setting will be applied to the bolts/nuts in the correct sequence, followed by one or more stages of tightening through specified angles.

When checking or retightening a nut or bolt to a specified torque setting, slacken the nut or bolt by a quarter of a turn, and then retighten to the specified setting. However, this should not be attempted where angular tightening has been used.

Locknuts, locktabs and washers

Any fastening which will rotate against a component or housing during tightening should always have a washer between it and the relevant component or housing.

Spring or split washers should always be renewed when they are used to lock a critical component such as a big-end bearing retaining bolt or nut. Locktabs which are folded over to retain a nut or bolt should always be renewed.

Self-locking nuts can be re-used in non-critical areas, providing resistance can be felt when the locking portion passes over the bolt or stud thread. However, it should be noted that self-locking stiffnuts tend to lose their effectiveness after long periods of use, and should then be renewed as a matter of course.

Split pins must always be replaced with new ones of the correct size for the hole.

When thread-locking compound is found on the threads of a fastener which is to be re-used, it should be cleaned off with a wire brush and solvent, and fresh compound applied on reassembly.

Special tools

Some repair procedures in this manual entail the use of special tools such as a press, two or three-legged pullers, spring compressors, etc. Wherever possible, suitable readily-available alternatives to the manufacturer's special tools are described, and are shown in use. In some instances, where no alternative is possible, it has been necessary to resort to the use of a manufacturer's tool, and this has been done for reasons of safety as well as the efficient completion of the repair operation. Unless you are highly-skilled and have a thorough understanding of the procedures described, never attempt to bypass the use of any special tool when the procedure described specifies its use. Not only is there a very great risk of personal injury, but expensive damage could be caused to the components involved.

Environmental considerations

When disposing of used engine oil, brake fluid, antifreeze, etc, give due consideration to any detrimental environmental effects. Do not, for instance, pour any of the above liquids down drains into the general sewage system, or onto the ground to soak away. Many local council refuse tips provide a facility for waste oil disposal, as do some garages. You can find your nearest disposal point by calling the Environment Agency on 08708 506 506 or by visiting www.oilbankline.org.uk.

Note: It is illegal and anti-social to dump oil down the drain. To find the location of your local oil recycling bank, call 08708 506 506 or visit www.oilbankline.org.uk.

The jack supplied with the vehicle tool kit should only be used for changing the roadwheels – see Wheel changing at the front of this manual. When carrying out any other kind of work, raise the vehicle using a hydraulic trolley jack, and always supplement the jack with axle stands positioned under the vehicle jacking points.

When using a trolley jack or axle stands, position the jack head or axle stand head adjacent to one of the relevant wheel changing jacking points under the sills **(see illustrations)**. Use a block of wood between the jack or axle stand and the sill.

Do not attempt to jack the vehicle under the sump, or any of the suspension components.

The jack supplied with the vehicle locates in the jacking points on the underside of the sills – see Wheel changing at the front of this manual. Ensure that the jack head is correctly engaged before attempting to raise the vehicle.

 Warning: Never work under, around, or near a raised car, unless it is adequately supported in at least two places.

Use a trolley jack at the rear...

...and always place axle stands under the sill jacking points

Raise the front of the vehicle and position the axle stand as shown

Introduction

A selection of good tools is a fundamental requirement for anyone contemplating the maintenance and repair of a motor vehicle. For the owner who does not possess any, their purchase will prove a considerable expense, offsetting some of the savings made by doing-it-yourself. However, provided that the tools purchased meet the relevant national safety standards and are of good quality, they will last for many years and prove an extremely worthwhile investment.

To help the average owner to decide which tools are needed to carry out the various tasks detailed in this manual, we have compiled three lists of tools under the following headings: *Maintenance and minor repair*, *Repair and overhaul*, and *Special*. Newcomers to practical mechanics should start off with the *Maintenance and minor repair* tool kit, and confine themselves to the simpler jobs around the vehicle. Then, as confidence and experience grow, more difficult tasks can be undertaken, with extra tools being purchased as, and when, they are needed. In this way, a *Maintenance and minor repair* tool kit can be built up into a *Repair and overhaul* tool kit over a considerable period of time, without any major cash outlays. The experienced do-it-yourselfer will have a tool kit good enough for most repair and overhaul procedures, and will add tools from the *Special* category when it is felt that the expense is justified by the amount of use to which these tools will be put.

Maintenance and minor repair tool kit

The tools given in this list should be considered as a minimum requirement if routine maintenance, servicing and minor repair operations are to be undertaken. We recommend the purchase of combination spanners (ring one end, open-ended the other); although more expensive than open-ended ones, they do give the advantages of both types of spanner.

☐ *Combination spanners:*
  Metric - 8 to 19 mm inclusive
☐ *Adjustable spanner - 35 mm jaw (approx.)*
☐ *Spark plug spanner (with rubber insert) - petrol models*
☐ *Spark plug gap adjustment tool - petrol models*
☐ *Set of feeler gauges*
☐ *Brake bleed nipple spanner*
☐ *Screwdrivers:*
  Flat blade - 100 mm long x 6 mm dia
  Cross blade - 100 mm long x 6 mm dia
  Torx - various sizes (not all vehicles)
☐ *Combination pliers*
☐ *Hacksaw (junior)*
☐ *Tyre pump*
☐ *Tyre pressure gauge*
☐ *Oil can*
☐ *Oil filter removal tool (if applicable)*
☐ *Fine emery cloth*
☐ *Wire brush (small)*
☐ *Funnel (medium size)*
☐ *Sump drain plug key (not all vehicles)*

Repair and overhaul tool kit

These tools are virtually essential for anyone undertaking any major repairs to a motor vehicle, and are additional to those given in the *Maintenance and minor repair* list. Included in this list is a comprehensive set of sockets. Although these are expensive, they will be found invaluable as they are so versatile - particularly if various drives are included in the set. We recommend the half-inch square-drive type, as this can be used with most proprietary torque wrenches.

The tools in this list will sometimes need to be supplemented by tools from the *Special* list:

☐ *Sockets to cover range in previous list (including Torx sockets)*
☐ *Reversible ratchet drive (for use with sockets)*
☐ *Extension piece, 250 mm (for use with sockets)*
☐ *Universal joint (for use with sockets)*
☐ *Flexible handle or sliding T "breaker bar" (for use with sockets)*
☐ *Torque wrench (for use with sockets)*
☐ *Self-locking grips*
☐ *Ball pein hammer*
☐ *Soft-faced mallet (plastic or rubber)*
☐ *Screwdrivers:*
  Flat blade - long & sturdy, short (chubby), and narrow (electrician's) types
  Cross blade - long & sturdy, and short (chubby) types
☐ *Pliers:*
  Long-nosed
  Side cutters (electrician's)
  Circlip (internal and external)
☐ *Cold chisel - 25 mm*
☐ *Scriber*
☐ *Scraper*
☐ *Centre-punch*
☐ *Pin punch*
☐ *Hacksaw*
☐ *Brake hose clamp*
☐ *Brake/clutch bleeding kit*
☐ *Selection of twist drills*
☐ *Steel rule/straight-edge*
☐ *Allen keys (inc. splined/Torx type)*
☐ *Selection of files*
☐ *Wire brush*
☐ *Axle stands*
☐ *Jack (strong trolley or hydraulic type)*
☐ *Light with extension lead*
☐ *Universal electrical multi-meter*

Sockets and reversible ratchet drive

Torx key, socket and bit

Brake bleeding kit

Hose clamp

Angular-tightening gauge

Special tools

The tools in this list are those which are not used regularly, are expensive to buy, or which need to be used in accordance with their manufacturers' instructions. Unless relatively difficult mechanical jobs are undertaken frequently, it will not be economic to buy many of these tools. Where this is the case, you could consider clubbing together with friends (or joining a motorists' club) to make a joint purchase, or borrowing the tools against a deposit from a local garage or tool hire specialist.

The following list contains only those tools and instruments freely available to the public, and not those special tools produced by the vehicle manufacturer specifically for its dealer network. You will find occasional references to these manufacturers' special tools in the text of this manual. Generally, an alternative method of doing the job without the vehicle manufacturers' special tool is given. However, sometimes there is no alternative to using them. Where this is the case and the relevant tool cannot be bought or borrowed, you will have to entrust the work to a dealer.

- ☐ Angular-tightening gauge
- ☐ Valve spring compressor
- ☐ Valve grinding tool
- ☐ Piston ring compressor
- ☐ Piston ring removal/installation tool
- ☐ Cylinder bore hone
- ☐ Balljoint separator
- ☐ Coil spring compressors (where applicable)
- ☐ Two/three-legged hub and bearing puller
- ☐ Impact screwdriver
- ☐ Micrometer and/or vernier calipers
- ☐ Dial gauge
- ☐ Tachometer
- ☐ Fault code reader
- ☐ Cylinder compression gauge
- ☐ Hand-operated vacuum pump and gauge
- ☐ Clutch plate alignment set
- ☐ Brake shoe steady spring cup removal tool
- ☐ Bush and bearing removal/installation set
- ☐ Stud extractors
- ☐ Tap and die set
- ☐ Lifting tackle

Buying tools

Reputable motor accessory shops and superstores often offer excellent quality tools at discount prices, so it pays to shop around.

Remember, you don't have to buy the most expensive items on the shelf, but it is always advisable to steer clear of the very cheap tools. Beware of 'bargains' offered on market stalls, on-line or at car boot sales. There are plenty of good tools around at reasonable prices, but always aim to purchase items which meet the relevant national safety standards. If in doubt, ask the proprietor or manager of the shop for advice before making a purchase.

Care and maintenance of tools

Having purchased a reasonable tool kit, it is necessary to keep the tools in a clean and serviceable condition. After use, always wipe off any dirt, grease and metal particles using a clean, dry cloth, before putting the tools away. Never leave them lying around after they have been used. A simple tool rack on the garage or workshop wall for items such as screwdrivers and pliers is a good idea. Store all normal spanners and sockets in a metal box. Any measuring instruments, gauges, meters, etc, must be carefully stored where they cannot be damaged or become rusty.

Take a little care when tools are used. Hammer heads inevitably become marked, and screwdrivers lose the keen edge on their blades from time to time. A little timely attention with emery cloth or a file will soon restore items like this to a good finish.

Working facilities

Not to be forgotten when discussing tools is the workshop itself. If anything more than routine maintenance is to be carried out, a suitable working area becomes essential.

It is appreciated that many an owner-mechanic is forced by circumstances to remove an engine or similar item without the benefit of a garage or workshop. Having done this, any repairs should always be done under the cover of a roof.

Wherever possible, any dismantling should be done on a clean, flat workbench or table at a suitable working height.

Any workbench needs a vice; one with a jaw opening of 100 mm is suitable for most jobs. As mentioned previously, some clean dry storage space is also required for tools, as well as for any lubricants, cleaning fluids, touch-up paints etc, which become necessary.

Another item which may be required, and which has a much more general usage, is an electric drill with a chuck capacity of at least 8 mm. This, together with a good range of twist drills, is virtually essential for fitting accessories.

Last, but not least, always keep a supply of old newspapers and clean, lint-free rags available, and try to keep any working area as clean as possible.

Micrometers

Dial test indicator ("dial gauge")

Oil filter removal tool (strap wrench type)

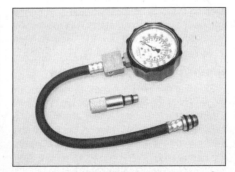

Compression tester

Bearing puller

This is a guide to getting your vehicle through the MOT test. Obviously it will not be possible to examine the vehicle to the same standard as the professional MOT tester. However, working through the following checks will enable you to identify any problem areas before submitting the vehicle for the test.

It has only been possible to summarise the test requirements here, based on the regulations in force at the time of printing. Test standards are becoming increasingly stringent, although there are some exemptions for older vehicles.

An assistant will be needed to help carry out some of these checks.

The checks have been sub-divided into four categories, as follows:

1 Checks carried out **FROM THE DRIVER'S SEAT**

2 Checks carried out **WITH THE VEHICLE ON THE GROUND**

3 Checks carried out **WITH THE VEHICLE RAISED AND THE WHEELS FREE TO TURN**

4 Checks carried out on **YOUR VEHICLE'S EXHAUST EMISSION SYSTEM**

---

1 Checks carried out **FROM THE DRIVER'S SEAT**

Handbrake (parking brake)

☐ Test the operation of the handbrake. Excessive travel (too many clicks) indicates incorrect brake or cable adjustment.
☐ Check that the handbrake cannot be released by tapping the lever sideways. Check the security of the lever mountings.

☐ If the parking brake is foot-operated, check that the pedal is secure and without excessive travel, and that the release mechanism operates correctly.
☐ Where applicable, test the operation of the electronic handbrake. The brake should engage and disengage without excessive delay. If the warning light does not extinguish when the brake is disengaged, this could indicate a fault which will need further investigation.

Footbrake

☐ Depress the brake pedal and check that it does not creep down to the floor, indicating a master cylinder fault. Release the pedal,

wait a few seconds, then depress it again. If the pedal travels nearly to the floor before firm resistance is felt, brake adjustment or repair is necessary. If the pedal feels spongy, there is air in the hydraulic system which must be removed by bleeding.

☐ Check that the brake pedal is secure and in good condition. Check also for signs of fluid leaks on the pedal, floor or carpets, which would indicate failed seals in the brake master cylinder.
☐ Check the servo unit (when applicable) by operating the brake pedal several times, then keeping the pedal depressed and starting the engine. As the engine starts, the pedal will move down slightly. If not, the vacuum hose or the servo itself may be faulty.

Steering wheel and column

☐ Examine the steering wheel for fractures or looseness of the hub, spokes or rim.
☐ Move the steering wheel from side to side and then up and down. Check that the steering wheel is not loose on the column, indicating wear or a loose retaining nut. Continue moving the steering wheel as before, but also turn it slightly from left to right.

☐ Check that the steering wheel is not loose on the column, and that there is no abnormal movement of the steering wheel, indicating wear in the column support bearings or couplings.
☐ Check that the ignition lock (where fitted) engages and disengages correctly.
☐ Steering column adjustment mechanisms (where fitted) must be able to lock the column securely in place with no play evident.

Windscreen, mirrors and sunvisor

☐ The windscreen must be free of cracks or other significant damage within the driver's field of view. (Small stone chips are acceptable.) Rear view mirrors must be secure, intact, and capable of being adjusted.

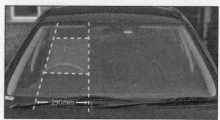

☐ The driver's sunvisor must be capable of being stored in the "up" position.

Seat belts and seats

Note: *The following checks are applicable to all seat belts, front and rear.*

☐ Examine the webbing of all the belts (including rear belts if fitted) for cuts, serious fraying or deterioration. Fasten and unfasten each belt to check the buckles. If applicable, check the retracting mechanism. Check the security of all seat belt mountings accessible from inside the vehicle, ensuring any height adjustable mountings lock securely in place.

☐ Seat belts with pre-tensioners, once activated, have a "flag" or similar showing on the seat belt stalk. This, in itself, is not a reason for test failure.

☐ The front seats themselves must be securely attached and the backrests must lock in the upright position.

Doors

☐ Both front doors must be able to be opened and closed from outside and inside, and must latch securely when closed.

Bonnet and boot/tailgate

☐ The bonnet and boot/tailgate must latch securely when closed.

2 Checks carried out WITH THE VEHICLE ON THE GROUND

Vehicle identification

☐ Number plates must be in good condition, secure and legible, with letters and numbers correctly spaced – spacing at (A) should be 33 mm and at (B) 11 mm. At the front, digits must be black on a white background and at the rear black on a yellow background. Other background designs (such as honeycomb) are not permitted.

☐ The VIN plate and/or homologation plate must be permanently displayed and legible.

Electrical equipment

☐ Switch on the ignition and check the operation of the horn.

☐ Check the windscreen washers and wipers, examining the wiper blades; renew damaged or perished blades. Also check the operation of the stop-lights.

☐ Check the operation of the sidelights and number plate lights. The lenses and reflectors must be secure, clean and undamaged.

☐ Check the operation and alignment of the headlights. The headlight reflectors must not be tarnished and the lenses must be undamaged.

☐ Switch on the ignition and check the operation of the direction indicators (including the instrument panel tell-tale) and the hazard warning lights. Operation of the sidelights and stop-lights must not affect the indicators - if it does, the cause is usually a bad earth at the rear light cluster. Indicators should flash at a rate of between 60 and 120 times per minute – faster or slower than this could indicate a fault with the flasher unit or a bad earth at one of the light units.

☐ Check the operation of the rear foglight(s), including the warning light on the instrument panel or in the switch.

☐ The warning lights must illuminate in accordance with the manufacturer's design. For most vehicles, the ABS and other warning lights should illuminate when the ignition is switched on, and (if the system is operating properly) extinguish after a few seconds. Refer to the owner's handbook.

Footbrake

☐ Examine the master cylinder, brake pipes and servo unit for leaks, loose mountings, corrosion or other damage. If ABS is fitted, this unit should also be examined for signs of leaks or corrosion.

☐ The fluid reservoir must be secure and the fluid level must be between the upper (A) and lower (B) markings.

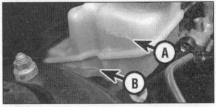

☐ Inspect both front brake flexible hoses for cracks or deterioration of the rubber. Turn the steering from lock to lock, and ensure that the hoses do not contact the wheel, tyre, or any part of the steering or suspension mechanism. With the brake pedal firmly depressed, check the hoses for bulges or leaks under pressure.

Steering and suspension

☐ Have your assistant turn the steering wheel from side to side slightly, up to the point where the steering gear just begins to transmit this movement to the roadwheels. Check for excessive free play between the steering wheel and the steering gear, indicating wear or insecurity of the steering column joints, the column-to-steering gear coupling, or the steering gear itself.

☐ Have your assistant turn the steering wheel more vigorously in each direction, so that the roadwheels just begin to turn. As this is done, examine all the steering joints, linkages, fittings and attachments. Renew any component that shows signs of wear or damage. On vehicles with power steering, check the security and condition of the steering pump, drivebelt and hoses.

☐ Check that the vehicle is standing level, and at approximately the correct ride height.

Shock absorbers

☐ Depress each corner of the vehicle in turn, then release it. The vehicle should rise and then settle in its normal position. If the vehicle continues to rise and fall, the shock absorber is defective. A shock absorber which has seized will also cause the vehicle to fail.

Exhaust system

☐ Start the engine. With your assistant holding a rag over the tailpipe, check the entire system for leaks. Repair or renew leaking sections.

3 Checks carried out
WITH THE VEHICLE RAISED AND THE WHEELS FREE TO TURN

Jack up the front and rear of the vehicle, and securely support it on axle stands. Position the stands clear of the suspension assemblies. Ensure that the wheels are clear of the ground and that the steering can be turned from lock to lock.

Steering mechanism

☐ Have your assistant turn the steering from lock to lock. Check that the steering turns smoothly, and that no part of the steering mechanism, including a wheel or tyre, fouls any brake hose or pipe or any part of the body structure.
☐ Examine the steering rack rubber gaiters for damage or insecurity of the retaining clips. If power steering is fitted, check for signs of damage or leakage of the fluid hoses, pipes or connections. Also check for excessive stiffness or binding of the steering, a missing split pin or locking device, or severe corrosion of the body structure within 30 cm of any steering component attachment point.

Front and rear suspension and wheel bearings

☐ Starting at the front right-hand side, grasp the roadwheel at the 3 o'clock and 9 o'clock positions and rock gently but firmly. Check for free play or insecurity at the wheel bearings, suspension balljoints, or suspension mount-ings, pivots and attachments.
☐ Now grasp the wheel at the 12 o'clock and 6 o'clock positions and repeat the previous inspection. Spin the wheel, and check for roughness or tightness of the front wheel bearing.

☐ If excess free play is suspected at a component pivot point, this can be confirmed by using a large screwdriver or similar tool and levering between the mounting and the component attachment. This will confirm whether the wear is in the pivot bush, its retaining bolt, or in the mounting itself (the bolt holes can often become elongated).

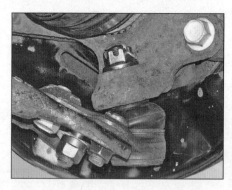

☐ Carry out all the above checks at the other front wheel, and then at both rear wheels.

Springs and shock absorbers

☐ Examine the suspension struts (when applicable) for serious fluid leakage, corrosion, or damage to the casing. Also check the security of the mounting points.
☐ If coil springs are fitted, check that the spring ends locate in their seats, and that the spring is not corroded, cracked or broken.
☐ If leaf springs are fitted, check that all leaves are intact, that the axle is securely attached to each spring, and that there is no deterioration of the spring eye mountings, bushes, and shackles.

☐ The same general checks apply to vehicles fitted with other suspension types, such as torsion bars, hydraulic displacer units, etc. Ensure that all mountings and attachments are secure, that there are no signs of excessive wear, corrosion or damage, and (on hydraulic types) that there are no fluid leaks or damaged pipes.
☐ Inspect the shock absorbers for signs of serious fluid leakage. Check for wear of the mounting bushes or attachments, or damage to the body of the unit.

Driveshafts (fwd vehicles only)

☐ Rotate each front wheel in turn and inspect the constant velocity joint gaiters for splits or damage. Also check that each driveshaft is straight and undamaged.

Braking system

☐ If possible without dismantling, check brake pad wear and disc condition. Ensure that the friction lining material has not worn excessively, (A) and that the discs are not fractured, pitted, scored or badly worn (B).

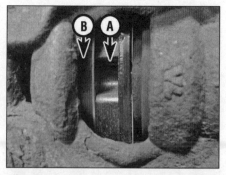

☐ Examine all the rigid brake pipes underneath the vehicle, and the flexible hose(s) at the rear. Look for corrosion, chafing or insecurity of the pipes, and for signs of bulging under pressure, chafing, splits or deterioration of the flexible hoses.
☐ Look for signs of fluid leaks at the brake calipers or on the brake backplates. Repair or renew leaking components.
☐ Slowly spin each wheel, while your assistant depresses and releases the footbrake. Ensure that each brake is operating and does not bind when the pedal is released.

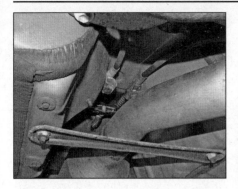

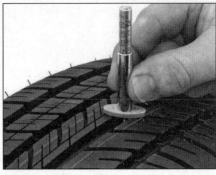

□ Examine the handbrake mechanism, checking for frayed or broken cables, excessive corrosion, or wear or insecurity of the linkage. Check that the mechanism works on each relevant wheel, and releases fully, without binding.

□ It is not possible to test brake efficiency without special equipment, but a road test can be carried out later to check that the vehicle pulls up in a straight line.

Fuel and exhaust systems

□ Inspect the fuel tank (including the filler cap), fuel pipes, hoses and unions. All components must be secure and free from leaks. Locking fuel caps must lock securely and the key must be provided for the MOT test.

□ Examine the exhaust system over its entire length, checking for any damaged, broken or missing mountings, security of the retaining

clamps and rust or corrosion.

Wheels and tyres

□ Examine the sidewalls and tread area of each tyre in turn. Check for cuts, tears, lumps, bulges, separation of the tread, and exposure of the ply or cord due to wear or damage. Check that the tyre bead is correctly seated on the wheel rim, that the valve is sound and properly seated, and that the wheel is not distorted or damaged.

□ Check that the tyres are of the correct size for the vehicle, that they are of the same size and type on each axle, and that the pressures

are correct.

□ Check the tyre tread depth. The legal minimum at the time of writing is 1.6 mm over the central three-quarters of the tread width. Abnormal tread wear may indicate incorrect front wheel alignment or wear in steering or suspension components.

□ If the spare wheel is fitted externally or in a separate carrier beneath the vehicle, check that mountings are secure and free of excessive corrosion.

Body corrosion

□ Check the condition of the entire vehicle structure for signs of corrosion in load-bearing areas. (These include chassis box sections, side sills, cross-members, pillars, and all suspension, steering, braking system and seat belt mountings and anchorages.) Any corrosion which has seriously reduced the thickness of a load-bearing area (or is within 30 cm of safety-related components such as steering or suspension) is likely to cause the vehicle to fail. In this case professional repairs are likely to be needed.

□ Damage or corrosion which causes sharp or otherwise dangerous edges to be exposed will also cause the vehicle to fail.

Towbars

□ Check the condition of mounting points (both beneath the vehicle and within boot/hatchback areas) for signs of corrosion, ensuring that all fixings are secure and not worn or damaged. There must be no excessive play in detachable tow ball arms or quick-release mechanisms.

4 Checks carried out on **YOUR VEHICLE'S EXHAUST EMISSION SYSTEM**

Petrol models

□ The engine should be warmed up, and running well (ignition system in good order, air filter element clean, etc).

□ Before testing, run the engine at around 2500 rpm for 20 seconds. Let the engine drop to idle, and watch for smoke from the exhaust. If the idle speed is too high, or if dense blue or black smoke emerges for more than 5 seconds, the vehicle will fail. Typically,

blue smoke signifies oil burning (engine wear); black smoke means unburnt fuel (dirty air cleaner element, or other fuel system fault).

□ An exhaust gas analyser for measuring carbon monoxide (CO) and hydrocarbons (HC) is now needed. If one cannot be hired or borrowed, have a local garage perform the check.

CO emissions (mixture)

□ The MOT tester has access to the CO limits for all vehicles. The CO level is measured at idle speed, and at 'fast idle' (2500 to 3000 rpm). The following limits are given as a general guide:

At idle speed – Less than 0.5% CO
At 'fast idle' – Less than 0.3% CO
Lambda reading – 0.97 to 1.03

□ If the CO level is too high, this may point to poor maintenance, a fuel injection system problem, faulty lambda (oxygen) sensor or catalytic converter. Try an injector cleaning treatment, and check the vehicle's ECU for fault codes.

HC emissions

□ The MOT tester has access to HC limits for all vehicles. The HC level is measured at 'fast idle' (2500 to 3000 rpm). The following limits are given as a general guide:

At 'fast idle' – Less then 200 ppm

□ Excessive HC emissions are typically caused by oil being burnt (worn engine), or by a blocked crankcase ventilation system ('breather'). If the engine oil is old and thin, an oil change may help. If the engine is running badly, check the vehicle's ECU for fault codes.

Diesel models

□ The only emission test for diesel engines is measuring exhaust smoke density, using a calibrated smoke meter. The test involves accelerating the engine at least 3 times to its maximum unloaded speed.

Note: *On engines with a timing belt, it is VITAL that the belt is in good condition before the test is carried out.*

□ With the engine warmed up, it is first purged by running at around 2500 rpm for 20 seconds. A governor check is then carried out, by slowly accelerating the engine to its maximum speed. After this, the smoke meter is connected, and the engine is accelerated quickly to maximum speed three times. If the smoke density is less than the limits given below, the vehicle will pass:

Non-turbo vehicles: 2.5m-1
Turbocharged vehicles: 3.0m-1

□ If excess smoke is produced, try fitting a new air cleaner element, or using an injector cleaning treatment. If the engine is running badly, where applicable, check the vehicle's ECU for fault codes. Also check the vehicle's EGR system, where applicable. At high mileages, the injectors may require professional attention.

Engine

- ☐ Engine fails to rotate when attempting to start
- ☐ Engine rotates, but will not start
- ☐ Engine difficult to start when cold
- ☐ Engine difficult to start when hot
- ☐ Starter motor noisy or excessively-rough in engagement
- ☐ Engine starts, but stops immediately
- ☐ Engine idles erratically
- ☐ Engine misfires at idle speed
- ☐ Engine misfires throughout the driving speed range
- ☐ Engine hesitates on acceleration
- ☐ Engine stalls
- ☐ Engine lacks power
- ☐ Engine backfires
- ☐ Oil pressure warning light illuminated with engine running
- ☐ Engine runs-on after switching off
- ☐ Engine noises

Cooling system

- ☐ Overheating
- ☐ Overcooling
- ☐ External coolant leakage
- ☐ Internal coolant leakage
- ☐ Corrosion

Fuel and exhaust systems

- ☐ Excessive fuel consumption
- ☐ Fuel leakage and/or fuel odour
- ☐ Excessive noise or fumes from exhaust system

Clutch

- ☐ Pedal travels to floor – no pressure or very little resistance
- ☐ Clutch fails to disengage (unable to select gears)
- ☐ Clutch slips (engine speed increases, with no increase in vehicle speed)
- ☐ Judder as clutch is engaged
- ☐ Noise when depressing or releasing clutch pedal

Manual transmission

- ☐ Noisy in neutral with engine running
- ☐ Noisy in one particular gear
- ☐ Difficulty engaging gears
- ☐ Jumps out of gear
- ☐ Vibration
- ☐ Lubricant leaks

Driveshafts

- ☐ Vibration when accelerating or decelerating
- ☐ Clicking or knocking noise on turns (at slow speed on full-lock)

Braking system

- ☐ Vehicle pulls to one side under braking
- ☐ Noise (grinding or high-pitched squeal) when brakes applied
- ☐ Excessive brake pedal travel
- ☐ Brake pedal feels spongy when depressed
- ☐ Excessive brake pedal effort required to stop vehicle
- ☐ Judder felt through brake pedal or steering wheel when braking
- ☐ Pedal pulsates when braking hard
- ☐ Brakes binding
- ☐ Rear wheels locking under normal braking

Steering and suspension

- ☐ Vehicle pulls to one side
- ☐ Wheel wobble and vibration
- ☐ Excessive pitching and/or rolling around corners, or during braking
- ☐ Wandering or general instability
- ☐ Excessively-stiff steering
- ☐ Excessive play in steering
- ☐ Lack of power assistance
- ☐ Tyre wear excessive

Electrical system

- ☐ Battery will not hold a charge more than a few days
- ☐ Ignition/no-charge warning light remains illuminated with engine running
- ☐ Ignition/no-charge warning light fails to come on
- ☐ Lights inoperative
- ☐ Instrument readings inaccurate or erratic
- ☐ Horn inoperative, or unsatisfactory in operation
- ☐ Windscreen/tailgate wipers inoperative, or unsatisfactory in operation
- ☐ Windscreen washers inoperative, or unsatisfactory in operation
- ☐ Electric windows inoperative, or unsatisfactory in operation
- ☐ Central locking system inoperative, or unsatisfactory in operation

Introduction

The vehicle owner who does his or her own maintenance according to the recommended service schedules should not have to use this section of the manual very often. Modern component reliability is such that, provided those items subject to wear or deterioration are inspected or renewed at the specified intervals, sudden failure is comparatively rare. Faults do not usually just happen as a result of sudden failure, but develop over a period of time. Major mechanical failures in particular are usually preceded by characteristic symptoms over hundreds or even thousands of miles. Those components which do occasionally fail without warning are often small and easily carried in the vehicle.

With any fault-finding, the first step is to decide where to begin investigations. Sometimes this is obvious, but on other occasions, a little detective work will be necessary. The owner who makes half a dozen haphazard adjustments or replacements may be successful in curing a fault (or its symptoms), but will be none the wiser if the fault recurs, and ultimately may have spent more time and money than was necessary. A calm and logical approach will be found to be more satisfactory in the long run. Always take into account any warning signs or abnormalities that may have been noticed in the period preceding the fault – power loss, high or low gauge readings, unusual smells, etc – and remember that failure of components such as fuses or spark plugs may only be pointers to some underlying fault.

The pages which follow provide an easy-reference guide to the more common problems which may occur during the operation of the vehicle. These problems and their possible causes are grouped under headings denoting various components or systems, such as Engine, Cooling system, etc. The general Chapter which deals with the problem is also shown in brackets; refer to the relevant part of that Chapter for system-specific information. Whatever the fault, certain basic principles apply. These are as follows:

Verify the fault. This is simply a matter of being sure that you know what the symptoms are before starting work. This is particularly important if you are investigating a fault for someone else, who may not have described it very accurately.

Don't overlook the obvious. For example, if the vehicle won't start, is there fuel in the tank? (Don't take anyone else's word on this particular point, and don't trust the fuel gauge either!) If an electrical fault is indicated, look for loose or broken wires before digging out the test gear.

Cure the disease, not the symptom. Substituting a flat battery with a fully-charged one will get you off the hard shoulder, but if the underlying cause is not attended to, the new battery will go the same way. Similarly, changing oil-fouled spark plugs for a new set will get you moving again, but remember that the reason for the fouling (if it wasn't simply an incorrect grade of plug) will have to be established and corrected.

Don't take anything for granted. Particularly, don't forget that a new component may itself be defective (especially if its been rattling around in the boot for months), and don't leave components out of a fault diagnosis sequence just because they are new or recently-fitted. When you do finally diagnose a difficult fault, you'll probably realise that all the evidence was there from the start.

Engine

Engine fails to rotate when attempting to start

☐ Battery terminal connections loose or corroded (see Weekly checks).
☐ Battery discharged or faulty (Chapter 5A).
☐ Broken, loose or disconnected wiring in the starting circuit (Chapter 5A).
☐ Defective starter solenoid or switch (Chapter 5A).
☐ Defective starter motor (Chapter 5A).
☐ Starter pinion or flywheel/driveplate ring gear teeth loose or broken (Chapter 2A, 2B or 2C and 5A).
☐ Engine earth strap broken or disconnected (Chapter 5A or 12).

Engine rotates, but will not start

☐ Fuel tank empty.
☐ Battery discharged (engine rotates slowly) (Chapter 5A).
☐ Battery terminal connections loose or corroded (see Weekly checks).
☐ Ignition components damp or damaged (Chapters 1A and).
☐ Broken, loose or disconnected wiring in the ignition circuit (Chapters 1A and).
☐ Worn, faulty or incorrectly-gapped spark plugs (Chapter 1A).
☐ Fuel injection system fault (Chapter 4A or 4B).
☐ Major mechanical failure (eg, timing belt/chain) (Chapter 2A, 2B or 2C).

Engine difficult to start when cold

☐ Battery discharged (Chapter 5A).
☐ Battery terminal connections loose or corroded (see Weekly checks).
☐ Worn, faulty or incorrectly-gapped spark plugs (Chapter 1A).
☐ Fuel injection system fault (Chapter 4A or 4B).
☐ Other ignition system fault (Chapters 1A or1B and 5B).
☐ Low cylinder compressions (Chapter 2A, 2B or 2C).

Engine difficult to start when hot

☐ Air filter element dirty or clogged (Chapter 1A or 1B).
☐ Fuel injection system fault (Chapter 4A or 4B).
☐ Low cylinder compressions (Chapter 2A, 2B or 2C).

Starter motor noisy or excessively-rough in engagement

☐ Starter pinion or flywheel ring gear teeth loose or broken (Chapter 2A, 2B or 2C and 5A).
☐ Starter motor mounting bolts loose or missing (Chapter 5A).
☐ Starter motor internal components worn or damaged (Chapter 5A).

Engine starts, but stops immediately

☐ Loose or faulty electrical connections in the ignition circuit (Chapters 1A or 1B and).
☐ Vacuum leak at the throttle body or intake manifold (Chapter 4A or 4B).
☐ Blocked injector/fuel injection system fault (Chapter 4A or 4B).

Engine idles erratically

☐ Air filter element clogged (Chapter 1A or 1B).
☐ Vacuum leak at the throttle body, intake manifold or associated hoses (Chapter 4A or 4B).
☐ Worn, faulty or incorrectly-gapped spark plugs (Chapter 1A).
☐ Uneven or low cylinder compressions (Chapter 2A, 2B or 2C).
☐ Camshaft lobes worn (Chapter 2A, 2B or 2C).
☐ Timing belt incorrectly fitted (Chapter 2A, 2B or 2C).
☐ Blocked injector/fuel injection system fault (Chapter 4A or 4B).

Engine misfires at idle speed

☐ Worn, faulty or incorrectly-gapped spark plugs (Chapter 1A).
☐ Vacuum leak at the throttle body, intake manifold or associated hoses (Chapter 4A or 4B).
☐ Blocked injector/fuel injection system fault (Chapter 4A or 4B).
☐ Uneven or low cylinder compressions (Chapter 2A, 2B or 2C).
☐ Disconnected, leaking, or perished crankcase ventilation hoses (Chapter 4C).

Engine misfires throughout the driving speed range

☐ Fuel pump faulty, or delivery pressure low (Chapter 4A or 4B).
☐ Fuel tank vent blocked, or fuel pipes restricted (Chapter 4A or 4B).
☐ Vacuum leak at the throttle body, intake manifold or associated hoses (Chapter 4A or 4B).
☐ Worn, faulty or incorrectly-gapped spark plugs (Chapter 1A).
☐ Faulty ignition coil (Chapter).
☐ Uneven or low cylinder compressions (Chapter 2A, 2B or 2C).
☐ Blocked injector/fuel injection system fault (Chapter 4A or 4B).

Engine hesitates on acceleration

☐ Worn, faulty or incorrectly-gapped spark plugs (Chapter 1A).
☐ Vacuum leak at the throttle body, intake manifold or associated hoses (Chapter 4A or 4B).
☐ Blocked injector/fuel injection system fault (Chapter 4A or 4B).

Engine (continued)

Engine stalls

- [ ] Vacuum leak at the throttle body, intake manifold or associated hoses (Chapter 4A or 4B).
- [ ] Fuel pump faulty, or delivery pressure low (Chapter 4A or 4B).
- [ ] Fuel tank vent blocked, or fuel pipes restricted (Chapter 4A or 4B).
- [ ] Blocked injector/fuel injection system fault (Chapter 4A or 4B).
- [ ] Faulty injector(s) (Chapter 4A or 4B).

Engine lacks power

- [ ] Timing belt incorrectly fitted or tensioned (Chapter 2A, 2B or 2C).
- [ ] Fuel pump faulty, or delivery pressure low Chapter 4A or 4B).
- [ ] Uneven or low cylinder compressions (Chapter 2A a, 2B or 2C).
- [ ] Worn, faulty or incorrectly-gapped spark plugs (Chapter 1A).
- [ ] Vacuum leak at the throttle body, intake manifold or associated hoses (Chapter 4A or 4B).
- [ ] Blocked injector/fuel injection system fault (Chapter 4A or 4B).
- [ ] Brakes binding (Chapter 9).
- [ ] Clutch slipping (Chapter 6).
- [ ] Air filter element clogged (Chapter 1A or 1B).

Engine backfires

- [ ] Timing belt incorrectly fitted or tensioned (Chapter 2A, 2B or 2C).
- [ ] Vacuum leak at the throttle body, intake manifold or associated hoses (Chapter 4A or 4B).
- [ ] Blocked injector/fuel injection system fault (Chapter 4A or 2B).

Oil pressure warning light illuminated with engine running

- [ ] Low oil level, or incorrect oil grade (Weekly checks).
- [ ] Faulty oil pressure switch (Chapter 5A).
- [ ] Worn engine bearings and/or oil pump (Chapter 2A, 2B or 2C).
- [ ] High engine operating temperature (Chapter 3).
- [ ] Oil pressure relief valve defective (Chapter 2A, 2B or 2C).
- [ ] Oil pick-up strainer clogged (Chapter 2A, 2B or 2C).

Engine runs-on after switching off

- [ ] Excessive carbon build-up in engine (Chapter 2A, 2B or 2C).
- [ ] High engine operating temperature (Chapter 3).
- [ ] Fuel injection system fault (Chapter 4A or 4B).

Engine noises

Pre-ignition (pinking) or knocking during acceleration or under load

- [ ] Ignition system fault (Chapters 1A and).
- [ ] Incorrect grade of spark plug (Chapter 1A).
- [ ] Vacuum leak at the throttle body, intake manifold or associated hoses (Chapter 4A or 4B).
- [ ] Excessive carbon build-up in engine (Chapter 2A, 2B or 2C).
- [ ] Blocked injector/fuel injection system fault (Chapter 4A or 4B).

Whistling or wheezing noises

- [ ] Leaking intake manifold or throttle body gasket (Chapter 4A or 4B).
- [ ] Leaking exhaust manifold gasket or pipe-to-manifold joint (Chapter 4A or 4B).
- [ ] Leaking vacuum hose (Chapters 4A, 4B and 9).
- [ ] Blowing cylinder head gasket (Chapter 2A, 2B or 2C).

Tapping or rattling noises

- [ ] Worn valve gear or camshaft (Chapter 2A, 2B or 2C).
- [ ] Ancillary component fault (coolant pump, alternator, etc) (Chapters 3, 5A, etc).

Knocking or thumping noises

- [ ] Worn big-end bearings (regular heavy knocking, perhaps less under load) (Chapter 2A, 2B or 2C).
- [ ] Worn main bearings (rumbling and knocking, perhaps worsening under load) (Chapter 2A, 2B or 2C).
- [ ] Piston slap (most noticeable when cold) (Chapter 2A, 2B or 2C).
- [ ] Ancillary component fault (coolant pump, alternator, etc) (Chapters 3, 5A, etc).

Cooling system

Overheating

☐ Insufficient coolant in system (Weekly checks).
☐ Thermostat faulty (Chapter 3).
☐ Radiator core blocked, or grille restricted (Chapter 3).
☐ Electric cooling fan or thermostatic switch faulty (Chapter 3).
☐ Inaccurate temperature gauge sender unit (Chapter 3).
☐ Airlock in cooling system.
☐ Expansion tank pressure cap faulty (Chapter 3).

Overcooling

☐ Thermostat faulty (Chapter 3).
☐ Inaccurate engine coolant temperature sensor (Chapter 3).

External coolant leakage

☐ Deteriorated or damaged hoses or hose clips (Chapter 1A or 1B).

☐ Radiator core or heater matrix leaking (Chapter 3).
☐ Pressure cap faulty (Chapter 3).
☐ Coolant pump internal seal leaking (Chapter 3).
☐ Coolant pump-to-housing seal leaking (Chapter 3).
☐ Boiling due to overheating (Chapter 3).
☐ Core plug leaking (Chapter 2A, 2B or 2C).

Internal coolant leakage

☐ Leaking cylinder head gasket (Chapter 2A, 2B or 2C).
☐ Cracked cylinder head or cylinder block (Chapter 2A, 2B or 2C).

Corrosion

☐ Infrequent draining and flushing (Chapter 1A or 1B).
☐ Incorrect coolant mixture or inappropriate coolant type (see Weekly checks).

Fuel and exhaust systems

Excessive fuel consumption

☐ Air filter element dirty or clogged (Chapter 1A or 1B).
☐ Fuel injection system fault (Chapter 4A or 4B).
☐ Ignition system fault (Chapters 1A and).
☐ Tyres under-inflated (see Weekly checks).

Fuel leakage and/or fuel odour

☐ Damaged fuel tank, pipes or connections (Chapter 4A or 4B)

Excessive noise or fumes from exhaust system

☐ Leaking exhaust system or manifold joints (Chapters 1A, 1B and 4A and 4B).
☐ Leaking, corroded or damaged silencers or pipe (Chapters 1A, 1B, 4A and 4B).
☐ Broken mountings causing body or suspension contact (Chapter 1A or 1B).

Clutch

Pedal travels to floor – no pressure or very little resistance

- [ ] Faulty master or slave cylinder (Chapter 6).
- [ ] Faulty hydraulic release system (Chapter 6).
- [ ] Broken clutch release bearing or arm (Chapter 6).
- [ ] Broken diaphragm spring in clutch pressure plate (Chapter 6).

Clutch fails to disengage (unable to select gears)

- [ ] Faulty master or slave cylinder (Chapter 6).
- [ ] Faulty hydraulic release system (Chapter 6).
- [ ] Clutch disc sticking on gearbox input shaft splines (Chapter 6).
- [ ] Clutch disc sticking to flywheel or pressure plate (Chapter 6).
- [ ] Faulty pressure plate assembly (Chapter 6).
- [ ] Clutch release mechanism worn or incorrectly assembled (Chapter 6).

Clutch slips (engine speed increases, with no increase in vehicle speed)

- [ ] Faulty hydraulic release system (Chapter 6).

- [ ] Clutch disc linings excessively worn (Chapter 6).
- [ ] Clutch disc linings contaminated with oil or grease (Chapter 6).
- [ ] Faulty pressure plate or weak diaphragm spring (Chapter 6).

Judder as clutch is engaged

- [ ] Clutch disc linings contaminated with oil or grease (Chapter 6).
- [ ] Clutch disc linings excessively worn (Chapter 6).
- [ ] Faulty or distorted pressure plate or diaphragm spring (Chapter 6).
- [ ] Worn or loose engine or gearbox mountings (Chapter 2A, 2B, or 2C).
- [ ] Clutch disc hub or gearbox input shaft splines worn (Chapter 6).

Noise when depressing or releasing clutch pedal

- [ ] Worn clutch release bearing (Chapter 6).
- [ ] Worn or dry clutch pedal pivot (Chapter 6).
- [ ] Faulty pressure plate assembly (Chapter 6).
- [ ] Pressure plate diaphragm spring broken (Chapter 6).
- [ ] Broken clutch friction plate cushioning springs (Chapter 6).

Manual transmission

Noisy in neutral with engine running

- [ ] Input shaft bearings worn (noise apparent with clutch pedal released, but not when depressed) (Chapter 7A).*
- [ ] Clutch release bearing worn (noise apparent with clutch pedal depressed, possibly less when released) (Chapter 6).

Noisy in one particular gear

- [ ] Worn, damaged or chipped gear teeth (Chapter 7A).*

Difficulty engaging gears

- [ ] Clutch fault (Chapter 6).
- [ ] Worn or damaged gear linkage (Chapter 7A).
- [ ] Worn synchroniser units (Chapter 7A).*

Jumps out of gear

- [ ] Worn or damaged gear linkage (Chapter 7A).

- [ ] Worn synchroniser units (Chapter 7A).*
- [ ] Worn selector forks (Chapter 7A).*

Vibration

- [ ] Lack of oil (Chapter 7A).
- [ ] Worn bearings (Chapter 7B).*

Lubricant leaks

- [ ] Leaking oil seal (Chapter 7A).
- [ ] Leaking housing joint (Chapter 7A).
- [ ] *Leaking input shaft oil seal (Chapter 7A).

Note: *Although the corrective action necessary to remedy the symptoms described is beyond the scope of the home mechanic, the above information should be helpful in isolating the cause of the condition, so that the owner can communicate clearly with a professional mechanic.*

Driveshafts

Vibration when accelerating or decelerating

☐ Worn inner constant velocity joint (Chapter 8).
☐ Bent or distorted driveshaft (Chapter 8).

Clicking or knocking noise on turns (at slow speed on full-lock)

☐ Worn outer constant velocity joint (Chapter 8).
☐ Lack of constant velocity joint lubricant, possibly due to damaged gaiter (Chapter 8).

Braking system

Vehicle pulls to one side under braking

☐ Worn, defective, damaged or contaminated front or rear brake pads/shoes on one side (Chapters 1A or 1B and 9).
☐ Seized or partially-seized front or rear brake caliper or wheel cylinder (Chapter 9).
☐ A mixture of brake pad/shoe lining materials fitted between sides (Chapter 9).
☐ Brake caliper mounting bolts loose (Chapter 9).
☐ Worn or damaged steering or suspension components (Chapters 1A or 1B and 10).

Noise (grinding or high-pitched squeal) when brakes applied

☐ Brake pad/shoe friction lining material worn down to metal backing (Chapters 1A or 1B and 9).
☐ Excessive corrosion of brake disc/drum – may be apparent after the vehicle has been standing for some time (Chapters 1A or 1B and 9).
☐ Foreign object (stone chipping, etc) trapped between brake disc and shield (Chapters 1A or 1B and 9).

Excessive brake pedal travel

☐ Faulty master cylinder (Chapter 9).
☐ Air in hydraulic system (Chapter 9).
☐ Faulty vacuum servo unit (Chapter 9).
☐ Faulty vacuum pump, where fitted (Chapter 9).

Brake pedal feels spongy when depressed

☐ Air in hydraulic system (Chapter 9).
☐ Deteriorated flexible rubber brake hoses (Chapters 1A or 1B and 9).
☐ Master cylinder mountings loose (Chapter 9).
☐ Faulty master cylinder (Chapter 9).

Excessive brake pedal effort required to stop vehicle

☐ Faulty vacuum servo unit (Chapter 9).
☐ Disconnected, damaged or insecure brake servo vacuum hose (Chapters 1A or 1B and 9).
☐ Faulty vacuum pump, where fitted (Chapter 9).
☐ Primary or secondary hydraulic circuit failure (Chapter 9).
☐ Seized brake caliper/wheel cylinder (Chapter 9).
☐ Brake pads/shoes incorrectly fitted (Chapter 9).
☐ Incorrect grade of brake pads/shoes fitted (Chapter 9).
☐ Brake pads/shoes contaminated (Chapter 9).

Judder felt through brake pedal or steering wheel when braking

☐ Excessive run-out or distortion of brake disc(s)/drums (Chapter 9).
☐ Brake pad/shoe linings worn (Chapters 1A or 1B and 9).
☐ Brake caliper mounting bolts loose (Chapter 9).
☐ Wear in suspension or steering components or mountings (Chapters 1A or1B and 10).

Pedal pulsates when braking hard

☐ Normal feature of ABS – no fault

Brakes binding

☐ Seized brake caliper piston(s)/wheel cylinder (Chapter 9).
☐ Incorrectly-adjusted handbrake mechanism (Chapter 9).
☐ Faulty master cylinder (Chapter 9).

Rear wheels locking under normal braking

☐ Rear brake pad/shoe linings contaminated (Chapters 1A or 1B and 9).
☐ Rear brake discs/drums warped (Chapters 1A or 1B and 9).

Steering and suspension

Vehicle pulls to one side

- [ ] Defective tyre (see Weekly checks).
- [ ] Excessive wear in suspension or steering components (Chapters 1A or 1B and 10).
- [ ] Incorrect front wheel alignment (Chapter 10).
- [ ] Accident damage to steering or suspension components (Chapters 1A or 1B and 10).

Wheel wobble and vibration

- [ ] Front roadwheels out of balance (vibration felt mainly through the steering wheel) (Chapter 10).
- [ ] Rear roadwheels out of balance (vibration felt throughout the vehicle) (Chapter 10).
- [ ] Roadwheels damaged or distorted (Chapter 10).
- [ ] Faulty or damaged tyre (Weekly checks).
- [ ] Worn steering or suspension joints, bushes or components (Chapters 1A or 1B and 10).
- [ ] Wheel nuts loose (Chapters 1A or 1B and 10).

Excessive pitching and/or rolling around corners, or during braking

- [ ] Defective shock absorbers (Chapters 1A or 1B and 10).
- [ ] Broken or weak coil spring and/or suspension component (Chapters 1A or 1B and 10).
- [ ] Worn or damaged anti-roll bar or mountings (Chapter 10).

Wandering or general instability

- [ ] Incorrect front wheel alignment (Chapter 10).
- [ ] Worn steering or suspension joints, bushes or components (Chapters 1A or 1B and 10).
- [ ] Roadwheels out of balance (Chapter 10).
- [ ] Faulty or damaged tyre (Weekly checks).
- [ ] Wheel nuts loose (Chapter 10).
- [ ] Defective shock absorbers (Chapters 1A or 1B and 10).

Excessively-stiff steering

- [ ] Seized track rod end balljoint or suspension balljoint (Chapters 1A or 1B and 10).
- [ ] Broken or incorrectly adjusted auxiliary drivebelt (Chapters 1A or 1B and 10).

- [ ] Incorrect front wheel alignment (Chapter 10).
- [ ] Steering gear damaged (Chapter 10).

Excessive play in steering

- [ ] Worn steering column universal joint(s) (Chapter 10).
- [ ] Worn steering track rod end balljoints (Chapters 1A or 1B and 10).
- [ ] Worn steering gear (Chapter 10).
- [ ] Worn steering or suspension joints, bushes or components (Chapters 1A or 1B and 10).

Lack of power assistance

- [ ] Broken or incorrectly-adjusted auxiliary drivebelt (Chapters 1A or 1B).
- [ ] Incorrect power steering fluid level (Weekly checks).
- [ ] Restriction in power steering fluid hoses (Chapter 10).
- [ ] Faulty power steering pump (Chapter 10).
- [ ] Faulty steering gear (Chapter 10).

Tyre wear excessive

Tyres worn on inside or outside edges

- [ ] Incorrect camber or castor angles (Chapter 10).
- [ ] Worn steering or suspension joints, bushes or components (Chapters 1A or 1B and 10).
- [ ] Excessively-hard cornering.
- [ ] Accident damage.

Tyre treads exhibit feathered edges

- [ ] Incorrect toe setting (Chapter 10).

Tyres worn in centre of tread

- [ ] Tyres over-inflated (Weekly checks).

Tyres worn on inside and outside edges

- [ ] Tyres under-inflated (Weekly checks).
- [ ] Worn shock absorbers (Chapter 10).

Tyres worn unevenly

- [ ] Tyres/wheels out of balance (Weekly checks).
- [ ] Excessive wheel or tyre run-out (Chapter 10).
- [ ] Worn shock absorbers (Chapters 1A or 1B and 10).
- [ ] Faulty tyre (Weekly checks).

Electrical system

Battery will not hold a charge more than a few days

- [ ] Battery defective internally (Chapter 5A).
- [ ] Battery electrolyte level low – where applicable (Weekly checks).
- [ ] Battery terminal connections loose or corroded (Weekly checks).
- [ ] Auxiliary drivebelt worn – or incorrectly adjusted, where applicable (Chapter 1A).
- [ ] Alternator not charging at correct output (Chapter 5A).
- [ ] Alternator or voltage regulator faulty (Chapter 5A).
- [ ] Short-circuit causing continual battery drain (Chapters 5A and 12).

Ignition/no-charge warning light remains illuminated with engine running

- [ ] Auxiliary drivebelt broken, worn, or incorrectly adjusted (Chapter 1A or 1B).
- [ ] Internal fault in alternator or voltage regulator (Chapter 5A).
- [ ] Broken, disconnected, or loose wiring in charging circuit (Chapter 5A).

Ignition/no-charge warning light fails to come on

- [ ] Broken, disconnected, or loose wiring in warning light circuit (Chapter 12).
- [ ] Alternator faulty (Chapter 5A).

Lights inoperative

- [ ] Bulb blown (Chapter 12).
- [ ] Corrosion of bulb or bulbholder contacts (Chapter 12).
- [ ] Blown fuse (Chapter 12).
- [ ] Faulty relay (Chapter 12).
- [ ] Broken, loose, or disconnected wiring (Chapter 12).
- [ ] Faulty switch (Chapter 12).

Instrument readings inaccurate or erratic

Fuel or temperature gauges give no reading

- [ ] Faulty coolant temperature sensor (Chapter 3).
- [ ] Wiring open-circuit (Chapter 12).
- [ ] Faulty gauge (Chapter 12).

Fuel or temperature gauges give continuous maximum reading

- [ ] Faulty coolant temperature sensor (Chapters 3).
- [ ] Wiring short-circuit (Chapter 12).
- [ ] Faulty gauge (Chapter 12).

Horn inoperative, or unsatisfactory in operation

Horn operates all the time

- [ ] Horn contacts permanently bridged or horn push stuck down (Chapter 12).

Horn fails to operate

- [ ] Blown fuse (Chapter 12).
- [ ] Cable or cable connections loose, broken or disconnected (Chapter 12)
- [ ] Faulty horn (Chapter 12).

Horn emits intermittent or unsatisfactory sound

- [ ] Cable connections loose (Chapter 12).
- [ ] Horn mountings loose (Chapter 12).
- [ ] Faulty horn (Chapter 12).

Windscreen/tailgate wipers inoperative, or unsatisfactory in operation

Wipers fail to operate, or operate very slowly

- [ ] Wiper blades stuck to screen, or linkage seized or binding (eekly checks and Chapter 12).
- [ ] Blown fuse (Chapter 12).
- [ ] Cable or cable connections loose, broken or disconnected (Chapter 12).

- [ ] Faulty relay (Chapter 12).
- [ ] Faulty wiper motor (Chapter 12).

Wiper blades sweep over too large or too small an area of the glass

- [ ] Wiper arms incorrectly positioned on spindles (Chapter 12).
- [ ] Excessive wear of wiper linkage (Chapter 12).
- [ ] Wiper motor or linkage mountings loose or insecure (Chapter 12).

Wiper blades fail to clean the glass effectively

- [ ] Wiper blade rubbers worn or perished (Weekly checks).
- [ ] Wiper arm tension springs broken, or arm pivots seized (Chapter 12).
- [ ] Insufficient windscreen washer additive to adequately remove road film (Weekly checks).

Windscreen washers inoperative, or unsatisfactory in operation

One or more washer jets inoperative

- [ ] Blocked washer jet (Chapter 12).
- [ ] Disconnected, kinked or restricted fluid hose (Chapter 12).
- [ ] Insufficient fluid in washer reservoir (Weekly checks).

Washer pump fails to operate

- [ ] Broken or disconnected wiring or connections (Chapter 12).
- [ ] Blown fuse (Chapter 12).
- [ ] Faulty washer switch (Chapter 12).
- [ ] Faulty washer pump (Chapter 12).

Electric windows inoperative, or unsatisfactory in operation

Window glass will only move in one direction

- [ ] Faulty switch (Chapter 12).

Window glass slow to move

- [ ] Regulator seized or damaged, or in need of lubrication (Chapter 11).
- [ ] Door internal components or trim fouling regulator (Chapter 11).
- [ ] Faulty motor (Chapter 11).

Window glass fails to move

- [ ] Blown fuse (Chapter 12).
- [ ] Faulty relay (Chapter 12).
- [ ] Broken or disconnected wiring or connections (Chapter 12).
- [ ] Faulty motor (Chapter 12).
- [ ] Faulty BCM (Chapter 12).

Central locking system inoperative, or unsatisfactory in operation

Complete system failure

- [ ] Blown fuse (Chapter 12).
- [ ] Faulty BCM (Chapter 12).
- [ ] Broken or disconnected wiring or connections (Chapter 12).

Latch locks but will not unlock, or unlocks but will not lock

- [ ] Faulty switch (Chapter 12).
- [ ] Broken or disconnected latch operating rods or levers (Chapter 11).
- [ ] Faulty BCM (Chapter 12).

One lock fails to operate

- [ ] Broken or disconnected wiring or connections (Chapter 12).
- [ ] Faulty motor (Chapter 11).
- [ ] Broken, binding or disconnected lock operating rods or levers (Chapter 11).
- [ ] Fault in door lock (Chapter 11).

A

ABS (Anti-lock brake system) A system, usually electronically controlled, that senses incipient wheel lockup during braking and relieves hydraulic pressure at wheels that are about to skid.

Air bag An inflatable bag hidden in the steering wheel (driver's side) or the dash or glovebox (passenger side). In a head-on collision, the bags inflate, preventing the driver and front passenger from being thrown forward into the steering wheel or windscreen.

Air cleaner A metal or plastic housing, containing a filter element, which removes dust and dirt from the air being drawn into the engine.

Air filter element The actual filter in an air cleaner system, usually manufactured from pleated paper and requiring renewal at regular intervals.

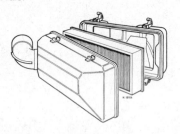

Air filter

Allen key A hexagonal wrench which fits into a recessed hexagonal hole.

Alligator clip A long-nosed spring-loaded metal clip with meshing teeth. Used to make temporary electrical connections.

Alternator A component in the electrical system which converts mechanical energy from a drivebelt into electrical energy to charge the battery and to operate the starting system, ignition system and electrical accessories.

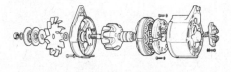

Alternator (exploded view)

Ampere (amp) A unit of measurement for the flow of electric current. One amp is the amount of current produced by one volt acting through a resistance of one ohm.

Anaerobic sealer A substance used to prevent bolts and screws from loosening. Anaerobic means that it does not require oxygen for activation. The Loctite brand is widely used.

Antifreeze A substance (usually ethylene glycol) mixed with water, and added to a vehicle's cooling system, to prevent freezing of the coolant in winter. Antifreeze also contains chemicals to inhibit corrosion and the formation of rust and other deposits that would tend to clog the radiator and coolant passages and reduce cooling efficiency.

Anti-seize compound A coating that reduces the risk of seizing on fasteners that are subjected to high temperatures, such as exhaust manifold bolts and nuts.

Anti-seize compound

Asbestos A natural fibrous mineral with great heat resistance, commonly used in the composition of brake friction materials. Asbestos is a health hazard and the dust created by brake systems should never be inhaled or ingested.

Axle A shaft on which a wheel revolves, or which revolves with a wheel. Also, a solid beam that connects the two wheels at one end of the vehicle. An axle which also transmits power to the wheels is known as a live axle.

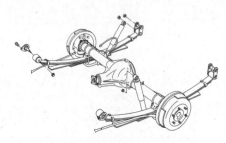

Axle assembly

Axleshaft A single rotating shaft, on either side of the differential, which delivers power from the final drive assembly to the drive wheels. Also called a driveshaft or a halfshaft.

B

Ball bearing An anti-friction bearing consisting of a hardened inner and outer race with hardened steel balls between two races.

Bearing

Bearing The curved surface on a shaft or in a bore, or the part assembled into either, that permits relative motion between them with minimum wear and friction.

Big-end bearing The bearing in the end of the connecting rod that's attached to the crankshaft.

Bleed nipple A valve on a brake wheel cylinder, caliper or other hydraulic component that is opened to purge the hydraulic system of air. Also called a bleed screw.

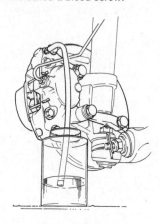

Brake bleeding

Brake bleeding Procedure for removing air from lines of a hydraulic brake system.

Brake disc The component of a disc brake that rotates with the wheels.

Brake drum The component of a drum brake that rotates with the wheels.

Brake linings The friction material which contacts the brake disc or drum to retard the vehicle's speed. The linings are bonded or riveted to the brake pads or shoes.

Brake pads The replaceable friction pads that pinch the brake disc when the brakes are applied. Brake pads consist of a friction material bonded or riveted to a rigid backing plate.

Brake shoe The crescent-shaped carrier to which the brake linings are mounted and which forces the lining against the rotating drum during braking.

Braking systems For more information on braking systems, consult the *Haynes Automotive Brake Manual*.

Breaker bar A long socket wrench handle providing greater leverage.

Bulkhead The insulated partition between the engine and the passenger compartment.

C

Caliper The non-rotating part of a disc-brake assembly that straddles the disc and carries the brake pads. The caliper also contains the hydraulic components that cause the pads to pinch the disc when the brakes are applied. A caliper is also a measuring tool that can be set to measure inside or outside dimensions of an object.

Camshaft A rotating shaft on which a series of cam lobes operate the valve mechanisms. The camshaft may be driven by gears, by sprockets and chain or by sprockets and a belt.

Canister A container in an evaporative emission control system; contains activated charcoal granules to trap vapours from the fuel system.

Canister

Carburettor A device which mixes fuel with air in the proper proportions to provide a desired power output from a spark ignition internal combustion engine.

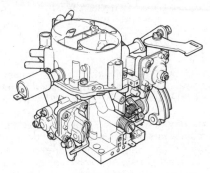

Carburettor

Castellated Resembling the parapets along the top of a castle wall. For example, a castellated balljoint stud nut.

Castellated nut

Castor In wheel alignment, the backward or forward tilt of the steering axis. Castor is positive when the steering axis is inclined rearward at the top.

Catalytic converter A silencer-like device in the exhaust system which converts certain pollutants in the exhaust gases into less harmful substances.

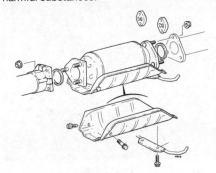

Catalytic converter

Circlip A ring-shaped clip used to prevent endwise movement of cylindrical parts and shafts. An internal circlip is installed in a groove in a housing; an external circlip fits into a groove on the outside of a cylindrical piece such as a shaft.

Clearance The amount of space between two parts. For example, between a piston and a cylinder, between a bearing and a journal, etc.

Coil spring A spiral of elastic steel found in various sizes throughout a vehicle, for example as a springing medium in the suspension and in the valve train.

Compression Reduction in volume, and increase in pressure and temperature, of a gas, caused by squeezing it into a smaller space.

Compression ratio The relationship between cylinder volume when the piston is at top dead centre and cylinder volume when the piston is at bottom dead centre.

Constant velocity (CV) joint A type of universal joint that cancels out vibrations caused by driving power being transmitted through an angle.

Core plug A disc or cup-shaped metal device inserted in a hole in a casting through which core was removed when the casting was formed. Also known as a freeze plug or expansion plug.

Crankcase The lower part of the engine block in which the crankshaft rotates.

Crankshaft The main rotating member, or shaft, running the length of the crankcase, with offset "throws" to which the connecting rods are attached.

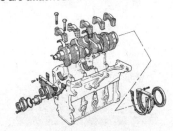

Crankshaft assembly

Crocodile clip See Alligator clip

D

Diagnostic code Code numbers obtained by accessing the diagnostic mode of an engine management computer. This code can be used to determine the area in the system where a malfunction may be located.

Disc brake A brake design incorporating a rotating disc onto which brake pads are squeezed. The resulting friction converts the energy of a moving vehicle into heat.

Double-overhead cam (DOHC) An engine that uses two overhead camshafts, usually one for the intake valves and one for the exhaust valves.

Drivebelt(s) The belt(s) used to drive accessories such as the alternator, water pump, power steering pump, air conditioning compressor, etc. off the crankshaft pulley.

Accessory drivebelts

Driveshaft Any shaft used to transmit motion. Commonly used when referring to the axleshafts on a front wheel drive vehicle.

Driveshaft

Drum brake A type of brake using a drum-shaped metal cylinder attached to the inner surface of the wheel. When the brake pedal is pressed, curved brake shoes with friction linings press against the inside of the drum to slow or stop the vehicle.

Drum brake assembly

E

EGR valve A valve used to introduce exhaust gases into the intake air stream.

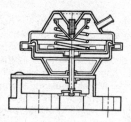

EGR valve

Electronic control unit (ECU) A computer which controls (for instance) ignition and fuel injection systems, or an anti-lock braking system. For more information refer to the *Haynes Automotive Electrical and Electronic Systems Manual*.

Electronic Fuel Injection (EFI) A computer controlled fuel system that distributes fuel through an injector located in each intake port of the engine.

Emergency brake A braking system, independent of the main hydraulic system, that can be used to slow or stop the vehicle if the primary brakes fail, or to hold the vehicle stationary even though the brake pedal isn't depressed. It usually consists of a hand lever that actuates either front or rear brakes mechanically through a series of cables and linkages. Also known as a handbrake or parking brake.

Endfloat The amount of lengthwise movement between two parts. As applied to a crankshaft, the distance that the crankshaft can move forward and back in the cylinder block.

Engine management system (EMS) A computer controlled system which manages the fuel injection and the ignition systems in an integrated fashion.

Exhaust manifold A part with several passages through which exhaust gases leave the engine combustion chambers and enter the exhaust pipe.

Exhaust manifold

F

Fan clutch A viscous (fluid) drive coupling device which permits variable engine fan speeds in relation to engine speeds.

Feeler blade A thin strip or blade of hardened steel, ground to an exact thickness, used to check or measure clearances between parts.

Feeler blade

Firing order The order in which the engine cylinders fire, or deliver their power strokes, beginning with the number one cylinder.

Flywheel A heavy spinning wheel in which energy is absorbed and stored by means of momentum. On cars, the flywheel is attached to the crankshaft to smooth out firing impulses.

Free play The amount of travel before any action takes place. The "looseness" in a linkage, or an assembly of parts, between the initial application of force and actual movement. For example, the distance the brake pedal moves before the pistons in the master cylinder are actuated.

Fuse An electrical device which protects a circuit against accidental overload. The typical fuse contains a soft piece of metal which is calibrated to melt at a predetermined current flow (expressed as amps) and break the circuit.

Fusible link A circuit protection device consisting of a conductor surrounded by heat-resistant insulation. The conductor is smaller than the wire it protects, so it acts as the weakest link in the circuit. Unlike a blown fuse, a failed fusible link must frequently be cut from the wire for replacement.

G

Gap The distance the spark must travel in jumping from the centre electrode to the side

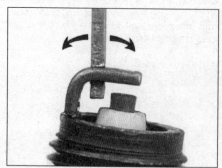

Adjusting spark plug gap

electrode in a spark plug. Also refers to the spacing between the points in a contact breaker assembly in a conventional points-type ignition, or to the distance between the reluctor or rotor and the pickup coil in an electronic ignition.

Gasket Any thin, soft material - usually cork, cardboard, asbestos or soft metal - installed between two metal surfaces to ensure a good seal. For instance, the cylinder head gasket seals the joint between the block and the cylinder head.

Gasket

Gauge An instrument panel display used to monitor engine conditions. A gauge with a movable pointer on a dial or a fixed scale is an analogue gauge. A gauge with a numerical readout is called a digital gauge.

H

Halfshaft A rotating shaft that transmits power from the final drive unit to a drive wheel, usually when referring to a live rear axle.

Harmonic balancer A device designed to reduce torsion or twisting vibration in the crankshaft. May be incorporated in the crankshaft pulley. Also known as a vibration damper.

Hone An abrasive tool for correcting small irregularities or differences in diameter in an engine cylinder, brake cylinder, etc.

Hydraulic tappet A tappet that utilises hydraulic pressure from the engine's lubrication system to maintain zero clearance (constant contact with both camshaft and valve stem). Automatically adjusts to variation in valve stem length. Hydraulic tappets also reduce valve noise.

I

Ignition timing The moment at which the spark plug fires, usually expressed in the number of crankshaft degrees before the piston reaches the top of its stroke.

Inlet manifold A tube or housing with passages through which flows the air-fuel mixture (carburettor vehicles and vehicles with throttle body injection) or air only (port fuel-injected vehicles) to the port openings in the cylinder head.

J

Jump start Starting the engine of a vehicle with a discharged or weak battery by attaching jump leads from the weak battery to a charged or helper battery.

L

Load Sensing Proportioning Valve (LSPV) A brake hydraulic system control valve that works like a proportioning valve, but also takes into consideration the amount of weight carried by the rear axle.

Locknut A nut used to lock an adjustment nut, or other threaded component, in place. For example, a locknut is employed to keep the adjusting nut on the rocker arm in position.

Lockwasher A form of washer designed to prevent an attaching nut from working loose.

M

MacPherson strut A type of front suspension system devised by Earle MacPherson at Ford of England. In its original form, a simple lateral link with the anti-roll bar creates the lower control arm. A long strut - an integral coil spring and shock absorber - is mounted between the body and the steering knuckle. Many modern so-called MacPherson strut systems use a conventional lower A-arm and don't rely on the anti-roll bar for location.

Multimeter An electrical test instrument with the capability to measure voltage, current and resistance.

N

NOx Oxides of Nitrogen. A common toxic pollutant emitted by petrol and diesel engines at higher temperatures.

O

Ohm The unit of electrical resistance. One volt applied to a resistance of one ohm will produce a current of one amp.

Ohmmeter An instrument for measuring electrical resistance.

O-ring A type of sealing ring made of a special rubber-like material; in use, the O-ring is compressed into a groove to provide the sealing action.

O-ring

Overhead cam (ohc) engine An engine with the camshaft(s) located on top of the cylinder head(s).

Overhead valve (ohv) engine An engine with the valves located in the cylinder head, but with the camshaft located in the engine block.

Oxygen sensor A device installed in the engine exhaust manifold, which senses the oxygen content in the exhaust and converts this information into an electric current. Also called a Lambda sensor.

P

Phillips screw A type of screw head having a cross instead of a slot for a corresponding type of screwdriver.

Plastigage A thin strip of plastic thread, available in different sizes, used for measuring clearances. For example, a strip of Plastigage is laid across a bearing journal. The parts are assembled and dismantled; the width of the crushed strip indicates the clearance between journal and bearing.

Plastigage

Propeller shaft The long hollow tube with universal joints at both ends that carries power from the transmission to the differential on front-engined rear wheel drive vehicles.

Proportioning valve A hydraulic control valve which limits the amount of pressure to the rear brakes during panic stops to prevent wheel lock-up.

R

Rack-and-pinion steering A steering system with a pinion gear on the end of the steering shaft that mates with a rack (think of a geared wheel opened up and laid flat). When the steering wheel is turned, the pinion turns, moving the rack to the left or right. This movement is transmitted through the track rods to the steering arms at the wheels.

Radiator A liquid-to-air heat transfer device designed to reduce the temperature of the coolant in an internal combustion engine cooling system.

Refrigerant Any substance used as a heat transfer agent in an air-conditioning system. R-12 has been the principle refrigerant for many years; recently, however, manufacturers have begun using R-134a, a non-CFC substance that is considered less harmful to the ozone in the upper atmosphere.

Rocker arm A lever arm that rocks on a shaft or pivots on a stud. In an overhead valve engine, the rocker arm converts the upward movement of the pushrod into a downward movement to open a valve.

Rotor In a distributor, the rotating device inside the cap that connects the centre electrode and the outer terminals as it turns, distributing the high voltage from the coil secondary winding to the proper spark plug. Also, that part of an alternator which rotates inside the stator. Also, the rotating assembly of a turbocharger, including the compressor wheel, shaft and turbine wheel.

Runout The amount of wobble (in-and-out movement) of a gear or wheel as it's rotated. The amount a shaft rotates "out-of-true." The out-of-round condition of a rotating part.

S

Sealant A liquid or paste used to prevent leakage at a joint. Sometimes used in conjunction with a gasket.

Sealed beam lamp An older headlight design which integrates the reflector, lens and filaments into a hermetically-sealed one-piece unit. When a filament burns out or the lens cracks, the entire unit is simply replaced.

Serpentine drivebelt A single, long, wide accessory drivebelt that's used on some newer vehicles to drive all the accessories, instead of a series of smaller, shorter belts. Serpentine drivebelts are usually tensioned by an automatic tensioner.

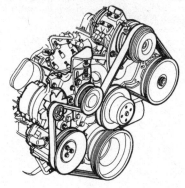

Serpentine drivebelt

Shim Thin spacer, commonly used to adjust the clearance or relative positions between two parts. For example, shims inserted into or under bucket tappets control valve clearances. Clearance is adjusted by changing the thickness of the shim.

Slide hammer A special puller that screws into or hooks onto a component such as a shaft or bearing; a heavy sliding handle on the shaft bottoms against the end of the shaft to knock the component free.

Sprocket A tooth or projection on the periphery of a wheel, shaped to engage with a chain or drivebelt. Commonly used to refer to the sprocket wheel itself.

Starter inhibitor switch On vehicles with an automatic transmission, a switch that prevents starting if the vehicle is not in Neutral or Park.

Strut See MacPherson strut.

T

Tappet A cylindrical component which transmits motion from the cam to the valve stem, either directly or via a pushrod and rocker arm. Also called a cam follower.

Thermostat A heat-controlled valve that regulates the flow of coolant between the cylinder block and the radiator, so maintaining optimum engine operating temperature. A thermostat is also used in some air cleaners in which the temperature is regulated.

Thrust bearing The bearing in the clutch assembly that is moved in to the release levers by clutch pedal action to disengage the clutch. Also referred to as a release bearing.

Timing belt A toothed belt which drives the camshaft. Serious engine damage may result if it breaks in service.

Timing chain A chain which drives the camshaft.

Toe-in The amount the front wheels are closer together at the front than at the rear. On rear wheel drive vehicles, a slight amount of toe-in is usually specified to keep the front wheels running parallel on the road by offsetting other forces that tend to spread the wheels apart.

Toe-out The amount the front wheels are closer together at the rear than at the front. On front wheel drive vehicles, a slight amount of toe-out is usually specified.

Tools For full information on choosing and using tools, refer to the *Haynes Automotive Tools Manual*.

Tracer A stripe of a second colour applied to a wire insulator to distinguish that wire from another one with the same colour insulator.

Tune-up A process of accurate and careful adjustments and parts replacement to obtain the best possible engine performance.

Turbocharger A centrifugal device, driven by exhaust gases, that pressurises the intake air. Normally used to increase the power output from a given engine displacement, but can also be used primarily to reduce exhaust emissions (as on VW's "Umwelt" Diesel engine).

U

Universal joint or U-joint A double-pivoted connection for transmitting power from a driving to a driven shaft through an angle. A U-joint consists of two Y-shaped yokes and a cross-shaped member called the spider.

V

Valve A device through which the flow of liquid, gas, vacuum, or loose material in bulk may be started, stopped, or regulated by a movable part that opens, shuts, or partially obstructs one or more ports or passageways. A valve is also the movable part of such a device.

Valve clearance The clearance between the valve tip (the end of the valve stem) and the rocker arm or tappet. The valve clearance is measured when the valve is closed.

Vernier caliper A precision measuring instrument that measures inside and outside dimensions. Not quite as accurate as a micrometer, but more convenient.

Viscosity The thickness of a liquid or its resistance to flow.

Volt A unit for expressing electrical "pressure" in a circuit. One volt that will produce a current of one ampere through a resistance of one ohm.

W

Welding Various processes used to join metal items by heating the areas to be joined to a molten state and fusing them together. For more information refer to the *Haynes Automotive Welding Manual*.

Wiring diagram A drawing portraying the components and wires in a vehicle's electrical system, using standardised symbols. For more information refer to the *Haynes Automotive Electrical and Electronic Systems Manual*.

Note: *References throughout this index are in the form "Chapter number" • "Page number". So, for example, 2C•15 refers to page 15 of Chapter 2C.*

A

ABS hydraulic unit – 9•12
ABS wheel sensor – 9•13
Accelerator pedal – 4A•4
Aerial – 12•18
Air conditioning system – 3•12
Air filter – 1A•12, 1B•14, 4A•5, 4B•5
Airbag system – 12•19, 12•20
Alternator – 5A•4
Anti-theft alarm system – 12•21
Audio system – 12•18
Automatic transmission – 7B•1 *et seq*
    fault finding – 7B•2
Auxiliary drivebelt – 1A•14, 1B•14

B

Balancer shafts – 2C•27
Balancer/oil pump drive chain – 2C•25
Battery – 0•17, 5A•2, 5A•3
Body electrical systems – 12•1 *et seq*
Bodywork and fittings – 11•1 *et seq*
Bonnet – 11•6
    lock and cable – 11•6
Braking system – 9•1 *et seq*
    caliper – 9•8, 9•11
    checks – 1A•8
    disc – 9•8, 9•12
    fault finding – REF•22
    fluid – 0•15, 1A•17, 1B•17
    light switch – 9•13
    master cylinder – 9•5
    pads – 9•6, 9•9
    pedal – 9•3
    pipes and hoses – 9•5
Bulbs – 12•8, 12•10
Bumper covers – 11•4

C

Camshaft – 2A•13, 2B•12
    oil seals – 2A•23, 2B•18
Camshaft, followers and hydraulic tappets – 2C•14
Catalytic converter – 4C•2
Central locking system – 12•17
Centre console – 11•17
Charging system – 5A•4
Clutch – 6•1 *et seq*
    assembly – 6•5
    fault finding – REF•21
    fluid – 0•15
    hydraulic system – 6•5
    master cylinder – 6•3
    pedal – 6•2
    release bearing and fork – 6•8
    slave cylinder – 6•4
Common rail – 4B•12
Compression and leakdown tests – 2C•5
Compression test – 2A•4, 2B•4
Conversion factors – REF•6
Coolant – 0•14 , 1A•17, 1B•17
Cooling, heating and air conditioning systems – 3•1 *et seq*
    fault finding – REF•20
    sensors and switches – 3•8
Crankcase emission control system – 4C•2
Crankshaft – 2D•10, 2D•14, 2D•18
    oil seals – 2A•24, 2B•19, 2C•29
    pilot bearing – 2C•29
    pulley – 2A•10, 2B•9, 2C•7
Cylinder block/crankcase – 2D•11
Cylinder head – 2A•16, 2B•13, 2C•18, 2D•6, 2D•8
    and valves – 2D•7
    cover – 2A•5, 2B•5, 2C•6

D

Diesel engine (2.2 litre) in-care repair procedures – 2C•1 *et seq*
Dimensions and weights – REF•1

Note: *References throughout this index are in the form "Chapter number" • "Page number". So, for example, 2C•15 refers to page 15 of Chapter 2C.*

Door – 11•11
    handle and lock components – 11•10
    inner trim panel – 11•7
    window glass – 11•8
    window regulator – 11•9
Driveshafts – 8•1 *et seq*
    damper – 8•8
    oil seals – 7A•1
    rubber gaiter – 1A•10
    rubber gaiter and joint – 1B•11
    fault finding – REF•22

E

Electrical systems – 0•17
    connectors – 12•4
    fault finding – 12•2, REF•24
Electronic control modules – 12•21
Electronic diesel control (EDC) system components – 4B•6
Emission control systems – 4C•1 *et seq*
Engine fault finding – REF•18
Engine oil – 0•13, 1A•6, 1B•6
Engine removal and overhaul procedures – 2D•1 *et seq*
Engine/transmission mountings – 2A•25, 2B•21, 2C•31
Evaporative emission control (EVAP) system – 4C•3
Exhaust emission control systems – 4C•4
Exhaust manifold – 4A•17, 4B•19
Exhaust system – 1A•9, 4A•18
Expansion tank – 3•7
Exterior mirror and glass – 11•12

F

Facia and crossmember – 11•19
Fault finding – REF•16
    automatic transmission – 7B•2
    braking system – REF•22
    clutch – REF•21
    cooling system – REF•20
    driveshafts – REF•22
    electrical system – 12•2, REF•24
    engine – REF•18
    fuel and exhaust systems – REF•20
    manual transmission – REF•21
    steering and suspension – REF•23

Flywheel – 2A•25, 2C•28
Flywheel/driveplate – 2B•20
Front anti-roll bar components – 10•8
Front subframe – 10•8
Front suspension control arm – 10•7
Front suspension strut – 10•5
Front swivel hub – 10•2
Front wheel bearings – 10•3
Fuel and exhaust systems – diesel engines – 4B•1 *et seq*
Fuel and exhaust systems – petrol engines – 4A•1 *et seq*
Fuel and exhaust systems fault finding – REF•20
Fuel economy – REF•2
Fuel filler cap – 4A•8
Fuel filter – 1B•13, 1B•8
Fuel gauge sender – 4B•6
Fuel injection system – 4A•8
Fuel injectors – 4B•12
Fuel pipes and connections – 4A•3, 4B•3
Fuel pump – 4B•10
Fuel pump/fuel gauge sender unit – 4A•5
Fuel system, depressurising, priming and bleeding – 4A•3, 4B•3
Fuel tank – 4A•7, 4B•6
Fuses and relays – 12•4

G

Gearbox – 7A•3
    overhaul – 7A•5
Gearchange mechanism and cables – 7A•2
Glossary of technical terms – REF•26
Glovebox – 11•18
Glow plugs – 5C•2
    control module – 5C•2
Grille – 11•5

H

Handbrake cables – 9•14
Handbrake lever – 9•13
Heater/ventilation system components – 3•9
Horns – 12•17
Hydraulic system bleeding – 9•4

Note: *References throughout this index are in the form "Chapter number" • "Page number". So, for example, 2C•15 refers to page 15 of Chapter 2C.*

I

Ignition system – 5B•1 *et seq*
   coils – 5B•2
   switch – 12•6
   timing – 5B•3
Inlet manifold – 4A•14, 4B•15
Inner constant velocity joint gaiter – 8•6
Instrument panel – 12•14
Intercooler – 4B•5
Interior mirror – 11•12
Interior trim panels – 11•15
Interlock system – 7B•4
Intermediate driveshaft – 8•4
   support bearing– 8•7
Introduction – 0•4

J

Jacking and vehicle support – REF•9
Jump starting – 0•7

K

Knock sensor – 5B•3

L

Leaks – 0•10, 1A•7, 1B•8
Light units – 12•12
Lubricants and fluids – 0•18

M

Main and big-end bearings – 2D•15
Manual transmission – 7A•1 *et seq*
   fault finding – REF•21
MOT test checks – REF•12

O

Oil cooler – 2C•30
Oil filter – 1A•6, 1B•6
Oil filter/oil cooler/water pump housing – 2C•30
Oil pressure switch – 2A•22, 2B•18
Oil pump – 2A•21, 2B•17, 2C•23
Outer constant velocity joint gaiter – 8•4

P

Parking aid components – 12•17
Petrol engine 1.8 litre in-car repair procedures – 2B•1 *et seq*
Petrol engine 1.4 litre in-car repair procedures – 2A•1 *et seq*
Pilot bearing – 2A•25, 2B•21
Piston rings – 2D•17
Pistons/connecting rods – 2D•9, 2D•12, 2D•22
Pollen filter renewal – 1A•16, 1B•16
Pre-heating system – 5C•1 *et seq*

R

Radiator – 3•6
   and condenser cooling fans – 3•5
Rear axle – 10•11

Note: *References throughout this index are in the form "Chapter number" • "Page number". So, for example, 2C•15 refers to page 15 of Chapter 2C.*

Rear coil spring – 10•10
Rear hub – 10•9
Rear shock absorber – 10•11
Remote control battery renewal – 1A•17, 1B•17
Reverse light switch – 7A•3
Reverse lock-out solenoid – 7A•3
Rocker shaft and VTEC control – 2B•10
Rocker shaft assembly – 2A•12
Routine maintenance and servicing – diesel models – 1B•1 *et seq*
Routine maintenance and servicing – petrol models – 1A•1 *et seq*

S

Safety first! – 0•5
Seats – 11•13
    belts – 11•14
Selector cable – 7B•3
Selector lever – 7B•3
Spark plug – 1A•13
Speakers – 12•19
Starter motor – 5A•5
Starting and charging systems – 5A•1 *et seq*
Steering and suspension fault finding – REF•23
Steering column – 10•12
Steering rack – 10•14
    gaiters – 10•14
Steering wheel – 10•12
Sump – 2A•19, 2B•16, 2C•21
Sunroof – 11•13
Suspension and steering – 10•1 *et seq*
Switches – 12•6

T

Tailgate – 11•12
Tailgate lock components – 11•13
Tailgate support struts – 11•13
Thermostat – 3•3
Timing chain and related components – 2A•6, 2B•6, 2C•10

Timing chain case – 2C•8
Timing chain tensioner and sprockets – 2C•12
Top Dead Centre – 2C•6
    (TDC) for No. 1 piston – 2A•4, 2B•4
Towing – 0•9
Track rod end – 10•14
Transmission fluid – 1A•16, 1B•16
Transmission range switch – 7B•3
Turbocharger – 4B•19
Tyres – 0•16
    pressures – 0•18

V

Vacuum pump – 9•14
Vacuum servo unit – 9•3
    check valve – 9•4
Valve clearances – 1A•12
Vehicle identification numbers – REF•7
VSA (Vehicle Stability Assist) – 9•13

W

Washer fluid – 0•14
Water pump – 3•7
Wheel alignment and steering angle – 10•15
Wheel arch liner – 11•21
Wheel changing – 0•8
Windscreen and fixed windows – 11•13
Windscreen washer system – 12•16
Windscreen wiper – 12•15
Wiper blades – 0•14
Wiring diagrams – 12•23 *et seq*

X

Xenon gas discharge headlight system – 12•13

Preserving Our Motoring Heritage

< *The Model J Duesenberg Derham Tourster. Only eight of these magnificent cars were ever built – this is the only example to be found outside the United States of America*

Almost every car you've ever loved, loathed or desired is gathered under one roof at the Haynes Motor Museum. Over 300 immaculately presented cars and motorbikes represent every aspect of our motoring heritage, from elegant reminders of bygone days, such as the superb Model J Duesenberg to curiosities like the bug-eyed BMW Isetta. There are also many old friends and flames. Perhaps you remember the 1959 Ford Popular that you did your courting in? The magnificent 'Red Collection' is a spectacle of classic sports cars including AC, Alfa Romeo, Austin Healey, Ferrari, Lamborghini, Maserati, MG, Riley, Porsche and Triumph.

A Perfect Day Out

Each and every vehicle at the Haynes Motor Museum has played its part in the history and culture of Motoring. Today, they make a wonderful spectacle and a great day out for all the family. Bring the kids, bring Mum and Dad, but above all bring your camera to capture those golden memories for ever. You will also find an impressive array of motoring memorabilia, a comfortable 70 seat video cinema and one of the most extensive transport book shops in Britain. The Pit Stop Cafe serves everything from a cup of tea to wholesome, home-made meals or, if you prefer, you can enjoy the large picnic area nestled in the beautiful rural surroundings of Somerset.

John Haynes O.B.E., Founder and Chairman of the museum at the wheel of a Haynes Light 12. >

< *Graham Hill's Lola Cosworth Formula 1 car next to a 1934 Riley Sports.*

The Museum is situated on the A359 Yeovil to Frome road at Sparkford, just off the A303 in Somerset. It is about 40 miles south of Bristol, and 25 minutes drive from the M5 intersection at Taunton.
Open 9.30am - 5.30pm (10.00am - 4.00pm Winter) 7 days a week, *except Christmas Day, Boxing Day and New Years Day*
Special rates available for schools, coach parties and outings Charitable Trust No. 292048